Lanthanide/Actinide Chemistry

Lanthanide/Actinide Chemistry

A symposium co-sponsored by the Division of Inorganic Chemistry and the Division of Nuclear Chemistry and Technology at the 152nd Meeting of the American Chemical Society, New York, N. Y., Sept. 13-14, 1966

Paul R. Fields and Therald Moeller

Symposium Chairmen

ADVANCES IN CHEMISTRY SERIES **71**

AMERICAN CHEMICAL SOCIETY

WASHINGTON, D.C. 1967

Library of Congress Catalog Card 67-31656

PRINTED IN THE UNITED STATES OF AMERICA

Advances in Chemistry Series

Robert F. Gould, *Editor*

AMERICAN CHEMICAL SOCIETY PUBLICATIONS

FOREWORD

ADVANCES IN CHEMISTRY SERIES was founded in 1949 by the American Chemical Society as an outlet for symposia and collections of data in special areas of topical interest that could not be accommodated in the Society's journals. It provides a medium for symposia that would otherwise be fragmented, their papers distributed among several journals or not published at all. Papers are refereed critically according to ACS editorial standards and receive the careful attention and processing characteristic of ACS publications. Papers published in ADVANCES IN CHEMISTRY SERIES are original contributions not published elsewhere in whole or major part and include reports of research as well as reviews since symposia may embrace both types of presentation.

CONTENTS

Preface ix

1. **Recent Advances in Actinide and Lanthanide Chemistry** 1
   K. W. Bagnall, Chemistry Division, A.E.R.E., Harwell, Didcot, Berks., England

2. **Donor Properties of Pyrophosphate Derivatives. Complexes of Rare Earth Ions with Octamethylpyrophosphoramide** 13
   Melvin D. Joesten and Robert A. Jacob, Southern Illinois University, Carbondale, Ill.

3. **Developments in Chemical Thermodynamics of the Lanthanides** .. 25
   Edgar F. Westrum, Jr., University of Michigan, Ann Arbor, Mich.

4. **Preparation and Identification of Divalent Lanthanide Ions as Dilute Solutes in Alkaline Earth Halide Solid Solutions** 51
   P. N. Yocom, Radio Corporation of America, Princeton, N. J.

5. **Physical Characterization of the Metallic LaI_2 and CeI_2 and of the Phase $LaI_{2.42}$** 56
   John D. Corbett, Robert A. Sallach, and Donald A. Lokken, Institute for Atomic Research and Department of Chemistry, Iowa State University, Ames, Iowa

6. **Fluorite-Related Oxide Phases of the Rare Earth and Actinide Elements** 67
   Leroy Eyring, Arizona State University, Tempe, Ariz.

7. **Lanthanide and Actinide Absorption Spectra in Solution** 86
   W. T. Carnall and P. R. Fields, Chemistry Division, Argonne National Laboratory, Argonne, Ill.

8. **Electronic Spectra of Lanthanide Compounds in the Vapor Phase** .. 102
   D. M. Gruen, C. W. DeKock, and R. L. McBeth, Argonne National Laboratory, Argonne, Ill.

9. **Preparation, Structure, and Spectra of Some Tetravalent Praseodymium Compounds** 122
   Larned B. Asprey, James S. Coleman, and Martin J. Reisfeld, University of California, Los Alamos Scientific Laboratory, Los Alamos, N. M.

10. **Thermodynamic Parameters of Fluoride Complexes of the Lanthanides** 127
    Jeffrey B. Walker and Gregory R. Choppin, Florida State University, Tallahassee, Fla.

11. **Volatile Rare Earth Chelates of β-Diketones** 141
Robert E. Sievers, Kent J. Eisentraut, and Charles S. Springer, Jr., Aerospace Research Laboratories, ARC, Wright-Patterson Air Force Base, Ohio and Devon W. Meek, Ohio State University, Columbus, Ohio

12. **Europium Chelates as Laser Materials** 155
Daniel L. Ross and Joseph Blanc, RCA Laboratories, Princeton, N. J.

13. **Complexes of the Rare Earths. *N*-Substituted Iminodiacetic Acids** .. 169
Larry C. Thompson, Barbara L. Shafer, John A. Edgar, and Kathleen D. Mannila, University of Minnesota, Duluth, Minn.

14. **Electronic Structure of the Actinide Elements** 180
Mark Fred, Argonne National Laboratory, Argonne, Ill.

15. **Optical and Electron Paramagnetic Resonance Spectroscopy of Actinide Ions in Single Crystals** 203
N. Edelstein, W. Easley, and R. McLaughlin, Lawrence Radiation Laboratory, University of California, Berkeley, Calif.

16. **Some Uranium-Transition Element Double Oxides** 211
Henry R. Hoekstra, Chemistry Division, Argonne National Laboratory, Argonne, Ill. and Robert H. Marshall, Department of Chemistry and Physics, Memphis State University, Memphis, Tenn.

17. **The Solid-State Chemistry of Americium Oxides** 228
C. Keller, University of Karlsruhe and Nuclear Research Centre, Karlsruhe, Germany

18. **Tetra- and Pentavalent Actinide Fluoride Complexes. Protactinium to Curium** 248
Robert A. Penneman, Thomas K. Keenan, and Larned B. Asprey, University of California, Los Alamos Scientific Laboratory, Los Alamos, N. M.

19. **Actinide Chemistry in Saturated Potassium Fluoride Solution** 256
Conrad E. Thalmayer and Donald Cohen, Argonne National Laboratory, Argonne, Ill.

20. **Aqueous Oxidation-Reduction Reactions of Uranium, Neptunium, Plutonium, and Americium** 268
T. W. Newton and F. B. Baker, University of California, Los Alamos Scientific Laboratory, Los Alamos, N. M.

21. **A Contribution to the Study of the Oxidation Potential of Berkelium (III)-(IV) Couple in Various Media** 296
C. Musikas and R. Berger, Department de Chimie, Services de Chimie des Combustibles Irradies, Section d'Etudes Chimiques et Radioactives, Commisariat a l'Energie Atomique, Centre d'Etudes Nucléaires, Fontenay aux Roses, France

22. **Condensed Phase Equilibria in the Molybdenum Hexafluoride-Uranium Hexafluoride System** 308
L. E. Trevorrow, M. J. Steindler, and D. V. Steidl, Chemical Engineering Division, Argonne National Laboratory, Argonne, Ill. and J. T. Savage, University of Oregon, Eugene, Ore.

23. **Uranyl Metaborate and Sodium Uranyl Borate** 320
Henry R. Hoekstra, Argonne National Laboratory, Argonne, Ill.

24. **Octahedral Hexahalide Complexes of the Trivalent Actinides** 331
J. L. Ryan, Battelle Memorial Institute, Pacific Northwest Laboratory, Richland, Wash.

25. **Anionic Acetato Complexes of the Hexavalent Actinides. Anion Exchange and Amine Extraction of Hexavalent Actinide Acetates** 335
J. L. Ryan and W. E. Keder, Battelle-Northwest Laboratories, Richland, Wash.

Index 353

PREFACE

Lanthanide chemistry is approaching its 200th Anniversary, but except for data on thorium and uranium the chemistry of the actinides is a comparative youngster of some 30 years. However, the two chemistries are intimately associated because their elements are of the *f* transition type and thus formally comparable with each other and different from other elements. Indeed, these parallels made it possible to unravel actinide behavior in the early days of transuranium element production. In addition to their chemical similarities, the two series also share the properties of magnetism and radiant energy absorption and emission characteristic of *f*-electron species. However, important differences exist also, particularly in oxidation states, in bonding, and in complex-ion formation.

Substantial new information has been accumulated in the past few years. In part, new applications for the lanthanides and actinides have prompted this surge. In part, the general quest for knowledge, the application of new techniques and instruments, and the advances in data interpretation have contributed as well. Although developments in the two areas have not been exactly parallel, the underlying chemistry is fundamentally the same. It seemed appropriate, therefore, to summarize the significant areas of current chemical research and, as has not been done previously, to bring together both lanthanide and actinide chemistry to emphasize their parallel and divergent behavior. The consistent retention of the terms lanthanide and actinide, rather than the substitution of the terms lanthanoid and actinoid as recommended by the IUPAC Commission on the Nomenclature of Inorganic Chemistry, has been dictated by common usage.

In arranging the symposium, we wished to make the presentations both informative and instructive. Therefore, new and original research were interspersed with information available in specific areas, and the program was balanced in terms of current interest and activity. We regret that not all of the papers presented could be included, but we believe the volume does cover lanthanide and actinide chemistry as it is currently being emphasized and practiced.

We express our sincere appreciation to the participants in the symposium for their contributions and to the officers of the Division of Inorganic Chemistry for their assistance in making the final arrangements.

Argonne, Ill.
Urbana, Ill.
March 27, 1967.

PAUL R. FIELDS
THERALD MOELLER

1

Recent Advances in Actinide and Lanthanide Chemistry

K. W. BAGNALL

Chemistry Division, A.E.R.E., Harwell, Didcot, Berks., England

The chemistry of the lighter actinides from thorium to americium, all being available in substantial quantities, is now well understood. In the +4, or higher oxidation states, these elements are best considered as an inner transition series. Their chemistry shows both horizontal similarities within the actinide group and to a lesser degree, some vertical similarities with the group 4, 5, and 6 d-*transition elements. All of the actinides in their +3 oxidation states behave in much the same way as the lanthanides. The chemistry of the actinides is reviewed within this context and compared with the corresponding lanthanides.*

In reviewing the chemistry of the actinides as a group, the simplest approach is to consider each valence state separately. In the tervalent state, and such examples of the divalent state as are known, the actinides show similar chemical behavior to the lanthanides. Experimental difficulties with the terpositive actinides up to plutonium are considerable because of the ready oxidation of this state. Some correlation exists with the actinides in studies of the lanthanide tetrafluorides and fluoro complexes. For other compounds of the 4-valent actinides, protactinium shows almost as many similarities as differences between thorium and the uranium-americium set; thus investigating the complex forming properties of their halides has attracted attention. In the 5- and 6-valent states, the elements from uranium to americium show a considerable degree of chemical similarity. Protactinium (V) behaves in much the same way as these elements in the 5-valent state except for water, where its hydrolytic behavior is more reminiscent of niobium and tantalum.

This review is largely restricted to work which has been published in the 1960's with emphasis on the chemistry of the halides and their complexes. These have been the subject of most of the recent research, and a complete comparison of all the known chemistry of the lanthanides and actinides has not been attempted previously.

Divalent State

Compounds of divalent samarium, europium, and ytterbium are well-known. In recent years, lower halides of other lanthanides, such as neodymium (*48*), praseodymium (*45, 49, 90*), and thulium (*4*) have been obtained by reducing the trihalide with the metal. The corresponding reaction of thorium tetraiodide with thorium metal has led to the identification of two crystalline forms of ThI_2 (*41, 91*); it is unlikely that the Th^{2+}, or even Th^{3+}, ion is present in ThI_2, but like PrI_2, which is formulated as $Pr^{3+}(I^-)_2(e^-)$ (*2*), the compound is probably of the type $Th^{4+}(I^-)_2(2e^-)$ (*41*). Certainly one crystal form is diamagnetic (*41*), suggesting the latter formulation.

In addition, all of the lanthanides have now been obtained in the divalent state in dilute solution in a CaF_2 matrix by γ-irradiation (*74*), fused salt electrolysis (*52*), or alkaline earth metal reduction (*68*). Attempts to reduce americium, the analog of europium, to this lower oxidation state have also been successful under similar conditions (*51*); the Am^{2+} ion, which occupies Ca^{2+} sites in the crystal, was identified by its ESR spectrum. Similar attempts to obtain uranium (II) have been unsuccessful (*51*).

Tervalent State

In the lanthanides, the basic chemistry of promethium has become better known because of the availability of relatively large quantities of ^{147}Pm (*103*), the observed behavior of the element being much as one would expect. In the actinides, ThI_3 has been prepared by reaction of ThI_4 with thorium metal (*41, 91*) and appears to be an ionic compound; if so, it will presumably be paramagnetic. With the higher actinides being produced in large quantities, it is pleasing to see crystallographic data reported for californium compounds, the emerald green trichloride being hexagonal (UCl_3), and the sesquioxide monoclinic (Sm_2O_3) (*58*) while, with the identification of a longer-lived (79 days) isotope of fermium [^{257}Fm (*60*)] it appears as though microchemical studies of all the actinides up to element 100 will become practicable.

Studies of the complex chemistry of the tervalent lanthanides show that coordination numbers higher than six are common, for example in the tetrakistropolonates (*79*), the complexes of the perchlorates with *N,N*-dimethylacetamide (DMA) (*77*) or octamethylpyrophosphoramide (*61*), of the iodides with *N,N*-dimethylformamide (DMF) (*76*), the nitrates with triphenylphosphine (or arsine) oxide (*46*), and the β-diketone chelates (*28*); many of these complexes are discussed later in this volume. Actinide (III) analogs do not seem to have been prepared.

In their halo complexes, the lanthanides (III) and actinides (III) show a considerable similarity. Thus tetrafluorolanthanides (III) (*100*) and -actinides (II) (*65, 72*) have been reported, all of them having hexagonal symmetry, and hexahalolanthanides (III) and some actinide (III) analogs have also been prepared; the triphenylphosphonium hexachlorolanthanides (III) have been isolated from nonaqueous solvents, and their visible spectra have been discussed in some detail (*62, 89*). The corresponding americium (III) salt can be made in a similar manner (*87*), but the aqueous alkali chloride/$AmCl_3$ system is more complicated, the species $CsAmCl_4 \cdot 4H_2O$ and $Cs_2NaAmCl_6$ being isolated from aqueous solution and "Cs_3AmCl_6" from ethanolic hydrochloric acid solutions of the components (*25*); this last may, however, be $Cs_8Am_3Cl_{17}$. The plutonium compound, $Cs_3PuCl_6 \cdot 2H_2O$, has been isolated from aqueous hydrochloric acid (*95*). Many more lanthanide and actinide halo complex species have been reported for fused salt melts, ranging in the case of the chlorides from the simple MCl_4^- ion to $M_2Cl_9^{3-}$ and $M_3Cl_{10}^{3-}$; some examples are shown in Table I. Many of them exist only in fused salts and have not been prepared by other means.

Table I. Anionic Chlorocomplexes in Fused Salts

Anion	*Metal (M)*	*Reference*
MCl_4^-	La	*9*
MCl_5^{2-}	La, Ce, Pr, Nd, Sm, Pu	*9, 72, 78, 80, 97, 98*
MCl_6^{3-}	Sc, Y, La, Ce, Pr, Nd, Sm, Yb, Pu	9, 59, 69, 72, 78, 80, 97, 98
MCl_9^{6-}	Pu	*72*
$M_2Cl_7^-$	Sm, Pu	*72, 80*
$M_2Cl_9^{3-}$	Sc, Ce, Pr, Nd	*9, 59*
$M_3Cl_{10}^-$	Y, La, Ce	*9, 69*

Tetravalent State

In the 4-valent state of the elements, one of the most remarkable preparative reactions reported recently is the isolation of PrF_4 by washing sodium fluoride from the complex Na_2PrF_6 with anhydrous HF in the presence of fluorine (*92*). The structures of PrF_4 and its fluoro complexes are analogous to those of the corresponding uranium compounds (*1*), and evidence has been obtained for the formation of Pr (IV) nitrato species in the reaction of Pr_6O_{11} or PrO_2 with dinitrogen pentoxide (*93*). A variety of fluoro complexes formed by the 4-valent elements from protactinium to curium have also been reported recently (*82*).

An unusual layer structure has been found for ThI_4 (*104*), and the existence of $PaCl_4$ has now been confirmed. $PaOCl_2$, $PaOBr_2$ (*31*),

$PaBr_4$ (*33*), $PaOI_2$, and PaI_4 (*31*) and some of their complexes, including hexachloro-, hexabromo-, and hexaiodoprotactinates (IV) (*33*) have been prepared. $PaBr_4$ appears to be isostructural with one form of $ThBr_4$ and not with monoclinic UBr_4. Hexachloro complexes of all the actinides (IV) from thorium to plutonium are now on record, only $(NEt_4)_2ThCl_6$ being reported as dimorphic. All the analogous hexabromo complexes are also known since the neptunium (IV) and plutonium (IV) compounds have been isolated from ethanolic hydrobromic acid (*88*). Protactinium (IV) (*37*), thorium (IV), and uranium (IV) (*16*) hexaiodo complexes are more difficult to obtain, in accordance with the marked Chatt-Ahrland A-class behavior of both lanthanides and actinides, but have been made by reaction of the tetraiodides with the appropriate cation iodide in methyl cyanide solution, the tetraphenyl- [Th (IV), U (IV)] and triphenylmethylarsonium [Pa (IV)] salts being the most stable hexaiodo compounds.

Although plutonium tetrachloride is unknown, its complexes with oxygen donor ligands, such as amides, can be prepared by treating Cs_2PuCl_6 with a solution of the ligand in a nonaqueous solvent (*22*); some of the complexes formed by the actinide tetrachlorides with amides are shown in Table II. The *N,N*-dimethylacetamide (DMA) complexes appear to be chlorine-bridged dimers in which the metal exhibits 8-coordination (*17*), whereas thorium forms the simple 8-coordinate complex $ThCl_4 \cdot 4DMA$ (*19*). The thorium (*19*), uranium (*26*), and neptunium (*70*) tetranitrate complexes with DMA, $2M(NO_3)_4 \cdot 5DMA$, are probably nitrate-bridged dimers analogous to the UCl_4 complex, but the thorium and uranium tetrathiocyanate complexes with DMA (*11, 19*) are 1:4 monomers and are 8-coordinate like the octaisothiocyanato complexes (*75*). Unfortunately, these tetrachloride—DMA complexes decompose in an x-ray beam, and evidence for their structures has been obtained by indirect chemical methods and is therefore somewhat speculative.

Table II. Actinide Tetrachloride-Acetamide Complexes

$MCl_4 \cdot 6CH_3CONH_2$	M = U, Np, Pu (*22*)
$MCl_4 \cdot 4CH_3CONH(CH_3)$	M = U (*19*)
$2MCl_4 \cdot 5CH_3CON(CH_3)_2$	M = U, Np, Pu (*22*)
$MCl_4 \cdot 4CH_3CON(CH_3)_2$	M = Th (*19*)

Unusual coordination numbers have been reported for dimethyl sulfoxide (DMSO) and hexamethylphosphoramide (HMPA) complexes of some actinide tetrahalides, notably 7-coordination in $UCl_4 \cdot 3DMSO$ and $ThBr_4 \cdot 3HMPA$, and 9-coordination in $ThCl_4 \cdot 5DMSO$, all of which appear to be monomeric (*18*). Interestingly, $ThBr_4 \cdot 6DMSO$ appears to behave as a 1:1 electrolyte in nitromethane (*18*), so that thorium may well be 9-coordinate in this complex also. Some infrared data are shown in Table III. Complexes of the tetrahalides with methylenebissulfoxides (*50*), phosphine oxides (*55*) and with dicarboxylic acid amides (*14*) have also been prepared, but all appear to be polymeric and *cis*-chelates do not seem to be formed.

Table III. MX_4 Complexes with Oxygen Donors (*18*)

	$S=O$, $cm.^{-1}$	$\Delta^{\nu}S=O$, $cm.^{-1}$
$ThCl_4 \cdot 5DMSO$	942	108
$UCl_4 \cdot 3DMSO$	947	103
$ThBr_4 \cdot 6DMSO$	948	102
$UBr_4 \cdot 6DMSO$	938	112
	$P=O$, $cm.^{-1}$	$\Delta^{\nu}P=O$, $cm.^{-1}$
$ThCl_4 \cdot 2HMPA$	1042	159
$ThBr_4 \cdot 2HMPA$	1027	174
$ThBr_4 \cdot 3HMPA$	1071	130
$UCl_4 \cdot 2HMPA$	1034	167
$UBr_4 \cdot 2HMPA$	1017	184

Pentavalent State

Considerable advances have been made in our knowledge of the 5-valent actinides, again mainly in the halides and halo complexes. Np_2O_5 is now known, made from $NpO_3 \cdot H_2O$ (*23*) or by reaction of neptunium metal with molten lithium perchlorate (*43*). Protactinium has received the most attention, the pentafluoride (*94*), pentachloride (*10, 36*), pentabromide (*34*) and pentaiodide (*38*), as well as their complexes with oxygen donors and their halo complexes, all having been thoroughly investigated in the past few years. Unlike $NbCl_5$ and UCl_5, which are chlorine-bridged dimers, $PaCl_5$ appears to be an infinite linear chlorine-bridged polymer (*47*), its symmetry being approximately D_{5h}.

The oxyhalides of the 5-valent actinides have proved to be of considerable interest, oxygen bridged species such as Pa_2OF_8 (*94*) and Pa_2OCl_8 (*36*), analogous to U_2OF_8 (*67*) being reported. The infrared spectra of the range of oxygen-bridged protactinium (V) oxychlorides (*36*) suggest that these represent successive stages in the chlorination of the polymeric pentoxide (Figure 1). The other known protactinium (V) oxyhalides—$PaOBr_3$, $PaOI_3$, PaO_2Br, and PaO_2I—are similar in nature (*34*), but there are no data for the uranium analog—$UOBr_3$ (*85*) and UO_2Br (*73*)—which may also be polymers.

Hydrated $NpOF_3$ (*12*) has been prepared by the action of hydrogen fluoride on the recently reported pentoxide, Np_2O_5 (*23, 43*), but NpF_5 itself has not yet been recorded.

Salts of the fluoro complex ions MF_6^-, MF_7^{2-}, and MF_8^{3-} have been reported for Pa (V) (*5, 7, 29, 30, 40, 66*), U (V) (*6, 56, 57, 81, 83, 84, 86,*

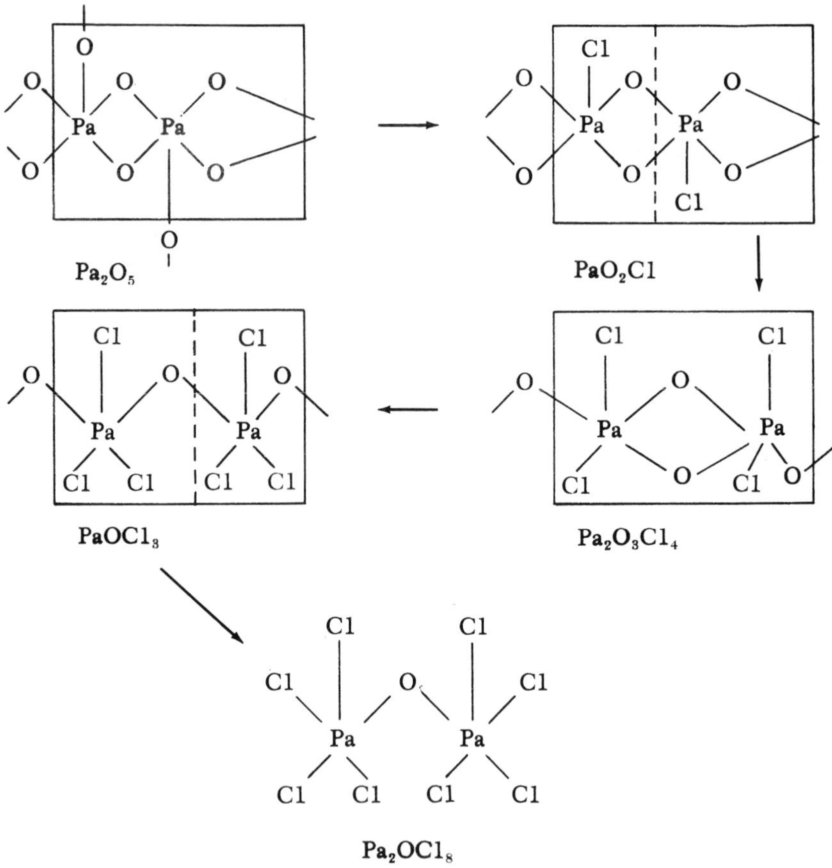

Figure 1. Pa (V) Oxychlorides

96), Np (V) (*3*) and Pu (V) (*8*), the last two being the first non-oxygenated neptunium (V) and plutonium (V) compounds. Some of the preparative procedures used for uranium (V) fluoro complexes are shown in Table IV.

A recent study of the alkali metal/uranium fluoride complex systems has shown that K_3UF_6, K_3UF_7, and K_3UF_8 are isomorphous (*99*), the crystal symmetry being unaffected by the fluoride ion absences. The structure of K_2PaF_7 has been determined only recently (*39*), and it has been shown that each protactinium atom is surrounded by nine fluorine atoms in what is effectively a trigonal prism with three added equatorial fluorine atoms; the PaF_9 groups are linked in infinite chains by two fluorine bridges.

Salts of the analogous protactinium (V) (*10*) and uranium (V) (*20*) chloro complex ions, MCl_6^- and MCl_8^{3-}, have been obtained from thionyl chloride solutions of the 5-valent elements, but no heptachloro complexes have been isolated. Similarly, so far only the hexabromo- and hexaiodo-protactinates (V) have been obtained, prepared from methyl cyanide solutions of the components (*38*).

Cesium hexachlorouranate (V) has been used to prepare $UCl_5 \cdot R_3PO$ complexes by reaction with the ligand in methylene dichloride (*21*), a reaction analogous to that used to prepare $PuCl_4$ complexes, and the corresponding $PaCl_5$ complexes have also been made (*32*); some infrared data are given in Table V. Whereas $NbCl_5 \cdot Ph_3PO$ reacts with an excess of the ligand, forming $NbOCl_3 \cdot 2Ph_3PO$, the $PaCl_5$ and UCl_5 complexes do not. On the other hand, neither the $NbCl_5$ nor $PaCl_5$ complexes with hexamethylphosphoramide (HMPA) react with an excess of ligand.

Alkali metal dioxofluorides of the type $A^IMO_2F_2$ (M = Np, Pu (*64*) and Am (*2, 64*) have been prepared from aqueous solution and chloro complex salts of neptunium (V) (*24*) and americium (V) (*25*) are now

Table IV. Preparation of Uranium (V) Fluoro Complexes

M^IUF_6 M^I = (a) NO^+, NO_2^+ (b, c) Li^+, Na^+, K^+, Rb^+, Cs^+

(a) $NO + UF_6 \rightarrow NOUF_6$ (*57*)

$NOF + UF_5 \rightarrow NOUF_6$ (*57*)

(b) $M^IF + UF_5 \xrightarrow{\text{in 10–27}M\text{ HF}} M^IUF_6$ (*6*)

(c) $M^IF + UF_5 \xrightarrow{300°C.} M^IUF_6$ (*83*)

$M_2^IUF_7$ M^I = K^+, Rb^+, Cs^+

$$2M^IF + UF_5 \xrightarrow{300°C.} \tfrac{1}{2}M^IUF_6 + \tfrac{1}{2}M_3^IUF_8 \xrightarrow{350°C.} M_2^IUF_7$$

$M_3^IUF_8$ M^I = Na^+, K^+, Rb^+, Cs^+

$3M^IF + UF_5 \xrightarrow{350°C.} M_3^IUF_8$ (*84*)

$Na_3UF_7 + \tfrac{1}{2}F_2 \xrightarrow{390°C.} Na_3UF_8$ (*86*)

Table V. Infrared Data for $MCl_5 \cdot Ph_3PO$ Complexes

	P = O, cm.$^{-1}$	*$\Delta_\nu P$ = O, cm.$^{-1}$*	*Reference*
$NbCl_5 \cdot Ph_3PO$	977	215	*32*
$TaCl_5 \cdot Ph_3PO$	987	205	*32*
$PaCl_5 \cdot Ph_3PO$	990	202	*32*
$UCl_5 \cdot Ph_3PO$	973	219	*21*
$NbOCl_3 \cdot 2Ph_3PO$	1167	25	*32, 44*

known; the former are salts of the "$NpO_2Cl_4^{3-}$" and $NpOCl_5^{2-}$ ions. The formation of Cs_2NpOCl_5 from aqueous solution indicates that the NpO_2^+ ion is more easily chlorinated than had been suspected, but further chlorination results only in disproportionation. "$Cs_3AmO_2Cl_4$" is isostructural with the neptunium (V) compound (*25*), and there is some doubt as to whether these compounds are monomeric or more correctly formulated as $Cs_8(MO_2)_3Cl_{11}$.

A few derivatives of oxyanions have also been prepared; protactinium (V) forms hexanitrato complexes, $Pa(NO_3)_6^-$, by reaction of the hexachloro complex with dinitrogen pentoxide, in contrast to niobium and tantalum which, under similar conditions, yield only tetranitrato complexes, $MO(NO_3)_4^-$ (*35*). Neptunium (V) nitrates, NpO_2NO_3 and $NpO(NO_3)_3$ have also been reported (*71*). Protactinium (V) sulfato- and selenato complex acids, $H_3PaO(SO_4)_3$ and $H_3PaO(SeO_4)_3$, have been obtained from aqueous solution (*13*), but no fully sulfated or selenated species have been recorded.

Hexavalent State

Much less work has been reported for the 6-valent elements as compared with the volume of literature for the actinides in lower valence states. Hydrated neptunium and plutonium trioxides are now known, $NpO_3 \cdot H_2O$ and $PuO_3 \cdot (0.8)H_2O$ being readily obtained by the action of ozone on an aqueous suspension of neptunium (V) or plutonium (IV) hydroxides at 90°C. (*23*); $NpO_3 \cdot 2H_2O$ is obtained in a similar manner at 18°C. (*23*) or by ozone oxidation of neptunium (V) in a molten lithium-potassium nitrate eutectic at 150°C. (*42*).

Another unsuccessful attempt has been made to prepare AmF_6, by fluorinating Am_2O_3 in the presence of PtF_6 (*100*). Complexes of UF_6 such as Na_2UF_8 (*63*), NH_4UF_7 (*102*) and $NOUF_7$ (*56*) are now known, but the complexing behavior of neptunium and plutonium hexafluorides and uranium hexachloride has scarcely been investigated.

The most stable form of the actinides (VI) is the oxygenated ion MO_2^{2+}, and this type of species has received much attention.

Although americium (VI) is rapidly reduced to americium (III) by chloride ion in aqueous solution, the insoluble red $Cs_2AmO_2Cl_4$ is readily obtained when the americium (V) chloro complex is treated with concentrated hydrochloric acid; the mechanism of the reaction is not yet known, but it is not a result of disproportionation (*25*).

Anhydrous neptunyl fluoride, previously obtained by fluorinating sodium neptunyl acetate (*52*), is more conveniently made by treating $NpO_3 \cdot H_2O$ with liquid bromine trifluoride at room temperature, hydrogen fluoride at 300°C., or fluorine at 230°C., and even by vacuum drying a hydrofluoric acid solution of $NpO_3 \cdot H_2O$ (*12*), from which it appears that the neptunyl compound is less strongly hydrated than uranyl fluoride.

Complexes of uranyl chloride with a variety of oxygen donor ligands continue to be reported, notably with phosphine oxides (*55*), pyridine *N*-oxides (*27*), *N,N*-dimethylformamide (*71*), acetamide (*15*), and with the *N,N,N′,N′*-tetramethyldicarboxylic acid amides (*14*), the last being mainly polymeric compounds. A few similar complexes of uranyl bromide (*54*) and iodide (*71*) are also known.

In conclusion, compared with the *d*-transition elements and the lanthanides, little information is available on the magnetic and spectral properties of the actinides as a group, so that there is considerable scope for further work in this area. The symmetry properties of *f*-orbitals are scarcely mentioned in the textbooks, and one must search to find any treatment of them in the literature. This reflects the complex magnetic behavior of many apparently magnetically dilute actinide complexes, together with the obvious complexity of their spectra, particularly of species of high coordination number and unknown, but probably low, symmetry. In this connection there is an obvious need for more structural work, for in nearly every case crystallographic data are lacking and structures have been inferred by indirect methods.

Literature Cited

(1) Asprey, L. B., Coleman, J. S., Reisfeld, M. J., ADVAN. CHEM. SER. **71,** 122 (1967).
(2) Asprey, L. B., Ellinger, F. H., Zachariasen, W. H., *J. Am. Chem. Soc.* **76,** 5235 (1954).
(3) Asprey, L. B., Keenan, T. K., Penneman, R. A., Sturgeon, G. D., *Inorg. Nucl. Chem. Letters* **2,** 19 (1966).
(4) Asprey, L. B., Kruse, F. H., *J. Inorg. Nucl. Chem.* **13,** 32 (1960).
(5) Asprey, L. B., Kruse, F. H., Penneman, R. A., *J. Am. Chem. Soc.* **87,** 3518 (1965).
(6) Asprey, L. B., Penneman, R. A., *Inorg. Chem.* **3,** 727 (1964).
(7) Asprey, L. B., Penneman, R. A., *Science* **145,** 924 (1964).
(8) Asprey, L. B., Sturgeon, G. D., Penneman, R. A., *J. Am. Chem. Soc.* **87,** 5803 (1965).
(9) Baev, A. K., Novikov, G. I., *Zh. Neorgan. Khim.* **6,** 2610 (1961).
(10) Bagnall, K. W., Brown, D., *J. Chem. Soc.* **1964,** 3021.
(11) Bagnall, K. W., Brown, D., Colton, R., *J. Chem. Soc.* **1964,** 2527.
(12) Bagnall, K. W., Brown, D., Easey, J. F., *J. Chem. Soc.* (to be published).
(13) Bagnall, K. W., Brown, D., Jones, P. J., *J. Chem. Soc.* **1965,** 176.
(14) Bagnall, K. W., Brown, D., Jones, P. J., *J. Chem. Soc.* **1966,** 741.
(15) Bagnall, K. W., Brown, D., Jones, P. J., *J. Chem. Soc.* (to be published).
(16) Bagnall, K. W., Brown, D., Jones, P. J., du Preez, J. G. H., *J. Chem. Soc.* **1965,** 350.
(17) Bagnall, K. W., Brown, D., Jones, P. J., du Preez, J. G. H., *J. Chem. Soc.* **1965,** 3594.
(18) Bagnall, K. W., Brown, D., Jones, P. J., du Preez, J. G. H., *J. Chem. Soc.* **1966,** 737.
(19) Bagnall, K. W., Brown, D., Jones, P. J., Robinson, P. S., *J. Chem. Soc.* **1964,** 2531.

(20) Bagnall, K. W., Brown, D., du Preez, J. G. H., *J. Chem. Soc.* **1964,** 2603.
(21) Bagnall, K. W., Brown, D., du Preez, J. G. H., *J. Chem. Soc.* **1965,** 5217.
(22) Bagnall, K. W., Deane, A. M., Markin, T. L., Robinson, P. S., Stewart, M. A. A., *J. Chem. Soc.* **1961,** 1611.
(23) Bagnall, K. W., Laidler, J. B., *J. Chem. Soc.* 1964, 2693.
(24) Bagnall, K. W., Laidler, J. B., *J. Chem. Soc.* 1966, 516.
(25) Bagnall, K. W., Laidler, J. B., Stewart, M. A. A. (to be published).
(26) Bagnall, K. W., Robinson, P. S., Stewart, M. A. A., *J. Chem. Soc.* **1961,** 4060.
(27) Balakrishnan, P. V., Patil, S. K., Venkatasetty, H. V., *J. Inorg. Nucl. Chem.* **28,** 537 (1966).
(28) Bauer, H., Blanc, J., Ross, D. L., *J. Am. Chem. Soc.* **86,** 5125 (1964).
(29) Brown, D., Easey, J. F., *Nature* **205,** 589 (1965).
(30) Brown, D., Easey, J. F., *J. Chem. Soc.* **1966,** 254.
(31) Brown, D., Easey, J. F., Jones, P. J., *J. Chem. Soc.* (to be published).
(32) Brown, D., Easey, J. F., du Preez, J. G. H., *J. Chem. Soc.* **1966,** 258.
(33) Brown, D., Jones, P. J., *Chem. Commun.* **1966,** 280.
(34) Brown, D., Jones, P. J., *J. Chem. Soc.* **1966,** 262.
(35) Brown, D., Jones, P. J., *J. Chem. Soc.* **1966,** 733.
(36) Brown, D., Jones, P. J., *J. Chem. Soc.* **1966,** 874.
(37) Brown, D., Jones, P. J., *J. Chem. Soc.* (to to published).
(38) Brown, D., Jones, P. J., private communication.
(39) Brown, D., Smith, A. J., *Chem. Commun.* **1965,** 554.
(40) Bukhsh, M. N., Flegenheimer, J., Hall, F. M., Maddock, A. G., Miranda, C. Ferreira de, *J. Inorg. Nucl. Chem.* **28,** 421 (1966).
(41) Clark, R. J., Corbett, J. D., *Inorg. Chem.* **2,** 460 (1963).
(42) Cohen, D., *Inorg. Chem.* **2,** 866 (1963).
(43) Cohen, D., Walter, A. J., *J. Chem. Soc.* **1964,** 2696.
(44) Copley, D. B., Fairbrother, F., Thompson, A., *J. Less-Common Metals* **8,** 256 (1965).
(45) Corbett, J. D., Druding, L. F., Burkhard, W. J., Lindahl, C. B., *Discussions Faraday Soc.* **32,** 79 (1961).
(46) Cousins, D., Hart, A., *J. Inorg. Nucl. Chem.*, in press.
(47) Dodge, R. P., Smith, G. S., Johnson, Q., Elson, R. W., *U.S. Report* **UCRL-14581** (1966).
(48) Druding, L. F., Corbett, J. D., *J. Am. Chem. Soc.* **83,** 2462 (1961).
(49) Druding, L. F., Corbett, J. D., Ramsey, B. N., *Inorg. Chem.* **2,** 869 (1963).
(50) Du Preez, J. G. H., private communication.
(51) Edelstein, N., Easley, W., McLaughlin, R., *J. Chem. Phys.* **44,** 3130 (1966).
(52) Fong, F. K., *J. Chem. Phys.* **41,** 2291 (1964).
(53) Fried, S., *Nat. Nucl. Energy Ser., Div. IV,* **14 A,** 471 (1954).
(54) Gans, P., Ph.D. Thesis, London (1964).
(55) Gans, P., Smith, B. C., *J. Chem. Soc.* **1964,** 4172.
(56) Geichman, J. R., Smith, E. A., Ogle, P. R., *Inorg. Chem.* **2,** 1012 (1963).
(57) Geichman, J. R., Smith, E. A., Trond, S. S., Ogle, P. R., *Inorg. Chem.* **1,** 661 (1962).
(58) Green, J. L., *U.S. Report* **UCRL-16516** (1965).
(59) Gut, R., Gruen, D. M., *J. Inorg. Nucl. Chem.* **21,** 259 (1961).
(60) Hulet, E. K., Hoff, R. W., Evans, J. E., Lougheed, R. W., *Phys. Rev. Letters* **13,** 343 (1964).

(61) Joesten, M. D., Jacob, R. A., ADVAN. CHEM. SER. **71,** 13 (1967).
(62) Jørgensen, C. K., *Proc. Conf. Rare Earth Res., 5th, Ames, Iowa, 1965,* Paper No. CERI-TIC-P99.
(63) Katz, S., *Inorg. Chem.* **3,** 1598 (1964).
(64) Keenan, T. K., *Inorg. Chem.* **4,** 1500 (1965).
(65) Keller, C., Schmutz, H., *Z. Naturforsch.* **19B,** 1080 (1964).
(66) Keller, O. L., Chetham-Strode, A., *Proc. Colloque Phys.-chim. Protactinium* **1965,** 119.
(67) Kirslis, S. S., McMillan, T. S., Bernhardt, H. A., *U.S. Report* **K-567** (1950).
(68) Kiss, Z. J., Yocom, P. N., *J. Chem. Phys.* **41,** 1511 (1964).
(69) Korshunov, B. G., Drobot, D. V., *Zh. Neorgan. Khim.* **9,** 222 (1964).
(70) Laidler, J. B., *J. Chem. Soc.* **1966,** 780.
(71) Lamisse, M., Heimburger, R., Rohmer, R., *Compt. rend.* **258,** 2078 (1964).
(72) Leary, J. A., *U.S. Report* **LA-2661** (1962).
(73) Levet, J. C., *Compt. rend.* **260,** 4775 (1965).
(74) McClure, D. S., Kiss, Z., *J. Chem. Phys.* **39,** 3251 (1963).
(75) Markov, V. P., Traggeim, E. N., *Zh. Neorgan. Khim.* **6,** 2316 (1961).
(76) Moeller, T., Galasyn, V., *J. Inorg. Nucl. Chem.* **12,** 259 (1960).
(77) Moeller, T., Vicentini, G., *J. Inorg. Nucl. Chem.* **27,** 1477 (1965).
(78) Morozov, I. S., Ionov, V. I., Korshunov, B. G., *Zh. Neorgan. Khim.* **4,** 1457 (1959).
(79) Muetterties, E. L., Wright, C. M., *J. Am. Chem. Soc.* **87,** 4706 (1965).
(80) Novikov, G. I., Polyachenok, O. G., Frid, S. A., *Zh. Neorgan. Khim.* **9,** 472 (1964).
(81) Penneman, R. A., Asprey, L. B., Sturgeon, G., *J. Am. Chem. Soc.* **84,** 4608 (1962).
(82) Penneman, R. A., Keenan, T. K., Asprey, L. B., ADVAN. CHEM. SER. **71,** 248 (1967).
(83) Penneman, R. A., Kruse, F. H., George, R. S., Coleman, J. S., *Inorg. Chem.* **3,** 309 (1964).
(84) Penneman, R. A., Sturgeon, G. D., Asprey, L. B., *Inorg. Chem.* **3,** 126 (1964).
(85) Prigent, J., *Ann. Chim.* (Paris), **15,** 65 (1960).
(86) Rüdorff, W., Leutner, H., *Ann.* **632,** 1 (1960).
(87) Ryan, J. L., ADVAN. CHEM. SER. **71,** 331 (1967).
(88) Ryan, J. L., Jørgensen, C. K., *Mol. Phys.* **7,** 17 (1963).
(89) Ryan, J. L., Jørgensen, C. K., Cyanamid European Research Institute, Geneva, *Rep.* **CERI-TIC-P95** (1965).
(90) Sallach, R. A., Corbett, J. D., *Inorg. Chem.* **2,** 457 (1963).
(91) Scaife, D. E., Wylie, A. W., *J. Chem. Soc.* **1964,** 5450.
(92) Soriano, J., Givon, M., Shamir, J., *Inorg. Nucl. Chem. Letters* **2,** 13 (1966).
(93) Soriano, J., Marcus, Y., *Inorg. Chem.* **3,** 901 (1964).
(94) Stein, L., *Inorg. Chem.* **3,** 995 (1964).
(95) Stevens, R. E., *J. Inorg. Nucl. Chem.* **27,** 1873 (1965).
(96) Sturgeon, G. D., Penneman, R. A., Kruse, F. H., Asprey, L. B., *Inorg. Chem.* **4,** 748 (1965).
(97) Sun, I. C., Morozov, I. S., *Zh. Neorgan. Khim.* **3,** 1914 (1958).
(98) Sung, Yu-Lin, Novikov, G. I., *Zh. Neorgan. Khim.* **8,** 700 (1963).
(99) Thoma, R. E., Friedman, H. A., Penneman, R. A., *J. Am. Chem. Soc.* **88,** 2046 (1966).
(100) Thoma, R. E., Insley, H., Hebert, G. M., *Inorg. Chem.* **5,** 1222 (1966).
(101) Tsujimura, S., Cohen, D., Chernick, C. L., Weinstock, B., *J. Inorg. Nucl. Chem.* **25,** 226 (1963).

(102) Volavsek, B., *Croat. Chem. Acta.* **33**, 181 (1961).
(103) Weigel, F., *Proc. Conf. Rare Earth Res., 5th, Ames, Iowa, 1965,* Paper No. 650804-7 (*Nucl. Sci. Abstr.* **19**, 43988 (1965)).
(104) Zalkin, A., Forrester, J. D., Templeton, D. H., *Inorg. Chem.* **3**, 639 (1964).

RECEIVED August 7, 1966.

2

Donor Properties of Pyrophosphate Derivatives

Complexes of Rare Earth Ions with Octamethylpyrophosphoramide

MELVIN D. JOESTEN[1] and ROBERT A. JACOB
Southern Illinois University, Carbondale, Ill.

Complexes of rare earth ions with octamethylpyrophosphoramide (OMPA) have been prepared and characterized. The stoichiometry of the complexes is either $Ln(ClO_4)_3 \cdot 3$ *OMPA* $\cdot$ x H_2O *where Ln is La, Ce, Pr, Nd, Sm, Eu, Gd, Tb, Dy, Ho, Er, and Y, and* x *is 1-4 or* $Ln(ClO_4)_3 \cdot 4$ *OMPA* $\cdot$ x H_2O *where Ln is La, Eu, and Ho, and* x *is 0,1,4. The infrared spectra of both types of complexes are interpreted on the basis of a coordination number of eight or more for the lanthanide ions.*

Previous work in this laboratory (*5, 6, 14*) has demonstrated the versatility of octamethylpyrophosphoramide (OMPA) as a ligand. Stable complexes of OMPA

$$
\begin{array}{ccccccc}
 & & O & & O & & \\
 & & \| & & \| & & \\
(CH_3)_2N & — & P & —O— & P & — & N(CH_3)_2 \\
 & & | & & | & & \\
 & & N(CH_3)_2 & & N(CH_3)_2 & &
\end{array}
$$

Octamethylpyrophosphoramide

with alkali, alkaline earth, and transition metal ions have been isolated.

The stability of complexes of rare earth ions is often compared with that of the alkaline earth ions (*11*). Since complexes such as $Mg(ClO_4)_2 \cdot 3$ OMPA and $Ca(ClO_4)_2 \cdot 3$ OMPA are quite stable (*14*), we decided to extend our studies to the reactions of OMPA with rare earth ions.

[1] Present address: Department of Chemistry, Vanderbilt University, Nashville, Tenn.

Experimental

Reagents. The OMPA used was 91% pure (Pennsalt Chemicals). This compound is extremely toxic and must be handled with care. OMPA was purified by vacuum distillation (*6*). The hydrated rare earth chlorides used were 99.9% pure (Lindsay Division of American Potash and Chemical Corp.).

Preparation of Complexes. *$Ln(ClO_4)_3 \cdot 3$ OMPA $\cdot$ x H_2O.* The hydrated metal chloride (0.0015 moles) was dissolved in 8 ml. of methanol. A stoichiometric amount of $AgClO_4 \cdot H_2O$ was added to precipitate AgCl. The filtrate was dehydrated with 2 ml. of 2,2-dimethoxypropane (*16*) for 45 min., and 0.0077 moles of OMPA was added. Excess ether was added to precipitate the complex. The compounds were dried under vacuum at room temperature. The complexes where Ln is La, Ce, Sm, Eu, Dy were recrystallized from a methanol-ether solution.

$Ln(ClO_4)_3 \cdot 4$ OMPA $\cdot$ x H_2O. The compounds where Ln is La and Eu were prepared as outlined above except that a large excess of OMPA was added (0.012 moles). The complex of Eu(III) was recrystallized from a methanol-ether solution. However, attempts to recrystallize $La(ClO_4)_3 \cdot 4$ OMPA resulted in the formation of $La(ClO_4)_3 \cdot 3$ OMPA $\cdot 2H_2O$.

The Ho(III) complex, $Ho(ClO_4)_3 \cdot 4$ OMPA $\cdot 4H_2O$, was prepared in much the same way except that the solution was cooled to 0°C. after adding an excess of OMPA (0.012 moles). At this temperature, crystals of the complex separated from solution. The complex was filtered off, recrystallized from a methanol-ether solution, and dried under vacuum at room temperature.

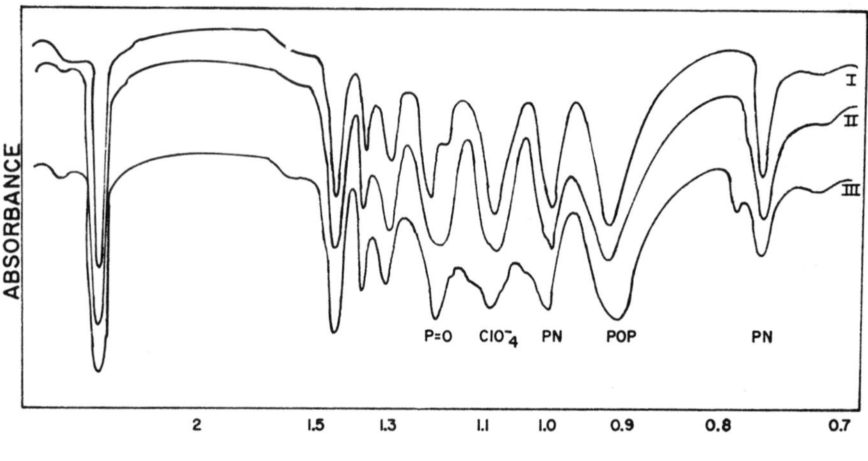

Figure 1. Infrared Spectra of $Mg(OMPA)_3(ClO_4)_2$, $La(ClO_4)_3 \cdot 4$ OMPA, and $La(ClO_4)_3 \cdot 3$ OMPA $\cdot 2H_2O$

I $Mg(OMPA)_3(ClO_4)_2$

II $La(ClO_4)_3 \cdot 4$ OMPA

III $La(ClO_4)_3 \cdot 3$ OMPA $\cdot 2H_2O$

$LaCl_3 \cdot 2$ OMPA $\cdot$ H_2O. Hydrated lanthanum chloride (0.0031 mole) was dissolved in a mixture of 2 ml. of 2,2-dimethoxypropane and 4 ml. of methanol. The solution was stirred for 1¼ hours at room temperature, and 0.0124 moles of OMPA was added. When ether was added, an oil separated from solution, which was extracted several times until a white precipitate formed.

Oils obtained by reaction of other rare earth chlorides with OMPA by the above procedure were intractable.

Spectral Measurements. Infrared spectra of Nujol mulls of the complexes were obtained with a Beckman IR5-A spectrophotometer. Ultraviolet and visible spectra were recorded on a Beckman DK-1A spectrophotometer. A Varian A-56/60 NMR spectrometer was used to measure the proton signals of solutions of OMPA, $Mg(ClO_4)_2 \cdot 3$ OMPA, $La(ClO_4)_3 \cdot 4$ OMPA, $La(ClO_4)_3 \cdot 3$ OMPA $\cdot$ 2 H_2O, and $Y(ClO_4)_3 \cdot$ 3 OMPA $\cdot$ 2 H_2O in methylene chloride. The NMR measurements were made at 35°C. with tetramethylsilane as reference.

Conductance Measurements. A conductance bridge (Industrial Instruments, Inc.) was used to measure molar conductivities of 1×10^{-3} *M* solutions of the complexes in nitromethane.

Analyses. Carbon, hydrogen, and nitrogen analyses were performed by Alfred Bernhardt, Max-Planck-Institute, Mulheim, Germany.

Results and Discussion

Elemental analyses for the rare earth complexes of OMPA are reported in Table I. The complexes are of two types:

(1) $Ln(ClO_4)_3 \cdot 3$ OMPA $\cdot$ x H_2O where Ln is La, Ce, Pr, Nd, Sm, Eu, Gd, Tb, Dy, Ho, Er, Y, and x is 1-4.

(2) $Ln(ClO_4)_3 \cdot 4$ OMPA $\cdot$ x H_2O where Ln is La, Eu, Ho, and x is 0,1,4.

The molar conductivity values for nitromethane solutions of the complexes (Table I) are in the range expected (*14*) for 3:1 electrolytes (200–250). The molar conductivity value for $LaCl_3 \cdot 2$ OMPA $\cdot$ H_2O indicates that it is a 1:1 electrolyte in nitromethane. The conductivities of methylene chloride solutions of OMPA complexes of Sm(III), Tb(III), Dy(III), and Er(III) were also measured. All of these complexes have ionic species present in methylene chloride (Table I, footnote c).

Variations in Infrared Spectra. Table II summarizes the positions of the infrared bands of P=O, P—O—P, P—N, and ClO_4^-. The features of the infrared bands of $Ln(ClO_4)_3 \cdot 3$ OMPA $\cdot$ x H_2O and $Ln(ClO_4)_3 \cdot 4$ OMPA $\cdot$ x H_2O are different from those observed for the alkaline earth complexes, but the infrared spectrum of $La(ClO_4)_3 \cdot 4$ OMPA is similar to that of $Mg(ClO_4)_3 \cdot 3$ OMPA. Figure 1 illustrates the similarity in the P=O, P—O—P, ClO_4^-, and P—N bands for $Mg(ClO_4)_2 \cdot 3$ OMPA and $La(ClO_4)_3 \cdot 4$ OMPA. The differences that appear in the spectrum of $La(ClO_4)_3 \cdot 3$ OMPA $\cdot$ 2 H_2O (Figure 1) are even more apparent in complexes of OMPA with heavier lanthanides (Figure 2). The main differ-

Table I. Analytical and Conductivity Data

	% Carbon	
	Calcd.	*Found*
$LaCl_3 \cdot 2\ OMPA \cdot H_2O$ [a]	23.0	23.2
$La(ClO_4)_3 \cdot 3\ OMPA \cdot 2H_2O$	21.6	21.5
$La(ClO_4)_3 \cdot 4\ OMPA$	24.3	24.1
$Ce(ClO_4)_3 \cdot 3\ OMPA \cdot 2H_2O$	21.6	21.6
$Pr(ClO_4)_3 \cdot 3\ OMPA \cdot H_2O$	21.9	22.3
$Nd(ClO_4)_3 \cdot 3\ OMPA \cdot H_2O$	21.9	22.2
$Sm(ClO_4)_3 \cdot 3\ OMPA \cdot 2H_2O$	21.4	21.2
$Eu(ClO_4)_3 \cdot 3\ OMPA \cdot 2H_2O$	21.4	21.2
$Eu(ClO_4)_3 \cdot 4\ OMPA \cdot H_2O$	23.8	23.9
$Gd(ClO_4)_3 \cdot 3\ OMPA \cdot 2H_2O$	21.3	21.3
$Tb(ClO_4)_3 \cdot 3\ OMPA \cdot 3H_2O$	21.0	21.3
$Dy(ClO_4)_3 \cdot 3\ OMPA \cdot 4H_2O$	20.7	20.7
$Ho(ClO_4)_3 \cdot 3\ OMPA \cdot 4H_2O$	20.7	20.5
$Ho(ClO_4)_3 \cdot 4\ OMPA \cdot 4H_2O$	22.9	22.7
$Er(ClO_4)_3 \cdot 3\ OMPA \cdot 2H_2O$	21.2	21.3
$Y(ClO_4)_3 \cdot 3\ OMPA \cdot 2H_2O$	22.5	22.3

[a] % Cl; Calcd., 12.8; Found, 12.6.
[b] 1×10^{-3} M nitromethane solutions at 25°C.

ences include a shoulder at 930–940 cm.$^{-1}$ on the main P—O—P band that becomes a separate peak for the heavier lanthanides; a shoulder at 1030–1035 cm.$^{-1}$ on the $P—N_1$ band for the lighter lanthanide complexes; the splitting of the $P—N_2$ band in all 3:1 complexes; the appearance of shoulders at 1120–1130 cm.$^{-1}$ and 1070 cm.$^{-1}$ on the perchlorate band; and the presence of water bands at 3350 and 1625 cm.$^{-1}$ (*10*).

The differences in the infrared spectra may be caused by:

(1) Coordinated Perchlorate. The shoulders at 1123, 1035, and 930-940 cm.$^{-1}$ which appear in the infrared spectra of several of the lanthanide complexes of OMPA could be caused by coordinated perchlorate (*4, 13, 17*).

The infrared spectra of $Tb(ClO_4)_3 \cdot 3\ OMPA \cdot 3H_2O$ and $Er(ClO_4)_3 \cdot 3\ OMPA \cdot 2H_2O$ in methylene chloride are of interest since the splitting of the P—O—P band is still observed even though the perchlorate band is that expected for ionic perchlorate. Since the perchlorate bands in these complexes are not as sharp or as well resolved as those observed previously for coordinated perchlorate (*4, 13, 17*), the presence of coordinated perchlorate is unlikely.

(2) Hydrogen Bonding. Some of the water molecules could be coordinated to the metal ion, and some could be hydrogen bonding with OMPA, ClO_4^-, or other water molecules. [We would like to thank one of the referees for this suggestion.]

The reported structure of $Y(acac)_3 \cdot 3H_2O$, where acac represents acetylacetonate, has two water molecules attached to yttrium and one water molecule which acts as a bridge by hydrogen bonding with water molecules coordinated to two different yttrium ions (*3*). In the OMPA

for OMPA Complexes of Rare Earth Ions

% Hydrogen		% Nitrogen		Λ_M [b] Cm.[2] ohm[-1] mole[-1]
Calcd.	*Found*	*Calcd.*	*Found*	
6.03	6.12	13.4	13.3	60
5.75	5.52	12.6	12.6	206
6.17	6.15	14.2	13.5	289
5.75	5.60	12.6	12.4	218
5.66	5.72	12.8	12.7	227
5.66	5.66	12.8	12.6	230
5.70	5.60	12.5	12.5	228 [c]
5.68	5.65	12.5	12.3	234
6.12	6.23	13.9	13.6	—
5.67	5.58	12.4	12.3	250
5.74	5.97	12.3	12.3	258 [c]
5.79	5.50	12.1	11.9	264 [c]
5.78	5.72	12.1	12.0	266
6.24	6.10	13.3	13.0	—
5.63	5.63	12.3	12.2	268 [c]
5.97	5.86	13.1	13.0	257

[c] Λ_M in CH_2Cl_2 is 50, 46, 43, 41 for OMPA complexes of Sm(III), Tb(III), Dy(III), and Er(III), respectively.

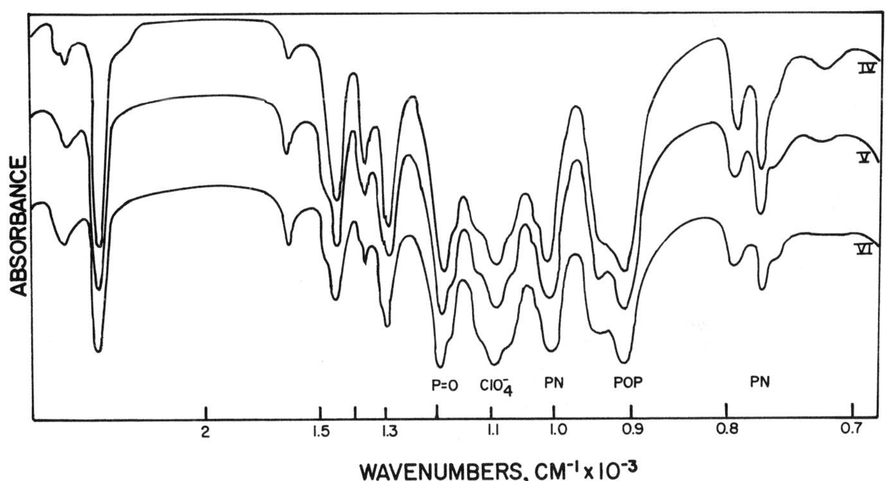

Figure 2. Infrared Spectra of $Nd(ClO_4)_3 \cdot 3$ OMPA $\cdot H_2O$, $Tb(ClO_4)_3 \cdot 3$ OMPA $\cdot 3H_2O$, and $Ho(ClO_4)_3 \cdot 3$ OMPA $\cdot 4H_2O$

IV $Nd(ClO_4)_3 \cdot 3$ OMPA $\cdot H_2O$

V $Tb(ClO_4)_3 \cdot 3$ OMPA $\cdot 3H_2O$

VI $Ho(ClO_4)_3 \cdot 3$ OMPA $\cdot 4H_2O$

Table II. Infrared

Compound	$\nu_{P=O}$ cm.$^{-1}$	ν_{P-O-P} cm.$^{-1}$
OMPA	1237	914
$LaCl_3 \cdot 2\ OMPA \cdot H_2O$	1198	908
$La(ClO_4)_3 \cdot 4\ OMPA$	1197	927
$La(ClO_4)_3 \cdot 3\ OMPA \cdot 2H_2O$	1195	909 (903)
$Ce(ClO_4)_3 \cdot 3\ OMPA \cdot 2H_2O$	1193	911 (924)
$Pr(ClO_4)_3 \cdot 3\ OMPA \cdot H_2O$	1197	912 (935)
$Nd(ClO_4)_3 \cdot 3\ OMPA \cdot H_2O$	1196	911 (940)
$Sm(ClO_4)_3 \cdot 3\ OMPA \cdot 2H_2O$	1195	908 (940)
$Eu(ClO_4)_3 \cdot 3\ OMPA \cdot 2H_2O$	1194	909 (945)
$Eu(ClO_4)_3 \cdot 3\ OMPA \cdot x\ H_2O$ [c]	1195	912 (930)
$Eu(ClO_4)_3 \cdot 4\ OMPA \cdot H_2O$	1177	917
$Gd(ClO_4)_3 \cdot 3\ OMPA \cdot 2H_2O$	1197	911, 943
$Tb(ClO_4)_3 \cdot 3\ OMPA \cdot 3H_2O$	1197	911, 945
$Tb(ClO_4)_3 \cdot 3\ OMPA \cdot x\ H_2O$ [c]	1194	915, 935
$Tb(ClO_4)_3 \cdot 3\ OMPA \cdot 3H_2O$ in CH_2Cl_2	1188	935 (895)
$Dy(ClO_4)_3 \cdot 3\ OMPA \cdot 4H_2O$	1191	910 (940)
$Ho(ClO_4)_3 \cdot 3\ OMPA \cdot 4H_2O$	1197	908 (942)
$Ho(ClO_4)_3 \cdot 4\ OMPA \cdot 4H_2O$	1176	908
$Er(ClO_4)_3 \cdot 3\ OMPA \cdot 2H_2O$	1192	900 (940)
$Er(ClO_4)_3 \cdot 3\ OMPA \cdot 2H_2O$ in CH_2Cl_2	1185	934 (892)
$Y(ClO_4)_3 \cdot 3\ OMPA \cdot 2H_2O$ [b]	1198	903, 940
$Y(ClO_4)_3 \cdot 3\ OMPA \cdot x\ H_2O$ [c]	1195	903

[a] Numbers in parentheses are shoulders on main peaks.
[b] All complexes with water molecules in formula have water bands at 3350 and 1625 cm.$^{-1}$.

complexes of lanthanide ions the splitting of the P—O—P and P—N bands would be expected if water molecules are hydrogen bonding to the oxygen or nitrogen sites.

The infrared spectra of the OMPA complexes of Y(III), Eu(III), and Tb(III) were obtained both before and after the complexes had been heated at 100°C. under vacuum for several hours. After the heat treatment, the water bands were less intense, the P—O—P band was smoothed out in the Y(III) complex, and the P—N bands were unchanged. Since the water bands did not disappear after the heat treatment, at least part of the water molecules are tightly held.

(3) Interaction of the Metal Ion with P—O—P Oxygens or P—N Nitrogens. Since the differences in infrared spectra are observed for both $Ln(ClO_4)_3 \cdot 4\ OMPA \cdot x\ H_2O$ and $Ln(ClO_4)_3 \cdot 3\ OMPA \cdot x\ H_2O$ but not for $La(ClO_4)_3 \cdot 4$ OMPA, the effect of the water molecules is probably more important than the secondary bonding of metal ions with P—O—P oxygens or P—N nitrogens.

Recently, rare earth complexes of β-diketone derivatives have been isolated in which the lanthanides are octacoordinate (*1, 3, 9*). We propose that the coordination number of the lanthanide ions in the OMPA complexes is at least eight. The fact that the P=O stretching frequency

Spectral Data

νP—N$_1$ cm.$^{-1}$	νP—N$_2$ cm.$^{-1}$	νClO_4^- cm.$^{-1}$
988	756 (773)[a]	—
1003 (980) (1015)	792, 760 (770)	—
1000	765	1097
1000	769, 787	1089 (1123)
1000 (1035)	771, 792	1093 (1070) (1123)
1010 (1035)	771, 792	1099 (1075) (1097)
1010 (1035)	770, 792	1097 (1072) (1123)
1002 (1035)	770, 792	1092 (1075)
1010	772, 793	1101 (1075)
1010	772, 792	1095
1010	750, 771, 790	1088
1010	771, 793 (765)	1097 (1065)
1012	772, 799 (760)	1097 (1122) (1070)
1010	774, 795 (760)	1097 (1070)
1000	—[d]	1098 (1070)
1017	771, 792 (760)	1088 (1065)
1012	771, 795 (760)	1093 (1075)
1002	748, 771, 793	1087
1008	771, 794 (757)	1090 (1065) (1120)
1010	—[d]	1096
1003	772, 793 (760)	1090 (1123) (1070)
1005	774, 794 (760)	1095 (1123) (1070)

[c] Spectrum taken after complex was heated at 100°C. under vacuum for several hours.
[d] Solvent absorption.

of OMPA is shifted to lower wave numbers upon coordination to the lanthanide ions is support for coordination of the metal ion to the phosphoryl oxygens. Lanthanum (III) in $La(ClO_4)_3 \cdot 4$ OMPA is probably octacoordinate with OMPA acting as a bidentate ligand.

$$\left[La \leftarrow \left(\begin{matrix} & X & \\ O — & P & — X \\ & O & \\ O — & P & — X \\ & X & \end{matrix} \right)_4 \right]^{3+} \qquad X = N(CH_3)_2$$

The metal ions in the compounds $Eu(ClO_4)_3 \cdot 4$ OMPA $\cdot H_2O$ and $Ho(ClO_4)_3 \cdot 4$ OMPA $\cdot 4H_2O$ may be coordinating to water molecules in addition to coordinating to four OMPA molecules. However, it is more likely that the water molecules are hydrogen bonding with the ligand.

In the complexes with the stoichiometry $Ln(ClO_4)_3 \cdot 3$ OMPA $\cdot\ x$ H_2O the first six coordination positions are occupied by the OMPA molecules while the remaining two (or more) positions are probably occupied by water molecules.

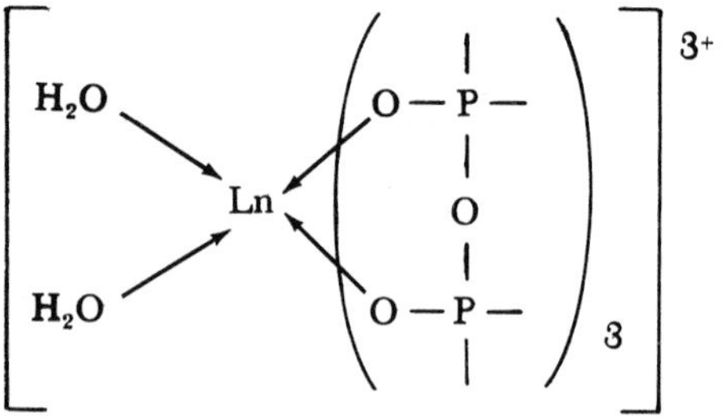

Proton NMR Shifts. The proton NMR spectra for several diamagnetic rare earth complexes of OMPA are shown in Figure 3, and the data are tabulated in Table III. The proton NMR spectrum of free OMPA contains a doublet which is caused by coupling between the phosphorus

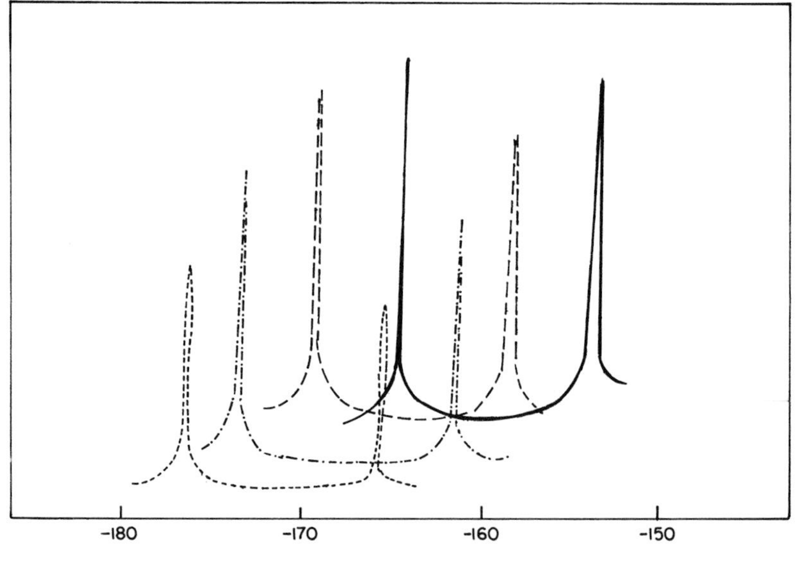

Figure 3. Proton Magnetic Resonance Spectra of Lanthanide Complexes of OMPA

——— *OMPA*
— — — *$La(ClO_4)_3 \cdot 4$ OMPA*
· — · — · *$La(ClO_4)_3 \cdot 3$ OMPA $\cdot\ 2\ H_2O$*
.... *$Y(ClO_4)_3 \cdot 3$ OMPA $\cdot\ 2\ H_2O$*

and the hydrogen (2). In the complexes of OMPA the doublet is shifted downfield in increasing order: $La(ClO_4)_3 \cdot 4$ OMPA $=$ $Mg(ClO_4)_2 \cdot 3$ OMPA $<$ $La(ClO_4)_3 \cdot 3$ OMPA $<$ $Y(ClO_4)_3 \cdot 3$ OMPA. Although the chemical shifts are quite small, they are outside experimental error. The donor sites of the ligand in these complexes must be arranged in a manner which allows all of the protons to be equivalent. The shifting downfield can be explained as being caused by increased covalent bonding between the metal ion and OMPA with the strongest interaction for Y(III). This can be understood by considering the following shifts in electron density (only one methyl group is shown).

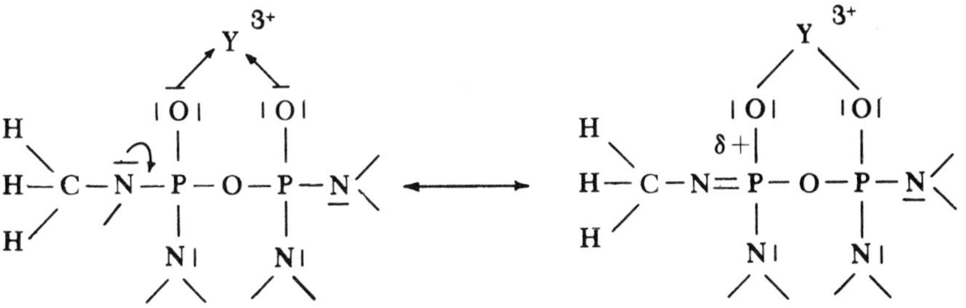

The increase in d_π—p_π bonding in the P—N bond gives the nitrogen a partial positive charge. This causes a drain in electron density from the C—N and C—H bonds. The stronger the bonding of the phosphoryl oxygens to the metal ion, the greater the drain of electron density from the C—H bonds.

The proton NMR data for other OMPA complexes of diamagnetic metal ions are also included in Table III for comparison. The increasing order of OMPA—metal ion interaction as indicated by NMR shifts is

Table III. Proton NMR Data

Compound	*Position of Doublet,*[a] *c.p.s.*
OMPA	-153, -164
$Mg(ClO_4)_2 \cdot 3$ OMPA	-159, -170
$La(ClO_4)_3 \cdot 4$ OMPA	-158, -169
$La(ClO_4)_3 \cdot 3$ OMPA $\cdot$ $2 H_2O$	-161, -172
$Y(ClO_4)_3 \cdot 3$ OMPA $\cdot$ $2 H_2O$	-165, -176
$NaClO_4 \cdot$ OMPA	-156, -167
$LiClO_4 \cdot 2$ OMPA	-157, -168
$Ba(ClO_4)_2 \cdot 2$ OMPA	-157, -168
$Zn(ClO_4)_2 \cdot 3$ OMPA	-160, -171
$Cd(ClO_4)_2 \cdot 3$ OMPA	-160, -171

[a] Relative to tetramethylsilane in methylene chloride at 35°C.

Na(I) < Li(I) = Ba(II) < Mg(II) < Zn(II) = Cd(II) < La(III) < Y(III). This agrees with the expected order of interaction for complexes of these ions.

Visible Spectral Data. The visible spectrum of $Pr(ClO_4)_3 \cdot 3$ OMPA $\cdot H_2O$ is shown in Figure 4. Spectral data for complexes of OMPA with Pr(III), Nd(III), Eu(III), Ho(III), and Er(III) are listed in Table IV. In general, the peaks for OMPA complexes appear at slightly shorter wavelengths than those reported for aquo complexes (*7, 12*). This trend is opposite that which has been observed for complexes of rare earth ions with all ligands except D_2O and F^- (*15*).

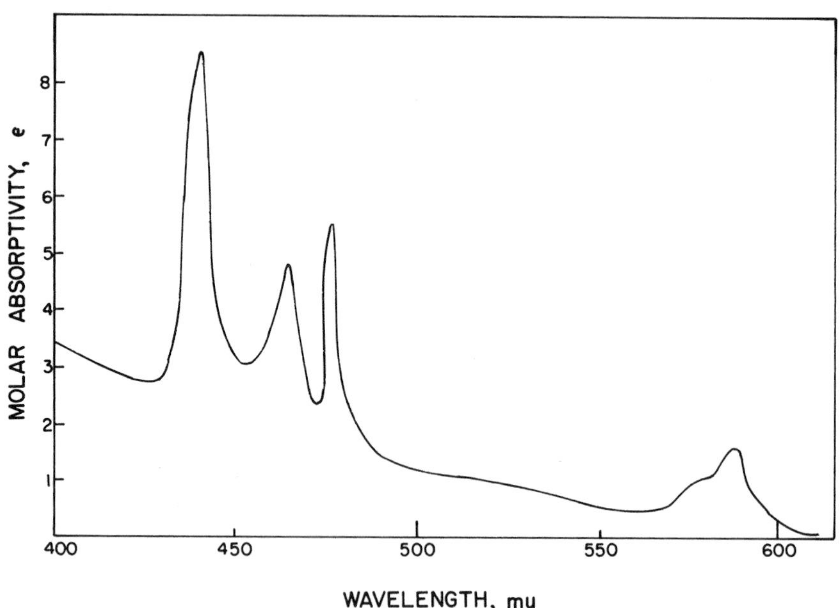

Figure 4. Visible Spectrum of $Pr(ClO_4)_3 \cdot 3$ OMPA $\cdot H_2O$

Jørgensen (*8*) has proposed that the red shift observed for most complexes of rare earth ions can be used as a measure of the amount of covalent bonding present in the metal-ligand bond (nephelauxetic series). Sinha (*15*) has modified Jørgensen's method of calculating the percent of covalent contributions to the metal-ligand bond and has examined spectral data for several complexes of Nd(III). The peaks for $Nd(ClO_4)_3 \cdot 3$ OMPA $\cdot H_2O$ in methanol are at slightly shorter wavelengths than those reported for Nd(III) in methanol (*15*). The spectrum of $Nd(ClO_4)_3 \cdot 3$ OMPA $\cdot H_2O$ in acetone was also measured, and the peaks are again shifted to slightly shorter wavelengths. If these shifts are an accurate measure of covalent bonding, the bonding in complexes of OMPA with rare earth ions must be essentially electrostatic. Earlier work with

Table IV. Visible Spectral Data

Compound	*In Methanol* $\lambda m\mu$	ϵ	*In Acetone* $\lambda m\mu$	ϵ
$Pr(ClO_4)_3 \cdot 3\ OMPA \cdot H_2O$	442	6.3		
	467	2.9		
	479	4.0		
	591	1.4		
$Nd(ClO_4)_3 \cdot 3\ OMPA \cdot H_2O$	430	0.6	428	0.5
	468	0.3	468	0.3
	476	0.5	474	0.4
	510	1.6	508	1.6
	522	3.0	520	3.1
	526 (sh)	1.8	523 (sh)	1.9
	570	5.3	568	6.8
	579	10.3	575	12.7
	581 (sh)	9.1	577	10.9
	683	0.4	682	0.4
$Eu(ClO_4)_3 \cdot 3\ OMPA \cdot 2H_2O$	361	0.5		
	375	0.3		
	392	2.9		
	463	0.4		
$Ho(ClO_4)_3 \cdot 3\ OMPA \cdot 4H_2O$	359	3.8	358	6.2
	381	0.2	380	0.3
	385	0.4	382	0.4
	418	1.9	416	2.3
	421 (sh)	0.7	419 (sh)	0.6
	449	10.0	448	15.7
	451	10.6	452	16.7
	457	6.0	457	10.7
	468	0.6	466	0.8
	472	0.7	471	0.9
	485	1.1	484	1.3
	538	3.3	536	4.0
	543 (sh)	1.3	541 (sh)	1.5
	641	1.9	639	2.1
	655 (sh)	0.6	653 (sh)	0.6
$Er(ClO_4)_3 \cdot 3\ OMPA \cdot 2H_2O$	362	2.2		
	375	14.0		
	378	9.0		
	403	0.6		
	441	0.3		
	448	0.6		
	486	2.0		
	518	8.2		
	521	5.6		
	541	0.5		
	652	1.7		

$Ni(ClO_4)_2 \cdot 3$ OMPA supports this conclusion since the ligand field parameters calculated for the Ni(II) complex place OMPA at the lower end of both the spectrochemical and nephelauxetic series (*6*).

Summary

The rare earth complexes of octamethylpyrophosphoramide are the first examples of isolated complexes with rare earth ions coordinated to the pyrophosphate linkage. Experimental evidence supports the coordination of the phosphoryl oxygens to the metal ion with additional coordination positions occupied by water.

Literature Cited

(1) Bauer, H., Blanc, J., Ross, D. L., *J. Am. Chem. Soc.* **86**, 5125 (1964).
(2) Cowley, A. H., Pinnell, R. P., *J. Am. Chem. Soc.* **87**, 4454 (1965).
(3) Cunningham, J. A., Sands, D. E., Wagner, W. F., *Inorg. Chem.* **6**, 499 (1967).
(4) Hathaway, B. J., Underhill, A. E., *J. Chem. Soc.* **1961**, 3091.
(5) Joesten, M. D., Forbes, J. F., *J. Am. Chem. Soc.* **88**, 5465 (1966).
(6) Joesten, M. D., Nykerk, K. M., *Inorg. Chem.* **3**, 548 (1964).
(7) Jørgensen, C. K., *Acta Chem. Scand.* **11**, 981 (1957).
(8) Jørgensen, C. K., "Absorption Spectra and Chemical Bonding in Complexes," pp. 143-145, Pergamon Press, 1962.
(9) Melby, L. R., Rose, N. J., Abramson, E., Caris, J. C., *J. Am. Chem. Soc.* **86**, 5117 (1964).
(10) Miller, F. A., Wilkins, C. H., *Anal. Chem.* **24**, 1253 (1952).
(11) Moeller, T., Martin, D. F., Thompson, L. C., Ferrús, R., Feistel, G. R., Randall, W. J., *Chem. Rev.* **65**, 1 (1965).
(12) Moeller, T., Horwitz, E. P., *J. Inorg. Nucl. Chem.* **12**, 49 (1959).
(13) Pavkovic, S. F., Meek, D. W., *Inorg. Chem.* **4**, 1091 (1965).
(14) Popp, C. J., Joesten, M. D., *Inorg. Chem.* **4**, 1418 (1965).
(15) Sinha, S. P., *Spectrochim. Acta* **22**, 57 (1966).
(16) Starke, K., *J. Inorg. Nucl. Chem.* **11**, 77 (1959).
(17) Wickenden, A. E., Krause, R. A., *Inorg. Chem.* **4**, 404 (1965).

RECEIVED October 4, 1966.

3

Developments in Chemical Thermodynamics of the Lanthanides

EDGAR F. WESTRUM, JR.

University of Michigan, Ann Arbor, Mich.

The present status of thermochemical and thermal data for lanthanide metals, chalcogenides, borides, pnictides, and halides is examined and assessed. Many ambiguities occur concerning entropies, stabilities, and enthalpies of formation even of the oxides—the most extensively studied of the lanthanide compounds. Here, as in related compounds, magnetic and electronic phenomena, cooperative transitions, Schottky anomalies, and low lying electronic levels make significant contributions to the thermal properties and are the motivation for further investigations. Schemes have been devised to estimate the entropies associated with known but presently unmeasured transitions. Binary chalcogenides, halides, and oxygen-contaminated metals have provided solid-state physicists with cryothermal anomalies, the temperatures of which often do not coincide with those of magnetic anomalies or (for impure metals) with transitions in sesquioxides.

It is the function of the present evaluation to present developments since 1960 which have made a significant contribution to the advancement of our understanding of the chemical thermodynamics of the lanthanide compounds. It will largely neglect the aqueous solution thermochemistry because relatively little progress has been made in this area during the past decade and because it has been discussed by Cunningham (*31*). Motivations for thermal and thermochemical investigations are usually predicated upon inherent phenomenological interest rather than upon the utility of the derived chemical thermodynamic data. This necessarily short assessment will endeavor to present evidence that the area is a viable one with ample opportunities for precise, skilled, and ingenious experimentation and correlation. At least in terms of the challenge, there is no occasion for mourning.

One of the barren regions of chemical thermodynamic values involves fundamental thermal and entropy data for lanthanide compounds despite the fact that these substances provide an unexcelled opportunity for studying the influence of electronic structure on key thermodynamic properties.

Lanthanide Chalcogenides—Mostly Oxides

The lanthanide chalcogenides represent a fertile and interesting field for investigation because of the magnetic (electronic) structure of the cations. Relatively little spectroscopic data, magnetic susceptibility values (taken at sufficiently low temperatures), and paramagnetic resonance work have been reported on the chalcogenides; heat capacity data have had to fill the experimental void. Interesting, short isostructural series occur in the lanthanide chalcogenides suitable for studying the dependence of lattice thermal properties on variations in the atomic mass of the cation, lattice dimensions, and force constants of these substances. The great elements of similarity between actinide and lanthanide chalcogenides provide a further nuclear energetic motivation for a more intensive study of lanthanide substances. Although many interesting analogies might be pointed out, this discussion will concern itself exclusively with the lanthanides.

Prior to 1960, cryogenic thermal data covering an adequate range of temperature to permit entropy evaluation at 298°K. existed only for six lanthanide compounds (*95*): CeF_3 (*97*), CeS (*99*), Ce_2S_3 (*99*), $EuSO_4 \cdot 8H_2O$ (*116*), $GdSO_4 \cdot 8H_2O$ (*3, 35, 36, 54, 106*), and $SmSO_4 \cdot 8H_2O$ (*2, 4*), although empirical estimates were formulated for several others. The four enthalpy increment determinations above 300°K. available were (with one exception) limited to oxides (*94*): CeF_3 (to 1799°K.) (*26*), La_2O_3 (to 1173°K.) (*12*), Nd_2O_3 (to 2000°K.) (*12*), and Pr_6O_{11} (to 1172°K.) (*12*), although estimates for several oxides (*29*), all the Ln(III) halides (*5*), plus the Ln(II) halides of europium, samarium, and ytterbium (*5*) existed and are tabulated elsewhere (*199*).

Cryothermal Measurements

It will be of interest to consider the thermal measurements since this area has been one of major activity in recent years. It is well known that the measurement of heat capacities at low temperatures provides a powerful tool for studying many solid-state phenomena, including the energy separation degeneracy of low lying energy levels in crystalline substances. The advantage of low temperature heat capacity measurements for providing insight into the energetic situation in these substances is that the contribution of the Schottky (*165*) anomalies to the heat capacity may be as large as or larger than the contribution of the vibrational modes of the lattice heat capacity.

Lanthanide(III) Oxides. The lanthanide(III) oxides will be used to illustrate the present breadth of our most extensive knowledge of the chemical thermodynamics of lanthanide compounds. Cryogenic heat capacities of hexagonal(III) lanthanum, neodymium, and samarium oxides, together with those of cubic(III) oxides of gadolinium, dysprosium, holmium, erbium, and ytterbium, have been reported (*90, 91, 195*). In addition, those of thulium, lutetium, and a composition approaching that of cerium(III) oxide have also been determined, and five well-characterized compositions between $PrO_{1.714}$ and $PrO_{1.833}$ are currently under study (*193*).

Table I. Properties of the Lanthanide(III) Ions

Atomic number	*Ion*	*Configuration*	*Ground term*	*Experimental magnetic moment*[a]
57	La		$^1S_0$	0.00[b]
58	Ce	$4f^1$	$^2F_{5/2}$	[2.56][c]
59	Pr	$4f^2$	$^3H_4$	3.55[d]
60	Nd	$4f^3$	$^4I_{9/2}$	3.66[b]
61	Pm	$4f^4$	$^5I_4$	[2.83][c]
62	Sm	$4f^5$	$^6H_{5/2}$	1.54[e]
63	Eu	$4f^6$	$^7F_0$	3.51[f]
64	Gd	$4f^7$	$^8S_{7/2}$	7.90[e]
65	Tb	$4f^8$	$^7F_6$	9.63[d]
66	Dy	$4f^9$	$^6H_{15/2}$	10.5[g]
67	Ho	$4f^{10}$	$^5I_8$	10.5[g]
68	Er	$4f^{11}$	$^4I_{15/2}$	9.5[g]
69	Tm	$4f^{12}$	$^3H_6$	7.39[e]
70	Yb	$4f^{13}$	$^2F_{7/2}$	4.34[h]
71	Lu	$4f^{14}$	$^1S_0$	[0.0][c]

[a] In Bohr magnetons.
[b] (*183*)
[c] (*111*)
[d] (*185*)
[e] (*179*)
[f] (*180*)
[g] (*20*)
[h] (*101*)

As shown in Table I, lanthanum and lutetium oxides have $^1S_0$ ground states and consequently their heat capacities should be attributed to lattice vibration. Data on these substances may be used to represent the lattice contribution to a first approximation for neighboring isostructural (and nearly so) sesquioxides. Cubic gadolinium oxide provides a mid-series lattice heat capacity approximation at relatively high temperatures because the crystal field acts mainly on the orbital angular momentum of the ion and has only a small effect on levels which are compounded purely from electron spin. In the absence of data on lutetium, resolution of magnetic heat capacity in the cubic oxides has been made from a combination of the low temperature heat capacity of ytterbium oxide and the higher temperature data on the gadolinium oxide. This resolution can be improved when data on lutetium are interpreted. Subtraction of the lattice heat capacity from the apparent or total heat capacity yields the magnetic heat capacity. Differences between C_p and C_v (arising from the anharmonicity of the lattice vibrations) should be cancelled in the proposed resolution, and if both para- and diamagnetic compounds are measured in the same laboratory, errors from systematic experimental discrepancies are minimized.

The excess (magnetic) heat capacity may be represented to a good approximation as the sum of (a) the electronic transitional (or Schottky) heat capacity, (b) the effects of interaction between the electrons and the nuclear spin of the paramagnetic ion, (c) the dipolar interaction between these ions, and (d) interactions for other types of interionic coupling. The last three terms are often small above 2°K. and in some instances can be obtained from paramagnetic relaxation data. In principle, the second and third can also be obtained from paramagnetic resonance data.

Entropy evaluations from published cryothermal data on the lanthanide(III) oxides are summarized in Table II with an indication of the lowest temperature of the measurements and the estimated magnetic entropy increments below this temperature. Their original assignment of crystalline field levels from thermal data still appears to be in good accord with recent findings (*e.g.*, *17*). Unfortunately, measurements on these substances were made only down to about 8°K. because the finely divided oxide samples tend to absorb the helium gas utilized to enhance thermal equilibration between sample and calorimeter.

Extension of heat capacity studies to lower temperatures is urgently desired from the chemical thermodynamicist's point of view because of evidence in many instances of cooperative or other magnetic anomalies below 8°K. in these substances. Neutron diffraction studies (*103*) indicate antiferromagnetic ordering in holmium oxide between 1.25° and 4.2°K., and antiferromagnetic ordering in erbium oxide at about 4°K. (*200*) confirmed earlier studies (*102, 202*) which indicated paramagnetic diffuse scattering and antiferromagnetic sub-lattice structures in the latter substance. Magnetization studies indicate the existence of a Néel (antiferromagnetic) transition at 2.5°K. in Yb_2O_3 (*69*), and at 1.2°K., 3.4°K., and 2.3°K. in Dy_2O_3, Er_2O_3, and Yb_2O_3, respectively (*14*). Cooperative transitions probably occur in other rare-earth oxides at or below liquid helium temperatures.

To facilitate chemical thermodynamic calculations, a nearly empirical scheme was devised recently by Grønvold and Westrum (*62*) for evaluating entropies for transition-element chalcogenides after a survey of available entropy data on such compounds. The scheme represents an extension of the approach used by Latimer (*112, 113*) in which the entropy of a compound is resolved into components for its atomic species. The new scheme incorporates a magnetic contribution based upon the spin-only moments and modifies the cationic contributions from those proposed by Latimer for the central region of the periodic system. The scheme has been shown to be in accordance with extensive data on transition-element chalcogenides. For the lanthanide oxides, the following metal and oxygen contributions obtain:

Cation contributions [in cal./(g.f.m.°K.)]:

Sc	*Y*	*La* → *Lu*
9.7	12	13.8

Oxygen contributions:

O_1	$O_{1.33}$	$O_{1.5}$	$O_{1.67}$	O_2
−2	−1	0	1	2

Comparison of the predictions of this scheme with the data for the diamagnetic sesquioxides of lanthanum and lutetium (*193*) suggests that if all of the entropy variation is to be ascribed to the cation, the contributions would have to decrease with increasing mass (or atomic number) from 15.2 for lanthanum to 13.0 for lutetium. As an approximation, the decrease is taken proportional to that of the cationic radius obtained by x-ray diffraction measurements. The following (improved) values then apply:

Improved cation contributions (La through Lu):

La	*Ce*	*Pr*	*Nd*	*Pm*	*Sm*	*Eu*	*Gd*
15.2	14.7	14.6	14.5	(14.3)	14.2	14.1	14.0

Tb	*Dy*	*Ho*	*Er*	*Tm*	*Yb*	*Lu*
13.8	13.6	13.5	13.3	13.2	13.1	13.0

Table II. Experimental Entropies of Lanthanide(III) Oxides at 298.15°K.[a]

Oxide	T_1	Entropies: Measured $^{S}T_{298} - {}^{S}T_1$	Entropies: Estimated $^{S}T_1 - {}^{S}0°K.$	$S°_{298}$
Y_2O_3	16	23.58[b]	0.11	23.69
Sc_2O_3	51	17.88[f]	0.48	18.4
La_2O_3	5	30.43[c]	0.002	30.43
	16	30.43[b]	0.15	30.58
Ce_2O_3		30.35[f]	5.67	36.0
Nd_2O_3	5	35.05[c]	2.8	37.9
	16	33.61[b]	3.31	36.92
Sm_2O_3	10	33.22[d]	2.9	36.1
Gd_2O_3	10	28.33[d]	7.8	36.0
Dy_2O_3	10	33.06[e]	2.7	35.8
Ho_2O_3	10	32.38[e]	5.4	37.8
Er_2O_3	10	33.81[e]	2.8	36.6
Yb_2O_3	10	29.01[d]	2.8	31.8

[a] Units: cal., g.f.m., °K.
[b] *(55)*
[c] *(90)*
[d] *(91)*
[e] *(195)*
[f] *(192)*

Application of these values plus the appropriate magnetic contributions leads to good agreement between observed and estimated entropies for Gd_2O_3 if the magnetic contributions to the experimental entropy are taken into account. The magnetic contributions have been obtained as $\Delta S_{mag} = R \ln_e (2J + 1)$ cal./(gram atom °K.) (in which J is the multiplicity of the ground level) except for Eu_2O_3. Here the high value for the effective magnetic moment of the Eu(III) ion has been explained in terms of the small energy differences between the ground and excited levels, $J = 1, 2, \ldots,$ in comparison with those of the multiplet components. A rough estimate on this basis leads to a magnetic entropy of 3.5 cal./(gram atom °K.) for Eu(III) in Eu_2O_3. Values of the entropy thus estimated for the lanthanide(III) oxides are presented in Table III.

Other Oxides. Apart from the sesquioxides, the only other lanthanide oxides on which sufficient cryothermal data exist to permit an entropy evaluation are diamagnetic CeO_2 (*194*) and ferromagnetic EuO (*63*). The measured entropy of CeO_2 suggests that the estimated cationic entropy contribution should be reduced about two entropy units in going from Ce(III) to Ce(IV), and thus about the same lattice entropy contribution is expected for all cerium oxides in the range $CeO_{1.5}$ to CeO_2. Since heavier lanthanide(IV) compounds contain $4f$ electrons, the effect will probably not be so pronounced for them. The value for Pr(IV) is reduced by a unit, while that for Tb(IV) is unchanged. Entropy estimates for such lanthanide oxides are found in Table IV. The magnetic contributions have been added with their full spin-only entropy value since the effective magnetic moments for the compounds investigated so far are not much lower than those expected for the corresponding "free ion" state.

Table III. Estimated Entropies of Lanthanide(III) Oxides at 298.15°K.[a]

Oxide	*Entropies*			
	Lattice	*Magnetic*	*Estimated* S°_{298}	*Observed* S°_{298}[b]
Y_2O_3	24.9	0	22.4	—
Sc_2O_3	19.4	0	19.4	—
La_2O_3	30.4	0	30.4	30.58
Ce_2O_3	29.3	7.12	36.4	—
Pr_2O_3	29.2	8.72	37.9	37.9
Nd_2O_3	28.9	9.14	38.0	36.92
Pm_2O_3	—	8.72	—	—
Sm_2O_3	28.3	7.12	35.4	36.1
Eu_2O_3	28.1	—	35	—
Gd_2O_3	28.0	8.26	36.3	36.0
Tb_2O_3	27.3	10.19	37.5	—
Dy_2O_3	27.1	11.02	38.1	35.8
Ho_2O_3	26.9	11.26	38.2	37.8
Er_2O_3	26.6	11.02	37.6	36.6
Tm_2O_3	26.3	10.19	36.5	—
Yb_2O_3	26.2	8.26	34.5	31.8
Lu_2O_3	26.0	0	26.0	—

[a] Units: cal., g.f.m., °K.
[b] *Cf.* Table II.

New heat capacity data on oxides over the cryogenic region from 51°K. to 300°K. have been reported by Weller and King (*190*) on scandium(III) oxide and on a composition ($Ce_2O_{3.33}$) assumed to be cerium(III) oxide with CeO_2 as a contaminant. The entropies at 298.15°K. are 17.88 and 6.00 cal./(mole °K.), respectively. Extrapolation below 51°K. on Sc_2O_3 amounts to 0.48 cal./(mole °K.), that on the cerium compound to 5.67 since the total spin entropy ($2R \ln 2$) was included in addition to the sizeable lattice contribution.

Data on Metals. A compilation of the available entropy values for lanthanide metals is given in Table V. It will be noted that these values also include significant estimated magnetic contributions to the entropy and the precision indicated may be deceptive. Experimental values are

Table IV. Entropy Estimates for Other Lanthanide Oxides at 298.15°K.[a]

Oxide	Entropies		
	Lattice	*Magnetic*	S°_{298}
$CeO_{1.67}$	14.7	2.5	17.2
$CeO_{1.72}$	14.7	1.8	16.5
$CeO_{1.78}$	14.7	1.5	16.2
$CeO_{1.81}$	14.7	1.5	16.2
CeO_2	14.7	—	14.7
$PrO_{1.70}$	15.1	[4.0]	[19.1]
$PrO_{1.74}$	15.2	[4.0]	[19.2]
$PrO_{1.83}$	15.3	3.8	19.1
PrO_2	15.6	3.5	19.1
SmO	12.2	[3.5]	[15.7]
EuO	12.1	[4.2]	[16.3]
$TbO_{1.72}$	14.8	4.5	19.3
$TbO_{1.81}$	15.1	4.3	19.4
TbO_2	15.8	4.0	19.8

[a] Units: cal., g.f.m., °K. By Westrum and Grønvold scheme (*192*).

still lacking for Sc, Pm, Eu, and Yb. Some discrepancies occur among the results of the various investigators listed in Table V, usually in the magnetic heat-capacity contribution.

Data on several metals are especially pertinent since observed cryogenic anomalies are interpreted as resulting from contaminant oxides and are noted beyond mere mention in Table V. For example, measurement of the low temperature heat capacity of gadolinium metal (*107*) revealed a large anomaly extending from about 0.5°K. to 5°K. To resolve the dilemma, Crane (*30*) measured metal samples with 0.22, 0.12, and 0.11 weight % oxygen contamination; peaks increasing in magnitude with greater oxygen concentration were again observed at roughly the same temperatures as those found previously. Lounasmaa (*119*) confirmed the presence of these anomalous peaks at 1.6° and 3.7°K. and, in addition, found a shoulder near 1.1°K. Crane found the total excess entropy below 5°K. (attributed to contaminant Gd_2O_3) to be close to the value of R ln 8 expected for the magnetic ordering of Gd(III) ions. Lounasmaa's analysis also attributes the anomalous heat capacity to the presence of sesquioxide in the metal. Although the anomaly does appear to be associated with the amount of oxygen present, it is perhaps a debatable question whether or not Gd_2O_3 rather than a lower oxide is responsible. In an endeavor to resolve this discrepancy, heat-capacity measurements on the sesquioxides at sufficiently low temperatures are obvious desirable. Recent heat capacity measurements on terbium metal by Gerstein, *et al.* (*52*) provide evidence that the anomaly at 2.42°K. found in earlier measurements was indeed occasioned by the presence of Tb_2O_3, as indicated by the discovery of antiferromagnetic ordering at 2.42°K. in the terbium(III) oxide.

Table V. Entropies of Lanthanide Metals at 298.15°K.[a]

Metal	*Lattice Entropies + cond. elec.*[b]	*Magnetic*[c]	*Exp. S°*[d]	*Ref.*
Sc	—	0	[8.20]	*62,131,141,191*
Y	—	0	10.63	*9,87,131*
La	13.35	0	13.64	*15,156*
Ce	13.22	3.56	16.68	*15,124,155*
Pr	13.09	4.37	17.49	*15,84,122*
Nd	12.96	4.58	17.54	*15,84,122*
Pm	12.88	4.37	[17.2]	*177*
Sm	12.76	3.56	16.64	*37,38,40,85,117,120,163*
Eu	—	4.13	[17.0]	*124,127,177*
Gd	12.52	4.13	15.77	*60,107,187*
Tb	12.40	5.10	17.48	*37,52,68,88,96,107,120,126,129,173*
Dy	12.29	5.51	17.87	*32,37,39,61,120126,128,157*
Ho	12.18	5.63	18.00	*51,58,59,96,118,120,174*
Er	12.11	5.10	17.52	*37,40,157,168*
Tm	12.00		17.37	*86,125*
Yb	—	0	[15.0]	*53,119,120,121,126,127,177*
Lu	11.79	0	12.19	*87,123*

[a] Units: cal., g.f.m., °K.
[b] Contribution of lattice vibration and conduction electrons to entropy estimated by Skochdopole, Griffel, and Spedding (*168*).
[c] Magnetic contribution to entropy estimated by Skochdopole, Griffel, and Spedding (*168*).
[d] Experimental (estimated if in brackets) entropy values based on first-mentioned source of heat-capacity data.

Thermochemical Values and the Thermodynamics of Formation

The enthalpies and entropies of formation of the lanthanide(III) oxides based on data in Tables II, III, IV, and V are presented in Table VI, together with the Gibbs energies derived from them. A semi-critical evaluation of the several sources of these values is contained in the superscripted references and notes. This compilation updates that of Montgomery (*142*) and those of Westrum (*191, 192*) because of the availability of better enthalpy of formation data, low temperature heat capacities for eight oxides, and a better understanding of the causes governing the magnitudes of the entropies of these substances. A similar tabulation for other lanthanide oxides is found in Table VII.

From aqueous calorimetry Burnett and Cunningham (*18*) found the $\Delta Hf°_{298}$ of $EuO_{1.02}$ to be −153.5 kcal./mole and, assuming the deviation from stoichiometry to be caused by the presence of Eu_2O_3, calculated that of EuO to be −145.2 kcal./mole. Formulas for the calculation of the enthalpy of formation, Gibbs energy of formation, entropy, and heat capacity of crystallohydrates $Ln_2O_3 \cdot nH_2O$ for Ln = Nd, Pr, and Ce have been devised by Maslov and Maslov (*134*).

Table VI. Enthalpies, Entropies, and Gibbs Energies of Formation of Lanthanide(III) Oxides at 298.15°K.[a]

Oxide	*Structure*[b]	$-\Delta Hf° \times 10^{-3}$	$-\Delta Sf°$[s]	$-\Delta Ff° \times 10^{-3}$
$ScO_{1.5}$	bcc	228.1 ± 0.05[c]	[35.6]	217.5
$YO_{1.5}$	bcc	227.73 ± 0.27[d]	35.54[t]	[217.1]
$LaO_{1.5}$	hex	214.29 ± 0.19[e]	35.18[u]	203.80
$CeO_{1.5}$	hex	217.46 ± 0.05[f]	[35.2]	[207.0]
$PrO_{1.5}$	hex	217.9 ± 0.8[g]	[35.4]	[207.4]
	bcc	218.4 ± 0.8[g]	[35.4]	[207.8]
$NdO_{1.5}$	hex	216.08 ± 0.12[h]	[35.3]	[205.6]
$PmO_{1.5}$	—	[216.5]	[35.4]	[206]
$SmO_{1.5}$	m	216.95 ± 0.24[i]	[35.4]	[206.4]
$EuO_{1.5}$	m	−196.9 ± 0.5[j]	[36]	[186]
$GdO_{1.5}$	m	216.97 ± 0.43[k]	[34.4]	[206.7]
$TbO_{1.5}$	bcc	218.4 ± 1.0[l]	[35.8]	[207.7]
$DyO_{1.5}$	bcc	222.92 ± 0.47[m]	[35.7]	[212.3]
$HoO_{1.5}$	bcc	224.78 ± 0.58[n]	[35.7]	[214.1]
$ErO_{1.5}$	bcc	226.80 ± 0.23[o]	[35.5]	[216.2]
$TmO_{1.5}$	bcc	225.7 ± 0.7[p]	[35.7]	[215.1]
$YbO_{1.5}$	bcc	216.84 ± 0.27[q]	[34.5]	[206.6]
$LuO_{1.5}$	bcc	224.5 ± 0.9[r]	[35.6]	[213.9]

[a] On basis discussed in text. Units: cal., g.f.m., °K.
[b] bcc = body-centered cubic (C-type), hex = hexagonal (A-type), m = monoclinic (B-type).
[c] Huber, *et al.* (*71*); *cf.* also Mah (*133*).
[d] Huber, Head, and Holley (*75*).
[e] La_2O_3; the combustion value [−428.59] of Huber and Holley (*80*) is adopted. This is in good accord with that [−428.57 ± 0.19] of Fitzgibbon, Holley, and Wadsö (*47*), that of Spedding and Flynn (*171*), and that of Montgomery (*142*), as well as with the value [−430.0] of Von Wartenberg (*186*), provided the enthalpy of solution data of Spedding and Flynn (*171*) are used rather than the Bommer and Hohmann (*13*) value. Four earlier determinations differ by more than 10 kcal., but the solution value of Matignon (*135*) is close [−427.7].
[f] Kuznetsov, *et al.* (*110*) which accords with Gerassimov, *et al.* (*49*). The value of Brauer, Gingerich, and Holtschmidt (*16*) for the reaction $CeO_{1.5} + 0.25\ O_2 = CeO_2$ is about 4 kcal. more negative. Mah (*132*) obtains −213.5 ± 0.4 kcal./mole.
[g] Stubblefield, Eick, and Eyring (*175*).
[h] Nd_2O_3; the combustion value of Huber and Holley (*79*) taken in preference to those of Spedding, Eberts, and Naumann (*170*) [−214.88 and −213.82] because of uncertainty in the latter due to lack of analytical data for non-metallic impurities.
[i] Sm_2O_3; the combustion value of Huber, Matthews, and Holley (*83*) is taken in preference to that of Spedding, Eberts, and Naumann (*170*) [−212.40] for the reason cited in (*h*); *cf.* Montgomery and Hubert (*143*).
[j] Huber, *et al.* (*72*) by combustion in oxygen. Their enthalpies of solution indicate $\Delta H° = -4.3 \pm 0.6$ kcal./mole for the reaction $Eu_2O_3(\text{cubic}) \rightarrow Eu_2O_3(\text{monoclinic})$. [*Cf.* Stuve (*178*)].
[k] Gd_2O_3; the combustion value of Huber and Holley (*82*) is preferred to that of Spedding, Eberts, and Naumann (*170*) [−213.46] for the reason cited in (*h*).

[l] Stubblefield, Eick, and Eyring (*176*).
[m] Huber, Head, and Holley (*73*).
[n] Huber, Head, and Holley (*76*).
[o] Er_2O_3; the combustion value of Huber, Head, and Holley (*74*) is taken in preference to that of Spedding, Eberts, and Naumann (*170*); *cf.* (*h*).
[p] Huber, Head, and Holley (*77*).
[q] Huber, Head, and Holley (*73*).
[r] Huber, Head, and Holley (*78*).
[s] Although the values in brackets are properly indicated as estimated, they have been taken from Tables II, III, and V and are based (as noted in these Tables) on experimental data for oxygen, most metals, and many oxides.
[t] Y_2O_3; Goldstein, *et al.* (*55*).
[u] La_2O_3; the entropy data of Justice and Westrum (*92*) have been taken in preference to those of Goldstein, *et al.* (*55*).

Table VII. Thermodynamics of Formation of Other Lanthanide Oxides at 298.15°K.[a]

Oxide	*Structure*[b]	$-\Delta Hf° \times 10^{-3}$	$-\Delta Sf°$[f]	$-\Delta Ff° \times 10^{-3}$
$CeO_{1.67}$	bcc	[233]	[40.3]	[221]
$CeO_{1.72}$	rh	[238]	[42.4]	[255]
$CeO_{1.78}$	rh	[244]	[44.1]	[231]
$CeO_{1.81}$	rh	[247]	[44.8]	[234]
CeO_2	bcc	260.18 ± 0.16[c]	50.80[g]	245.0
$PrO_{1.71}$	bcc	223.5 ± 0.8[d]	[40.1]	[211.5]
$PrO_{1.74}$	rh	[225]	[40.9]	[212.8]
$PrO_{1.80}$	bcc	227.6 ± 0.8[d]	[43.2]	[214.7]
PrO_2	bcc	232.9[d]	[47.4]	[218.8]
$TbO_{1.72}$	rh	223.3 ± 1.0[e]	[40.4]	[211.2]
$TbO_{1.81}$	tri	226.4 ± 1.0[e]	[42.4]	[213.8]
TbO_2	bcc	[231]	[46.7]	[217]

[a] On basis discussed in text. Units: cal., g.f.m., °K.
[b] bcc = body-centered cubic (C-type), rh = rhombohedral, tri = trigonal.
[c] Huber and Holley (*81*).
[d] Stubblefield, Eick, and Eyring (*175*).
[e] Stubblefield, Eick, and Eyring (*176*).
[f] Although the values in brackets are properly indicated as estimated, they have been taken from Tables IV and V and are based (as noted in these Tables) on experimental data for oxygen, most metals, and many oxides.
[g] CeO_2; Westrum and Beale (*194*).

Higher Temperature Thermodynamic Measurements

Oxides. Determinations of the enthalpy and derived functions by the method of mixtures have also been made for purposes of metallurgical and ceramic applications on most of the lanthanide(III) oxides usually to temperatures of about 2000°K. (*100, 152, 153, 154*). The results of these determinations have been summarized in Table VIII.

King and Christensen (*98*) and Kuznetsov and Rezukhina (*108*) have independently determined the high temperature enthalpy of CeO_2. The latter workers (*109*) have also determined the enthalpy of cerium(III) oxide from 578° to 1168°K. Earlier studies have been summarized in the compilation by Kelley (*94*). In addition to studies on the sesquioxides reported in Table VIII, Pankratz made high temperature enthalpy determinations on $PrO_{1.833}$, $TbO_{1.719}$, and $TbO_{1.812}$ to at least 850°K. (*150*). Enthalpy increments for the *C* and *B* forms of Eu_2O_3, Tm_2O_3, and Yb_2O_3 were determined from 298° to 1600°K. by drop calorimetry by Tsagareishvili and Gvelesiani (*182*).

Table VIII. High Temperature Entropies of the Lanthanide(III) Oxides[a]

Oxide	*Structure*	$S°_T - S°_{298}$		*Transitions*	
		1000°K.	*2000°K.*	T_t	ΔHt
Sc_2O_3[b]	cubic	32.34	54.02		
Y_2O_3[c]	cubic	31.22	56.00	1330°	310
La_2O_3[d]	hex.	35.42	58.40		
Ce_2O_3[e]	α, hex.	39.12	—		
	β, hex.	40.96	—		
Pr_2O_3[f]	—	38.26	—		
Nd_2O_3[c]	hex.	37.03	62.48		
Sm_2O_3[c]	cubic	38.65	—		
	mono.	38.31	63.79		
Eu_2O_3[c]	cubic	40.13	—		
	mono.	39.38	64.98	895°	130
Gd_2O_3[c]	cubic	34.75	—		
	mono.	34.21	56.56		
Tb_2O_3[f]	cubic	37.42	—		
Dy_2O_3[e]	cubic	36.73	60.17		
Ho_2O_3[g]	cubic	35.62	58.23		
Er_2O_3[g]	cubic	34.99	57.36		
Tm_2O_3[g]	cubic	36.28	58.54	1680°	310
Yb_2O_3[g]	cubic	36.62	58.83	1365°	150
Lu_2O_3[e]	cubic	33.76	55.62		

[a] Units: cal., g.f.m., °K.
[b] (*151*)
[c] (*154*)
[d] (*100*)
[e] (*152*)
[f] (*150*)
[g] (*153*)

Metals. High temperature thermal functions plus enthalpies of transition and melting of cerium, neodymium, and samarium metal have been determined to 1370°K. from enthalpy increment determinations using a Bunsen ice calorimeter by Spedding, McKeown, and Daane (*172*). These properties for eight other lanthanide metals were reported by Dennison, Gschneidner, and Daane (*34*). Their results are summarized in Table IX. Values for yttrium, praseodymium, europium, and ytterbium have been determined by Berg (*8*), and are to be published by Berg, Spedding, and Daane (*9, 10*).

Table IX. High Temperature Thermal Properties of Lanthanide Metals[a]

Element	$S°_T - S°_0$		*Transition*		*Melting*	
	1000°K.	*1800°K.*	T_t	ΔSt	T_m	ΔSm
Sc[b]	16.16	21.92	1608	0.60	1812	1.86
Ce[c]	27.11	—	1003	0.70	1077	1.15
Nd[c]	26.82	—	1135	0.63	1297	1.31
Sm[c]	27.72	—	1190	0.63	1345	1.53
Gd[b]	25.06	—	1533	0.61	1585	1.52
Tb[b]	26.25	34.25(*l*)	1560	0.77	1630	1.58
Dy[b]	26.12	33.90(*l*)	1657	[0.56]	1682	[1.53]
Ho[b]	26.23	34.13(*l*)	1701	[0.66]	1743	[1.67]
Er[b]	25.95	33.73(*l*)	—	—	1795	2.65
Tm[b]	25.44	20.25	—	—	1818	2.21
Lu[b]	20.07	25.03	—	—	—	—

[a] Units: cal., g.atom, °K.
[b] (*34*)
[c] (*173*)

Thermodynamics of Vaporization and Decomposition

Oxides. Decomposition pressure measurements on the TbO_x system by Eyring and his collaborators (*64*) have been supplemented by similar and related studies on the PrO_x system (*46*) and on other lanthanide-oxygen systems (*43, 44*). Extensive and systematic studies of vaporization processes in lanthanide-oxide systems have been undertaken by White, *et al.* (*6, 188, 196*) using conventional Knudsen effusion measurements of the rates of vaporization of the oxides into high vacuum. Combination of these data with information on the entropies and Gibbs energy functions of reactants and products of the reaction yields enthalpies of reaction. In favorable instances (*i.e.,* if spectroscopic data on the gaseous species are available), the enthalpies of formation and the stabilities of previously undetermined individual species are also derived. The rates of vaporization of 17 lanthanide-oxide systems (*196*) and the vaporization of lanthanum, neodymium, and yttrium oxides at temperatures between 22° and 2700°K. have been reported (*188*).

Three significant studies by White, *et al.* involve the vaporization of La_2O_3 and Nd_2O_3 (*56*), mass spectrometric determination of the enthalpies of sublimation of rare-earth metals (*198*), and the thermodynamics of vaporization of the rare-earth oxides at elevated temperatures (*197*). The first and third studies also involve the dissociation energy of the gaseous monoxides. Their experimental work on the oxides included four types of measurements: (a) determination of the rates of vaporization of La_2O_3, Nd_2O_3, Sm_2O_3, Gd_2O_3, Lu_2O_3, and Y_2O_3 at high temperatures using the Knudsen effusion technique, (b) determination of the composition of the solid(III) oxides as a function of the extent of vaporization by x-ray powder diffraction methods, (c) determination of the composition of the vapors effusing from the Knudsen cell by mass spectrometric methods, and (d) determination of the equilibrium constants (as a function of temperature and the related thermodynamic function) for the isomolecular oxygen-exchange reactions,

$$Ln(g) + Ln'O(g) \rightleftarrows Ln'(g) + LnO(g),$$

in which Ln and Ln′ represent different rare-earth elements from the group: La, Ce, Pr, Nd, Sm, Eu, Tb, Lu, and Y. The thermodynamic analysis of the effusion data was performed by a modified "third-law" technique which did not require knowledge of the vapor-phase composition but only of the species present. A portion of the results of their vaporization studies is presented in Table X. In addition, these authors

Table X. Thermodynamics of Vaporization of Lanthanide(III) Oxides[a]

Oxide	$\Delta Hv°_0$ [b]	$\Delta Hf°_0$ [c] *For MO(g) (kcal./mole)*	$D°_0$ [d] *For MO (eV)*
Y_2O_3	502.6	−5.0 ± 5.0	7.10 ± 0.2
La_2O_3	430.2	−27.9 ± 5.0	8.26 ± 0.2
Nd_2O_3	428.0	−31.2 ± 7.0	7.24 ± 0.3
Sm_2O_3	443.2	−24.0 ± 7.0	5.77 ± 0.3
Gd_2O_3	453.3	−18.6 ± 7.0	7.02 ± 0.3
Lu_2O_3	495.7	−5.3 ± 7.0	6.90 ± 0.3

[a] White, *et al.* (*197*).
[b] $\Delta Hv°_0$, standard enthalpy of vaporization at 0°K. for the reaction $Ln_2O_3(c) \rightarrow 2LnO(g) + O(g)$.
[c] $\Delta Hf°_0$, standard enthalpy of formation for LnO(g) at 0°K.
[d] $D°_0$, standard dissociation energy of LnO(g) at 0°K.

examined the vaporization of Pr_6O_{11}, CeO_2, Eu_2O_3, and Tb_4O_7, but the results have not been reported since changes in the solid phase compositions yield time-dependent rates of vaporization.

A striking correlation results from a comparison of the dissociation energies of the gaseous monoxides with the variation of the enthalpies of sublimation of the metals given in Table XI. Although both show large variations, these variations are almost identical for both sets of data. The increments in the binding energies of the monoxides must coincide almost with those in the cohesive energies of the corresponding solid metals. The increment gradually (and essentially monotonically) becomes more positive with increasing atomic number. Since it is possible

Table XI. High Temperature Thermodynamic Functions for the Lanthanide Metals[a]

Metal	ΔHs°_{0} [b]	$S^{\circ}_{2000^{\circ}K.}$ [c]
Y	99.0	53.4
La	103.0	56.5
Nd	76.6	57.4
Sm	50.0	57.4
Gd	84.1	58.2
Lu	94.7	55.1

[a] White, *et al.* (*197, 198*).
[b] Standard enthalpy of sublimation at 0°K. kcal./gram atom.
[c] For the gaseous phase; units: cal./(gram atom °K.).

to predict the trends of the enthalpies of sublimation and of the dissociation energies for the gaseous lanthanide oxides, these values can be used to predict the thermodynamics of the vaporization of the solid sesquioxides. Previously mentioned work (*56*) on the vaporization of La_2O_3 and Nd_2O_3 indicated that the reaction proceeds essentially as follows:

$$Ln_2O_3(c) \rightarrow 2LnO(g) + O(g)$$

The vaporization of Pr_2O_3, Nd_2O_3, Sm_2O_3, and Eu_2O_3 at temperatures ranging from 1950° to 2350°K. has been studied by Panish (*149, 150*), who analyzed the species effusing from a Knudsen effusion cell with a time-of-flight mass spectrometer.

Mass spectrophotometric study of the vaporization equilibria in the system lanthanum-lanthanum oxide (*27*) yields $D_{0^{\circ}K.}$ (LaO) = 8.15 ± 0.35 *eV* and $\Delta H^{\circ}_{0^{\circ}K.}$ = 189 ± 8 kcal./mole for the reaction

$$LaO(g) = La(g) + O(g).$$

Vapor pressure *vs.* temperature data are presented graphically for the rare earths by Beavis (*7*).

The thermodynamics of gaseous yttrium monoxide have been investigated by Ackermann, *et al.* (*1*), and the dissociation energy of the scandium monoxide molecule mass-spectrometrically was determined by Smoes, *et al.* (*168*). These authors identified and determined atomization energies for the suboxides Sc_2O, Y_2O, Y_2O_2, La_2O, and La_2O_2. Vapor pressures of oxides of La, Ce, Pr, Nd, Sm, Eu, Gd, Dy, Ho, Er, and Lu were determined by the effusion method over the range 1980°–2400°C. by Kul'varskaya and Maslovskaya (*105*).

Although such data do not appear to have been taken, the facile reversibility of the PrO_x system, for example, suggests the desirability of the direct calorimetric determination of the partial molal thermodynamic quantities for the variation in *x*, as has been done for UO_{2+x} by Gerdanian and Dodé (*50*) utilizing a high temperature microcalorimeter. The greater rapidity of the oxygen evolution and adsorption at much lower temperatures in the PrO_x system would greatly facilitate the study even with intermediate temperature adiabatic calorimeters.

Semenov obtained enthalpies of sublimation of Sc_2O_3 and dissociation of ScO by mass spectrometry (*165*).

Metals. Kruglikh, *et al.* (*104*) measured saturated vapor pressures of erbium, samarium, and ytterbium by the Knudsen effusion method, and standard (average) sublimation entropies of 18.4, 20.7, and 25.6 cal./(gram atom °K.) were derived. Nesmeyanov, *et al.* (*146*) studied the vapor pressure of yttrium by an integral variant of the effusion technique. Similar studies at higher temperatures by Herrick (*70*) on samarium metal have been interpreted in good accord by both first and second law methods. Ideal gas thermodynamic functions have been derived from 100°K. to 6000°K. at 100° intervals for both actinide and lanthanide elements by Feber and Herrick (*45*).

Monochalcogenides

The discovery by Matthias, *et al.* (*136*) that EuO (both an oxide and an insulator) is ferromagnetic has stimulated considerable research on divalent europium chalcogenides. These are particularly interesting materials because they combine several features of the ideal Heisenberg ferromagnet with localized spin-only moments for the magnetic ions and the relatively simple fcc crystal structure. Only the telluride has antiferromagnetic ordering. EuO is the only monochalcogenide whose heat capacity has been determined over a sufficient region (15°–280°K.) to permit useful thermodynamic evaluations (*63*). Their data include a large and sharply defined anomaly at 69.2 ± 0.2°K. due to the onset of ferromagnetism.

The heat capacity of EuS was measured to test the predictions of spin-wave theory from 1° to 38°K. by McCollum and Callaway (*137*) and independently from 10° to 35°K. by Moruzzi and Teaney (*145*). A sharp Néel peak was found at 16.2°K. Magnetic and lattice contributions to the heat capacities were resolved on the assumption of a T^3 dependence for the lattice and a T^{-2} dependence for the magnetic contribution at temperatures above the Néel point. A plot of CT^2 *vs.* T^5 yields a straight line between 21° and 31°K. and a Debye temperature of 208°K.

An extended two-particle cluster approximation involving nearest- and next-nearest neighbor exchange for para- and ferromagnets (with particular reference to EuO, EuS, EuSe, and EuTe) has been developed (*22*). Heat capacity curves, Curie temperatures, magnetization curves, susceptibilities, and spin-correlation functions thus derived are in excellent accord with experimental results. A second neighbor exchange integral applicable for the EuS situation has been derived (*21*). Similar analyses for EuS based both on simple and complete spin-wave theory have also been presented (*24, 25*). Another application of spin-wave theory to EuO and EuS has been made by Low (*130*). His heat capacity values depart from the experimental values at a temperature about a third that of the Curie point. Considerable further evidence that EuS is nearly an ideal Heisenberg ferromagnet is provided by the accord of its calculated higher temperature heat capacity on this model (*201*) with experimental data.

Heat capacities taken over the range 1.3°–20°K. (*19*) show an extremely narrow peak at 4.58 ± 0.03°K. at the EuSe ferromagnetic Curie temperature and one at 9.64 ± 0.06°K. in EuTe identified with the antiferromagnetic transition. The magnetic transition entropy increments are 4 and 3 cal./(mole °K.).

The congruent vaporization of LaS has been studied over the range 2012°–2490°K. using the effusion technique with the aid of a vacuum balance and a mass spectrometer by Cater, *et al.* (*23*).

Pnictides

The heat capacities of sintered specimens of LaN and NdN were measured from 1.2°K. to 45°K. by Veyssie, *et al.* (*185*). LaN shows a slight anomaly attributed to magnetic impurities; NdN has a peak at 27.6 ± 0.1°K. corresponding to a (ferromagnetic) Curie transition. Debye θ values are 300° and ~360°K., respectively, but the data do not cover an adequate range to permit evaluation of the thermodynamic properties.

Carbides

Time-of-flight mass spectrometry and target collection techniques over the range 1130°–1600°K. on $EuC_{1.87 \pm 0.07}$ yield a value of the enthalpy and Gibbs energy of formation (*48*).

Hexaborides

Studies on the thermal properties of lanthanum, cerium, neodymium, and gadolinium hexaborides in the cryogenic region from 5° to 350°K. (*193*) have shown the presence of two types of anomalies in the latter three substances. At temperatures near 10°K. there appears a lambda-type anomaly in each which is rather characteristic of a magnetic transformation. At slightly higher temperatures this is followed by Schottky-like anomalies. To a first approximation these anomalies resemble those to be expected from a set of crystal-field Schottky levels and can be treated in the same fashion as those in the oxides. It seems evident that in the case of the gadolinium compound, the splitting deduced as a consequence of interpreting this anomaly as a Schottky effect is much larger than expected for the second-order interaction of the crystal field with the spin-orbit coupling vector, which mechanism is believed to hold for rare-earth ions. A Schottky anomaly with the ratio of 3:1 (for the excited to ground state) is needed to explain the curve. Difficulties of interpretation suggest caution in deriving chemical thermodynamic values based upon hexaboride data (except for lanthanum hexaboride) until the interpretation of the observed anomalies in these conducting materials has been clarified.

Enthalpies of sublimation based on Knudsen effusion measurements have been determined for LaB_6 by Gordienko, *et al.* (*57*). The thermodynamics of formation of lanthanide hexaborides from oxides have been deduced by Portnoi, *et al.* (*162*); vaporization and stabilities have been studied by Smith (*168*).

Halides

The interest in the crystalline field parameters and the magnetic transitions in the lanthanide trihalides has preceded determination of magnetocaloric and other thermal data. Recent magnetic susceptibility measurements on $CeCl_3$, $PrCl_3$, and $NdCl_3$ (*42*) have indicated unexplained cooperative anomalies. Heat capacity measurements over the range 0.26°K.–4.2°K. (*93*) revealed a single sharp peak at 0.27°K. indicating cooperative ordering but no anomaly at the previously reported susceptibility peak (0.345°K.). The data do not permit an entropy evaluation.

Heat capacities have been reported on $DyCl_3 \cdot 6H_2O$ and $NdCl_3 \cdot 6H_2O$ (1.1°–220°K.) (*160*), on $LuCl_3 \cdot 6H_2O$ (1.4°–223°K.) (*159*), on $LaCl_3 \cdot 7H_2O$ and $PrCl_3 \cdot 7H_2O$ (5°–262°K.) (*66*), on $GdCl_3 \cdot 6H_2O$ (1.1°–259°K.) (*67*), and on $HoCl_3 \cdot 6H_2O$ and $ErCl_3 \cdot 6H_2O$ (1.2°–230.8°K.) (*158*). Unfortunately, these data do not extend up to 298°K. so that precise entropy comparisons are not available at these temperatures. By plotting C/T *vs.* T for the above data, Cobble (*28*) found near linearity above 120°K., extrapolated the data to 298°K., and by means of an analysis similar (but not so detailed) to that already discussed for the oxides, the results given in Table XII are obtained.

By subtracting the total estimated magnetic contributions, net or lattice entropies are obtained which appear to be more variant than those for the sesquioxides. The last column indicates a near constancy of the ratio of $(S_{net}/C_p)_{298°K.}$. Therefore, $GdCl_3 \cdot 6H_2O$ and $ErCl_3 \cdot 6H_2O$ have

Table XII. Entropies for Hydrated Lanthanide Halides at 298.15°K.[a]

Compound	Ionic State	Entropy, 298°K. Total (Extrapolated)	Magnetic (Estimated)	Lattice[b] (S_{net})	C_p	(S_{net}/C_p)
$LaCl_3 \cdot 7H_2O$[c]	$^1S_0$	110.6	0	110.6	102.6	1.08
$PrCl_3 \cdot 7H_2O$[c]	$^3H_4$	112.7	4.4	108.3	[101.1][d]	1.07
$NdCl_3 \cdot 6H_2O$	$^4I_{9/2}$	99.5	4.6	94.9	86.8	1.09
$GdCl_3 \cdot 6H_2O$	$^8S_{7/2}$	93.6	4.1	89.5	82.7	1.08
$DyCl_3 \cdot 6H_2O$	$^6H_{15/2}$	96.9	5.5	91.4	82.8	1.10
$HoCl_3 \cdot 6H_2O$	$^5I_8$	96.6	5.6	91.0	82.5	1.10
$ErCl_3 \cdot 6H_2O$	$^4I_{15/2}$	95.3	5.5	89.8	82.3	1.08
$LuCl_3 \cdot 6H_2O$	$^1S_0$	90.9	0	90.9	83.4	1.09

[a] After Cobble (*28*) based on the data of Pfeffer, *et al.* (*66, 67, 158, 159, 160*).
[b] The net entropy is the difference between the measured entropy and the magnetic entropy.
[c] There is some uncertainty in the stoichiometry of these hydrates (*66*).
[d] Estimated from the authors' (*66*) data on the difference between the heat capacities of $LaCl_3 \cdot 7H_2O$ and $PrCl_3 \cdot 7H_2O$ from 150° to 250°K.

lower lattice entropies but correspondingly lower heat capacities at this temperature. Cobble concludes that measurements made to near 1°K. have included much of the magnetic entropy on these compounds. These and systematic trends make it possible to estimate entropies for a number of related substances.

The enthalpy of formation of YF_3 was determined by Rudzitis, Feder, and Hubbard (*164*) using fluorine bomb calorimetry. $NdCl_3$ was done by solution methods (*179*), and the enthalpies of formation of LaF_3 and PrF_3 were determined by Polyachenok (*161*) who employed an indirect equilibration technique. A recent torsion-effusion study of the vapor pressure of CeF_3 (*115*) yields second and third law values for the enthalpy of sublimation. The thermodynamics of the chlorination of rare earths with gaseous chlorine have also been investigated (*144*). Gibbs energies of formation were determined for $CeCl_3$ by solid-state electromotive force techniques (*41*).

Hydrides

Studies of the scandium—hydrogen system by isothermal equilibration were made by Lieberman and Wahlbeck (*114*). Parallel studies on the yttrium—hydrogen system have been reported by Yannopoulos, *et al.* (*203*). Heat capacities on YH_3 and $CeH_{2.86}$ over the usual cryogenic range are discussed by Bieganski, *et al.* (*11*). A pronounced anomaly at about 255°K. could not be ascribed to a phase change or magnetic ordering.

Miscellaneous Materials

Among the most interesting studies of thermal properties of rare-earth iron garnets are the heat capacity measurements at low temperature of Meyer and Harris (*65, 139*). Their data cover only the range 1.4°–20°K. Below 5°K. the heat capacity of yttrium iron garnet can be represented by the sum of the lattice term proportional to T^3 and by the spin-wave contribution of $2.15 \times 10^{-3}T^{3/2}$ j/(mole °K.). This last term is in good accord with a calculation based on spin-wave analysis, in which the exchange interaction coefficients were those derived from Pauthenet's magnetization data.

Data on the interesting Schottky transformations in the lanthanide hydrated ethyl sulfates by Meyer and his collaborators (*89, 138, 140*) are suggestive and of considerable interest, but they do not cover a sufficiently extended range to permit entropy calculations. Vapor pressure data of metallically bonded lanthanide-magnesium alloys have been used also to deduce enthalpies of formation of CsCl-type compounds. Since data were unavailable, ΔC_p values were assumed to be zero (*147*).

Finally, significant advances in the techniques of both thermal and thermochemical measurements have come to fruition in the last decade, notably "aneroid" rotating-bomb calorimetry and automatic adiabatic shield control, so that enhanced calorimetric precision is possible, and the tedium is greatly reduced by high speed digital computation. Non-calorimetric experimental approaches as well as theoretical ones, *e.g.*, calculation of electronic heat capacity contributions to di- and trivalent lanthanides by Dennison and Gschneidner (*33*), are also adding to definitive thermodynamic functions.

Current interest in high temperature chemistry and the closely related thermodynamics of the actinides will provide additional stimuli for determining precise thermodynamic data in cryogenic as well as in higher temperature regions. The "utopian era" in the chemical thermodynamics of the lanthanides is sufficiently far off to occasion extension of shrewdly devised schemes to other classes of compounds. Use of the semi-empirical schemes already discussed—or theoretically based ones—plus the key compound concept may prove as effective here (desipte magnetic and electronic complications) as it has for hydrocarbon thermodynamics.

Acknowledgment

The author expresses his gratitude to the U. S. Atomic Energy Commission for partial support of his research endeavors at the University of Michigan on the cryogenic thermal and magnetic properties of the rare-earth chalcogenides and related substances. He also wishes to thank

Lynne Lurie for meticulous attention to editorial and bibliographical details in this paper.

Literature Cited

(1) Ackermann, R. J., Rauh, E. G., Thorn, R. J., *J. Chem. Phys.* **40,** 883 (1964).
(2) Ahlberg, J. E., Blanchard, E. R., Lundberg, W. O., *J. Chem. Phys.* **5,** 539 (1937).
(3) Ahlberg, J. E., Clark, C. W., *J. Am. Chem. Soc.* **57,** 437 (1935).
(4) Ahlberg, J. E., Freed, S., *J. Am. Chem. Soc.* **57,** 431 (1935).
(5) Altshuller, A. P., *J. Chem. Phys.* **23,** 761 (1955).
(6) Ames, L. L., *Univ. Microfilms* (Ann Arbor, Mich.) *Order No.* **65-13,194;** *Dissertation Abstr.* **26,** 3643 (1966).
(7) Beavis, L. C., Sandia Corporation Technical Monograph **256a-60(14)** (Dec. 23, 1960); *cf. Nucl. Sci. Abstr.* **15,** 10931 (1961).
(8) Berg, J. R., Ph.D. Thesis, Iowa State University, Ames, Iowa, 1961.
(9) Berg, J. R., Spedding, F. H., Daane, A. H., *U. S. At. Energy Comm. Rept.* **IS-327** (1961); *cf. Nucl. Sci. Abstr.* **17,** 4929 (1963).
(10) Berg, J. R., Spedding, F. H., Daane, A. H. [to be published].
(11) Bieganski, Z., Fesenko, W., Stalinski, B., *Bull. Acad. Polon. Sci., Ser. Sci. Chim.* **13,** 227 (1965).
(12) Blomeke, J. O., Ziegler, W. T., *J. Am. Chem. Soc.* **73,** 5099 (1951).
(13) Bommer, H., Hohmann, E., *Z. Anorg. Allgem. Chem.* **248,** 357 (1941).
(14) Bonrath, H., Hellwege, K. H., Nicolay, K., Weber, G., *Physik Kondensierten Materie* **4,** 382 (1966).
(15) Boorse, H. A., Berman, A., Worley, R. C., Zemansky, M. W., *Bull. Inst. Intern. Froid Annexe,* 499 (1955).
(16) Brauer, G., Gingerich, K. A., Holtschmidt, U., *J. Inorg. Nucl. Chem.* **16,** 77 (1960).
(17) Brockhouse, B. N., Becka, L. N., Rao, K. R., Sinclair, R. N., Woods, A. D. B., *J. Phys. Soc. Japan* **17,** 63 (1962).
(18) Burnett, J. L., Cunningham, B. B., *U. S. At. Energy Comm. Rept.* **UCRL-11126** (1964); *cf. Nucl. Sci. Abstr.* **18,** 23453 (1964).
(19) Busch, G., Junod, P., Morris, R. G., Muheim, J., Stutius, W., *Phys. Letters* **11,** 9 (1964).
(20) Cabrera, B., Duperier, A., *Compt. Rend.* **188,** 1640 (1929).
(21) Callaway, J., McCollum, D. C., *Phys. Rev.* **130,** 1741 (1963).
(22) Callen, H. B., Callen, E., *Phys. Rev.* **136A,** 1675 (1964).
(23) Cater, E. D., Lee, T. E., Johnson, E. W., Rauh, E. G., Eick, H. A., *J. Phys. Chem.* **69,** 2684 (1965).
(24) Charap, S. H., *J. Appl. Phys.* **35,** 988 (1964).
(25) Charap, S. H., Boyd, E. L., *Phys. Rev.* **133A,** 811 (1964).
(26) Christensen, A. U., unpublished measurements, Berkeley Thermodynamics Laboratory, Region II, Bureau of Mines, Berkeley, California.
(27) Chupka, W. A., Inghram, M. G., Porter, R. F., *J. Chem. Phys.* **24,** 792 (1956).
(28) Cobble, J. W., in "Annual Review of Physical Chemistry," Vol. 17, H. Eyring, ed., p. 15, Annual Reviews, Inc., Palo Alto, California, 1966.
(29) Coughlin, J. P., "Contributions to the Data on Theoretical Metallurgy. XII. Heats and Free Energies of Formation of Inorganic Oxides," Bureau of Mines Bulletin 542, Washington, D. C., 1954.
(30) Crane, L. T., *J. Chem. Phys.* **36,** 10 (1962).
(31) Cunningham, B. B., in "XVIIth International Congress of Pure and Applied Chemistry," p. 64, Butterworths, London, 1964.

(32) Dash, J. G., Taylor, R. D., Craig, P. P., in "Proceedings of the VIIth International Conference on Low Temperature Physics," G. M. Graham and A. C. Hollis Hallett, eds., p. 705, University of Toronto Press, Toronto, 1961.

(33) Dennison, D. H., Gschneidner, K. A., Jr., *U. S. At. Energy Comm. Rept.* **IS-1156** (1965); *cf. Chem. Abstr.* **63,** 15628c (1965).

(34) Dennison, D. H., Gschneidner, K. A., Jr., Daane, A. H., *J. Chem. Phys.* **44,** 4273 (1966).

(35) van Dijk, H., *Physica* **10,** 248 (1943).

(36) van Dijk, H., *Physica* **12,** 371 (1946).

(37) Dreyfus, B., *J. Phys. Radium* **22,** 838 (1961).

(38) Dreyfus, B., Goodman, B. B., Trolliet, G., Weil, L., *Compt. Rend.* **252,** 1743 (1961).

(39) Dreyfus, B., Goodman, B. B., Trolliet, G., Weil, L., *Compt. Rend.* **253,** 1085 (1961).

(40) Dreyfus, B., Trolliet, G., Lacaze, A., *J. Phys. Radium* **22,** 665 (1961).

(41) Egan, J. J., McCoy, W., Bracker, J., in "Thermodynamics of Nuclear Materials," p. 163, International Atomic Energy Agency, Vienna, 1962.

(42) Eisenstein, J. C., Hudson, R. P., Mangum, B. W., *Phys. Rev.* **137,** 1886 (1965).

(43) Eyring, L., Schuldt, H. S., Vorres, K., *U. S. At. Energy Comm. Rept.* **TID-5914** (1959); *cf. Nucl. Sci. Abstr.* **14,** 15629 (1960).

(44) Eyring, L., Vorres, K., Schuldt, H. S., *U. S. At. Energy Comm. Rept.* **TID-5956** (1960); *cf. Nucl. Sci. Abstr.* **14,** 15997 (1960).

(45) Feber, R. C., Herrick, C. C., *U. S. At. Energy Comm. Rept.* **LA-3184** (1965); *cf. Chem. Abstr.* **63,** 3687f (1965).

(46) Ferguson, R. E., Guth, E. D., Eyring, L., *J. Am. Chem. Soc.* **76,** 3890 (1954).

(47) Fitzgibbon, G. C., Holley, C. E., Jr., Wadsö, I., *J. Phys. Chem.* **69,** 2464 (1965).

(48) Gebelt, R. E., Eick, H. A., *J. Chem. Phys.* **44,** 2872 (1966).

(49) Gerassimov, Ya. I., Lavrent, V. L., Kuznetsev, F. A., Rezuhina, T. N., in "Symposium on Chemical and Thermodynamic Properties at High Temperatures," (XVIIIth International Congress of Pure and Applied Chemistry, Montreal, Canada), p. 117, National Bureau of Standards, Washington, D. C., 1961.

(50) Gerdanian, P., Dodé, M., *Compt. Rend.* **262,** 796 (1966).

(51) Gerstein, B. C., Griffel, M., Jennings, L. D., Miller, R. E., Skochdopole, R. E., Spedding, F. H., *J. Chem. Phys.* **27,** 394 (1957).

(52) Gerstein, B. C., Jelinek, F. J., Spedding, F. H., *Phys. Rev. Letters* **8,** 425 (1962).

(53) Gerstein, B. C., Mullaly, J., Phillips, E., Miller, R. E., Spedding, F. H., *J. Chem. Phys.* **41,** 883 (1964).

(54) Giauque, W. F., Clark, C. W., *J. Am. Chem. Soc.* **54,** 3135 (1932).

(55) Goldstein, H. W., Neilson, E. F., Walsh, P. N., White, D., *J. Phys. Chem.* **63,** 1445 (1959).

(56) Goldstein, H. W., Walsh, P. N., White, D., *J. Phys. Chem.* **65,** 1400 (1961).

(57) Gordienko, S. P., Samsonov, G. V., Fesenko, V. V., *Poroshkovaya Met., Akad. Nauk Ukr. SSR* **5,** 70 (1965).

(58) Gordon, J. E., Dempsey, C. W., Soller, T., *Phys. Rev.* **124,** 724 (1961).

(59) Gordon, J. E., Dempsey, C. W., Soller, T., in "Rare Earth Research," J. F. Nachman and C. E. Lundin, eds., p. 203, Gordon and Breach, New York, 1962.

(60) Griffel, M., Skochdopole, R. E., Spedding, F. H., *Phys. Rev.* **93,** 657 (1954).

(61) Griffel, M., Skochdopole, R. E., Spedding, F. H., *J. Chem. Phys.* **25,** 75 (1956).
(62) Grønvold, F., Westrum, E. F., Jr., *Inorg. Chem.* **1,** 36 (1962).
(63) Guerci, C. F., Moruzzi, U. L., Teaney, D. T., *Bull. Am. Phys. Soc.* **9,** 225 (1964).
(64) Guth, E. D., Eyring, L., *J. Am. Chem. Soc.* **76,** 5242 (1954).
(65) Harris, A. B., Meyer, H., *Phys. Rev.* **127,** 101 (1962).
(66) Hellwege, K. H., Johnsen, U., Pfeffer, W., *Z. Physik* **154,** 301 (1959).
(67) Hellwege, K. H., Küch, F., Nieman, K., Pfeffer, W., *Z. Physik* **162,** 358 (1961).
(68) Heltemes, E. C., Swenson, C. A., *J. Chem. Phys.* **35,** 1264 (1961).
(69) Henry, W. E., *Phys. Rev.* **98,** 226 (1955).
(70) Herrick, C. C., *J. Less-Common Metals* **7,** 330 (1964).
(71) Huber, E. J., Jr., Fitzgibbon, G. C., Head, E. L., Holley, C. E., Jr., *J. Phys. Chem.* **67,** 1731 (1963).
(72) Huber, E. J., Jr., Fitzgibbon, G. C., Holley, C. E., Jr., *J. Phys. Chem.* **68,** 2720 (1964).
(73) Huber, E. J., Jr., Head, E. L., Holley, C. E., Jr., *J. Phys. Chem.* **60,** 1457 (1956).
(74) Huber, E. J., Jr., Head, E. L., Holley, C. E., Jr., *J. Phys. Chem.* **60,** 1582 (1956).
(75) Huber, E. J., Jr., Head, E. L., Holley, C. E., Jr., *J. Phys. Chem.* **61,** 497 (1957).
(76) Huber, E. J., Jr., Head, E. L., Holley, C. E., Jr., *J. Phys. Chem.* **61,** 1021 (1957).
(77) Huber, E. J., Jr., Head, E. L., Holley, C. E., Jr., *J. Phys. Chem.* **64,** 379 (1960).
(78) Huber, E. J., Jr., Head, E. L., Holley, C. E., Jr., *J. Phys. Chem.* **64,** 1768 (1960).
(79) Huber, E. J., Jr., Holley, C. E., Jr., *J. Am. Chem. Soc.* **74,** 5530 (1952).
(80) Huber, E. J., Jr., Holley, C. E., Jr., *J. Am. Chem. Soc.* **75,** 3594 (1953).
(81) Huber, E. J., Jr., Holley, C. E., Jr., *J. Am. Chem. Soc.* **75,** 5645 (1953).
(82) Huber, E. J., Jr., Holley, C. E., Jr., *J. Am. Chem. Soc.* **77,** 1444 (1955).
(83) Huber, E. J., Jr., Matthews, C. O., Holley, C. E., Jr., *J. Am. Chem. Soc.* **77,** 6493 (1955).
(84) Janovec, V., Morrison, J. A., *Phys. Letters* **17,** 226 (1965).
(85) Jennings, L. D., Hill, E. D., Spedding, F. H., *J. Chem. Phys.* **31,** 1240 (1959).
(86) Jennings, L. D., Hill, E., Spedding, F. H., *J. Chem. Phys.* **34,** 2082 (1961).
(87) Jennings, L. D., Miller, R. E., Spedding, F. H., *J. Chem. Phys.* **33,** 1849 (1960).
(88) Jennings, L. D., Stanton, R. M., Spedding, F. H., *J. Chem. Phys.* **27,** 909 (1957).
(89) Johnson, C. E., Meyer, H., *Proc. Roy. Soc. (London)* **A253,** 199 (1959).
(90) Justice, B. H., Westrum, E. F., Jr., *J. Phys. Chem.* **67,** 339 (1963).
(91) Justice, B. H., Westrum, E. F., Jr., *J. Phys. Chem.* **67,** 345 (1963).
(92) Justice, B. H., Westrum, E. F., Jr., unpublished data.
(93) Keen, B. E., Landau, D. P., Wolf, W. P., *Bull. Am. Phys. Soc.* **11,** Abstract GH1 (1966).
(94) Kelley, K. K., "Contributions to the Data on Theoretical Metallurgy. XIII. High-Temperature Heat-Content, Heat-Capacity, and Entropy Data for the Elements and Inorganic Compounds," Bureau of Mines Bulletin 584, Washington, D. C., 1960.
(95) Kelley, K. K., King, E. G., "Contributions to the Data on Theoretical Metallurgy. XIV. Entropies of the Elements and Inorganic Compounds," Bureau of Mines Bulletin 592, Washington, D. C., 1961.

(96) van Kempen, H., Miedema, A. R., Huiskamp, W. J., *Physica* **30**, 229 (1964).
(97) King, E. G., Christensen, A. U., Jr., *U. S. Bur. Mines Rept. Invest.* **5510** (1959).
(98) King, E. G., Christensen, A. U., Jr., *U. S. Bur. Mines Rept. Invest.* **5789** (1961).
(99) King, E. G., Weller, W. W., *U. S. Bur. Mines Rept. Invest.* **5485** (1959).
(100) King, E. G., Weller, W. W., Pankratz, L. B., *U. S. Bur. Mines Rept. Invest.* **5857** (1961).
(101) Klemm, W., Koczy, A., *Z. Anorg. Allgem. Chem.* **233,** 84 (1937).
(102) Koehler, W. C., Wollan, E. O., *Phys. Rev.* **92,** 1380 (1953).
(103) Koehler, W. C., Wollan, E. O., Wilkinson, M. K., Cable, J. W., *Bull. Am. Phys. Soc.* **2,** 127 (1957).
(104) Kruglikh, A. A., Kovtun, G. P., Pavlov, V. S., *Ukr. Fiz. Zh.* **10,** 432 (1965).
(105) Kul'varskaya, B. S., Maslovskaya, R. S., *Radiotekhn. i Elektron.* **5,** 1254 (1960).
(106) Kurti, N., *Z. Physik. Chem.* **20B,** 305 (1933).
(107) Kurti, N., Safrata, R. S., *Phil. Mag.* [8] **3,** 780 (1958).
(108) Kuznetsov, F. A., Rezukhina, T. N., *Zh. Fiz. Khim.* **34,** 2467 (1960); *Russ. J. Phys. Chem.* **34,** 1164 (1960).
(109) Kuznetsov, F. A., Rezukhina, T. N., *Zh Fiz. Khim.* **35,** 956 (1961).
(110) Kuznetsov, F. A., Rezukhina, T. N., Golubenko, A. N., *Zh. Fiz. Khim.* **34,** 2129 (1960).
(111) La Blanchetais, C. H., *J. Rech. Centre Natl. Rech. Sci., Lab. Bellevue (Paris)* **28,** 32 (1954).
(112) Latimer, W. M., *J. Am. Chem. Soc.* **43,** 818 (1921).
(113) Latimer, W. M., *J. Am. Chem. Soc.* **73,** 1480 (1951).
(114) Lieberman, M. L., Wahlbeck, P. G., *J. Phys. Chem.* **69,** 3514 (1965).
(115) Lim, M., Searcy, A. W., *J. Phys. Chem.* **70,** 1762 (1966).
(116) Long, E. A., Degraff, R. A., *J. Am. Chem. Soc.* **64,** 1346 (1942).
(117) Lounasmaa, O. V., *Phys. Rev.* **126,** 1352 (1962).
(118) Lounasmaa, O. V., *Phys. Rev.* **128,** 1136 (1962).
(119) Lounasmaa, O. V., *Phys. Rev.* **129,** 2460 (1963).
(120) Lounasmaa, O. V., in "Proceedings of the Eighth International Conference on Low Temperature Physics," R. O. Davies, ed., p. 223, Butterworths, London, 1963.
(121) Lounasmaa, O. V., *Bull. Am. Phys. Soc.* **9,** 657 (1964).
(122) Lounasmaa, O. V., *Phys. Rev.* **133A,** 211 (1964).
(123) Lounasmaa, O. V., *Phys. Rev.* **133A,** 219 (1964).
(124) Lounasmaa, O. V., *Phys. Rev.* **133A,** 502 (1964); *cf. Erratum, Phys. Rev.* **134AB,** 1 (1964).
(125) Lounasmaa, O. V., *Phys. Rev.* **134A,** 1620 (1964).
(126) Lounasmaa, O. V., in "Low Temperature Physics—LT9," J. G. Daunt, *et al.,* eds., Part B, p. 901, Plenum Press, New York, 1965.
(127) Lounasmaa, O. V., *Phys. Rev.* **143,** 399 (1966).
(128) Lounasmaa, O. V., Guenther, R. A., *Phys. Rev.* **126,** 1357 (1962).
(129) Lounasmaa, O. V., Roach, P. R., *Phys. Rev.* **128,** 622 (1962).
(130) Low, G. G., *Proc. Phys. Soc. (London)* **82,** 992 (1963).
(131) Lynam, P., Scurlock, R. G., Wray, E. M., in "Low Temperature Physics—LT9," J. G. Daunt, *et al.,* eds., Part B, p. 905, Plenum Press, New York, 1965.
(132) Mah, A. D., *U. S. Bur. Mines Rept. Invest.* **5676** (1961).
(133) Mah, A. D., *U. S. Bur. Mines Rept. Invest.* **5965** (1962).
(134) Maslov, P. G., Maslov, Yu. P., *Izv. Vysshikh Uchebn. Zavedenii, Khim. i Khim. Tekhnol.* **2,** 516 (1959).

(135) Matignon, C., *Ann. Chim. Phys.* **8,** 433 (1906).
(136) Matthias, B. T., Bozorth, R. M., Van Vleck, J. H., *Phys. Rev. Letters* **7,** 160 (1961).
(137) McCollum, D. C., Jr., Callaway, J., *Phys. Rev. Letters* **9,** 376 (1962).
(138) Meyer, H., *J. Phys. Chem. Solids* **9,** 296 (1959).
(139) Meyer, H., Harris, A. B., *J. Appl. Phys.* **31,** 49S (1960).
(140) Meyer, H., Smith, P. L., *J. Phys. Chem. Solids* **9,** 285 (1959).
(141) Montgomery, H., Pells, G. P., *Proc. Phys. Soc. (London)* **78,** 622 (1961).
(142) Montgomery, R. L., *U. S. Bur. Mines Rept. Invest.* **5468** (1959).
(143) Montgomery, R. L., Hubert, T. D., *U. S. Bur. Mines Rept. Invest.* **5525** (1959).
(144) Morozov, I. S., Korshunov, B. G., *Dokl. Akad. Nauk SSSR* **119,** 523 (1958).
(145) Moruzzi, V. L., Teaney, D. T., *Solid State Commun.* **1,** 127 (1963).
(146) Nesmeyanov, A. N., Priselkov, U. A., Karelin, V. V., in "Thermodynamics of Nuclear Materials," p. 667, International Atomic Energy Agency, Vienna, 1962.
(147) Ogren, J. R., *U. S. At. Energy Comm. Rept.* **IS-T-25** (1965); *cf. Chem. Abstr.* **63,** 17218h (1965).
(148) Panish, M. B., *J. Chem. Phys.* **34,** 1079 (1961).
(149) Panish, M. B., *J. Chem. Phys.* **34,** 2197 (1961).
(150) Pankratz, L. B., *U. S. Bur. Mines Rept. Invest.* **6781** (1966).
(151) Pankratz, L. B., Kelley, K. K., *U. S. Bur. Mines Rept. Invest.* **6198** (1963).
(152) Pankratz, L. B., Kelley, K. K., *U. S. Bur. Mines Rept. Invest.* **6248** (1963).
(153) Pankratz, L. B., King, E. G., *U. S. Bur. Mines Rept. Invest.* **6175** (1963).
(154) Pankratz, L. B., King, E. G., Kelley, K. K., *U. S. Bur. Mines Rept. Invest.* **6033** (1962).
(155) Parkinson, D. H., Roberts, L. M., *Proc. Phys. Soc. (London)* **B70,** 471 (1957).
(156) Parkinson, D. H., Simon, F. E., Spedding, F. H., *Proc. Roy. Soc. (London)* **A207,** 137 (1951).
(157) Parks, R. D., "Rare Earth Research," J. E. Nachman, C. F. Lundin, eds., p. 225, Gordon and Breach, New York, 1962.
(158) Pfeffer, W., *Z. Physik* **162,** 413 (1961).
(159) Pfeffer, W., *Z. Physik* **164,** 295 (1961).
(160) Pfeffer, W., *Z. Physik* **168,** 305 (1962).
(161) Polyachenok, O. G., *Zh. Neorgan. Khim.* **10,** 1939 (1965).
(162) Portnoi, K. I., Timofeev, V. A., Timofeeva, E. N., *Izv. Akad. Nauk SSSR, Neorgan. Materialy* **1,** 1513 (1965).
(163) Roberts, L. M., *Proc. Phys. Soc. (London)* **B70,** 434 (1957).
(164) Rudzitis, E., Feder, H. M., Hubbard, W. N., *J. Phys. Chem.* **69,** 2305 (1965).
(165) Schottky, W., *Physik. Z.* **23,** 448 (1922).
(166) Semenov, G. A., *Zh. Neorgan. Khim.* **10,** 2390 (1965).
(167) Skochdopole, R. E., Griffel, M., Spedding, F. H., *J. Chem. Phys.* **23,** 2258 (1955).
(168) Smith, P. K., *Univ. Microfilms* (Ann Arbor, Mich.) *Order No.* **65-1577;** *Dissertation Abstr.* **25,** 5591 (1965).
(169) Smoes, S., Drowart, J., Verhaegen, G., *J. Chem. Phys.* **43,** 732 (1965).
(170) Spedding, F. H., Eberts, R. E., Naumann, A. W., Ames Laboratory Research and Development Report **ISC-934,** Ames, Iowa, 1959.
(171) Spedding, F. H., Flynn, J. P., *J. Am. Chem. Soc.* **76,** 1474 (1954).
(172) Spedding, F. H., McKeown, J. J., Daane, A. H., *J. Phys. Chem.* **64,** 289 (1960).

(173) Stanton, R. M., Jennings, L. D., Spedding, F. H., *J. Chem. Phys.* **32**, 630 (1960).
(174) Strandburg, D. L., Legvold, S., Spedding, F. H., *Phys. Rev.* **127**, 2046 (1962).
(175) Stubblefield, C. T., Eick, H., Eyring, L., *J. Am. Chem. Soc.* **78**, 3018 (1956).
(176) Stubblefield, C. T., Eick, H., Eyring, L., *J. Am. Chem. Soc.* **78**, 3877 (1956).
(177) Stull, D. R., Sinke, G. C., ADVAN. CHEM. SER. **18** (1956).
(178) Stuve, J. M., *U. S. Bur. Mines Rept. Invest.* **6640** (1965).
(179) Stuve, J. M., *U. S. Bur. Mines Rept. Invest.* **6697** (1965).
(180) Sugden, S., Tailby, S. R., *J. Chem. Soc.* **1949**, 136.
(181) Trapnell, B. M. W., Selwood, P. W., *Nature* **169**, 840 (1952).
(182) Tsagareishvili, D. Sh., Gvelesiani, G. G., *Zh. Neorgan. Khim.* **10**, 319 (1965).
(183) Van Vleck, J. H., "The Theory of Electric and Magnetic Susceptibilities," Oxford University Press, London, 1944.
(184) Veyssie, J. J., Chaussy, J., Berton, A., *Phys. Letters* **13**, 29 (1964).
(185) Vickery, R. C., Ruben, A., *J. Chem. Soc.* **1959**, 510.
(186) Von Wartenberg, H., *Z. Anorg. Allgem. Chem.* **299**, 227 (1959).
(187) Voronel, A. V., Garber, S. R., Simkina, A. P., Charkina, I. A., *Zh. Eksperim. i Teor. Fiz.* **49**, 429 (1965); *cf. Soviet Phys. JETP* **22**, (1966).
(188) Walsh, P. N., Goldstein, H. W., White, D., *J. Am. Ceram. Soc.* **43**, 229 (1960).
(189) Weller, W. W., Kelley, K. K., *U. S. Bur. Mines Rept. Invest.* **5984** (1962).
(190) Weller, W. W., King, E. G., *U. S. Bur. Mines Rept. Invest.* **6245** (1963).
(191) Westrum, E. F., Jr., in "Progress in the Science and Technology of the Rare Earths," L. Eyring, ed., Vol. 1, p. 310, Pergamon Press, London, 1964.
(192) Westrum, E. F., Jr., in "Progress in the Science and Technology of the Rare Earths," L. Eyring, ed., Vol. 2, Pergamon Press, London. [In press]
(193) Westrum, E. F., Jr., *et al.* (unpublished data).
(194) Westrum, E. F., Jr., Beale, A. F., Jr., *J. Phys. Chem.* **65**, 353 (1961).
(195) Westrum, E. F., Jr., Justice, B. H., *J. Phys. Chem.* **67**, 659 (1963).
(196) White, D., Air Force Office of Technical Research Report **60-177**, Ohio State University Research Foundation, Columbus, Ohio, 1960.
(197) White, D., Walsh, P. N., Ames, L. L., Goldstein, H. W., in "Thermodynamics of Nuclear Materials," p. 417, International Atomic Energy Agency, Vienna, 1962.
(198) White, D., Walsh, P. N., Goldstein, H. W., Dever, D. F., *J. Phys. Chem.* **65**, 1404 (1961).
(199) Wicks, C. E., Block, F. E., "Thermodynamic Properties of 65 Elements —Their Oxides, Halides, Carbides, and Nitrides," Bureau of Mines Bulletin 605, Washington, D. C., 1963.
(200) Wilkinson, M. K., Koehler, W. C., Wollan, E. O., Cable, J. W., *Bull. Am. Phys. Soc.* **2**, 127 (1957).
(201) Wojtowicz, P. J., *J. Appl. Phys.* **35**, 991 (1964).
(202) Wollan, E. O., Koehler, W. C., *Phys. Rev.* **100**, 545 (1955).
(203) Wollan, Yannopoulos, L. N., Edwards, R. K., Wahlbeck, P. G., *J. Phys. Chem.* **69**, 2510 (1965).

RECEIVED October 10, 1967.

4

Preparation and Identification of Divalent Lanthanide Ions as Dilute Solutes in Alkaline Earth Halide Solid Solutions

P. N. YOCOM

Radio Corporation of America, Princeton, N. J.

Each of the lanthanide elements can be obtained as a divalent ion in dilute solution with the alkaline earth halides as the solvent in either the fused state (by metallic reduction with either lanthanide or alkaline earth metal or photoreduction with ultraviolet or gamma radiation) or solid state either by gamma irradiation, metallic reduction with alkaline earth metal or electrolysis. The divalent species has been identified by absorption and emission spectroscopy and/or electron paramagnetic resonance. Those divalent ions showing definite 4f *configuration in their ground states are Pr, Dy, Ho, Er, Tm and the well known Sm, Eu, and Yb. The remaining ions, La, Ce, Nd, Gd, and Tb have* 5d *ground states or a low lying* 4f *to* 5d *transition, as is probably the case with Nd.*

This paper reviews the work of the past few years on preparing and characterizing divalent lanthanide ions in dilute solid solution in alkaline earth halides. By dilute is meant < 0.5 mole % with most work being carried out at about 0.05 mole %. This work has been stimulated greatly by the desire to obtain efficient optical masers since it was felt that the allowed $4f$–$5d$ absorption bands of these ions, which occur in the visible portion of the spectrum, would permit efficient pumping. Because of the laser possibilities, those ions showing sharp line fluorescence are the ones studied most completely.

Until 1960 only samarium, europium, and ytterbium were indisputably known to exist in the divalent state. Divalent samarium was first isolated in 1906 by Matignon and Cazes (*17*). Divalent europium was found in 1911 by Urbain and Bourion (*22*). In 1929 Klemm and Schuth

(*14*) isolated divalent ytterbium. It had been argued for some years that because of the similarities of the light and heavy lanthanides thulium should show a divalent state in analogy to samarium. In 1960 Asprey and Kruse (*1*) prepared TmI_2.

Preparation

In 1961 Hayes and Twidell (*8*) found that if calcium fluoride crystals containing trivalent thulium were irradiated with x-rays, some of the thulium was converted to the divalent state. This discovery was the first of many in the study of dilute solutions of divalent rare earth ions. Most workers prefer to study the alkaline earth fluorides since these materials are stable with respect to air and have more attractive mechanical properties than the alkaline earth chlorides, bromides, and iodides. Enough work has been carried out in these softer materials to show that reactions similar to those in the fluorides do occur.

Gamma rays from spent reactor fuel rods were used for the photoreduction of the trivalent lanthanides. A spectral survey of these divalent containing crystals has been presented by McClure and Kiss (*16*). This photoreduction technique reduces only a minor fraction of the total trivalent concentration, and those divalent ions produced are unstable with respect to heat and/or light. Fong (*3*) has described these effects using divalent dysprosium as an example.

Friedman and Low (*6*) have shown that the trivalent lanthanides dissolved in the alkaline earth fluorides can be compensated by interstitial fluoride ions at either adjacent or remote sites. If the interstitial is adjacent, the crystal field of the trivalent is axial; but if it is remote, the crystal field of the trivalent is cubic. Measurement of the crystal field splitting of radiation-produced divalent lanthanide ions indicate cubic symmetry (*16*). More recent measurements by Sabisky (*20*) have shown a small percentage of non-cubic sites. It is thought that the trivalent ions in the cubic symmetry are the species predominantly reduced by radiation.

Because of the instability of the radiation produced divalents, their use in lasers was not desirable, and work on finding methods to prepare materials containing stable divalent lanthanides was stimulated. Reduction techniques were developed for the fused state from which crystals had to be grown and also for the solid state in which the as–grown crystals contained trivalent ions.

In the fused state, the straightforward method is to allow either the lanthanide metal or the alkaline earth metal to react with a melt of the alkaline earth halide and the lanthanide trihalide. This approach yields the desired divalent ions if inert containers are used. Satisfactory reduction has been obtained in molybdenum, tungsten, and tantalum. The divalent-containing melts wet these materials strongly, making the growth of large, high quality crystals difficult.

Divalent lanthanide ions have also been obtained in fused barium bromide by Pinch (*19*), who used ultraviolet radiation for the reduction. In this instance the photolysis produced bromine which was removed from the system by its volatility, and the remaining divalent lanthanide ions were stable. This reduction technique suffers from the same difficulty as the metallic reduction technique in that it is difficult to grow good crystals from this reactive melt.

For the solid-state reduction techniques, crystals are grown containing trivalent ions, as in the photoreduction process, but the divalents produced are now stabilized. One of these techniques involves heating the trivalent crystal with the appropriate alkaline earth metal. A convenient way of doing this is to heat the crystal with the alkaline earth metal in a vacuum so that the crystal is baked in metal vapor (*11*). The reduction can also be carried out by solid-state electrolysis (*4, 7*). An electric field is applied to the crystal at an elevated temperature such as above 600°C. for calcium fluoride or above 400°C. for strontium chloride. If the reduction is carried out below these temperatures, nonuniform results are obtained.

In light of the work of Ure (*23*) showing the conductivity of calcium fluoride being mainly caused by the motion of fluoride ion, the solid state reduction reactions have been interpreted in terms of a model which allows reduction to occur by diffusion of the interstitial, charge compensating ion out of the crystal while an electron is injected to reduce the trivalent lanthanide. Under these conditions there is no hole or electron deficiency remaining in the crystal, as in the case of radiation reduction; hence the divalent species is stable.

Identification

The divalent lanthanide ions produced by the described methods have been identified and studied mostly by electron paramagnetic resonance and/or optical spectroscopy. If the divalent ion has a $4f$ configuration for its ground state, it has an energy level scheme similar to the isoelectronic system of the trivalent ion of the element of next higher atomic number in the lanthanide series. The difference between these two isoelectronic systems is in the energy difference between states; the difference is less in the divalent ion than in the trivalent because of the smaller nuclear charge of the divalent. This contraction of the energy level scheme for the divalent ions brings the strong $4f$–$5d$ transition into the visible region of the spectrum. It is this property which makes the ions interesting for laser purposes because they can absorb efficiently in the region of the spectrum for which strong pumping lamps exist. The usual trivalent ions have only weak narrow line absorptions in this region.

Table I. Studies of the Divalent Lanthanides in Alkaline Earth Halide Solid Solutions

Divalent Ion	*Ground State Configuration*	*Method of Determination*	*Reference*
La	*d*	EPR	9
Ce	(*d*?)		*16*
Pr	*f*	EPR	*18*
Nd			
Pm			
Sm	*f*	optical	2, *21*, *25*
Eu	*f*	optical	2, *15*
Gd	(*d*?)		*16*
Tb	(*d*?)		*16*
Dy	*f*	optical	*12*
Ho	*f*	EPR	*10*
		EPR	*15*
		optical	*24*
Er	*f*	optical	*16*
Tm	*f*	EPR	8
		optical	*13*
Yb	*f*	optical	2

Table I summarizes the studies of the divalent lanthanides in alkaline earth halide solid solutions. The divalent ions of dysprosium, holmium, erbium, and thulium show the sharp-line fluorescent emission that is associated with unpaired *f* electrons. The emission lines of the divalent erbium seem to be abnormally broadened. Divalent praseodymium has been shown by EPR measurements to be in the 4*f* ground state (*18*), but a broad, low lying absorption band (4*f* to 5*d*?) has covered the energy region where one would expect to see fluorescent emission from 4*f* excited states (*16*). This low lying absorption band is also observed in divalent neodymium (*16*), and since the divalent ground state is non-magnetic, divalent neodymium has not been unequivocally shown to have 4*f* ground state. The *d* configuration of divalent cerium, gadolinium, and terbium is sho'vn in Table I with a question mark because a complete study has not been made of them; however, their known properties are consistent with the *d* configuration and would be hard to reconcile with an *f* configuration.

Acknowledgment

The research reported in this paper was sponsored by the Air Force Electronic Technology, Materials and Avionics Laboratories, of the Research and Technology Division, Air Force Systems Command, Wright Patterson AFB, Ohio, under contract numbers: AF33(657)11221, AF33(616)8199, and AF33(615)-1096 and RCA Laboratories, Princeton, N. J.

Literature Cited

(1) Asprey, L. B., Kruse, F. H., *J. Inorg. Nucl. Chem.* **13,** 32 (1960).
(2) Butement, F. D. S., *Trans. Faraday Soc.* **44,** 617 (1948).
(3) Fong, F. K., *J. Chem. Phys.* **41,** 245 (1964).
(4) Fong, F. K., *RCA Rev.* **25,** 303 (1964); *J. Chem. Phys.* **41,** 229 (1964).
(5) Freed, S., Katcoff, S., *Physica* **14,** 17 (1948).
(6) Friedman, E., Low, W., *J. Chem. Phys.* **33,** 1275 (1960).
(7) Guggenheim, H., Kane, J. V., *Appl. Phys. Letters* **4,** 172 (1964).
(8) Hayes, W., Twidell, J. W., *J. Chem. Phys.* **35,** 1521 (1961).
(9) Hayes, W., Twidell, J. W., *Proc. Phys. Soc.* **82,** 330 (1963).
(10) Hayes, W., Jones, G. D., Twidell, J. W., *Proc. Phys. Soc.* **81,** 371 (1963).
(11) Kiss, Z. J., Yocom, P. N., *J. Chem. Phys.* **41,** 1511 (1964).
(12) Kiss, Z. J., *Phys. Rev.* **137A,** 1749 (1965).
(13) Kiss, Z. J., *Phys. Rev.* **127,** 718 (1962).
(14) Klemm, W., Schuth, W., *Z. Anorg. Allgem. Chem.* **184,** 352 (1929).
(15) Lewis, H. R., Sabisky, E. S., *Phys. Rev.* **130,** 1370 (1963).
(16) McClure, D. S., Kiss, Z. J., *J. Chem. Phys.* **39,** 3251 (1963).
(17) Matignon, C., Cazes, E., *Compt. rend.* **142,** 83 (1906).
(18) Merritt, F. R., Guggenheim, H., Garrett, C. G. B., *Phys. Rev.* **145,** 188 (1966).
(19) Pinch, H. L., *J. Amer. Chem. Soc.* **86,** 3167 (1964).
(20) Sabisky, E. S., *Am. Phys. Soc. Meeting,* New York, Jan. 1967 (to be published).
(21) Sorokin, P., Stevenson, M. J., Lankard, J. R., Pettit, G. D., *Phys. Rev.* **127,** 503 (1962).
(22) Urbain, G., Bourion, F., *Compt. rend.* **153,** 1155 (1911).
(23) Ure, R. W., Jr., *J. Chem. Phys.* **26,** 1363 (1957).
(24) Weakliem, H. A., Kiss, Z. J., *Phys. Rev.* (to be published).
(25) Wood, D. L., Kaiser, W., *Phys. Rev.* **126,** 2079 (1962).

RECEIVED April 10, 1967.

5

Physical Characterization of the Metallic LaI_2 and CeI_2 and of the Phase $LaI_{2.42}$

JOHN D. CORBETT, ROBERT A. SALLACH and DONALD A. LOKKEN

Institute for Atomic Research and Department of Chemistry,
Iowa State University, Ames, Iowa

The specific resistance and magnetic susceptibility measured for LaI_2 clearly support the metallic formulation $La^{3+}(I^-)_2e^-$. A comparable temperature dependence of resistivity was obtained for a mixed phase sample of CeI_2. The formation of apparently metallic phases for only the iodides of five lanthanide and actinide elements is considered in terms of the stoichiometry, the electronic structure of the cation, the possible nature of the band, and the role of the anion. In contrast, the intermediate $LaI_{2.42}$ phase exhibits semiconduction. Its magnetic data between 80° and 300°K. can be best accounted for if the reduced component is considered to be La^{2+}, [Xe]$5d^1$, with a $^2T_{2g}$ ground term, a spin-orbit coupling constant λ ~650 cm.$^{-1}$, and only small covalency and asymmetry parameters.

Studies of binary rare earth metal-metal halide systems have revealed not only a considerable number of new, reduced phases, but also a substantially new class of halides possessing a metallic rather than a truly reduced or localized character. The reduction properties of the chlorides, bromides, and iodides of the first four rare earth elements are summarized as follows in terms of the compositions of new lower phases or, where absent, the limiting solution compositions in mole % metal in liquid MX_3:

X	*La*	*Ce*	*Pr*	*Nd*
Cl	9% soln. (*21*)	9% soln. (*27*)	$PrCl_{2.32}$ (*12*)	$NdCl_{2.00,\ 2.27,\ 2.37}$ (*11*)
Br	14% soln. (*30*)	12% soln. (*30*)	$PrBr_{2.38}$ (*30*)	- - - - - - - - -
I	$LaI_{2.00,\ 2.42}$ (*6*)	$CeI_{2.0,\ 2.4}$ (*6*)	$PrI_{2.00,\ 2.5}$ (*6*)	$NdI_{1.95}$ (*11*)

In most of these systems there is clear evidence for the formation of the reduced ion M^{2+}. For example, in NdX_2 salts this is on the basis of magnetic studies (*31*), and with the praseodymium chloride and bromide phases, from qualitative resistivity measurements and their structural relationships to the neodymium chlorides according to x-ray data. Cryoscopic data for all the systems listed are also consistent with the formation of a M^{2+}, as opposed to M^{+}, solute in dilute solution in MX_3 (*3, 7*).

The unexpected is found with the iodides of the first three in that they form rather stable diiodides, congruently melting for LaI_2, with a structure different from that of "NdI_2" ($SmBr_2$ or $SrBr_2$ type) (*11*). The appearance of the first three diiodides immediately suggested a more metal-like character, and this was supported by preliminary electrical and magnetic measurements (*6*). Such phases are relatively rare among halides, including, in addition, only the unique Ag_2F (*36, 37*) and the subsequently discovered GdI_2 (*26*) and ThI_2 (*4*). However, this property is known for most of the rare earth elements in the monochalcogenides (*16, 29*) and dicarbides (*33*), as well as with the oxides, sulfides, etc. of a number of transition elements. This article reports more completely the evidence for this character, especially for LaI_2 because of its favorable congruent melting property and diamagnetic core background, and considers some of the important criteria for the formation of the metallic halides. Some properties related to the constitution of the intermediate phase $LaI_{2.42}$ are also presented.

Experimental

Preparations were generally as previously described (*6*). Sublimation of the triiodides was carried out in glass-jacketed tantalum to avoid the reaction of the molten iodides with SiO_2 to form MOI and SiI_4. Rods of MI_2 $\frac{1}{4}$ in. diameter were grown from the melt in tantalum tubing by manual movement of this through a gradient furnace. This was a simple process for the congruently melting LaI_2, but single phase samples of the incongruently melting CeI_2 and PrI_2 were not obtained, even with metal reservoirs maintained only a short distance from the interface. Samples of $LaI_{2.42}$ and of neighboring mixtures were prepared by quenching suitable mixtures of the components from the all liquid region followed by annealing at $\sim$745°C. (m.p. 750°C.). Solution of samples for analysis was performed in closed, evacuated containers to avoid loss of up to 1 wt. % iodine as HI that occurs in open containers.

The resistivity apparatus shown in Figure 1 was constructed of Lavite and stainless steel, with tungsten probes and silver leads. The size of the sample rods accommodated was largely dictated by their low strength during peeling of the tantalum container and during the measurements. The original intent to make measurements up to near the melting point was defeated by the relatively large thermal expansion of the diiodides, which caused loss of current contact at low temperatures or compressive fracture too far above room temperature. The entire apparatus was baked out under vacuum, loaded in the dry box, and jacketed in glass under Ar. Direct current methods were abandoned when the insulating LaI_3 was found to form at the current leads; even with a sine wave source some rectification was observed until the current contact was made through a small wafer of the same metal as the iodide.

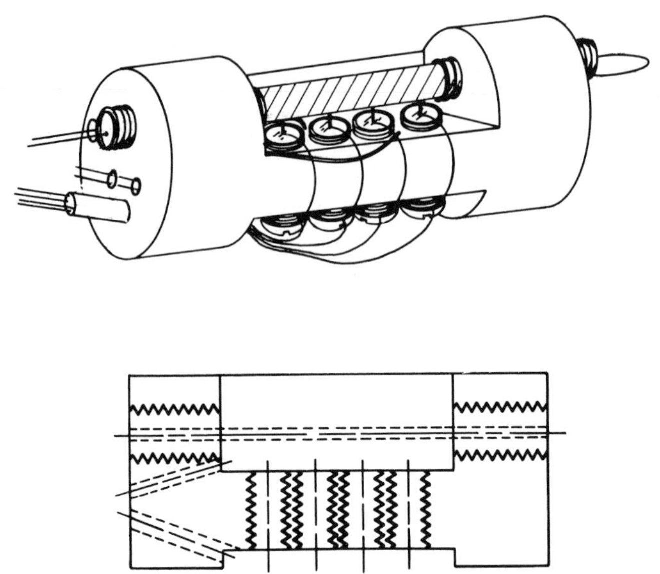

Figure 1. The resistivity sample holder

The potential drops were measured across the sample rod and a standard resistor in series with a sensitive VTVM (vacuum tube volt meter) while the wave form was monitored with an oscilloscope. Two samples of composition $LaI_{2.00 \pm 0.01}$ were measured from 77° to 344° and 186° to 408°K., respectively, without irreversible temperature effects. One sample of composition $CeI_{2.07}$ was studied from 153° to 300°K., but satisfactory PrI_2 samples could not be obtained. Because of phase relationships and the relatively high resistivity found, $LaI_{2.42}$ was studied as a pellet formed with a "KBr" press using a VTVM in the dry box. The results from one sample to another were somewhat erratic, partly because of extreme susceptibility to oxidation, but were sufficient to characterize the compound as salt-like as opposed to metallic.

Susceptibilities were determined by the Gouy method, extrapolated to infinite H (though the effect was small), and corrected for core diamagnetism with Selwood's values. Measurements on $LaI_{2.42}$ between 1.2 and 80°K. were made by the mutual inductance method.

Results and Discussion

The Diiodides. The resistivities obtained for two samples of LaI_2 between 77° and 408°K. are shown in Figure 2 (right ordinate). Values for lanthanum metal (*1, 32*), with its h.c.p.-c.c.p. transition near room temperature, are also shown to illustrate the remarkable similarity. The opposite curvature found for LaI_2 possibly arises because of its abnormally large thermal expansion (*see* Experimental), giving rise to a more rapid decrease in overlap (band narrowing). The room temperature value of 64 $\pm$ 2 μohm.-cm. may also be compared with 68 and 92 μohm.-cm. reported for the metallic LaC_2 (*33*) and LaS (*25*), respectively. It is interesting that the result of a linear extrapolation of the data shown to the melting point, ~350 μohm.cm. at 830°, is within a factor of three of that from a similarly long extrapolation of the melt's conductivity (as log T *vs.* N_{La}, which is nearly linear) (*13*) to pure LaI_2 (liq.), 330–100 μohm.-cm. Since the increase in resistivity on fusion is probably small, this suggests that the liquid retains the metal-like property, as has already been inferred from the cryoscopic behavior of LaI_3 in LaI_2 (*13*).

The incongruent melting characteristic of the cerium and praseodymium diiodides prevented the preparation of pure phase samples in the necessary size and shape. The resistivities obtained for a sample of composition $CeI_{2.07}$, Figure 2 (left ordinate), are meaningful in that the temperature dependence is similar to that of LaI_2. Since x-ray powder data suggest that the contaminant phase $CeI_{2.4}$ is isomorphous with $LaI_{2.42}$ (*6*), and presumably likewise effectively an insulator on this scale, the impurity would serve mainly to reduce the effective cross sectional area without masking the apparent metallicity of CeI_2. Lower resistivities on purer samples were obtained at room temperature by preliminary d.c. methods, 300 $\pm$ 100 μohm. for $CeI_{2.04}$ and ~350 μohm.-cm. for a $PrI_{2.07}$ composition. X-ray powder data again indicate that the first two diiodides are isomorphous, whereas PrI_2 may be slightly different.

The absence of localized states is clearly supported by the small, Pauli-type paramagnetism of LaI_2, 0 $\pm$ 5 and (30 $\pm$ 10) $\times$ 10^{-6} e.m.u. mole^{-1} at 299° and 78°K., respectively. Values of this magnitude are characteristic of metals where they are (ideally) associated with the Pauli spin paramagnetism of the conduction electrons. In the present case the results of correction for the diamagnetic contribution of the iodide ions in LaI_2 [(104 $\pm$ 5) and (134 $\pm$ 10) $\times$ 10^{-6}, respectively] are again remarkably (and probably fortuitously) close to those for the metal (113 and 139 $\times$ 10^{-6}) (*22*).

There is little doubt that LaI_2 is correctly formulated as La^{3+} $(I^-)_2e^-$, and that a similar constitution appears likely for CeI_2, and possible for PrI_2. LaI_2 does not yield solvated electrons in liquid NH_3 as do the divalent metals europium and ytterbium (*39*); the rapid evolution of hydrogen is probably a result of substantial ammonolysis of the La^{3+} ion.

At present five metallic diiodides are known—the above three, GdI_2 (*26*), and ThI_2 (*4*). No other examples of metallic phases are found in the other metal-metal halide systems of these elements which have been examined—specifically, the chlorides of all five and the bromides of all but gadolinium. The only other halide example is the enigmatic Ag_2F.

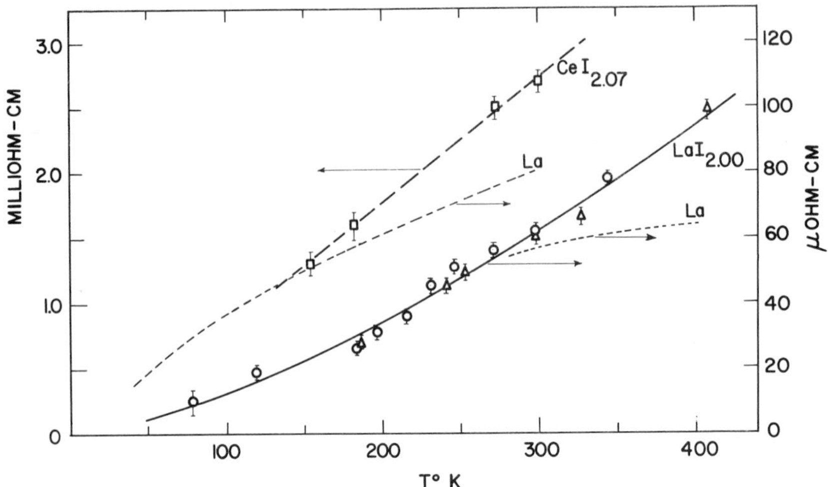

Figure 2. The resistivities of LaI_2 (○, Δ, right scale), La metal (dashed curve, right scale), and $CeI_{2.07}$ sample (□, left scale)

It is worthwhile to consider the conditions and criteria which appear important in accomplishing the necessary overlap and delocalization and in limiting this behavior substantially to the iodides cited. These are classified in terms of the stoichiometry, the electronic state of cation, and the nature of the band and the role of the anions.

Stoichiometry. At present the observed limit of two halide ions per metal does not seem particularly important as a necessity for close approach of the cations and hence suitable band formation; rather, it more probably results from other characteristics of this formal oxidation state for these elements. One possible fact to the contrary is that thorium(III) iodide is evidently not metallic (*4*), though it would probably meet the second criterion below. The general electronic conduction in sulfide *vs.* chloride melts in the metal-rich region (as well as in the solid state) may be attributed to the lower anion to cation ratio and therefore closer approach of the cations (*5*), although covalency as discussed below may be more significant.

Electronic State of Cation. A more important factor for the lanthanides appears to be the electronic configuration of the simple, reduced ion. As noted before (*19, 26*), it appears necessary and plausible that the isolated M^{2+} ion should have, or be close to the configuration $[Xe]4f^n5d^1$

([Rn]$6d^2$ for Th^{2+}) in order for overlap of some sort *(vide infra)* to lead to a suitable conduction band. The normal, salt-like behavior of $NdI_{1.95}$, SmI_2, EuI_2, DyI_2, TmI_2, and YbI_2 is entirely reasonable since the ground states all derive from stable, well-shielded $4f^{n+1}$ configurations. It appears more than coincidental that such "*d*" states generally pertain only to dipositive rare earth metal ions of lanthanum, cerium, gadolinium, terbium, and lutetium. (M-MI_3 systems for the last two have not been examined.) This fact was first generalized in spectral studies of the dipositive ions in fluorite hosts (*23*), although it has been recognized for many of these in spectroscopic studies of the gaseous ions as well. The ground state configuration for Pr^{2+}, [Xe]$4f^3$, is not consistent with the apparently metallic character of PrI_2. Although the lowest $4f^35d^1$ state in Pr^{2+} is 1.6 e.v. higher in the gas phase (*35*), it is only 0.4 e.v. above ground in a simple cubic environment in fluorite (*23*), so that greater crystal field or banding effects could readily result in an effective "*d*" state.

NATURE OF THE BAND AND THE ROLE OF THE ANIONS. The role of the anions and the type of banding are important in any consideration of the absence of metal-like phases for these metals with other halide anions. While it is probably true that the diiodides are electrostatically the most stable to disproportionation among the dihalides, as with normal iodide salts (*38*), the nature of the banding itself appears to be more significant in the present discussion. A considerable amount has been written about this property of the metallic MS (and M_3S_4) phases of the rare earth metals (*8, 24*), generally in terms of an implied or stated cation sublattice band involving the 5*d* and perhaps the 6*s* orbitals. For the c.c.p. monosulfides this cation band would result from a sufficient overlap of the $t_{2g}{}^1$ states, while the corresponding sulfur orbitals remain substantially nonbonding. A comparable behavior in the present diiodides (whatever their structure) is difficult to account for with this picture because they are uniquely limited to compounds with the largest anion, which presumably would be the least favorable for cation-cation overlap. Including pi bonding with iodide is more credible since it should be the most favorable here with regard to both energy and overlap criteria. Delocalization in this case would then result from the banding of the π^* orbitals in a periodic lattice. This would result from $(t_{2g}{}^*)^1$ states in the familiar octahedral environment, but with only one electron per metal to be accommodated, a lower degeneracy would present no problem. Covalency is critical for adequate delocalization in such a band (*17*), and this is most favorable with iodide anions. Of course the increased shielding of *d* orbitals so obtained, particularly through sigma bonding, will enhance overlap in either model [compare the effect of oxide *vs.* fluoride with the $3d$ elements (*28*)]. Some idea of possible bonding in the other metallic diiodides can be obtained from the structure recently determined for ThI_2, where a layer structure similar to that found for δ–TaS_2 indicates delocalization only within the sheets (*18*).

The rare earth elements under discussion appear to be unique in possessing sufficient radial extension in the $5d$ orbitals for adequate overlap with the iodides. [The inversely related small value of the third ionization energy is perhaps more important with regard to the alternate formation of localized states on reduced cations (*26*)]. Orbital contraction in the heavier lanthanides would be expected to reduce the likelihood of delocalized states so that lutetium(II) may not form a metallic iodide. The extensive disproportionation expected for this state (*7*) may preclude the formation of any new phase at all. A localized metal-metal bonding seems evident in the unusual $GdCl_{1.6}$ (*26*) while the $5d^1$ states of elements immediately following the lanthanides, having both increased coordination number and more tightly bound valence electrons, generally exhibit localized metal-metal interactions. For example, hafnium(III) iodide is an insulator and exhibits only a small temperature-independent paramagnetism (*34*), whereas the bonding is localized in TaI_4 with the formation of discrete dimers (*9*). There is no hafnium diiodide representing a constant stoichiometry, while the more numerous and tightly bound electrons in the closest thing to a tantalum diiodide, $TaI_{2.33}$ (*2*), find delocalized metal-metal-halogen bonding in discrete clusters much more profitable. Much more needs to be learned about transitions of this type.

The monosulfides of the rare earth elements behave differently from that discussed here since these are metal-like for all but those elements forming the most stable divalent states. Here a general proclivity towards forming tripositive ions seems more important (as in the metals themselves)—a property usually considered to result from a fortuitous balance between ionization and lattice or solvation energies. The sulfides have also been interpreted in terms of a degeneracy of the upper $4f$ levels with a $5d$ band (where applicable) (*10*). In contrast to the halides, there is little differentiation of the electrical properties among the monosulfides, monoselenides, and monotellurides (*29*).

The Intermediate Phase $LaI_{2.42}$. The composition of this phase was further defined with powder pattern data for nine samples ($2.36 < I/La < 2.51$) which were quenched from the liquid region and annealed just below the melting point for 2–7 days. Certain diffractions of the neighboring LaI_3 and LaI_2 phases were detectable in fairly small amounts ($< \pm 0.06$ in I/La) so that the interpolated composition is probably uncertain by not much more than ± 0.01 in I/La, exclusive of systematic errors in analysis.

The resistivities of pressed pellets of the compound were in the range of 10^2 to 10^3 ohm.-cm. at room temperature, with a negative temperature coefficient of about 10^{-2} deg.$^{-1}$. A more thorough investigation of the electrical properties was not made, because the semiconducting character is in such obvious contrast to that of LaI_2. It should be noted that localized states are evident in the melt up to at least this composition according to conductivity studies (*13*). In this case a resonant charge transfer process brought about by the iodide ions would account for not only the dependence of electronic conduction on temperature and on metal concentration but also for the presence of conduction with the d^1 ions considered here, but not with the inert f^{n+1} ions like Nd^{2+}.

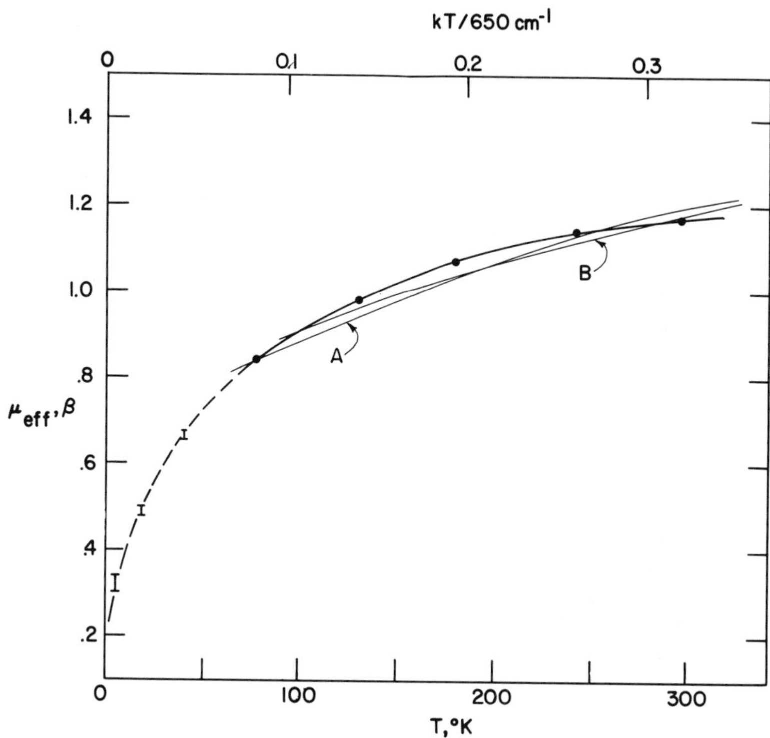

Figure 3. μ_{eff} vs. T *for* $LaI_{2.42}$

Solid curve with open circles: Gouy data.
Dashed curve: mutual inductance data (smoothed).
Lighter solid curves: theory for d^1, $^2T_{2g}$, *with* A: $\lambda = 550$ *cm.*$^{-1}$, k = *0.7*, $\Delta/\lambda =$ *0.4;* B: $\lambda = 750$ *cm.*$^{-1}$, k = *1.0*, $\Delta/\lambda = 0.9$.

Magnetic data suggest strongly that the reduced states so indicated for this phase are those of lanthanum(II), [Xe]$5d^1$. With $\chi_D = 1.46 \times$

10^{-4} e.m.u. the molar susceptibility of $LaI_{2.42}$ is described fairly well between 77° and 295°K. by a Curie-Weiss relationship, $\chi_p \times 10^6 = 0.151/(T + 151)$. For the presumed 58% lanthanum(II) content μ would be 1.45β, certainly not that of a $4f^1$ state (2.54β). Extending the measurements down to 1.2°K. by the (less sensitive) mutual inductance method failed to reveal the magnetic ordering that the Curie-Weiss description would imply. The room temperature result, $\chi_p = 5.77 \times 10^{-4}$ e.m.u. mole^{-1}, or $\mu_{eff} = 1.17\beta$ (based on 58% La^{2+}) is too low and the temperature dependence too great for a d^1 state with ground state terms ^2A or ^2E —that is, in an environment of fairly low symmetry. Assumption of a $^2T_{2g}$ ground term, corresponding to La^{2+} in octahedral symmetry, together with a plausible spin-orbit coupling constant gives the best description of the data, perhaps as good as frequently encountered in better known systems (*14*). The experimental dependence of μ_{eff} on temperature is shown in Figure 3, together with theoretical curves (*15*) for two extremes of spin-orbit coupling constant, covalency k, and tetragonal asymmetry parameter v ($= \Delta/\lambda$) that fit the Gouy data as well as possible. Intermediate choices of constants λ, k, and v, (650, 0.8, 0.6, for example) give appropriately intermediate curves. The λ value compares to 640 cm.$^{-1}$ estimated by Jørgensen for La^{2+} (*20*); in any case the value is not very critical in this range, and additional effects described empirically at this point by k and v are quite small. The agreement with theory at lower temperatures is poor; assuming the presence of a temperature-independent component in χ_p does not help, although more negative values for Pascal's constants would. This degree of agreement between theory and experiment cannot be obtained anywhere else with lower symmetries, larger v values, or for other configurations (d^2, f^1, *etc.*).

Meaningful ESR or spectral data have not been obtained. Only a band at 29800 cm.$^{-1}$, with a shoulder at 27800 cm.$^{-1}$, can be resolved in the reflectance spectrum of the black compound in KI; the energy and intensity both suggest these arise from charge transfer processes.

The indicated octahedral coordination at first may seem unusual when compared with the nine-fold coordination found in the barium halides, NdX_2, etc. and the eight-fold coordination of the smaller La^{3+} ion in its trihalides. However, the geometry in the latter may depend on attaining a maximum dispersion energy, whereas in the present case the d^1 state may be able to realize a good deal more from a crystal field effects in an environment of higher symmetry. The triiodide is evidently relatively loosely bound compared with the lower iodides. Density estimates of 5 to 5.3 gram cm.$^{-3}$ for $LaI_{2.42}$ and LaI_2 from measurements both on samples as prepared and on pressed pellets indicate molar volumes of these two phases are less than 50% of the appropriate average of those of the components La and LaI_3.

Acknowledgments

The use of the Gouy balance was made possible by P. E. Roughan, W. J. Gray, and A. H. Daane, and of the mutual inductance bridge by F. J. Jelinek and B. C. Gerstein.

Literature Cited

(1) Alstad, J. K., Colvin, R. V., Legvold, S., Spedding, F. H., *Phys. Rev.* **121,** 1637 (1961).
(2) Bauer, D., Schnering, H. G., Schafer, H., *J. Less-Common Metals* **6,** 388 (1965).
(3) Bredig, M. A., in "Molten Salt Chemistry," M. Blander, ed., p. 408, Wiley, New York, 1964.
(4) Clark, R. J., Corbett, J. D., *Inorg. Chem.* **2,** 460 (1963).
(5) Corbett, J. D., in "Fused Salts," B. R. Sundheim, Ed., Chap. 6, McGraw-Hill, New York, 1964.
(6) Corbett, J. D., Druding, L. F., Burkhard, W. J., Lindahl, C. B., *Discussions Faraday Soc.* **32,** 79 (1961).
(7) Corbett, J. D., Pollard, D. L., Mee, J. E., *Inorg. Chem.* **5,** 761 (1966).
(8) Cutler, M., Fitzpatrick, R. L., Leavy, J. F., *J. Phys. Chem. Solids* **24,** 319 (1963).
(9) Dahl, L. E., Wampler, D. L., *J. Am. Chem. Soc.* **81,** 315 (1959).
(10) Didchenko, R., Gortsema, F. P., *J. Phys. Chem. Solids* **24,** 863 (1963).
(11) Druding, L. F., Corbett, J. D., *J. Am. Chem. Soc.* **83,** 2462 (1961).
(12) Druding, L. F., Corbett, J. D., Ramsey, B. N., *Inorg. Chem.* **2,** 869 (1963).
(13) Dworkin, A. S., Sallach, R. A., Bronstein, H. R., Bredig, M. A., Corbett, J. D., *J. Phys. Chem.* **67,** 1145 (1963).
(14) Figgis, B. N., "Introduction to Ligand Fields," Chap. 10. Interscience, New York, 1966.
(15) Figgis, B. N., *Trans. Faraday Soc.* **57,** 198 (1961).
(16) Flahaut, J., Guittard, M., Patrie, M., *Bull. Soc. Chim. France* **1959,** 1917.
(17) Goodenough, J. B., *J. Appl. Phys.* **37,** 1415 (1966).
(18) Jacobson, R. A., Guggenberger, L. (to be published).
(19) Jørgensen, C. K., *Mol. Phys.* **7,** 420 (1964).
(20) Jørgensen, C. K., "Orbitals in Atoms and Molecules," p. 137, Academic Press, New York, 1962.
(21) Keneshea, F. J. Jr., Cubicciotti, D. D., *J. Chem. Eng. Data* **6,** 507 (1961).
(22) Lock, J. M., *Phil. Mag.* **2,** 726 (1957).
(23) McClure, D. S., Kiss, Z., *J. Chem. Phys.* **39,** 3251 (1963).
(24) McClure, J. W., *J. Phys. Chem. Solids* **24,** 871 (1963).
(25) Marchenko, V. I., Samsonov, G. V., *Russ. J. Inorg. Chem.* **8,** 1061 (1963).
(26) Mee, J. E., Corbett, J. D., *Inorg. Chem.* **4,** 88 (1965).
(27) Mellors, G. W., Senderoff, S., *J. Phys. Chem.* **63,** 1110 (1959).
(28) Morin, F. J., *J. Appl. Phys. (Suppl.)* **32,** 2195 (1961).
(29) Reid, F. J., Matson, L. K., Miller, J. F., Himes, R. C., *J. Phys. Chem. Solids* **25,** 969 (1964).
(30) Sallach, R. A., Corbett, J. D., *Inorg. Chem.* **2,** 457 (1963).
(31) Sallach, R. A., Corbett, J. D., *Ibid.* **3,** 933 (1964).
(32) Spedding, F. H., Daane, A. H., Herrmann, K. W., *J. Metals* **9,** 895 (1957).
(33) Spedding, F. H., Gschneidner, K., Daane, A. H., *Trans. Met. Soc.* AIME **215,** 192 (1959).
(34) Struss, A. W., Corbett, J. D. (to be published).

(35) Sugar, J., *J. Opt. Soc. Am.* **53,** 831 (1963).
(36) Terrey, H., Diamond, H., *J. Chem. Soc.* **1928**, 2820.
(37) Trzebiatowski, W., Różyczka, J., *Poczniki Chem.* **32,** 183 (1958).
(38) Van Arkel, A., *Research* **2,** 307 (1949).
(39) Warf, J. C., Korst, W. L., *J. Phys. Chem.* **60,** 1590 (1956).

RECEIVED October 17, 1966. Work performed in the Ames Laboratory of the U. S. Atomic Energy Commission. Contribution No. 1980.

6

Fluorite-Related Oxide Phases of the Rare Earth and Actinide Elements

LEROY EYRING

Arizona State University, Tempe, Ariz.

Cerium, praseodymium, and terbium oxides display homologous series of ordered phases of narrow composition range, disordered phases of wide composition range, and the phenomenon of chemical hysteresis among phases which are structurally related to the fluorite-type dioxides. Hence they must play an essential role in the satisfactory development of a comprehensive theory of the solid state. All the actinide elements form fluorite-related oxides, and the trend from ThO_x to CmO_x is toward behavior similar to that of the lanthanides already mentioned. The relationships among all these fluorite-related oxides must be recognized and clarified to provide the broad base on which a satisfactory theory can be built.

The incentive for scheduling a symposium on the chemistry of the lanthanides and actinides is derived in part from the value of examining the similarities and interrelationships which exist between these analogous sequences of elements. The chemical analogies which first suggested the ingenious actinide hypothesis many years ago are now well developed and generally recognized. It is now possible to go beyond this to examine subtle similarities and variations. Indeed, in the two chemically related *f*-shell groups nearly one third of the known elements provide extended series of elements and compounds whose properties vary continually in each sequence but with overlap to provide one of the most valuable testing grounds in all of chemistry for any theory which may be advanced. The isomorphism existing among the oxides of the actinide and lanthanide elements in the composition range RO_x, $1.5 \leq x \leq 2.0$, gave early support to the actinide hypothesis, but now a more careful scrutiny of the details is possible and should lead to a greater appreciation of the quality of the variation in chemical behavior along the two series. We are not discouraged by the fact that oxides in this composition range behave neither like lanthanum nor actinium oxides.

Perhaps of greater significance is that this double sequence of complex oxides will play a central role in elucidating the nature of nonstoichiometry in chemical systems. The phenomena of ordered intermediate phases of narrow composition (homologous series), nonstoichiometric phases of widely variable composition resulting from order-disorder transformations, and chemical hysteresis are exhibited among them with unusual variation. The entire question of the nature of nonstoichiometric behavior is rapidly approaching a new level of understanding, and continued careful development of knowledge of these oxides is necessary in evolving the total picture.

The state of knowledge of these oxide systems is not yet ready for a full review. Rather, this discussion sketches the present state of knowledge which is fairly complete for some oxide systems, skimpy for others, and virtually nonexistent for a few, with the hope that it shall be continued until this mother lode shall have been emptied of her treasure.

Studies and discussions of the past several years have led to the realization that binary inorganic compounds of elements exhibiting altervalent character, such as the transition metal oxides, tend to show an unmixing of previously observed ranges of composition into a sequence of ordered phases belonging to an homologous series whose structures are related by some simple structural principle. The earliest indications of this were seen by Magnéli (*36, 37*) on the molybdenum-oxygen system and have been enlarged and extended by him and his colleagues to a wide range of transition metal oxides. A general review of the extent of such studies and the structural principles involved has been presented by Wadsley (*48*), who has greatly extended our knowledge of ordered intermediate phases. Nonstoichiometry has been discussed in detail over the years by Anderson (*5, 6*), who has recently synthesized the extant ideas. The general pattern of behavior of metal oxides capable of variation in composition is to form a homologous series of phases having some simple relating structural principle, and disordered phases of wide composition range in which the disorder is not at the level of point defects but rather of defect complexes or domains of the order of five to 20 unit cells in linear dimension—*i.e.*, there is short- but not long-range order. Coherence makes such phases thermodynamically stable. The occurrence of hysteresis, the magnitude of the thermochemical properties, as well as considerations of the energy requirement for large concentrations of point defects, suggest that such domain structures exist (*11, 28*).

It must be kept in mind that each nonstoichiometric system is unique, and that each ordered phase, each polymorph, and each disordered phase has its own range of stability. Whenever tangents to the free energy curves (G, x) for the various stable phases can be constructed, two-phase regions are indicated. Such two-phase regions are usually realized only for the lowest surfaces in any region of T and x. This means that no two oxide systems are expected to be identical but will vary as the stability ranges of all possible species dictate. It is convenient to discuss the most thoroughly studied oxide systems and establish a nomenclature for the phases which could be expected in each of the oxide systems of the lanthanide and the actinide elements.

Fluorite Related Phases in the Rare Earth Oxides

Comprehensive studies of the PrO_x-O_2 system have culminated in a detailed paper by Hyde *et al.* (*30*), who rationalize previous work and describe isobaric studies whose results were a powerful tool in exposing the intricacies of that system. The TbO_x-O_2 system has likewise been studied by Hyde and Eyring (*32*) using the isobaric technique and the results of previous studies reviewed and discussed. In addition, the TbO_x-O_2 system is compared with that of PrO_x-O_2 (*30*) and CeO_x-O_2 (*13*). References *13, 30,* and *32* should be consulted for experimental details and for a discussion of previous work. Brauer (*15, 16*) has recently reviewed current studies on all the rare earth oxides.

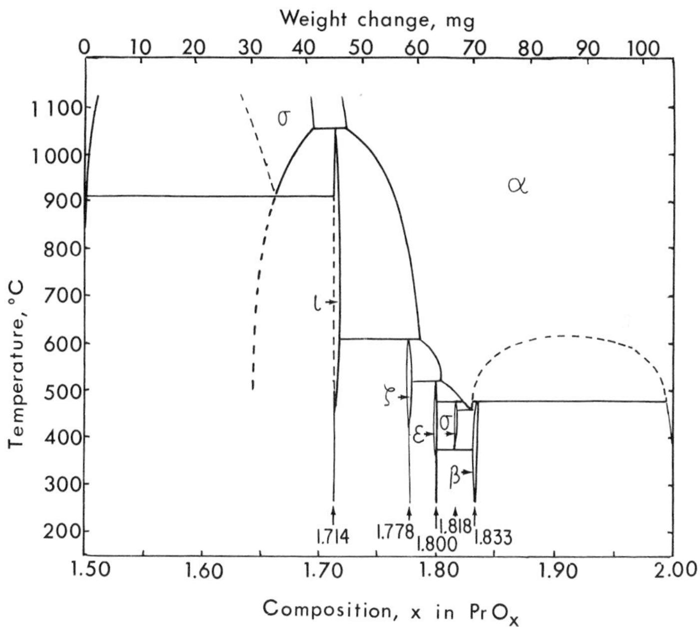

Figure 1. Projection of the PrO_x-O_2 phase diagram

A phase diagram of the system PrO_x, $1.5 \leq x \leq 2.0$, is shown in Figure 1. Apparent in this diagram are an homologous series (R_nO_{2n-2}, $n = 4,7,9,10,11,12$) of phases of narrow composition range which decompose to give disordered nonstoichiometric phases at higher temperature. Phase designations adopted for this system, shown in Table I, shall be used here to indicate phases believed to be isomorphous or analogous.

Table I. Members of the R_nO_{2n-2} Series and Disordered Phases of the Rare Earth Oxides

Value of n	*Stoichiometric formula*	*x in RO_x*	*Phase symbol*
4	Ce_2O_3 (hex.)	1.500	A
	Pr_2O_3 (hex.)		
	Tb_2O_3 (hex.)		
	Tb_2O_3 (moncl.)	1.500	B
	Pr_2O_3 (b.c.c.)	1.500	C
	Tb_2O_3 (b.c.c.)		
	$CeO_{1.6} \pm \delta$	1.5-1.7	σ
	$PrO_{1.6} \pm \delta$		
	$TbO_{1.6} \pm \delta$		
7	Ce_7O_{12}	1.714	ι
	Pr_7O_{12}		
	Tb_7O_{12}		
9	Ce_9O_{16}	1.778	ζ
	Pr_9O_{16}		
10	Ce_5O_9	1.800	ϵ
	Pr_5O_9		
11	$Ce_{11}O_{20}$	1.818	δ
	$Pr_{11}O_{20}$		
	$Tb_{11}O_{20}$		
12	Pr_6O_{11}	1.833	β
	Tb_6O_{11} (?)		
	$CeO_{1.7} + \delta$	1.7-2.0	α
	$PrO_{1.7} + \delta$		
	$TbO_{1.7} + \delta$ (?)		
∞	CeO_2	2.000	F
	PrO_2		
	TbO_2		

Praseodymium dioxide crystallizes in the fluorite-type structure (space group $Fm3m$) with four praseodymium atoms and eight oxygen atoms per unit cell. This structure may be visualized easily as an infinite array of coordination cubes (each consisting of a Pr atom at the center with eight O atoms at the corners) stacked so that all cube edges are shared.

If one views this configuration at right angles to the body diagonal of one of the cubes (perpendicular to the <111> axis of the unit cell), planes containing only metal or oxygen atoms appear stacked in the sequence *Ac aCb cBa bA*, where capital letters represent metal planes and lower case letters those of oxygen (*23*).

The *C*-type rare earth structure (space group Ia3), which is the other end-member of the fluorite-related series of phases, has the same stacking sequence, but one-fourth of the oxygens are missing from each oxygen plane in an ordered way. The result of this ordering is that in the *C*-type structure all the oxygen vacancies may be considered as laying in strings along the four <111> directions of the fluorite cell. These strings are non-intersecting, and their closest approach removes oxygens from the face diagonals of the intervening [RO_8] cubes giving six coordination of one of two types to all the metal atoms.

The intermediate ordered phases observed in the rare earth oxides have structures which are obviously related to those of the end-members described above if one compares the x-ray diffraction patterns (*46*). The structure of the ι phase, Pr_7O_{12}, has been determined. It may be represented in terms similar to those used above by visualizing it as consisting entirely of the strings of six coordinated metal atoms running in one <111> direction only. The creation of the string generates "sheaths" of seven coordinated metal atoms surrounding it forming a rod. When these rods are aligned parallel to one another yielding the Pr_7O_{12} structure (*23, 31, 32, 46*) only six and seven coordination exists. It is suggested (*32*) that the strings are the structural entity relating all the intermediate oxides and the end-members. Since $1/n$th of the cations are in the strings and each cation has two of its original eight oxygens missing, a composition $RO_{2(1-1/n)} = R_nO_{2n-2}$ is observed.

The other phases with $n > 7$ are believed to consist also of strings running in only one <111> direction, but for each of these there must be increasing regions of [RO_8] groups as the composition PrO_2 ($n = \infty$) is approached.

The disordered σ phase is believed to consist of a *C*-type oxide, with some of the oxygen positions along the strings filled, interrupting the strings but maintaining the cubic symmetry.

The α phase, on the other hand, must consist of a fluorite-type matrix with segments of strings bundled together in increasing amounts as oxygen is lost from the PrO_2 structure. The bundles are believed to be at random along the four <111> directions of the fluorite cell preserving cubic symmetry. Where the bundles so oriented approach each other, regions of *C*-type are created. This is suggested by the weak superstructure reflections in x-ray diffraction from the α phase of the CeO_2-Y_2O_3 mixed oxides (*12*). The complexes of rods are not fixed in the α phase but are free to translate. The α-σ miscibility gap represents the region in which the labile α transforms to the rigid σ.

Proposed partial (T,x) phase diagrams for the CeO_x (*13*) and TbO_x (*32*) are shown in Figures 2 and 3. The existence of some of the homologous series are seen in each, but the principle feature is the wide range of σ and α phases with a miscibility gap.

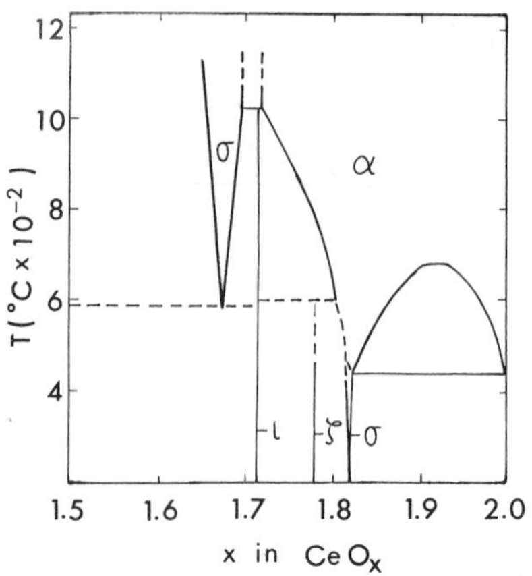

Figure 2. Projection of the CeO_x-O_2 phase diagram

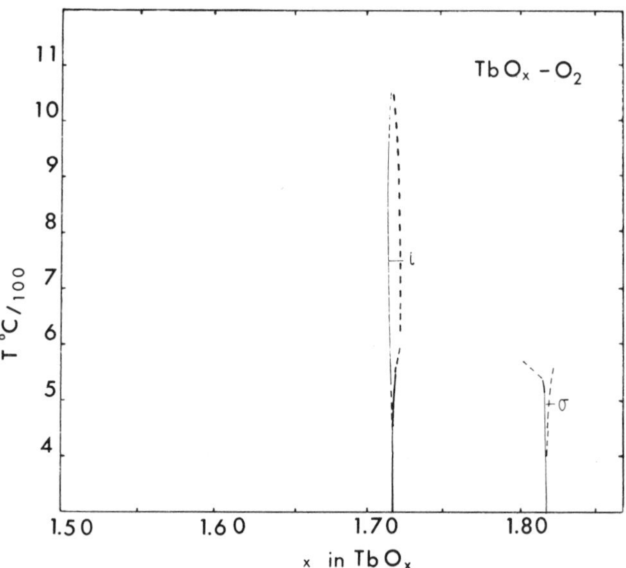

Figure 3. Projection of the TbO_x-O_2 phase diagram

All three polymorphs of the rare earth sesquioxides are shown by either Ce_2O_3 (A-type), Pr_2O_3 (*A* and *C*-type) or Tb_2O_3 (*A*, *B*, and *C*-type). Much work is now underway on the existence and relationship of these three types, and there is a great deal of disagreement as to whether they do in fact represent polymorphs in the thermodynamic sense. Brauer (*15, 16*) reviews progress in this area of research to the end of 1965, but considerable work has been reported since then with little agreement. The areas of high temperature transformation are discussed by Foëx (*24, 25*), who has observed phase transitions up to the melting point of the oxides; by Boganov and Rudenko (*14*) and Glushkova and Boganov (*27*) who address themselves to reversibility of the transitions and the differences in composition; by Hoekstra (*29*), who reports extensive work on the pressure dependence of the transitions and reversibility among them.

Fluorite Related Phases of the Actinide Metal Oxides

All the actinide elements whose oxides have been studied can be made as fluorite-type dioxides. For most of them this is their most stable form in air at room temperature. The fluorite-related phases of each actinide element known will be discussed individually before a comparison is made with the rare earth oxides (*45*).

Thorium. ThO_2 is one of the most thermally stable oxides known, but it forms a slightly oxygen-deficient, congruently-vaporizing solid $ThO_{1.998}$ (*3*) at temperatures of about 2500°C. ThO_2 is a fluorite-type dioxide with $a = 5.999$A.

Protoactinium. Fluorite-type PaO_2 is known, but no evidence exists for PaO_{2-x} phases which almost certainly could be made. Nonfluorite-type higher oxides (*i.e.*, Pa_2O_5) have been studied to some extent.

Uranium. Of all oxide systems investigated, those of uranium must be the most thoroughly studied, revealing it to be one of the most complex binary systems known. We shall concern ourselves here only with the fluorite-related phases $UO_{2\pm x}$. A phase diagram of the region of interest is shown in Figure 4, which is a composite of the UO_{2+x} region proposed by Roberts (*43*) and the UO_{2-x} region observed by Martin and Edwards (*39*).

The extra oxygen in fluorite-related UO_{2+x} has been located in neutron diffraction studies by Willis (*50*) to be accommodated in the fluorite lattice by the generation of complex groups described as 2:2:2 configurations consisting of two interstitial oxygens displaced about 1A. along the <110> direction from the holes in the center of the fluorite unit cell, and two oxygen interstitials displaced about 1A. along the <111> direction from the two normal sites vacated. The positions of the uranium atoms are unaffected by this rearrangement.

The U_4O_9 phase results when one of these 2:2:2 complexes in every two unit cells of the parent UO_2 is linked together with its neighbors in an ordered way. The complete structure is not known. At high temperatures the UO_{2+x} phase may exist with complex concentrations greater than in U_4O_9. According to Anderson (*6*) the transformation between U_4O_9 and $UO_{2+0.25}$ is accompanied by only a small entropy increase, indicating some but not great disordering in the transition.

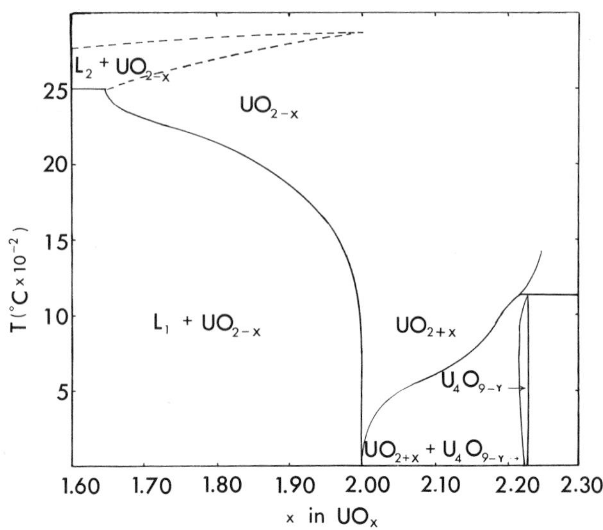

Figure 4. Projection of the $UO_{2\pm x}$-O_2 phase diagram

Martin and Edwards (*39*) have studied the phase diagram for the UO_2-U region, which shows a UO_{2-x} phase as sketched in Figure 4. Usually hyperstoichiometric UO_2 disproportionates when cooled to give UO_2 and U; however, Ackermann *et al.* (*2*) have observed a UO_2 phase of $a = 5.4714$A., a significantly larger unit cell than for $UO_{2.00}$.

The lattice parameter of the UO_{2+x} phase decreased with increasing O/U ratio from $a = 5.4705$A. for UO_2. Values of the lattice parameters of UO_{2+x} and U_4O_{9-y} are on smooth curves lying above a line joining the end-members UO_2 and U_4O_9 (*35*). (The pseudo-cell of the latter is $a = 5.4453$A.) Actually, the U_4O_9 structure is cubic with weak superstructure lines indicating that the true unit cell has an edge of $4a = 21.8$A. and the body-centered space-group $I\bar{4}3d$ (*50*).

Neptunium. The fluorite-type NpO_2 is the stable oxide formed in air when neptunium oxysalts are decomposed, but almost no studies have been carried out in the oxygen-defect region. Ackermann *et al.* (*1*) in studying the vaporization process of NpO_x observed A-type Np_2O_3 in quenched samples which had been 70% vaporized. It is likely that the two phases were formed from a nonstoichiometric NpO_{2-x} phase by disproportionation as the sample was cooled.

Roberts and Walter (*44*) studied the irreversible decomposition on Np_3O_8 but observed no phases intermediate to Np_3O_8 and NpO_2. Hyper-stoichiometric NpO_2 has not so far been reported.

Plutonium. Gardner *et al.* (*26*) have made a careful high temperature x-ray diffraction study of the plutonium-oxygen system in the range from room temperature to 900°C. observing diffraction from oxide samples contained in silica capillaries. They review briefly previous work *apropos* of phase transformations (*i.e.*, thermal and electrical measurements) and construct a phase diagram as shown in Figure 5.

The phases they observed were $PuO_{1.515}$ (b.c.c., $a = 11.05$); $PuO_{1.61}$ (assumed b.c.c., $a = 10.99$); $PuO_{1.98}$ (f.c.c., $a = 5.40$) which is the lower composition limit of PrO_2 (f.c.c., $a = 5.396$); β Pu_2O_3 ($PuO_{1.510} \pm 0.005$ hex., $a = 3.8417 \pm 0.0003$A., $c = 5.9530 \pm 0.005$A.); and at least one cubic phase of widely variable composition PuO_x, $1.61 \leq x \leq 2.0$. Between 300° and 600°C. in this composition range there is a miscibility gap which continuously narrows until it is supposedly closed.

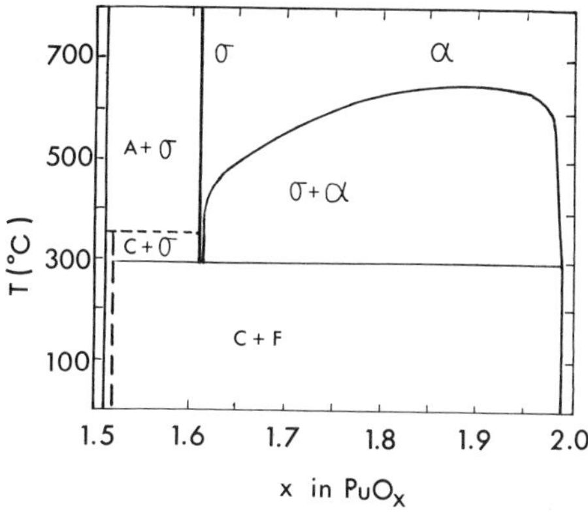

Figure 5. Projection of the PuO_x-O_2 phase diagram

Certain features of the study were emphasized such as the fact that although the $PuO_{1.61}$ phase was assumed b.c.c., the powder patterns were not good enough to show the superstructure lines. Also the eutectoid in the proposed diagram of Chikalla *et al.* (*22*) was not observed in the x-ray studies. No satisfactory explanation of electrical resistivity and thermal expansion measurements which led to this earlier construction has emerged. Gardner *et al.* (*26*) also looked for but did not see any indication of ordered intermediate phases at low temperatures such as were described above for the rare earth oxides nor did they observe a failure of the miscibility gap to close as would have occurred if the end members, $PuO_{1.61}$ and $PuO_{1.98}$, had different symmetries. They could not, however, have observed a narrow two-phase region since high resolution and sharp diagrams would have been required. One can observe from their published data that a shift occurs in slopes of the *a vs. x* lines for oxides between $PuO_{1.690}$ and $PuO_{1.717}$, which may suggest a discontinuity in this region permitting the construction of the narrow miscibility gap required if the $PuO_{1.61}$ and $PuO_{1.98}$ have different symmetries. A brief discussion of this point is given below.

If this gap exists, the system bears even greater resemblance to the cerium oxide system and for many mixed oxides (*12*)—especially if one assumes that ordering upon cooling is blocked in some way. This is not likely, however, since the high temperature disordered phase cannot easily be quenched in other systems. Brett (*18*) found that samples quenched from 900°C. in liquid nitrogen resulted in α-Pu_2O_3 and PuO_2. Tensimetric studies would help to settle the question of phase relationships if one could achieve equilibrium rapidly enough at reasonable temperatures and the extremely low pressures required.

Markin *et al.* (*38*) have determined the e.m.f. of high temperature galvanic cells involving the plutonium oxide-oxygen system. The plots of partial molal free energy of oxygen *vs.* temperature show a profound change in the composition interval 1.691 and 1.812. In many respects the behavior of PuO_x is quite similar to CeO_x.

Americium. Some years ago Asprey and Cunningham (*7*) studied the thermal decomposition of PrO_2 and AmO_2 in a calibrated reaction volume. This work presaged the tensimetric wonder of the PrO_x-O_2 system already discussed and indicated the relative simplicity of the AmO_x-O_2 system in the accessible temperature range. AmO_2 appeared to lose oxygen smoothly to a composition of $AmO_{1.85}$ at 1400°C. where it had an equilibrium oxygen pressure of 13 mm. Hg in contrast to the much easier but interrupted loss for PrO_x resulting from the several stable intermediate phases. Asprey's curves do show some minor breaks in the log *p vs.* $1/T$ plots with a change of slope at $AmO_{1.877}$ in one of the runs. It is not at all certain that these are significant since they were not corroborated in the work discussed below.

A recent study by Chikalla and Eyring (*21*) of the AmO_x system, including tensimetric and x-ray diffraction measurements, has been completed. The results agree with Asprey's measurements within the expected accuracy of his work. A reversible single phase AmO_{2-x} region for $0 \leq x \leq 0.2$ is observed at 1172°C. and $0 \leq x \leq 0.007$ at 866° C., which were the limits of composition available to the isothermal tensimetric technique. A striking feature of the isotherms is the distinct change in slope which occurs at a composition of $AmO_{1.99}$ at 866°C. The break occurs at decreasing compositions reaching $AmO_{1.97}$ at 1172°C. This feature is reminiscent of a break in the curve of lattice parameter *vs.* composition of the ternary oxide $Ce_yY_{1-y}O_x$ at $MO_{1.95}$ which was considered by Bevan *et al.* (*12*) to be caused by a transition from random to complexed defects. The change is not sharp but occurs reversibly over a considerable pressure range in all cases. This break naturally shows up in the derived thermodynamic quantities, $\Delta\overline{S}$ and $\Delta\overline{H}$. Chikalla also points out that the impurity concentration would undoubtedly affect the behavior in the region AmO_x, $2.0 \geq x \geq 1.99$.

X-ray diffraction studies by Chikalla (*21*) on cooled and quenched samples show that the single phase AmO_x, $1.8 \leq x \leq 2.0$, stable at high temperatures, disproportionates too rapidly to be quenched; all the room temperature diagrams show two phases—$AmO_{2.00}$ and $AmO_{1.8}$. In the range $AmO_{1.5+x}$, $0 \leq x \leq 0.20$, a continuously changing *C*-type phase is observed as shown by the continual shift in the lattice parameter as a function of composition. Both cooled and quenched samples give the same results; even one quenched from 460°C. seems to be in the single phase region.

In terms of the rare earth oxides a miscibility gap between AmO_2-$AmO_{1.8}$ exists, with some complications in the $AmO_{1.71}$ to $AmO_{1.8}$ region. Broad σ and α regions exist at high temperature and may be separated by a miscibility gap.

Curium. A central problem in the curium-oxygen system is the lack of precise knowledge of the compositions for the phases which have been observed. Generally, it has been assumed that there is an analogy between this system and those discussed above. The fluorite-type phase with the smallest lattice parameter is considered to be CmO_2, and the most fully reduced *C*-type oxide is assumed to have the composition $CmO_{1.5}$.

Wallmann (*49*) has prepared *C*-type Cm_2O_3 ($a = 11.01 \pm 0.01$) by igniting curium nitrate on a platinum plate in air (this yields a black intermediate oxide), followed by reduction with purified hydrogen at temperatures from 600° to 850°C. The *C*-type sesquioxide transforms spontaneously at room temperature in a few days to the hexagonal *A*-type sesquioxide ($a = 3.80 \pm 0.02$A., $c = 6.00 \pm 0.03$A.), presumably a result of radiation effects.

Using an automatic recording thermal balance Posey *et al.* (*41, 42*) have made isobaric and isothermal studies indicating the existence of regions of stability having approximate compositions $CmO_{1.71}$ and $CmO_{1.82}$, as well as phases of variable composition $CmO_{1.5+x}$ and CmO_{2-x}. The breaks are not usually sharp; hence, the stable phases show an appreciable range of composition especially for the $CmO_{1.83}$ to $CmO_{1.78}$ region which may involve several different phases.

A complete isobar at 159 mm. of Hg shows the normal breaks at $CmO_{1.8}$ and $CmO_{1.7}$ in the reduction half of the cycle but exhibits an extreme hysteresis loop in the oxidation part of the cycle which did not close until a composition near CmO_2 was reached. This behavior, to a lesser degree, is exhibited by the rare earth oxide systems discussed above.

Isothermal measurements seem to confirm the more expressive isobaric results and even indicate a possible complexity in the $CmO_{1.80-1.83}$ region.

Smith (*47*) has observed a CmO_x fluorite-type phase of variable lattice parameter (a = 5.38 to 5.52A.). This probably represents the entire composition range between CmO_2 and $CmO_{1.5}$—the diagrams not being good enough to see superstructure lines characteristic of a C-type, σ phase or any of the other intermediate phases. (Wallmann (*49*) observed $a = 2(5.50)$ for C-type Cm_2O_3).

Perhaps with such intense radioactivity complete ordering is impossible, and although the tensimetric measurements definitely show the greatly increased stability at certain concentrations the order is not well enough established to show up in the x-ray diagrams. This behavior is observed in the mixed $Ce_{0.2}Tb_{0.8}O_x$ system where the presence of Ce prevents the complete ordering necessary to give resolution in the high temperature x-ray diffraction patterns (*20*), but the tensimetric measurements indicate unmistakably the formation of the ι phase (*33*).

Ternary Actinide–Lanthanide Oxide Phases. An interesting link exists between the ordered oxide phases of the lanthanide elements on the one hand and the actinide oxides on the other. Bartram describes the preparation and structures of ternary oxides having the composition $UO_3 \cdot 3R_2O_3$ or UR_6O_{12}, where R represents a rare earth atom (*10*). These structures are isomorphous with the R_7O_{12} phases previously discussed for the binary Ce, Pr, and Tb oxides. In the ternary oxides the uranium atoms fill all the metal positions along the strings and the oxygens are shifted in toward the vacant sites along the string. The R atoms are seven coordinated in the sheaths surrounding the strings as indicated above.

Observed Trends

The fluorite-related oxide phases which are known in the lanthanide and actinide series are displayed in Table II for closer comparison. The most obvious feature is that the oxide systems of Ce, Pr, and Tb reveal greater complexity than any of the actinide elements so far studied. The dioxides of the actinide elements are more easily reduced as one goes from ThO_2 to CmO_2 showing an approach to the behavior of the lanthanides. More complete measurements on CmO_x and BkO_x may well show marked similarity to the rare earths.

All 12 elements listed in Table II form dioxides of the same structure. Most of them form sesquioxides having the *A*- ,*B*-, or *C*-type rare earth structure and demonstrate similar polymorphism. The analogous intermediate oxides are also obviously possible, and the R_nO_{2n-2} homologous series could exist. The question as to whether such phases are in fact observed depends entirely on the form of the free energy surface. The factors determining the shape and relative positions of the free energy minima of each phase are not understood. Even metastable phases are observed to be formed under circumstances where ordering is much slower than transformation to another disordered phase (*i.e.*, $\sigma^m \rightarrow \alpha^m$ in PrO_x).

Figure 6 shows the lattice parameters *vs.* composition of the phases discussed above. For the *C*-type sesquioxides or σ phases the pseudo-

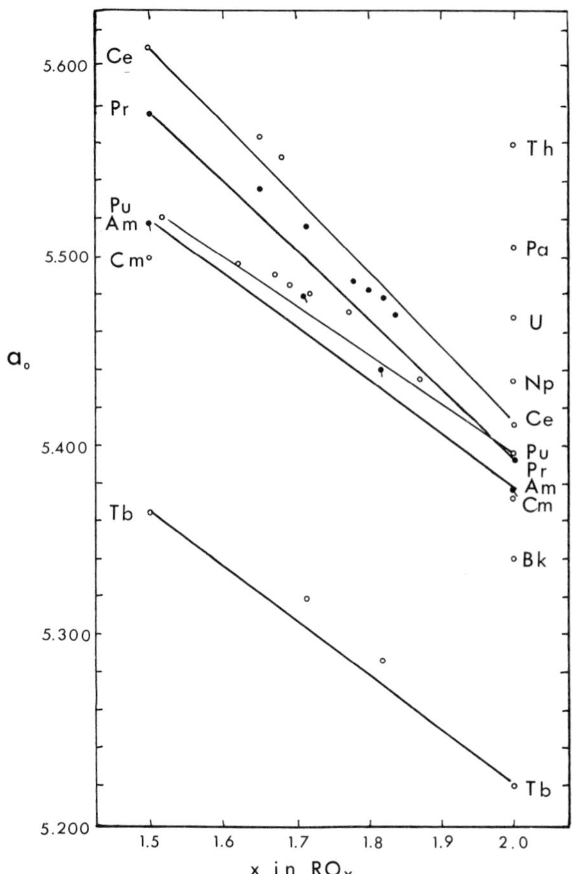

Figure 6. Lattice parameters of fluorite-related oxides of some lanthanide and actinide elements as a function of composition

fluorite cell dimension is used for comparison. The lattice parameters of all the intermediate oxide phases lie above a straight line joining values for the dioxide and *C*-type sesquioxide.

Table II. Existence Diagram for R_nO_{2n-2} Phases of Some Lanthanide and Actinide Elements

Phase Type	*A*	*B*	*C*	σ	ι	ζ	ϵ	δ	β	α	*F*
n	4	4	4	$1.5 \leq x$	7	9	10	11	12	$1.7 \leq x$	∞
$x(RO_x)$		1.50		≤ 1.7	1.71	1.78	1.80	1.82	1.83	≤ 2.0	2.00
Ce	X			X	X	X	X	X		X	X
Pr	X		X	X	X	X	X	X	X	X	X
Tb	X	X	X	X	X			X	?	?	X
U/Y			/X		X						X
Th										X	X
Pa											X
U										X	X
Np	X			?						X	X
Pu	X		X	X	?					X	X
Am	X	X	X	X	?			?		X	X
Cm	X		X	X	X	?	?	X	?	X	X
Bk											X

Correlation of the standard free energy change for the reaction $\frac{1}{2}R_2O_3 + \frac{1}{4}O_2 = RO_2$ with the change in the heats of atomization of the respective oxides per equivalent O_2 (Figure 7) illustrates well the observed trends in stability. A difference of 10 kcal. per equivalent of oxygen in the energies of atomization corresponds to oxygen dissociation pressure differences of about 100 orders of magnitude. The oxygen dissociation pressure of a particular oxide composition shows a definite trend within each series increasing with atomic number. The order, in the region of overlap of the two series, is indicated by the oxygen dissociation pressure, at some temperature, of $RO_{1.714}$ which increases in the order Pu, Ce, Am, Pr, Tb, and Cm.

Chemists, accustomed to the vagaries of the two series of elements, realize that facts forbid any simple progression in properties. This is true for the lanthanide elements because of the perturbation of properties accompanying the stabilizing effect on the electrons of an empty, half-filled and full 4*f* shell. It is accentuated in the case of the actinides where one has 6*d*, 7*s*, and 5*f* levels so close together in energy that the early members of the series behave as though they had no *f* electrons. However, as one progresses down the actinide series the *f* electrons definitely become less available for bonding as they do in the 4*f* elements.

Ackermann and Thorn (*4*) emphasize the importance, in interpreting high temperature vaporization results, of knowing the composition and nature of the solid phase. Even ThO_2 lost oxygen in congruent vaporization at 2500°C. (*4*). All other actinide dioxides studied have a higher oxygen dissociation pressure than ThO_2 at the same temperature and would be expected to form an α phase. This was observed to a great degree in UO_{2-x}, strongly suggested in NpO_{2-x}, and clearly demonstrated in PuO_{2-x}, AmO_{2-x}, and CmO_{2-x}. In addition, CmO_{2-x} showed stable intermediate phases at $CmO_{1.71}$ and $CmO_{1.8}$. The fact that Cm shows +3 and +4 valences with a $5f^7$ configuration for Cm^{3+} emphasizes the greater availability of the 5*f* electrons for bonding than exists in the rare earths where Gd^{3+} with $4f^7$ electrons forms only the sesquioxide.

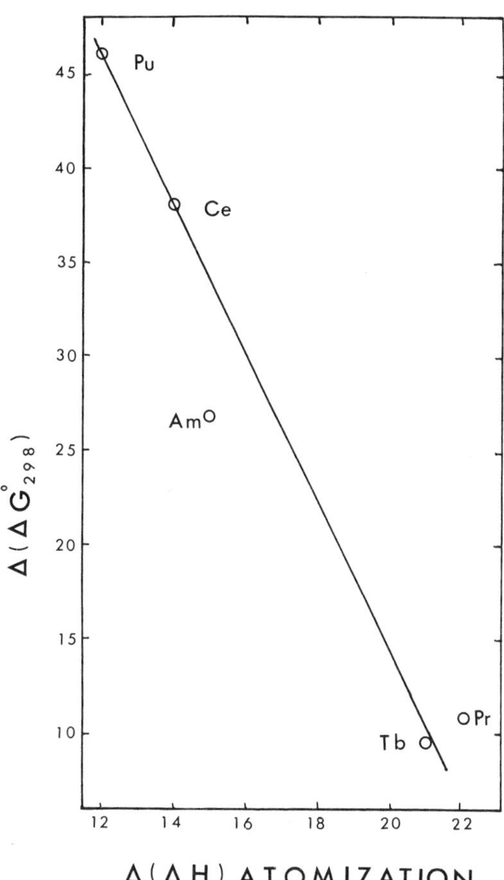

Figure 7. Free energy change for the reaction $RO_2(c) = \frac{1}{2}R_2O_3(c) + \frac{1}{4}O_2(g)$ correlated with the differences in atomization energy per equivalent of oxygen for $RO_2(c)$ and $R_2O_3(c)$. All values are given in kcal. per equivalent

The structural principles enumerated above for the intermediate phases of the rare earths, including the α phase, presuppose a structure which would be better characterized by oxygen vacancies than by metal interstitials. It is tacitly assumed that the α phases of the actinide oxides would be analogous. However, Atlas and Schlehman (8) have studied the pressure dependence of electrical conductivity on composition and oxygen pressure and conclude from mass-action analysis that the defects in PuO_{2-x} in the temperature region 1100°–1600°C. are predominantly interstitial plutonium ions, usually Pu^{4+}. In this treatment the arbitrary assumption is made that the defects do not interact. The data cover the composition range $PuO_{2.0-1.8}$, where one would expect extensive defect interactions. Chikalla (*21*) has considered the various attempts to determine the type of defects in the oxygen deficient fluorite phases, PuO_{2-x}, CeO_{2-x}, and AmO_{2-x}. He concludes that although the mass-action treatment agrees in all cases with a metal interstitial model an oxygen vacancy model might explain the results as well, especially if the defects are paired or complexed. On the other hand there may be no appreciable defect concentration at all in a well annealed α phase with domain structure.

As a matter of principle any of the systems showing both the sesquioxide (even the *C*-type) and the fluorite-type dioxide must exhibit a miscibility gap somewhere. For this reason the σ is distinguished from the α phase. In all cases where thorough studies have been possible, a gap has indeed been found.

Solid solubility in rare earth oxide systems has been studied extensively. There is no doubt of complete solubility, often called isomorphous replacement between oxide phases of the same symmetry as in mixtures of PrO_2 and CeO_2 or in the sesquioxides of one type. In these cases Vegard's law appears to hold precisely (*40*).

Because of the close relationship between the *C*-type and the fluorite-type structures much attention has been given to the range of solution between phases having these structures. Brauer and Gradinger (*17*) indicated that in solutions involving CeO_2 or ThO_2 with the trivalent rare earths, phase separation is most common, but there were cases which appeared to form complete solid solution (*i.e.*, CeO_2 with Sm_2O_3, Gd_2O_3, or Dy_2O_3) over the entire range of composition.

This is *apropos* of the basic question of whether or not one may go continuously between different structures having different symmetries. In principle this should not be possible (*19, 34*); however, certain cases have been reported, and the one mentioned above is used by Zernike (*51*) against the basic philosophic arguments.

Bevan (*12*) and his colleagues have studied precisely those systems reported to be single phase by Brauer and Gradinger and have shown them to be at least two phase. A miscibility gap at about 60% sesquioxide is observed in each case. This removes one of the principle arrows from the bow of those who would argue against the requirements of basic theory and raises the question as to whether, in fact, there are any exceptions. This is a question which can only be settled by principle since more and more careful structural determinations may be made and could reveal narrow two-phase regions.

Chikalla (*21*) has considered the possibility that radiation damage is a major cause of failure to order among the intermediate actinide oxides. This will certainly be a factor against ordering, but the decidedly greater tendency of the short lived CmO_x to show ordering indicates that it is only one of many factors. X-ray diffraction patterns may fail to reveal the presence of ordered intermediate phases in CmO_x because of the high radiation. However, tensimetric measurements may reveal order where x-ray measurements fail, as was true for the $Ce_yTb_{1-y}O_x$ system (*33*). High temperature x-ray diffraction measurements using high intensity tubes might be required to see the true structural changes at temperature and at equilibrium for highly radioactive materials.

Acknowledgment

This paper is dedicated to James C. Wallmann, actinide experimentalist extraordinary whose untimely death removed a devoted scientist from his laboratory in the peak of his productivity. The loss to science is great and to his family and friends is without relief.

This work was performed under the auspices of the Atomic Energy Commission whose resources and far sighted policies have made this paper and most of the work discussed herein possible. R. T. Sanderson and J. O. Sawyer have helpfully discussed certain aspects of this work.

Literature Cited

(1) Ackermann, R. J., Faircloth, R. L., Rauh, E. G., Thorn, R. J., *Inorg. Nucl. Chem.* **28**, 111 (1966).
(2) Ackermann, R. J., Gilles, P. W., Thorn, R. J., *J. Chem. Phys.* **25**, 1089 (1956).
(3) Ackermann, R. J., Rauh, E. G., Thorn, R. J., Cannon, M. C., *J. Phys. Chem.* **67**, 762 (1963).
(4) Ackermann, R. J., Thorn, R. J., *Proc. Symp. Thermodynamics, IAEA Vienna 1965,* **I**, 243 (1965).
(5) Anderson, J. S., ADVAN. CHEM. SER. **39,** 1 (1963).
(6) Anderson, J. S., *Proc. Chem. Soc.* p. 166 (1964).
(7) Asprey, L. B., Cunningham, B. B., *U. S. At. Energy Comm. Rept.* **UCRL-329** (1949).
(8) Atlas, L. M., Schlehman, G. J., *Proc. Intern. Conf. on Plutonium, 3rd, London* (1965).

(9) Baengiger, N. C., Eick, H. A., Schuldt, H. S., Eyring, L., *J. Am. Chem. Soc.* **83,** 2219 (1961).
(10) Bartram, S. F., *Inorg. Chem.* **5,** 749 (1966).
(11) Bertaut, E. F., *Acta Cryst.* **6,** 557 (1953).
(12) Bevan, D. J. M., Barker, W. W., Martin, R. L., Parks, T. C., "Rare Earth Research III," L. Eyring, ed., p. 441, Gordon & Breach, New York, 1965.
(13) Bevan, D. J. M., Kordis, J., *J. Inorg. Chem. Nucl. Chem.* **26,** 1509 (1964).
(14) Boganov, A. G., Rudenko, V. S., *Dokl. Akad. Nauk SSSR* **161,** 590 (1965).
(15) Brauer, G., "Progress in the Science and Technology of the Rare Earths," Vol. II, L. Eyring, ed., p. 312, Pergamon Press, Oxford, 1966.
(16) *Ibid.,* **I,** p. 152 (1964).
(17) Brauer, G., Gradinger, H., *Z. Anorg. Allgem. Chem.* **276,** 209 (1954).
(18) Brett, N. H., Russell, L. E., *Proc. Intern. Conf. Pu Metallurgy, 2nd,* Grenoble (1960).
(19) Bridgman, P. W., *Rev. Mod. Phys.* **7,** 17 (1935).
(20) Burnham, A., Eyring, L. (to be published).
(21) Chikalla, T. D., *J. Inorg. Nucl. Chem.* (in press).
(22) Chikalla, T. D., McNeilly, C. E., Skavdahl, R. E., *J. Nucl. Meter.* **122,** 131 (1964).
(23) Eyring, L., Baenziger, N. C., *J. Appl. Phys. (Suppl.)* **33,** 428 (1962).
(24) Foëx, M., *Z. Anorg. Allgem. Chem.* **337,** No. 5-6 (1965).
(25) Foëx, M., Traverse, J. P., Coutures, J., *C. R. Acad. Sc. Paris* **261,** 5497 (1965).
(26) Gardner, E. R., Markin, T. L., Street, R. S., *J. Inorg. Nucl. Chem.* **27,** 541 (1965).
(27) Glushkova, V. B., Boganov, A. G., *Izv. Akad. Nauk. SSSR, Ser. Khim.* **7,** 1131 (1965).
(28) Hoch, M., Yoon, H. S., "Rare Earth Research III," L. Eyring, ed., p. 665, Gordon & Breach, New York, 1965.
(29) Hoekstra, H. R., *Inorg. Chem.* **5,** 754 (1966).
(30) Hyde, B. G., Bevan, D. J. M., Eyring, L., *Phil. Trans. Roy. Soc. London A No. 1106* **259,** 583 (1966).
(31) Hyde, B. G., Bevan, D. J. M., Eyring, L., *Intern. Conf. Electron Diffraction Crystal Defects, Melbourne, Australia, 1965,* Pergamon Press, 1966.
(32) Hyde, B. G., Eyring, L., "Rare Earth Research III," L. Eyring, ed., p. 623, Gordon & Breach, New York, 1966.
(33) Kordis, J., Eyring, L. (to be published).
(34) Landau, L. D., Lifshitz, E. M., "Statistical Physics," p. 260, Pergamon Press, London, 1959.
(35) Lynds, L., Young, W. A., Mohl, J. S., Libowitz, G. G., ADVAN. CHEM. SER. **39** (1963).
(36) Magnéli, A., *Acta Chem. Scand.* **2,** 501 (1948).
(37) *Ibid.,* p. 861.
(38) Markin, T. L., Bones, R. J., Gardner, E. R., **Rept. AERE-R4724,** 1964.
(39) Martin, A. E., Edwards, R. K., *J. Phys. Chem.* **69,** 1788 (1965).
(40) McCullough, J. D., Britton, J. D., *J. Am. Chem. Soc.* **74,** 5225 (1952).
(41) Posey, J. C., Kuehn, P. R., McHenry, R. E., *Abstr. Papers, 150th Meeting ACS, Atlantic City,* 1965.
(42) Posey, J. C., Kuehn, P. R., McHenry, R. E. (private communication).
(43) Roberts, L. E. J., ADVAN. CHEM. SER. **39,** 66 (1963).
(44) Roberts, L. E. J., Walter, A. J., **Rept. AERE-R 3624** (1963).
(45) Roberts, L. E. J., *Quart. Rev.,* London, **15,** No. 4, 442 (1961).
(46) Sawyer, J. O., Hyde, B. G., Eyring, L., *Bull. Soc. Chim.* p. 1190 (1965).
(47) Smith, K. (private communication).
(48) Wadsley, A. D., "Non-Stoichiometric Compounds," L. Mandelcorn, ed., Chapt. 3, Academic Press, London, 1964.

(49) Wallmann, J. C., *J. Inorg. Nucl. Chem.* **26**, 2053 (1964).
(50) Willis, B. T. M., I. A. E. A. Symp., Vienna, 1964.
(51) Zernike, J., "Chemical Phase Theory," p. 169, N. V. Uitgevers-Maatschappij AE. E. Kluwer Antwerp.

RECEIVED October 17, 1966.

7

Lanthanide and Actinide Absorption Spectra in Solution

W. T. CARNALL and P. R. FIELDS

Chemistry Division, Argonne National Laboratory, Argonne, Ill.

We have calculated sets of theoretical energy levels for the trivalent actinides and lanthanides and correlated these levels with transitions observed in the solution absorption spectra of these elements. Using the eigenvectors resulting from this energy level calculation, we have computed the theoretical matrix elements required to account for the observed band intensities in the two series of elements. The extent to which the theoretical calculations can be correlated with experimental results has been discussed, and some applications for the intensity relationships are pointed out.

The solution absorption spectra of the trivalent lanthanides and actinides are comprised of distinctive sharp, rather weak absorption bands which have been observed primarily in the visible-near u.v. region of the spectrum. Most of these bands arise from transitions within the f^N-electron configuration. However, the extent to which both their energies and intensities can be correlated with theoretically calculated energies and intensities has been explored only recently (*2, 14*). In this paper we will emphasize the theoretical treatment of experimental results in two related stages. First, the energies of the transitions observed in dilute acid solution are related to calculated energy levels. The eigenvectors derived from the energy level calculations are then used as a basis to calculate band intensities.

Most published work on the energy levels in the trivalent lanthanides and actinides has been carried out in crystalline media, where the identity of a level in terms of a given coupling scheme can be experimentally established (*8, 19*). In attempting similar correlations in aqueous solution, one must rely heavily on the level identifications established in crystals. Where crystal data is not available, extrapolation of parameters from neighboring elements is required to make level assignments. One objective of this study is to correlate the energy levels and intensities of all the trivalent lanthanides and actinides in a single solvent medium. For the intensity study, relationships developed in aqueous solutions can then serve as a basis for comparing the results in many other media in which strong complexes are formed.

Experimental

The spectral measurements were made in fused silica cells whose path lengths varied from 1.0 to 5.0 cm. and were observed using a high resolution prism-grating recording spectrophotometer. The useful spectral range of the instrument was 0.18–2.6 μ. The lanthanides used were obtained commercially as oxides with a stated purity of $>$99.9%; however, each batch of oxide was checked spectrographically before use. These oxides were dissolved in either $DClO_4$ or $HClO_4$ for the absorption spectra measurements (*3*). Solutions of the actinides were prepared from highly purified stock solutions by techniques previously discussed (*4*).

Energy Level Calculations

The total energy of a system consisting of a point nucleus with an infinite mass, surrounded by N electrons can be represented by the Hamiltonian (*19*),

$$\mathfrak{H} = \mathfrak{H}_o + \mathfrak{H}_e + \mathfrak{H}_{so}$$

where $\mathfrak{H}_o$ represents the kinetic energy of all the electrons and their coulomb interaction with the nucleus; $\mathfrak{H}_e$ involves the coulomb interaction between pairs of electrons, and $\mathfrak{H}_{so}$ takes into account the magnetic interactions of the electrons, of which the coupling of spin and orbital angular momenta is the most important effect for f-electrons.

Using a central field approximation in which it is assumed that each electron moves independently in an average spherically symmetric potential, it is possible to solve for the energies of the different configurations. Calculations of this type show that the f^N-configuration is the lowest energy configuration for the trivalent lanthanides and actinides.

Since it can be demonstrated that the term $\mathfrak{H}_o$ does not affect the energy level structure within a given configuration and since the absorption spectra of the trivalent lanthanides and actinides involve transitions between states within the f^N-configuration, it is not necessary to concern ourselves with $\mathfrak{H}_o$ any further. A substantial simplification is also possible in formulating $\mathfrak{H}_e$. Including the effect of electrons in closed shells in the calculation merely shifts the energy of a configuration; thus, for our purposes it is only necessary to consider the electrostatic interaction between electrons in the incomplete $4f$ or $5f$ shell.

The solution of the remaining terms in the Hamiltonian, $\mathfrak{H}_e$ and $\mathfrak{H}_{so}$ can be written as

$$E = E_e + E_{so}$$

where

$$E_e = \sum_{k=0}^{6} f^k F_k \ (k \text{ even})$$

and

$$E_{so} = A_{so}\zeta_{nf}$$

The electrostatic energy is expressed as a sum of radial integrals F_k, and coefficients f^k which represent the angular part of the interaction. Similarly A_{so} represents the angular part of the spin-orbit interaction and ζ_{nf} is a radial integral, referred to as the spin orbit coupling constant. The angular parts of both perturbation energies can be evaluated using Racah's tensor operator formalism, and assuming the Russell-Saunders (SLJ) coupling scheme. The radial dependence is difficult to calculate theoretically, and in practice these functions are treated as parameters to be evaluated from experimental data. There are, therefore, three electrostatic parameters, F_2, F_4, and F_6 and one spin-orbit parameter, ζ_{nf}, to be determined by a fit to observed energy levels for which assignments have been made in an appropriate coupling scheme (in this case SLJ).

Since the spin-orbit interaction is large for the lanthanides and especially large for the actinides, the SLJ basis states are mixed, and the calculations are actually carried out in intermediate coupling.

To illustrate the effect of the various perturbations, consider as a typical example, Pr^{3+}. As shown in Figure 1, consideration of the electrostatic interaction of two 4*f*-electrons (Pr^{3+}) gives rise to a set of seven degenerate energy levels. These are further split by inclusion of spin-orbit interaction, to 13 levels which are called field-free levels since they represent the spectrum of Pr^{3+} as observed in Pr^{3+} vapor where there are no ligands about the Pr^{3+} ions. In fact, these levels are also degenerate. Additional splitting does occur when the ion is incorporated in either a solid or liquid matrix. This ligand field splitting is small compared with the other effects considered, and the individual levels are normally not resolved in solution spectra. For our purposes it is sufficient to identify the center of gravity of a given absorption band with the appropriate field-free level.

Since at this point we have no method of experimentally identifying a given absorption band in solution in terms of its description in the SLJ coupling scheme, we rely on the similarity in band energy with that established for Pr^{3+} in various crystal matrices. Figure 2 shows the experimentally determined positions of the center of gravity of the levels of Pr^{3+} in $LaCl_3$ (*17*), LaF_3 (*5*) and the levels found in Pr^{3+} vapor (*7, 18*).

For isolated bands there is no question of the proper assignment, but as can be seen, even when the bands are not isolated it may be reasonable to make assignments to the solution spectra. In the case of Pr^{3+}, the spectra in LaF_3 resembles quite closely that found in solution.

As the number of *f*-electrons increases, the process of assigning levels becomes more complicated. It is not often that the published results for lanthanide spectra in crystal media compare as favorably as those for

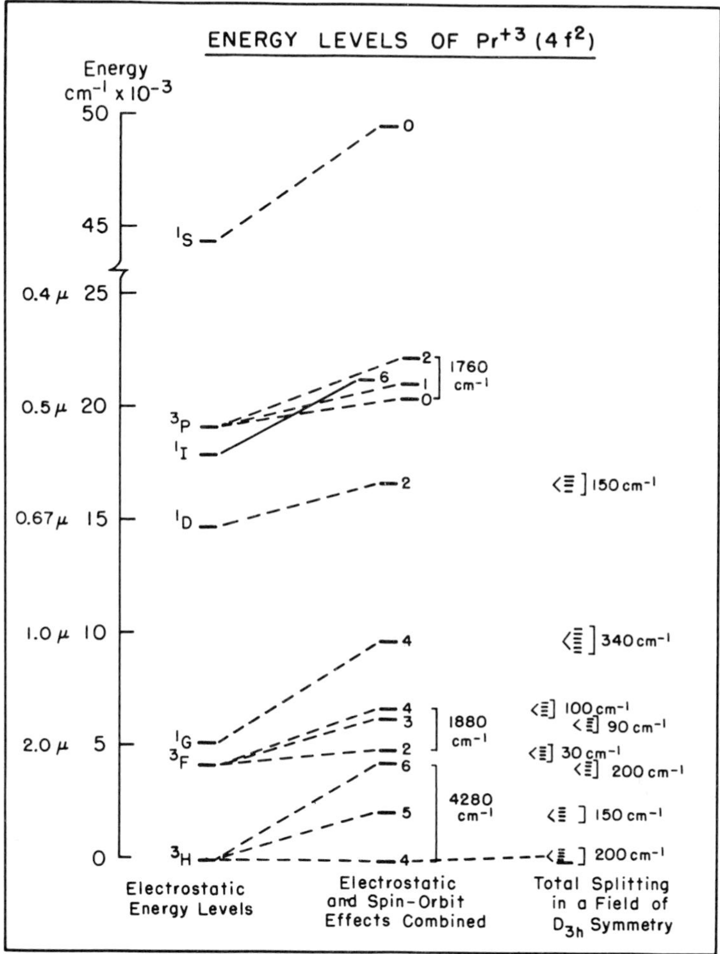

Figure 1. Energy levels due to electrostatic, spin-orbit and crystal field interactions in Pr^{3+}

Pr^{3+} in LaF_3 to Pr^{3+} in solution. For the lanthanides in the middle of the series where the most complex spectra occur, much of the work in crystals is still preliminary. This problem is even more acute for the actinides.

Where published values of F_2, F_4, F_6, and ζ were not available, initial assignments were based on levels calculated from the parameters F_k and ζ which were obtained by extrapolation from neighboring members of the series (*4*). Both F_2 and ζ can be assumed to be approximately linear functions of Z (atomic number) within the series, and by using the ratios F_4/F_2 and F_6/F_2 calculated for a 4*f* or 5*f* hydrogenic eigenfunction (*15*), all three electrostatic parameters can be evaluated from F_2 alone.

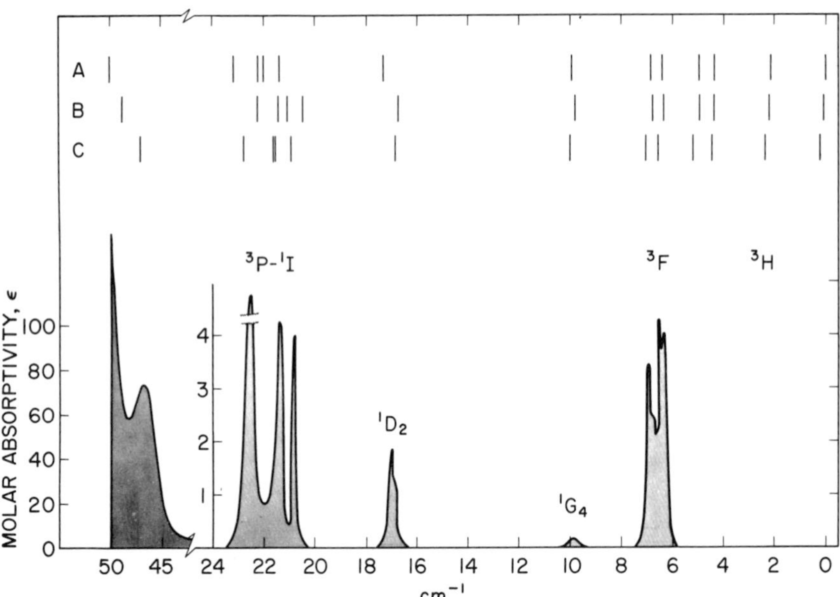

Figure 2. Comparison of the absorption spectra of Pr^{3+} *in aqueous solution with the energy levels found experimentally for* Pr^{3+} *in (A) vapor phase (free-ion levels)* (7, 18), *(B)* $LaCl_3$ *crystal* (17), *(C)* LaF_3 *crystal* (5)

The results of applying the foregoing discussion to a calculation of energy levels for spectra of the lanthanides in dilute acid solution are shown in Figures 3–5. The best values of the four parameters obtained from the data are summarized in Table I. Since the fit to the data at higher energies becomes quite poor in many cases, only the bands observed at $<$ 30000 cm.$^{-1}$ are shown except for Gd^{3+} (Figure 4), where all of the excited levels occur at $>$ 30000 cm.$^{-1}$.

The same type of approach in terms of fitting energy levels to the absorption bands observed in the trivalent actinide elements has already been reported (*4*). Here the problems were somewhat more formidable because of the paucity of crystal data and the much greater density of levels observed in the spectral region over which solution absorption spectra could be obtained. Experimental data and calculated energy levels are shown in Figure 6. The four parameters derived from the data are also shown in Table I.

The values of F_2 for the trivalent lanthanides and actinides are plotted vs. Z (atomic number) in Figure 7, and those of ζ are shown graphically in Figure 8. Values of F_2 and ζ_{5f} for actinides above curium were extrapolated from the light half of the series assuming a linear relationship for the parameters (*9*). These parameters, in turn, were used to calculate the expected energy levels for Bk^{3+}, Cf^{3+}, Es^{3+}, and Fm^{3+}. These, together with the absorption spectrum of Cf^{3+}, which was recently measured jointly with scientists from the Lawrence Radiation Laboratories (*6*), are shown in Figure 9.

Sets of eigenvectors which describe each of the states in intermediate coupling, are obtained from the calculations of the energy levels. These eigenvectors are an essential element in establishing the correlation between experimental band intensities and those calculated from theory.

Table I. Parameters Used to Calculate Energy Levels Observed in the Solution Absorption Spectra of the Trivalent Actinides and Lanthanides

	No. of f-electrons	F_2	F_4	F_6	ζ
Pr^{3+}	2	304.7	50.82	5.106	714.5
Nd^{3+}	3	333.6	48.06	5.450	874.1
Pm^{3+}	4	351.0	47.70	5.300	1030
Sm^{3+}	5	371.8	54.02	6.027	1171
Eu^{3+}	6	470.6	70.91	4.953	1297
Gd^{3+}	7	488.4	46.28	6.219	1454
Tb^{3+}	8	486.7	69.17	5.859	1681
Dy^{3+}	9	420.0	58.00	6.346	1900
Ho^{3+}	10	415.0	68.80	7.270	2163
Er^{3+}	11	433.2	67.10	7.360	2393
Tm^{3+}	12	447.6	67.12	7.336	2652
U^{3+}	3	196	27.9	3.16	1666
Np^{3+}	4	225	32.0	3.62	2070
Pu^{3+}	5	240	34.1	3.86	2292
Am^{3+}	6	419	55.6	1.98	2190
Cm^{3+}	7	370	21.0	4.90	2918
Bk^{3+}	8	299	42.5	4.81	3263
Cf^{3+}	9	318	45.2	5.12	3580
Es^{3+}	10	338	48.1	5.44	3900
Fm^{3+}	11	358	50.9	5.76	4220

Calculation of Intensities

Any theoretical treatment of the intensities of the intra f^N-electron transitions observed in trivalent lanthanide and actinide spectra must begin with a consideration of the possible mechanisms involved, and a number of authors have examined this problem in detail (*1, 2, 19*). The

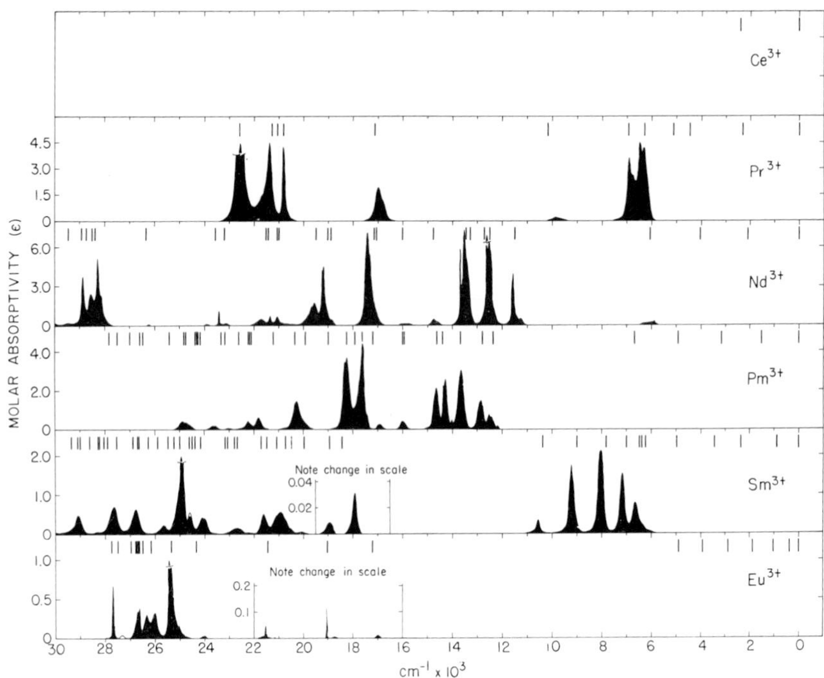

Figure 3. Absorption spectra of Ce^{3+}, Pr^{3+}, Nd^{3+}, Pm^{3+}, Sm^{3+}, and Eu^{3+} in dilute acid solution

results show that while there is some magnetic dipole character in a few transitions, only an induced electric dipole mechanism can account for the intensities observed for most of the bands. The designation induced or forced electric dipole is used to acknowledge the fact that true electric dipole transitions require a parity change and cannot occur within the same configuration because the initial and final states have the same parity. Since the intensities of the intra f^N-electron transitions are extremely weak compared with true electric dipole transitions, they can be accounted for by assuming that a small amount of the character of higher-lying configurations of opposite parity are mixed into the f^N-electron states. This mixing is assumed to be accomplished *via* the odd terms in the potential owing to the ligand field experienced by the lanthanide or actinide ion. It will be noted that the inversion operator cannot be one of the symmetry elements in such a ligand field.

Judd (*14*) has applied the forced electric dipole mechanism to transitions within the f^N-electron configuration and was able to develop an expression for the oscillator strength of a given transition. (For purposes of comparing results we have defined $\tau_\lambda = (2J + 1)\ T_\lambda$ where T_λ is the term used in Judd's paper (*2, 14*).)

This expression can be written:

$$P = \sigma\,[\tau_2(M_2)^2 + \tau_4(M_4)^2 + \tau_6(M_6)^2]$$

$$M_\lambda = (f^N\psi_J \,||\, \mathbf{U}^{(\lambda)} \,||\, f^N\psi'_J\,)\quad \lambda = 2,4,6.$$

P is the oscillator strength defined by $P = 4.31 \times 10^{-9} \int \epsilon_i\,(\sigma)\,d\sigma$ where $\int \epsilon_i\,(\sigma)\,d\sigma$ is the area under the observed absorption band, σ is the energy of the transition in wave numbers and ϵ_i its absorbance. M_λ are the matrix elements of the unit tensor operator $\mathbf{U}^{(\lambda)}$. This operator connects the initial and final states $\psi_J \rightarrow \psi'_{J}{}'$, which were in turn of the form:

$$|\, f^N\psi_J\rangle = \sum_{\alpha,S,L} C\,(\alpha,S,L)\,|\, f^N\alpha SLJ\rangle$$

$C(\alpha,S,L)$ are the intermediate coupling coefficients; α represents extra quantum numbers that might be necessary to describe the state completely and $|f^N\alpha\; SLJ\rangle$ are the basis states in the SLJ coupling scheme. Formulas for calculating the matrix elements M_λ, using the eigenvectors obtained on the basis of the energy level fits already discussed, are given in Ref. 2. The parameters τ_λ are a function of the quantities that describe the immediate environment of the ion, the index of refraction of the medium, and the radial wave functions of the states involved. Since we are not at this time able to calculate τ_λ, although in principle this can be done, we adopt a semiempirical procedure for testing the validity of the theory. The quantities, τ_λ, are evaluated by relating the experimentally determined oscillator strength, P, to the energy of the transition, σ, and the calculated matrix elements, M_λ.

In practice, we experimentally determine the area of as many bands in the absorption spectrum of a given lanthanide or actinide as we have been able to identify with distinct SLJ levels. In some cases a single band or group of bands extending over not more than a few hundred cm.$^{-1}$ results from several transitions of nearly the same energy. In such instances it is frequently possible to treat the band or group as a unit with the total matrix element equal to the sum of the elements associated with each transition contributing to the band. The extent to which this fitting procedure can be applied is limited by both the increasingly poor fit of the calculated levels and the greater density of levels at higher energies. Finally, a least-squares fit is made to determine the best set of values for τ_λ. Agreement between the theory and experiment can then be determined by comparing experimental oscillator strengths with those calculated based on the single "best" set of values for τ_λ.

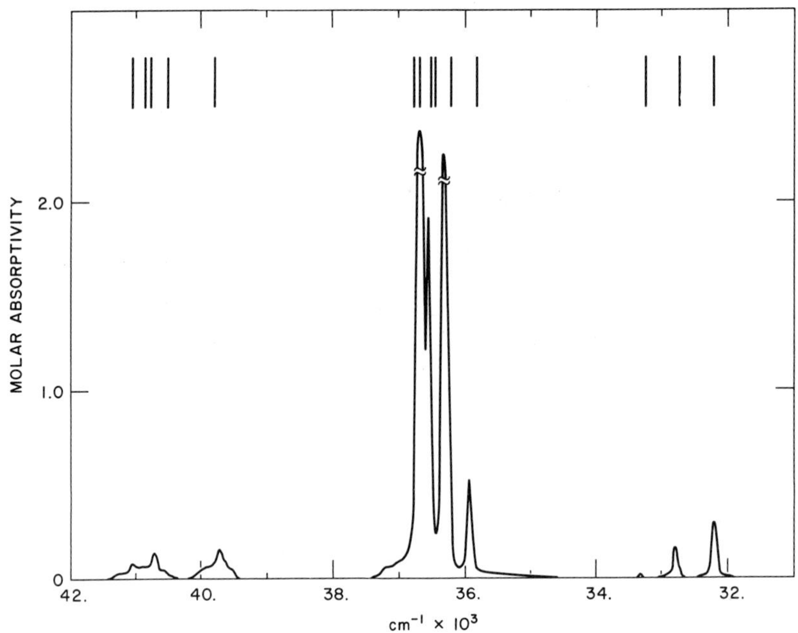

Figure 4. Absorption spectrum of Gd^{3+} in dilute acid solution

As an example, the experimental and calculated oscillator strengths for Ho^{3+} in dilute acid are shown in Table II. The fit is quite good for the levels shown but including bands beyond ~24000 cm.$^{-1}$ appreciably increases the deviation between P (calc.) and P (expt.). Similar results were reported earlier for Pr^{3+}, Nd^{3+}, Er^{3+}, Tm^{3+}, and Yb^{3+} in dilute acid (2).

The parameters τ_λ obtained for all of the lanthanides in dilute acid solution are summarized in Table III. Before appraising the significance of the data it should be noted that what amount to selection rules (triangular conditions on 6-j symbols involved in the calculations of the matrix elements) determine whether or not $[M_\lambda]^2$ can have positive values. Thus M_2 can only have non-zero values for $\Delta J \leq 2$; M_4 has non-zero values for $\Delta J \leq 4$, etc. Hence we find that M_6 has the largest number of non-zero matrix elements, M_4 has a moderate number of non-zero elements, and M_2 has relatively few non-zero matrix elements. It is clear from the data in Table III that τ_6 is the best determined of the three τ_λ parameters, as it should be. τ_2, in contrast, is poorly determined in most of the cases—indeed one can generalize that τ_2 has a probable magnitude of $\leq 1 \times 10^{-9}$ and makes essentially no contribution to $> 90\%$ of the calculated oscillator strengths in dilute acid solutions. Its important role in hypersensitive transitions will be mentioned later.

The parameters for Eu^{3+} and Gd^{3+} are based on a minimum of data. The ground state of Eu^{3+} has $J = 0$ ($^7F_0$). This imposes the special

Table II. Comparison of Calculated and Observed Oscillator Strengths for Ho^{3+} in 0.1M $HClO_4$

$E_{expt,}$ (cm.$^{-1}$)	$E_{calc,}$ (cm.$^{-1}$)	$P_{expt,} \times 10^6$	$P_{calc,} \times 10^6$
8,673	8,706	1.04	1.37
11,235	11,258	0.20	0.25
13,368	13,317	0.02	0.02
15,607	15,545	3.68	3.66
18,632	18,689	5.11	4.95
20,609	20,735	3.15	3.26
22,177	22,247	6.61	6.61
24,032	23,883	3.20	3.27

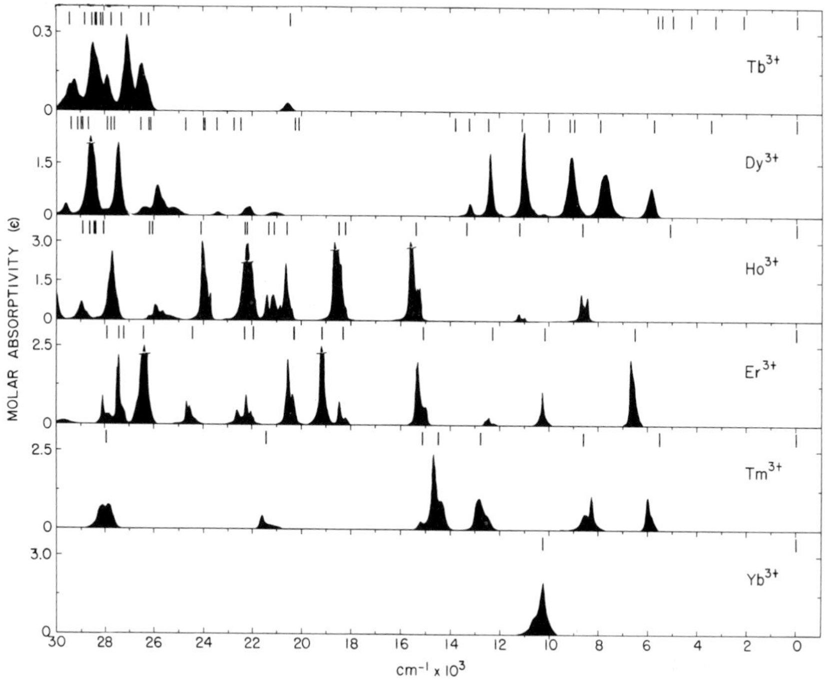

Figure 5. Absorption spectra of Tb^{3+}, Dy^{3+}, Ho^{3+}, Er^{3+}, Tm^{3+}, and Yb^{3+} in dilute acid solution

condition that M_2 is non-zero only for transitions in which $\Delta J = 2$; M_4 for $\Delta J = 4$; M_6 for $\Delta J = 6$. Thus, the transition ${}^7F_0 \rightarrow {}^5D_2$ determined the indicated value of τ_2. There is one other transition within the spectral range for which meaningful assignments seemed possible and this was a $\Delta J = 6$ transition. Similarly, the bands observed in Gd^{3+} were such that only values for τ_2 and τ_6 could be calculated.

In the case of Tb^{3+}, only one level (${}^5D_4$) can at present be fit. The indicated parameters for Tb^{3+} in Table III are extrapolated, based on those calculated for other members in the series. The values of τ_λ for Yb^{3+} are also extrapolated, since there is only one f^N-transition in Yb^{3+}. The indicated parameters allow a good fit to the observed intensity.

It is clear from the present data that the theory does successfully account for the experimentally observed intensities of lanthanide absorption bands up to ~30000 cm.$^{-1}$. Intensity calculations beyond ~30000 cm.$^{-1}$ are not presently feasible because of the difficulty in making energy

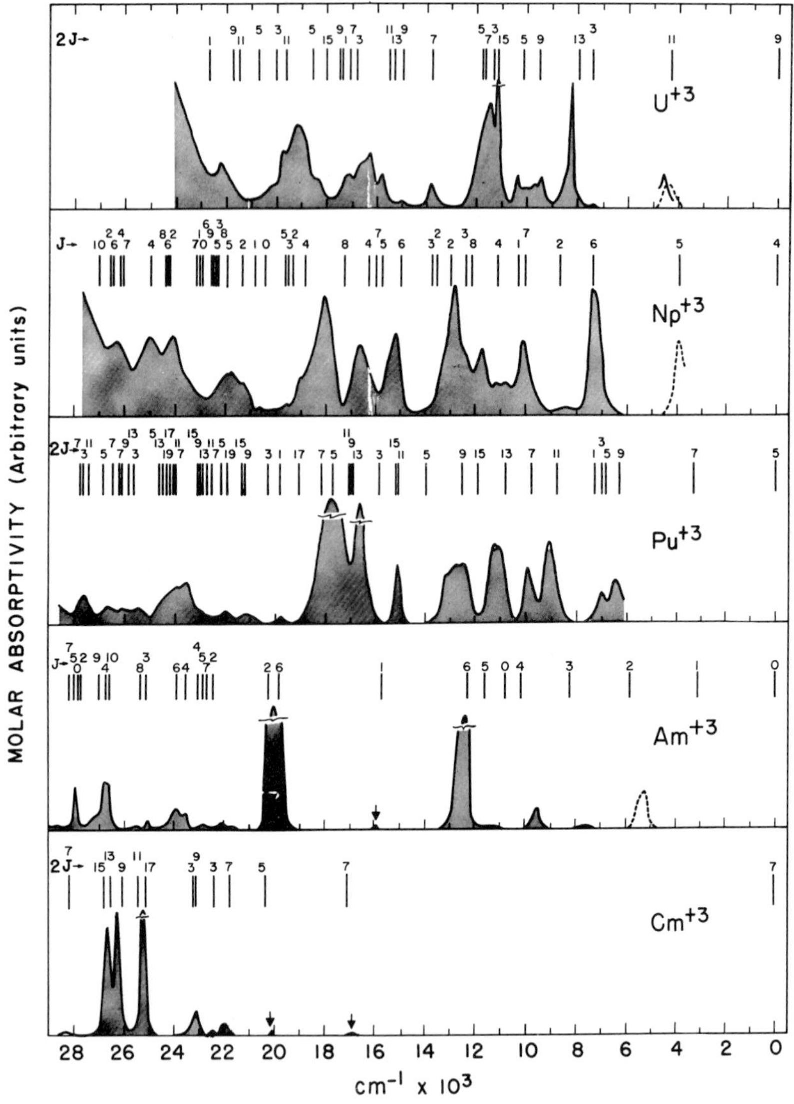

Figure 6. Absorption spectra of U^{3+}, Np^{3+}, Pu^{3+}, Am^{3+}, and Cm^{3+} in dilute acid solution

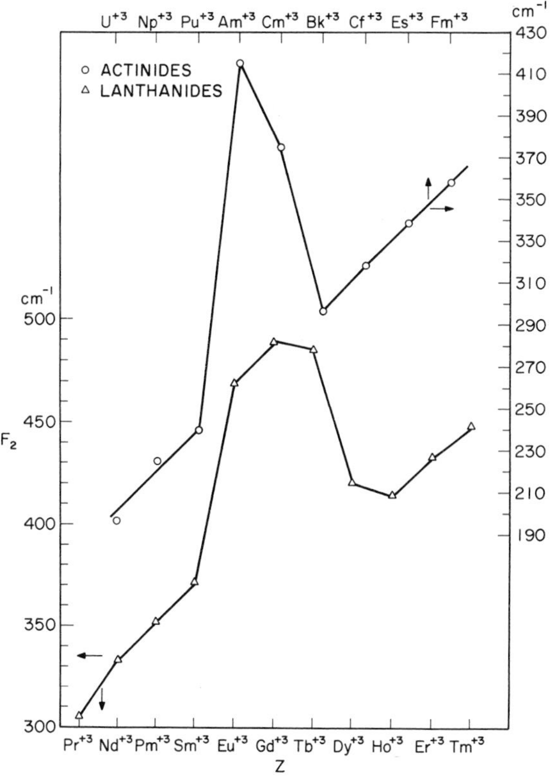

Figure 7. Variation of F_2 *with atomic number* Z *in the* 4f *and* 5f *series*

level assignments. In turning to similar attempted fitting procedures with the actinide elements one is immediately impressed by the poor correlations obtained. Tentative values of τ_λ for the light trivalent actinides are given in Table IV. To a certain extent the large errors in the parameters may be traced to poor correlation between levels observed in crystals and those found in solution, but a more detailed examination of the problem reveals that, for example, in Pu^{3+} (Figure 6) the matrix elements needed to account for the large double band centered near 17500 cm.$^{-1}$ are too small. The reason for these poor fits in the light actinides is not obvious since the assumptions made in deriving the theoretical expression for oscillator strength should apply to both the lanthanides and actinides. One possible explanation may arise from the fact that excited configurations in the actinides seem to occur at lower energies than their lanthanide counterparts.

It is, therefore, particularly significant that beginning with Am^{3+}-Cm^{3+} the fits to experimental intensity data appear to improve. The large deviations in τ_2 and τ_4 in Cm^{3+} reflect the fact that they are poorly determined—most of the band intensities observed are accounted for by τ_6. Based on a set of eigenvectors derived from the extrapolated values of F_2 and ζ for Cf^{3+}, the comparison between calculated and observed oscillator strengths for the first seven observed bands is satisfactory. An improved energy level fit to Cf^{3+} would be expected to improve the intensity correlation. Apparently, the agreement between theory and experiment improves as the actinides become more rare earth-like—that is, as atomic number increases and 3+ becomes the most stable valence state.

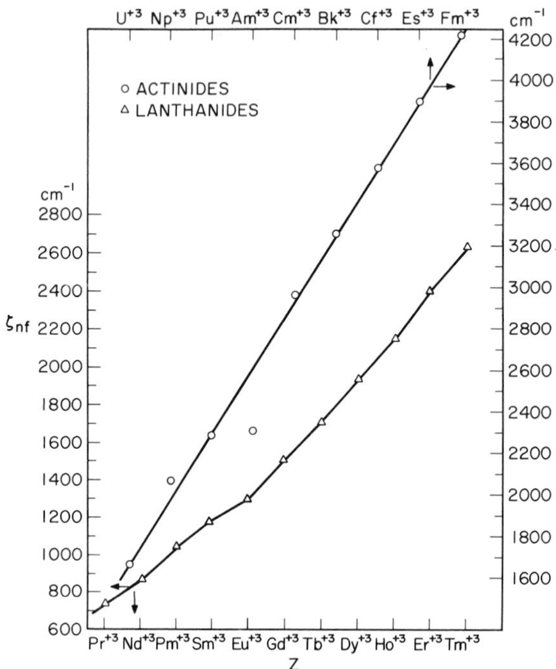

Figure 8. Variation of ζ with atomic number Z in the 4f and 5f series

One interesting and useful result of the present investigation is the indication that the intensity calculations may be used as the basis for refining the energy level fits. For example, if we examine the calculated matrix elements for Ho^{3+} in the 28000–31000 cm.$^{-1}$ region (Table V), we find that at least qualitatively the $^5G_2$ level should be weak, followed by a noticeably stronger transition to $^5G_3$ near 29000 cm.$^{-1}$; then the pattern should be weak, very strong, weak for $^3K_6$, $^3F_4$, $^5G_2$. If a very strong band were observed as low as 30200 cm.$^{-1}$, we would assign the $^3F_4$ level

Table III. Values for τ_λ for the Lanthanides in Dilute Acid Solution

	$\tau_2 \times 10^9$	$\tau_4 \times 10^9$	$\tau_6 \times 10^9$
Pr^{3+}	$-2.7 \pm 44.$	20.8 ± 1.61	27.4 ± 2.80
Nd^{3+}	1.58 ± 0.57	5.48 ± 0.51	10.2 ± 0.70
Pm^{3+}	3.26 ± 0.41	3.77 ± 0.68	5.20 ± 0.34
Sm^{3+}	1.54 ± 1.14	4.10 ± 1.10	3.42 ± 0.51
Eu^{3+}	0.84	—	4.8
Gd^{3+}	1.7	—	5.9
Tb^{3+}	~0	~2	~4
Dy^{3+}	1.73 ± 0.32	2.08 ± 0.48	4.96 ± 0.16
Ho^{3+}	0.49 ± 0.17	4.28 ± 0.34	3.69 ± 0.17
Er^{3+}	1.59 ± 0.22	2.26 ± 0.36	2.38 ± 0.18
Tm^{3+}	0.76 ± 0.88	2.36 ± 0.39	2.48 ± 0.23
Yb^{3+}	1.0	2.3	2.4

Table IV. Values of τ_λ for the Actinides in Dilute Acid Solution

	$\tau_2 \times 10^9$	$\tau_4 \times 10^9$	$\tau_6 \times 10^9$
U^{3+}	460 ± 30	70 ± 20	240 ± 20
Np^{3+}	-40 ± 30	30 ± 30	190 ± 7
Pu^{3+}	160 ± 130	-70 ± 80	90 ± 2
Am^{3+}	5	10	70
Cm^{3+}	54 ± 69	-35 ± 112	50.6 ± 2.7

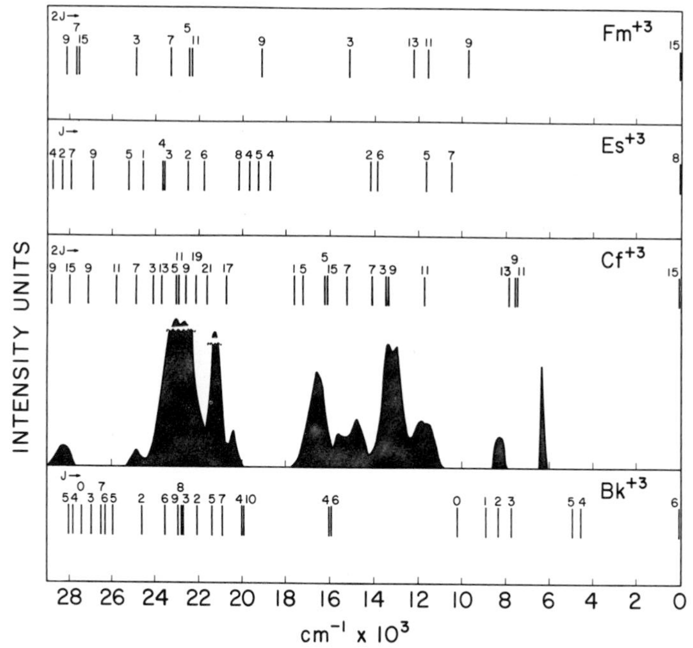

Figure 9. Calculated free-ion levels for Bk^{3+}, Cf^{3+}, Es^{3+}, and Fm^{3+} together with the experimentally determined absorption spectrum of Cf^{3+} in dilute acid solution

to that band and include this level in determining F_2, F_4, F_6, and ζ. Initial results show that such a procedure greatly increases the number of levels that can be assigned in solution spectra.

It is clear that the present results are consistent with the mechanism and formulation proposed by Judd. Of the three parameters τ_2, τ_4, and τ_6, it has been demonstrated that τ_2 has particularly interesting properties. Studies of lanthanide spectra in molten nitrate salts (*2*), in organic solvents (*2, 16*), and in the vapor phase (*10, 11*) have shown that the value of τ_2 can vary an order of magnitude or more depending upon the environment. Where it has been feasible to determine the values of τ_4 and τ_6 in systems where τ_2 was enhanced, it was found that they were nearly equal to those in aqueous solution.

Table V. Matrix Elements for Ho^{3+}

S'L'J'	*Calculated Energy (cm.⁻¹)*	$[M_2]^2$	$[M_4]^2$	$[M_6]^2$
$^3H_6$	28,396	0.1362	0.0828	0.0071
$^3L_9$	28,430	0.0186	0.0050	0.1548
$^5G_2$	28,635	0	0	0.0040
$^5G_3$	28,975	0	0	0.0135
$^3K_6$	30,264	0.0028	0.0004	0.0020
$^3F_4$	30,738	0	0.1526	0.0034
$^5G_2$	31,112	0	0	0.0009

During this investigation, we found that on the average, one or two transitions in the visible or near infrared spectral range in each lanthanide proved to have large matrix elements for M_2. In each case these transitions were the ones that showed a hypersensitivity to the environment and conformed to the selection rule $\Delta J = \pm 2$, as pointed out by Jørgensen and Judd (*12*). Various theories have been proposed to account for this hypersensitivity, and the magnitude of τ_2 has been used to test their validity (*10*).

Large values of τ_2 can be accounted for by assuming that the symmetry type of the ligands directly coordinated to the central ion is limited to the groups (*1*):

$$C_s,\ C_n \text{ where } n = 1,2,3,4,6 \text{ and } C_{nv} \text{ where } n = 2,3,4,6.$$

Future investigations will test this hypothesis and may in addition be able to correlate the magnitude of τ_2 with the type of bonding as well. The present study should prove useful to future work in a variety of media by serving as a basis for comparison.

Acknowledgment

The authors would like to acknowledge the large contribution of B. G. Wybourne, University of Canterbury, New Zealand, which made much of this work possible, and the valuable assistance of F. Clark in carrying out the computer calculations.

Literature Cited

(1) Broer, L. J. F., Gorter, C. J., Hoogschagen, J., *Physica* **11**, 231 (1945).
(2) Carnall, W. T., Fields, P. R., Wybourne, B. G., *J. Chem. Phys.* **42**, 3797 (1965).
(3) Carnall, W. T., Gruen, D. M., McBeth, R. L., *J. Phys. Chem.* **66**, 2159 (1962).
(4) Carnall, W. T., Wybourne, B. G., *J. Chem. Phys.* **40**, 3428 (1964).
(5) Caspers, H. H., Rast, H. E., Buchanan, R. A., *J. Chem. Phys.* **43**, 2124 (1965).
(6) Conway, J. G., Fried, S., Latimer, R. M., McLaughlin, R., Gutmacher, R. G., Carnall, W. T., Fields, P. R., *J. Inorg. Nucl. Chem.* **28**, 3064 (1966).
(7) Crosswhite, H. M., Dieke, G. H., Carter, W. J., *J. Chem. Phys.* **43**, 2047 (1965).
(8) El'yashevich, M. A., "Spectra of the Rare Earths," State Pub. House, Moscow, 1953; At. Energy Comm. transl. AEC-tr-4403 available from Office of Technical Information, Dept. of Commerce, Washington, D. C.
(9) Fields, P. R., Wybourne, B. G., Carnall, W. T., *Argonne National Lab. Rept.* **ANL-6911** (July 1964).
(10) Gruen, D. M., DeKock, C. W., *J. Chem. Phys.* **45**, 455 (1966).
(11) Gruen, D. M., DeKock, C. W., McBeth, R. L., ADVAN. CHEM. SER. **71**, 102 (1967).
(12) Jørgensen, C. K., Judd, B. R., *Mol. Phys.* **8**, 281 (1964).
(13) Judd, B. R., *J. Chem. Phys.* **44**, 839 (1966).
(14) Judd, B. R., *Phys. Rev.* **127**, 750 (1962).
(15) Judd, B. R., "Operator Techniques in Atomic Spectroscopy," McGraw-Hill, New York, 1963.
(16) Ryan, J. L., Jørgensen, C. K., *J. Chem. Phys.* (in press).
(17) Sarup, R., Crozier, M. H., *J. Chem. Phys.* **42**, 371 (1965).
(18) Sugar, J., *Phys. Rev. Letters* **14**, 731 (1965).
(19) Wybourne, B. G., "Spectroscopic Properties of Rare Earths," Wiley, New York, 1965.

RECEIVED November 2, 1966.

8

Electronic Spectra of Lanthanide Compounds in the Vapor Phase

D. M. GRUEN, C. W. DEKOCK, and R. L. MCBETH

Argonne National Laboratory, Argonne, Ill.

The vapor phase spectra of the tribromides and triiodides of Pr, Nd, Er and Tm and of the 2,2,6,6-tetramethyl-3,5-heptanedionates of Pr, Nd, Sm, Eu, Dy, Ho, Er and Tm have been measured in the range 4,000–30,000 cm.⁻. The transition intensities of most of the f ← f *transitions in the gaseous molecules are comparable with those found in crystal and solution spectra. The hypersensitive transitions obeying the selection rules* $\Delta J = \pm 2$, $\Delta L \leq 2$, $\Delta S = 0$, *are greatly enhanced, particularly in the gaseous halide molecules. This result led to reconsidering various intensity mechanisms. It appears that the vibronic mechanism can account for both the environmental sensitivity and the magnitude of the* τ_2 *parameter. The large oscillator strengths of the hypersensitive transitions in the vapor phase molecules can be rationalized in this manner.*

As part of a continuing study of the electronic spectra of lanthanide compounds in the vapor phase (*11*), we report here the spectra of the gaseous tribromides and triodides of Pr, Nd, Er, and Tm and of the gaseous 2,2,6,6-tetramethyl-3,5-heptanedionates of Pr, Nd, Sm, Eu, Dy, Ho, Er, and Tm (*9*). Spectra of gaseous lanthanide compounds are virtually unexplored, in contrast to crystal and solution spectra, and can be expected to contribute new information concerning energy levels and intensities of $f \leftarrow f$ transitions.

A recent development of interest in interpreting the absorption spectra of lanthanide ions has been a theory of absorption intensities developed independently by Judd (*14*) and by Ofelt (*21*) which represents an important advance from earlier treatments of this problem (*3*, *25*).

The relatively narrow, low intensity absorption bands of the rare-earths have been studied a great deal over the years, and most of the electronic transitions giving rise to the bands have by now been assigned. The energies of the bands are affected only to minor extents when the chemical environment of the rare-earth ion is changed, and this can be understood in terms of the effective shielding of the $4f$ electrons by the remainder of the electrons of the ion core. Similarly, for most transitions the band intensities are influenced only to a small degree by changes in chemical environment. There are about a dozen transitions distributed among eight of the rare earths whose intensities differ by factors of 10–100 depending on the ligand. These transitions have been the object of numerous experimental investigations, and their intensities in different media have been investigated extensively (*5, 12, 16, 19, 20, 23, 26*). They have been called "hypersensitive" transitions by Jørgensen and Judd (*13*).

A number of studies of rare-earth spectra in condensed phases (*2, 4, 17, 18*) have confirmed that the theory of Judd and of Ofelt can account for the observed intensities of electric-dipole transitions within the $4f^n$ configuration on the basis of three phenomenological parameters τ_2, τ_4, and τ_6. These studies have also shown that the parameter τ_2 is very sensitive to the rare-earth ion environment while τ_4 and τ_6 are relatively insensitive to the environment. In the earlier gas-phase neodymium trihalide study, it was found that τ_2 is enhanced to such an extent relative to the τ_4 and τ_6 parameters that the oscillator strength of the hypersensitive $^4I_{9/2} - {}^4G_{5/2}$ transition is a factor of 10 higher than in condensed phases (*11*).

With the general success of the three-parameter theory in accounting for transition intensities, it is appropriate to attempt an interpretation of the τ_λ parameters in terms of fundamental quantities. In view of the existence of hypersensitive transitions, it is interesting to find the origin for the remarkable variation of τ_2 with changes in the ligands surrounding the lanthanide ion. Jørgensen and Judd (*13*) examined a number of mechanisms for the variation of τ_2 and concluded that the sensitivity of τ_2 was attributed to a mechanism involving inhomogeneities induced in the dielectric. Judd has recently proposed a different mechanism which depends only on the point group symmetry provided by the ligand environment of the rare-earth ion. (*15*). The earlier work (*11*) on the gas phase spectra of the neodymium halides showed that neither of these mechanisms was able to account for the strong enhancement of τ_2 in the case of the gaseous molecules.

The present study was undertaken in order to test further the validity of the theoretical model on a number of gaseous rare earth compounds and to compare the relationships of the τ_λ parameters found for the gas phase spectra with those determined from solution spectra. Such comparisons hopefully will help establish the correct mechanism responsible for the environmental sensitivity of τ_2.

Calculations

The intensity of a transition is measured by its oscillator strength P which may be written

$$P = 4.31 \times 10^{-9}\left[\frac{9\eta}{(\eta^2+2)^2}\right]\int \epsilon_i(\nu)\, d\nu \qquad (1)$$

where η is the refractive index of the medium, ϵ is the molar extinction coefficient and ν is the energy of the transition in wavenumbers. The refractive index factor, $9\eta/(\eta^2+2)^2$ will be essentially unity for the gas phase and was neglected in our calculations.

Judd (*13*) has shown that the oscillator strength of an induced electric dipole transition may be related to the energy of the transition (ν, in cm.$^{1-}$) and the square of the matrix elements of the unit tensor operators $U^{(\lambda)}$ connecting the initial and final states *via* three phenomenological parameters T_λ ($\lambda = 2, 4,$ and 6) according to Equation 2.

$$P = \sum_{\lambda=2,4,6} T_\lambda \nu\, (\psi_J \,||\, U^{(\lambda)} \,||\, \psi'_{J'})^2 \ . \qquad (2)$$

To facilitate the comparison of the parameters for different ions and with the solution data of Carnall, Fields, and Wybourne (*4*) (subsequently referred to as CFW), we have followed their suggestion and rewritten

Equation 2 in the form

$$P = \sum_{\lambda \text{ even}} \tau_\lambda \nu (\psi_J \,||\, U^{(\lambda)} \,||\, \psi'_J)^2/2J+1 \ . \qquad (3)$$

For a more complete discussion of the theoretical treatment the reader should consult Ref. *4*.

The oscillator strengths were calculated from the observed spectra using Equation 1. For the two cases in which the magnetic-dipole transition intensity is appreciable, the $^4I_{15/2} - {}^4I_{13/2}$ transition of Er^{3+} and the $^3H_6 - {}^3H_5$ transition of Tm^{3+}, its value was subtracted from the total intensity, and the residual oscillator strength was ascribed to the electric dipole transition. The magnetic dipole oscillator strengths used were those calculated by CFW.

In those systems which could be analyzed by Equation 3, the parameters τ_λ were determined by a least-squares analysis. The $[U^{(\lambda)}]^2$ matrix elements were those calculated by CFW. The error in the parameters was computed in the usual manner. The measure of the fitting is expressed by the root mean square (rms) deviation defined by

$$\text{rms} = \left(\frac{\text{sum of squares of deviation}}{\text{number of observations—number of parameters}}\right)^{1/2} \qquad (4)$$

Results

Gaseous $ErBr_3$ and ErI_3. The spectrum of gaseous $ErBr_3$ is shown in Figure 1, while the calculated and observed oscillator strengths together with the $[U^2]^2$ matrix elements are given in Table I. The τ_λ parameters calculated from a least-squares fit of Equation 3 are given in Table V. The fit to Equation 3 for the $ErBr_3$ vapor spectra is as good as that obtained by CFW for their solution spectra. Although τ_4 and τ_6 are not well defined in the vapor spectra, they have nearly the same values as in solution. The τ_2 value is three times larger than most solution values making τ_2 30 times larger than τ_4 or τ_6. The increase in τ_2 is solely responsible for the large intensity of the transitions to the $^2H_{11/2}$ and $^4G_{11/2}$ states (Table I).

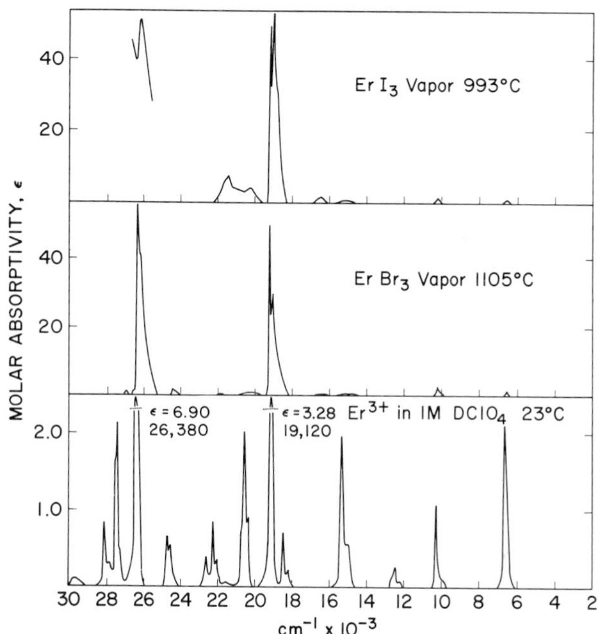

Figure 1. Absorption spectrum of gaseous ErI_3 and $ErBr_3$ compared with Er^{3+} ion in 1m $DClO_4$

The spectrum of gaseous ErI_3 was analyzed using Equation 3 even though only five transitions were available with which to fit the three parameters (Table I). The transitions located between 20,000 and 22,000 cm.$^{-1}$ were not used because of baseline difficulties. The parameters for ErI_3 vapor indicate the same trend as those for $ErBr_3$ vapor; τ_4 and τ_6 are nearly the same as the solution values, while τ_2 is a factor of 5 larger than many of the solution values (Table V).

Table I. Oscillator Strengths of $ErBr_3(g)$ and $ErI_3(g)$

			$P \times 10^6$			
			$ErBr_3$		*ErI_3*	
$S'L'J'$	*Calculated energy (cm.$^{-1}$)*	$[U^{(2)}]^2$	*Expt.*	*Calc.*	*Expt.*	*Calc.*
$^4I_{13/2}$	6547	0.0195	0.93	1.67	0.58	0.21
$^4I_{11/2}$	10177	0.0291	1.87	1.67	1.01	1.55
$^4I_{9/2}$	12325	0	0	.25	1.44	0.90
$^4F_{9/2}$	15144	0	1.25	1.62	2.3	2.5
$^4S_{3/2}$	18305	0	} 57.5	} 58.8	} 95.5	95.5
$^2H_{11/2}$	19211	0.7326				
$^4F_{7/2}$	20300	0	2.89	1.77		
$^4F_{5/2}$	21950	0	0.46	0.56		
$^4F_{3/2}$	22308	0	0	0.32		
$^2G_{9/2}$	24478	0	2.27	0.68		
$^4G_{11/2}$	26434	0.8970	99.2	98.3		
$^2K_{15/2}$	27226	0.0229	0.77	2.8		
$^4G_{9/2}$	27412	0				
$^2G_{7/2}$	27952	0				
rms deviation}[a]		1.22×10^{-6}		0.6×10^{-6}		

[a] Root-mean-square deviation calculated from Equation 4.

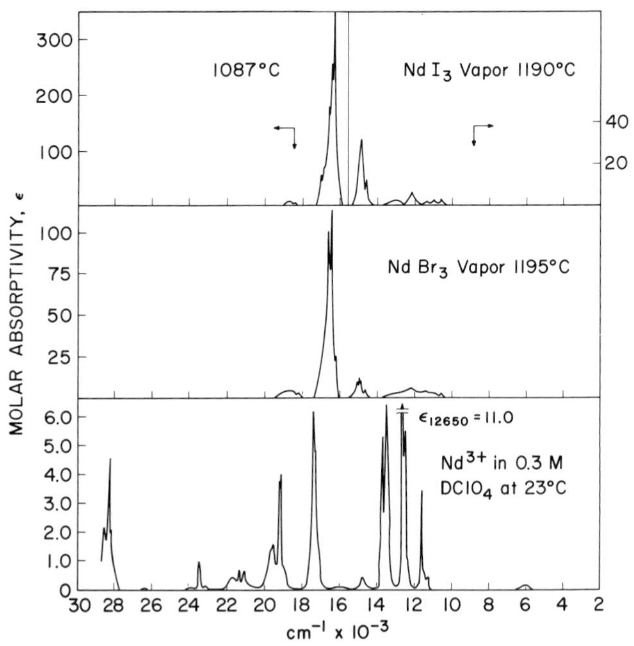

Figure 2. Absorption spectrum of gaseous NdI_3 and $NdBr_3$ compared with Nd^{3+} ion in 0.3m $DClO_4$

Gaseous $NdBr_3$ and NdI_3. The spectra of gaseous $NdBr_3$ and NdI_3 appear in Figure 2 together with a comparison of the aqueous spectra, while the observed oscillator strengths and $[U^2]^2$ matrix elements appear in Table II. The calculated τ_λ values appear in Table V. All of the non-hypersensitive transitions in the vapor phase have oscillator strengths which are approximately the same as those found by CFW in solution. The τ_λ values were calculated assuming that τ_4 and τ_6 were nearly the same as found in solution, $\sim 1 \times 10^{-8}$ and τ_2 was calculated from the intensity of the $^4I_{9/2}$ to $^4G_{5/2}$ hypersensitive transition.

Table II. Oscillator Strengths for NdBr(g) and NdI_3(g)

$S'L'J'$	Calculated energy (cm.$^{-1}$)	$[U^{(2)}]^2$	$P \times 10^6$ $NdBr_3$	NdI_3
$^4I_{13/2}$	3875	0.0001		
$^4I_{15/2}$	5950	0		
$^4F_{3/2}$	11232	0	36	46
$^4F_{5/2}$	12277	0.0009		
$^2H_{9/2}$	12527	0.0092		
$^4S_{3/2}$	13113	0		
$^4F_{7/2}$	13268	0.0010		
$^4F_{9/2}$	14587	0.0010	34	43
$^2H_{11/2}$	15864	0.0001		
$^4G_{5/2}$	16897	0.8968	330	530
$^2G_{7/2}$	17044	0.0755		
$^2K_{13/2}$	18803	0.0068	22	5
$^4G_{7/2}$	18823	0.0551		
$^4G_{9/2}$	19260	0.0046		
$^2K_{15/2}$	20806	0		
$^2G_{9/2}$	20897	0.0010		
$^2D_{3/2}$	21041	0		
$^4G_{11/2}$	21272	~0		
$^2P_{1/2}$	22903	0		
$^2D_{5/2}$	23549	0		
$^2D_{3/2}$	26047	0		
$^4D_{3/2}$	27945	0		

The $^4I_{11/2}$ state, which lies $\sim$ 2000 cm.$^{1-}$ above the ground $^4I_{9/2}$ and is thermally populated to the extent of about 20%, provides a complicating factor in calculating the observed intensities from Equation 3. For example, the transition located in the 14,000–15,000 cm.$^{-1}$ region has been assigned to the $^4I_{11/2} - {}^2G_{7/2}$ transition which is hypersensitive with $[U^2]^2 = 0.3663$ (*11*). The calculated oscillator strength for this transition is 2.7×10^{-5} for NdI_3 and 1.8×10^{-5} for $NdBr_3$ vapor. The agreement between the observed and calculated oscillator strengths substantiates this assignment.

Although the τ_λ parameters are not well defined for the gaseous $NdBr_3$ and NdI_3 spectra, the general result that τ_2 is enhanced with respect to its solution value is definitely established.

Gaseous $PrBr_3$ and PrI_3. The spectra of gaseous $PrBr_3$ and PrI_3 are shown in Figure 3 together with the spectrum of aqueous Pr^{3+}. The observed oscillator strengths with the corresponding $[U^2]^2$ matrix elements are shown in Table III. The τ_λ parameters appear in Table V.

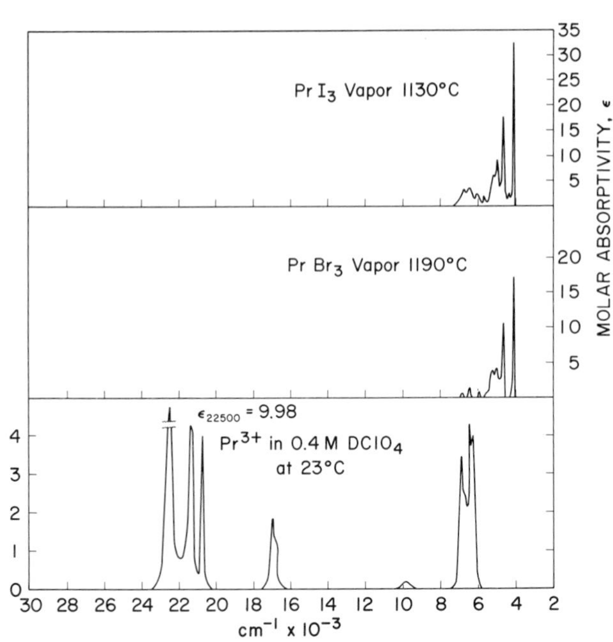

Figure 3. Absorption spectrum of gaseous PrI_3 and $PrBr_3$ compared with Pr^{3+} ion in 0.4m $CDlO_4$

Table III. Oscillator Strengths for $PrBr_3(g)$ and $PrI_3(g)$

$S'L'J'$	Energy cm.$^{-1}$	$(U^2)^2$	$P \times 10^6$ $PrBr_3$	$P \times 10^6$ PrI_3
$^3H_6$	4438	0.0001	20.0	40.0
$^3F_2$	4829	0.5081		
$^3F_3$	6267	0.0655	1.0	13.4
$^3F_4$	6910	0.0174		
$^1G_4$	10176	0.0019		
$^1D_2$	17741	0.0029		
$^3P_0$	20683	0		
$^3P_1$	21302	0		
$^1I_6$	21496	0.0087		
$^3P_2$	22690	~0		

The salient feature of the gaseous praeseodymium halide spectra is the absence of transitions with measurable intensities at energies greater than 7000 cm.$^{1-}$. The absence of transitions to the $^3P_{2,1,0}$, $^1I_6$ and $^1D_2$ states is particularly striking since these are the most intense transitions in aqueous solution. Since these transitions are not observed in the vapors, an estimate of the maximum value for the τ_4 and τ_6 parameters may be made on the assumption that the transitions have an oscillator strength $\leq 1 \times 10^{-6}$. On this basis, τ_4 and τ_6 are calculated to be $\leq 3 \times 10^{-9}$. An estimate of τ_2 can be made from the intensity of the transitions in the 4000–7000 cm.$^{1-}$ region which are to the ^3F_J ($J = 2,3,4$) states. Such an analysis again indicates that τ_2 is approximately 20 to 30 times larger than τ_4 and τ_6, which is significantly larger than observed in most solution spectra.

Some of the absorption intensity in the 4000 to 5000 cm.$^{-1}$ region is calculated to arise from the $^3H_5$–$^3F_3$ transition. The $^3H_5$ state lies $\sim$ 2100 cm.$^{-1}$ above the ground $^3H_4$ state and is 20% thermally populated at the temperature of the measurement. The $[U^2]^2$ matrix element for the $^3H_5$–$^3F_3$ transition is 0.3142 which leads to a calculated oscillator strength of $\sim 3 \times 10^{-6}$ for the iodide and 2×10^{-6} for the bromide at an energy of $\sim$ 4100 cm.$^{1-}$.

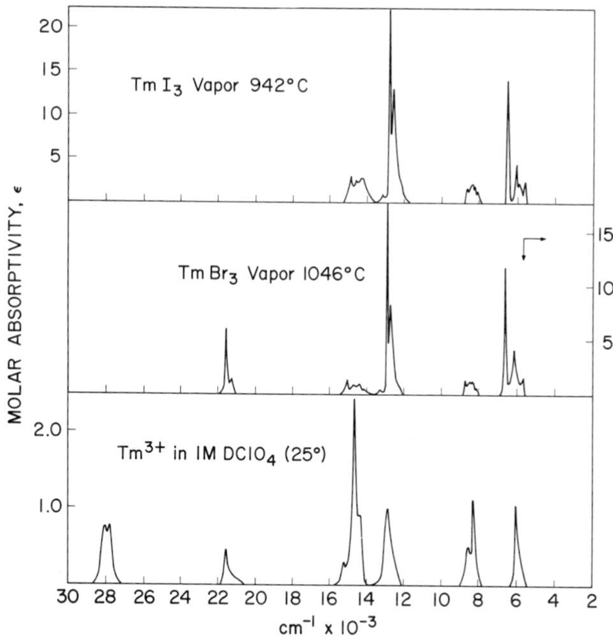

Figure 4. Absorption spectrum of gaseous TmI_3 and $TmBr_3$ compared with Tm^{3+} ion in 1m $DClO_4$

Gaseous $TmBr_3$ and TmI_3. The spectra of gaseous $TmBr_3$ and TmI_3 appear in Figure 4 together with the spectrum of aqueous Tm^{3+}. The experimental and calculated oscillator strengths appear in Table IV, while the τ_λ values are given in Table V.

Table IV. Oscillator Strengths of $TmBr_3(g)$ and $TmI_3(g)$

			$P \times 10^6$			
			$TmBr_3(g)$		$TmI_3(g)$	
S'L'J'	*Calculated energy (cm.⁻¹)*	$[U^{(2)}]^2$	*Expt.*	*Calc.*	*Expt.*	*Calc.*
$^3H_4$	5508	0.2300	12.0	12.0	10.7	10.7
$^3H_5$	8322	0.1073	2.7	4.8	4.6	4.4
$^3F_4$	12636	0.5470	15.3	12.2	25.3	11.1
$^3F_3$	14280	0	} 3.3	4.7	11.0	4.7
$^3F_2$	14996	0				
$^1G_4$	21421	0.0006	4.5	1.2		
$^1D_2$	28103	0				

Table V. Values of τ_λ

		Bromide	*Iodide*
Pr	τ_2	$\sim 5 \times 10^{-8}$	$\sim 1 \times 10^{-7}$
	τ_4	$< 3 \times 10^{-9}$	$< 3 \times 10^{-9}$
	τ_6	$< 3 \times 10^{-9}$	$< 3 \times 10^{-9}$
Nd[a]	τ_2	2×10^{-7}	3×10^{-7}
	τ_4	1×10^{-8}	1×10^{-8}
	τ_6	1×10^{-8}	1×10^{-8}
Er	τ_2	$6.51 \pm .16 \times 10^{-8}$	$10.6 \pm .1 \times 10^{-8}$
	τ_4	$1.6 \pm 2.7 \times 10^{-9}$	$6.4 \pm 1.5 \times 10^{-9}$
	τ_6	$1.8 \pm 1.2 \times 10^{-9}$	$-1.6 \pm 1.0 \times 10^{-9}$
Tm	τ_2	$5.9 \pm 1.2 \times 10^{-8}$	$9.8 \pm .5 \times 10^{-8}$
	τ_4	$-0.9 \pm 1.2 \times 10^{-8}$	$-4.4 \pm .6 \times 10^{-8}$
	τ_6	$0.5 \pm 3.5 \times 10^{-8}$	$1.3 \pm .2 \times 10^{-8}$
Tm[a]	τ_2	4.6×10^{-8}	4.06×10^{-8}
	τ_4	3×10^{-9}	3×10^{-9}
	τ_6	3×10^{-9}	3×10^{-9}

[a] Calculated assuming τ_4 and τ_6 are average solution values.

The τ_λ parameters were calculated both by a least-squares fit to Equation 3 and by setting τ_4 and τ_6 equal to their solution values and calculating τ_2 from a fit to the $^3F_4$ level. The least-squares method is not very reliable since only five transitions are available for $TmBr_3$ and only four for TmI_3. Since for the two most intense transitions, $^3F_4$ and $^3H_4$, all the $\mathbf{U}^\lambda$ matrix elements are large, the relationship between the τ_λ parameters cannot be evaluated. When τ_4 and τ_6 are set equal to their solution values, τ_2 again is a factor of 10 larger than τ_4 or τ_6, and there is little loss in the over-all fitting of Equation 3 except for the transition to $^3H_4$ for TmI_3.

Some General Remarks. The energies and intensities of the absorption maxima found in rare-earth halide vapor spectra are brought together in Table VI.

Only in the case of $ErBr_3$ were there enough transitions available to make a rigorous analysis of the spectrum in accordance with Equation 3. The chief reason limiting the number of observable $f \leftarrow f$ transitions for the other rare-earth halides was the appearance of a rather intense broad impurity band located at about 28,000 cm.$^{-1}$ for the tribromides, and at a somewhat lower energy for the triiodides. For the bromides, this transition increased in intensity with time when the temperature was above 1000°C., while for the iodides it was already detectable at 850°C. The nature of the impurity is not known at this time, but the shape and intensity of the band suggest that it is caused by a charge transfer transition of the impurity species. The impurity was not a volatile one since spectra taken below 800°C. on cells with the impurity present did not reveal any transition at 28,000 cm.$^{-1}$. Using the $0 \rightarrow 0.1$ o.d. recorder it was possible to obtain the spectra of $ErBr_3$ vapor to 30,000 cm.$^{-1}$ at a sufficiently low temperature so that the impurity transition did not appear. The presence of the impurity did not affect the intensity of the other rare-earth transitions, except for those near the tail of the impurity transition, $>$ 23,000 cm.$^{-1}$ for the bromides and $>$ 20,000 cm.$^{-1}$ for the iodides since it was difficult to determine the baselines in these regions.

Gaseous 2,2,6,6-Tetramethyl-3,5-Heptanedionates. With Eisentraut and Sievers's (9) discovery of a group of volatile lanthanide chelates, the lanthanide 2,2,6,6-tetramethyl-3,5-heptanedionates abbreviated $M(thd)_3$, an interesting group of compounds for vapor phase spectral investigation became available.

The vapor spectra of the $M(thd)_3$ compounds with M = Pr, Nd, Sm, Eu, Dy, Ho, Er, and Tm are shown in Figures 5 and 6. The arrows indicate absorption owing to vibrational overtone and combination bands of the organic chelate moiety. The remaining absorption bands arise from $f \leftarrow f$ transitions of the rare-earth constituents. The energies and molar absorptivities of the $f \leftarrow f$ absorption maxima are shown in Table VII.

The features of particular interest from the point of view of the present study are the hypersensitive transitions in the gaseous spectra. They constitute the most prominent features of the spectra, and their oscillator strengths are listed in Table IX.

Discussion

The unexpected finding that the oscillator strengths of the hypersensitive transitions in lanthanide vapor spectra are larger than in many

Table VI. Energies and Intensities of the

$PrBr_3$ $cm.^{-1}$	ϵ [a]	PrI_3	ϵ	$NdBr_3$	ϵ	NdI_3	ϵ
4103	17	4135	32	10570	2	10560	2
4629	6	4350	3	10990	3	10990	3
4677	10	4660sh	15	11430	6	11360	2
5025	4	4680	18	12220	7	12220	6
5150	3	5000	9	14672	7	13160	2
5620	1	5180	7	14900	11	14641	13
5960	1	5680	2	15000	13	14891	32
6470	1	5950sh	2	15090	10	14936sh	28
6850	0.5	6030	3	16260	25	16194	90
		6100sh	2	16469	115	16334	345
		6430	4	16598	85	16469	250
		6780	3	16656	105	16515	220
				16750	60	16611	175
				16806	45	16703	115
				16849	40	16778	85
				16975	30	16877	75
				18867	8	18900sh	64

[a] ϵ = liters/mole-cm.

condensed phases demonstrates the need for a better understanding of the intensity mechanisms involved in $f \leftarrow f$ transitions.

The hypersensitive transitions ($\Delta J \leq 2$) were given by Jørgensen and Judd (*13*) and are listed in Table VIII together with their energies. The pertinent oscillator strengths determined in the course of the present work are given in Table IX.

The best intercomparison of τ_2, τ_4, and τ_6 values between different solution and vapor spectra can be made in the case of Er^{3+} since data for a larger number of transitions have been obtained for it than for the other lanthanide ions. The τ_λ values for Er^{3+} in $DClO_4$ and $LiNO_3$–KNO_3 eutectic solutions (data of CFW) and for $Er(thd)_3$, $ErBr_3$, and ErI_3 vapors (present work) are listed in Table X. It can be seen that τ_4 and τ_6 are roughly constant in all of these systems while τ_2 increases by a factor of 66 in going from an aqueous solution to the triiodide vapor.

Although the data are not as complete for the other lanthanides, it is possible to give the approximate ranges of τ_2 which span the values assumed by this parameter in the systems which have been investigated up to now. The range of τ_2-values for solution and vapor spectra of the lanthanides based on the best currently available data are listed in Table XI. The salient conclusions to be drawn from this survey are that τ_2 has experimentally been found to vary by as much as a factor of 100 and that the largest values of τ_2 occur in the tribromide and triiodide vapor spectra.

Gaseous Rare-Earth Halide Absorption Maxims

$ErBr_3$	ϵ	ErI_3	ϵ	$TmBr_3$	ϵ	TmI_3	ϵ
6435	0.8	6450	3	5586	1.5	5571	2.3
6501	1.4	6515	4	6053	4	5903	2.3
6578	0.8	6561sh	2	6561	12	6016	4.6
10101sh	1.1			8110	0.6	6493	14
10162	2.8	10172	7	8210	1.1	8103	1.4
10204sh	1.8	10245	5	8237	1.2	8196	1.9
15151	0.4	15151	1	8319	1.2	8237	1.7
16393	2.5	16420	2	8417	1.1	8305	2.1
18903sh	17	18832	32	8547	1.0	8403	1.9
19047	29	19000	53	8650	1.3	8510	1.6
19197	50	19157	33	8673	1.2	8620	1.6
20161	0.9	19197	49	12453	2.0	12415sh	4.9
21929	0.4	20242	4	12682	8	12615	13
25773	13	21459	7	12853	18	12804	22
25974	24	26178		13262	0.3	13175	1
26178	41	26336		13937	0.4	14285	2.7
26350	56			14357	0.9	14577	2.4
26595sh	1			14662	0.8	14858	3
27000	1			15004	1.2		
				21254	1.3		
				21551	6		

It is appropriate to discuss the mechanisms which have been proposed to account for the variability of τ_2 since the correct mechanism is the key to understanding the intensities of the hypersensitive transitions.

Inhomogeneous Dielectric. After a detailed examination of a number of mechanisms, Jørgensen and Judd (*13*) concluded that the origin of the sensitivity of τ_2 is in the inhomogeneity of the dielectric. This mechanism supposes that there is an asymmetric distribution of the dipoles induced by the electromagnetic field in the medium surrounding the lanthanide ion. According to this model, the variation of the electric vector across the lanthanide ion becomes great enough to induce hypersensitive pseudoquadrupole transitions in the lanthanide ion. The effect depends on the square of the parameter ξ, given by

$$\xi = \frac{15}{4\pi^2} \frac{n^2 - 1}{n(n^2 + 2)} \left(\frac{a}{R}\right)^3 \left(\frac{\lambda}{R}\right) \qquad (8)$$

where a is the lattice constant, R is the nearest neighbor distance, λ is the wavelength of light, and n is the bulk refractive index. For $n = 1.5$, $\lambda = 5000$ A., $R = a = 2.5$ A., ξ is found to be equal to 150. Substituting for n in Equation 8 the value 1.001, a reasonable approximation of the bulk refractive index of gaseous substances, gives a value of ξ^2 which is lower by a factor of 10^6 than that obtained for the condensed phase.

It seems clear that this particular mechanism in the form originally presented cannot account for the gas phase intensities.

Forced Electric Dipole Transitions. In more recent work, Judd (*15*) has given further attention to the problem of intensities. According to this work, under certain symmetry restricted circumstances, the Hamiltonian for the interaction of a lanthanide ion with its neighbors can contain spherical harmonics Y_{km} with $k = 1$ if the electrons of the rare-earth ion produce an electric field at the nucleus that exactly cancels that

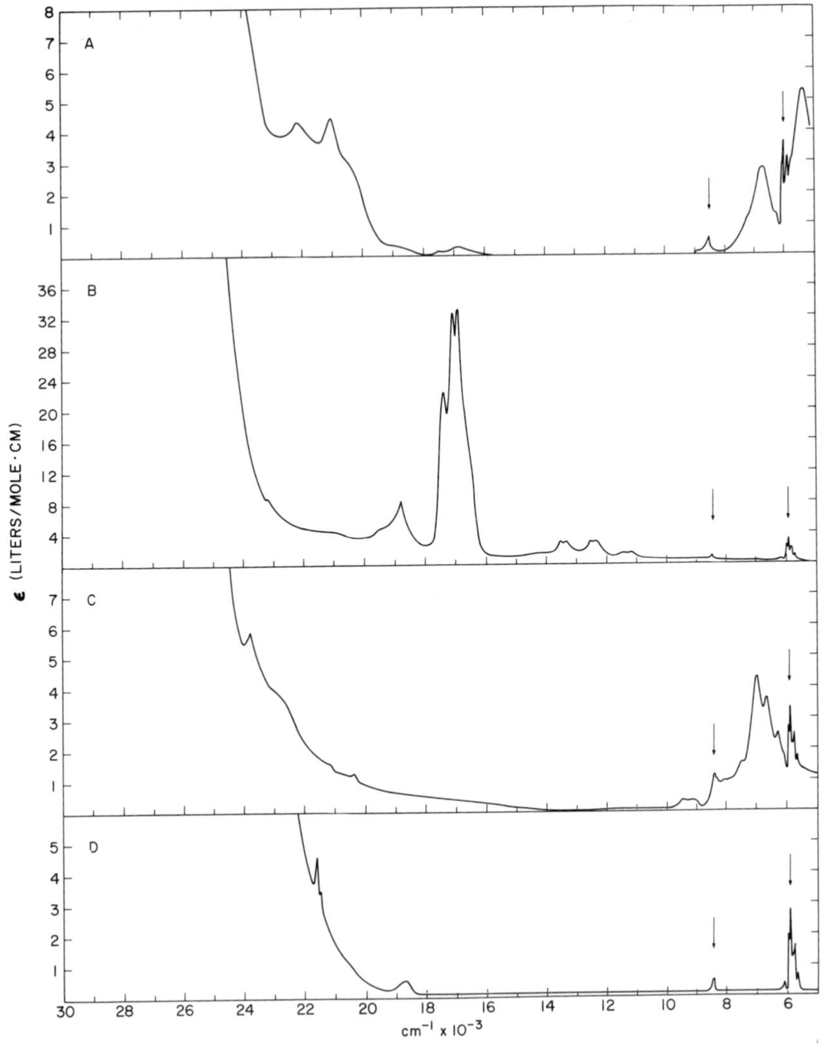

Figure 5. Absorption spectra of the rare-earth chelate vapors (A) $Pr(thd)_3$ at 320°C. (B) $Nd(thd)_3$ at 320°C. (C) $Sm(thd)_3$ at 309°C. (D) $Eu(thd)_3$ at 282°C.

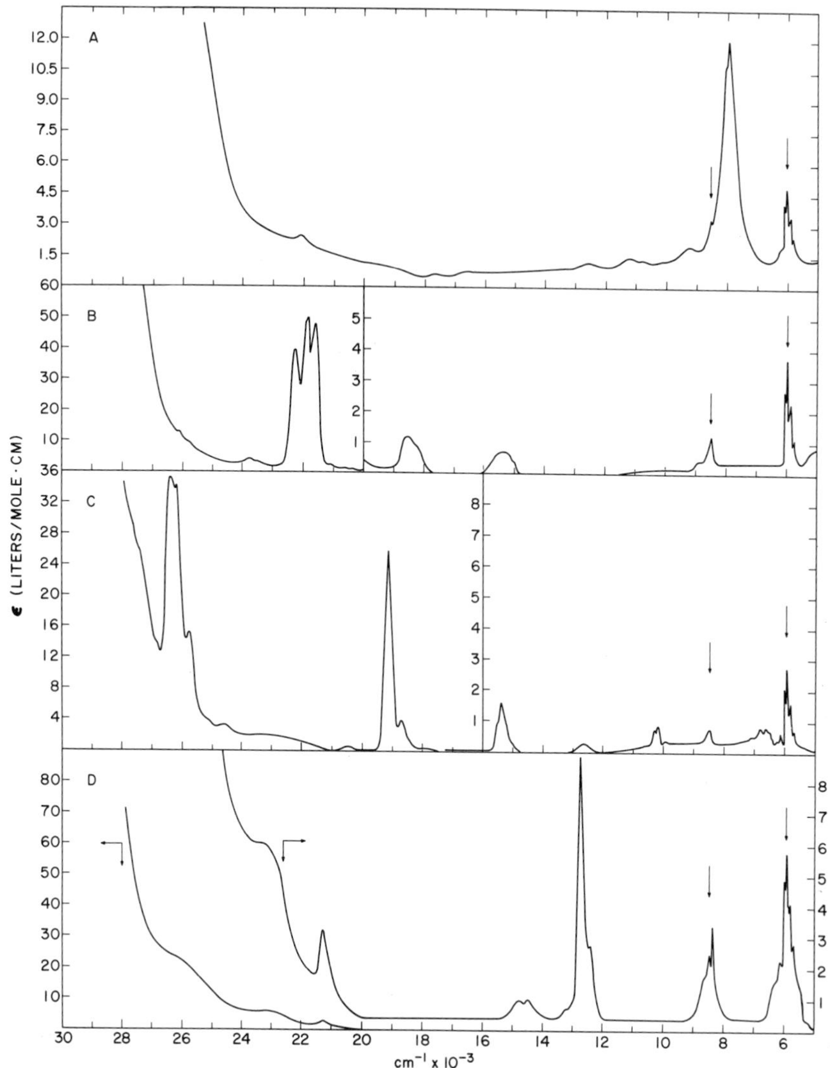

Figure 6. Absorption spectra of the rare-earth chelate vapors (A) $Dy(thd)_3$ at 286°C. (B) $Ho(thd)_3$ at 335°C. (C) $Er(thd)_3$ at 288°C. (D) $Tm(thd)_3$ at 294°C.

coming from the neighboring ions. Including the terms Y_{lm} in the Hamiltonian will affect only the parameter τ_2 and not τ_4 or τ_6. The intensities of spectral lines satisfying quadrupole selection rules should be particularly sensitive to the symmetry of the nearest neighbors surroundings.

An electron diffraction study of gaseous neodymium halides has been performed (*1*) and interpreted in terms of planar D_{3h} molecules. In the absence of evidence to the contrary, one must assume that $NdBr_3$ and NdI_3 and probably the halides of the other lanthanides are planar in the vapor phase. As already mentioned, in order for the forced electric dipole mechanism to display a strong τ_2 dependence, the presence of harmonics Y_{km} with $k = 1$ in the static electric field potential created by the ligands surrounding the 4f ions is required. Judd (*15*) gives a table of point group symmetries which satisfy this requirement. A point symmetry D_{3h} has $Y_{km's}$ with k odd but none with $k = 1$. This mechanism is ruled out in the case of the lanthanide halides if, as indicated by experiment, these molecules are not statically disorted. It would be desirable to obtain additional information on the symmetry of these molecules. The structures of the $M(thd)_3$ compounds in the vapor are not known. It is likely that the lanthanide metal atom is surrounded by six oxygens. For the forced electric dipole mechanism to be operative, the site symmetry would have to be lower than O_h.

Vibronic Mechanism. Jørgensen and Judd (*53*) considered and rejected the vibronic mechanism as the source of the observed hypersensitivity for lanthanide ion solutions since the calculated magnitude of τ_2 was too small by a factor of 10^3 compared with experimental values of τ_2.

The situation appears to be entirely different for gaseous molecules. It is convenient to use Equation 6 as given by Jørgensen and Judd (*13*) for the solution case although it should be modified for application to the gas phase. Accordingly

$$\tau_2/(2J + 1) \simeq 21[N(\rho'')^2 a_0^4/(\rho')^6] \times 10^{-7} \tag{9}$$

where ρ'' is the amplitude of oscillation, N is a dimensionless factor of the order of 10, and ρ' is the radius of the lanthanide ion for an isolated gaseous molecule. We consider appropriate vibrations (the out-of-plane bending vibrations of the NdX_3 molecules or a mode of an octahedral complex in which the central atom beats against the cage of the six ligands so as to leave the center of mass of the system unchanged) as the intensity giving ones and chose $\rho'' \simeq 0.1$A. With $\rho' = 1$ A. the value τ_2 calculated by means of Equation 9 turns out to be $\simeq 1 \times 10^{-7}$, in approximate agreement with experiment.

The difference in our estimate of the magnitude of τ_2 and the earlier estimate (*13*) is attributed to the fact that for the gaseous molecules ρ' may be taken to be the radius of rare-earth ion, $\sim$ 1 A., whereas ρ' was chosen to be 4 A. in the earlier work which related to the hydrated rare-earth ion in aqueous solution. Because of the inverse 6th power dependence on ρ' in Equation 9, a factor of $\sim$ 4000 is gained on decreasing ρ' from 4 to 1 A.

It would appear that the vibronic mechanism can account for the hypersensitivity and the observed magnitude of the gas phase intensities.

Table VII. Energies and Intensities of the Gaseous Rare-Earth Chelate Absorption Maxima

Compound	*cm.*$^{-1}$	ϵ	*Compound*	*cm.*$^{-1}$	ϵ
Pr(thd)$_3$	5235	5.3	Sm(thd)$_3$	6289	2.5
	6578	2.8		6578	3.6
	16835	0.3		6993	4.3
	17361	0.1		7462sh	1.5
	19230sh	0.4		8064	1.0
	20491sh	3.2		9174	0.3
	20920	4.5		9293	0.3
	22123	4.4		9469	0.3
				20408	1.3
Nd(thd)$_3$	11111	1.4		21367sh	1.6
	11337	1.4		22935	3.9
	12345	2.9		23809	5.8
	12500	2.9			
	13297	2.9	Eu(thd)$_3$	18656	0.6
	13513	2.9		21482	3.4
	16556sh	14.8		21598	4.5
	16883	32.8			
	17050	32.4	Dy(thd)$_3$	7836	12.0
	17346	22.2		7936sh	10.5
	18744	7.6		9090	2.0
	18779	8.2		10695	1.3
	18867	7.1		11111	1.4
	23148	8.5		12345	1.1
				17605	0.6
				22026	2.5
Ho(thd)$_3$	15337	0.7	Er(thd)$_3$	6578	0.8
	18181sh	0.8		6756	0.8
	18518	1.2		9900	0.4
	17497	2.7		10152	0.9
	20512	1.1		10257	0.7
	21645	48.0		12658	0.3
	21905	50.2		15384	1.6
	21978sh	48.1		15527sh	0.9
	22321	39.6		18518sh	1.6
	23584sh	3.5		18726	3.8
	23752	4.3		19157	25.9
	25706	8.1		20491	0.7
	26178	12.8		24630	3.3
				25316sh	4.5
Tm(thd)$_3$	6250sh	1.7		25773	15.3
	8305	3.4		26178	34.2
	12376	2.8		26385	35.3
	12706	8.8		26809sh	13.8
	14450	1.0		27100sh	19.1
	14792	1.0		27397sh	25.8
	21276	3.2			
	23364sh	6.0			
	25773sh	20.7			

Table VIII. Hypersensitive Transitions in the Lanthanides[a]

Tripositive Ion	*Configuration*	*Ground State*	*Excited State*	*Energy cm.$^{-1}$*
Pr	f^2	$^3H_4$	$^3F_2$	4,800
		$^3H_5$	$^3F_3$	4,100
Nd	f^3	$^4I_{9/2}$	$^4G_{5/2}$	17,300
		$^4I_{11/2}$	$^2G_{7/2}$	14,900
Sm	f^5	$^6H_{5/2}$	$^6F_{1/2}$	6,200
Eu	f^6	$^7F_0$	$^5D_2$	21,500
Dy	f^9	$^6H_{15/2}$	$^6F_{11/2}$	7,700
Ho	f^{10}	$^5I_8$	$^5G_6$	22,200
		$^5I_8$	$^3H_6$	26,200
Er	f^{11}	$^4I_{15/2}$	$^2H_{11/2}$	19,200
		$^4I_{15/2}$	$^4G_{11/2}$	26,500
Tm	f^{12}	$^3H_6$	$^3F_4$	12,600
		$^3H_6$	$^3H_4$	5,500

[a] Data from Jørgensen and Judd (*13*).

Table IX. Oscillator Strengths, *P*, of Hypersensitive Transitions in Gaseous Lanthanide Compounds

Ion	*Excited State*	*P × 10^6*		
		Bromide	*Iodide*	*Chelate*
Pr	$^3F_2$	~20	~40	15
Nd	$^4G_{5/2}$	330	530	120
Dy	$^6F_{11/2}$	—	—	32
Ho	$^5G_6$	—	—	178
Er	$^2H_{11/2}$	58	96	34
Tm	$^4G_{11/2}$	99	—	85
	$^3F_4$	15	25	12

The oscillator strengths of these transitions in aqueous solutions are in the range 1 to 10×10^{-6}.

Table X. τ_λ Values for Er^{3+} Solution and Vapor Spectra

Medium		$\tau_\lambda \times 10^8$		
		τ_2	τ_4	τ_6
$DClO_4$	Solution	0.16	0.23	0.24
$LiNO_3$-KNO_3	Solution	2.2	0.25	0.19
Chelate	Vapor	5	~0.3	~0.4
Tribromide	Vapor	6.5	0.16	0.18
Triiodide	Vapor	10.6	—	—

Table XI. Range of τ_2-Values for Solution and Vapor Spectra

Aqueous solutions	$1–2 \times 10^{-9}$
$LiNO_3$-KNO_3 eutectic solns.	$1–2 \times 10^{-8}$
Chelate vapors	$0.5–1 \times 10^{-7}$
Bromide and iodide vapors	$0.5–3 \times 10^{-7}$

Table XII.

Compound	*Experimental m.p., °C.*	*Literature m.p., °C. (7)*
Pr(thd)$_3$	222–225	222–224
Nd(thd)$_3$	215–217.5	215–218
Sm(thd)$_3$	198.5–200	195.5–198.5
Eu(thd)$_3$	188.5–189	187–189
Dy(thd)$_3$	181–183.5	180–183.5
Ho(thd)$_3$	182.5–185	180–182.5
Er(thd)$_3$	182.5–183.5	179–181
Tm(thd)$_3$	171–174	171.5–173.5

Experimental

Bromides and Iodides. The absorption spectra of the gaseous rare-earth halides were measured with a Cary 14 H spectrophotometer. The experimental procedure has been described previously (*11*). In this study a double furnace was used, allowing the rare-earth halide vapor to be heated to a higher temperature than the solid or liquid and allowing a baseline determination at the temperature of interest. In addition, a 0 → 0.1 full scale optical density slidewire was employed with the Cary 14 H spectrophotometer, increasing its sensitivity by a factor of 10. With this arrangement transitions with optical density of 0.005 could be observed easily.

The molar absorptivities for $PrBr_3$ and PrI_3 vapor were determined from Shimazaki and Niwa's (*22*) vapor pressure equations for the solids and the extrapolations used in the earlier gaseous $NdBr_3$ and NdI_3 study. The heat capacities and heats of fusion for $PrBr_3$ and PrI_3 were taken from Dworkin and Bredig's (*7, 8*) data. The vapor pressure equations obtained for solid and liquid $PrBr_3$ are given by Equations 5 and 6 respectively

$$\log P_{atm}(PrBr_3(s)) = \frac{-16743}{T} - 4.28 \log T + 24.279 \qquad (5)$$

$$\log P_{atm}(PrBr_3(l)) = \frac{-15434}{T} - 7.04 \log T + 31.189 \qquad (6)$$

and for solid and liquid PrI_3 by Equations 7 and 8 respectively

$$\log P_{atm}(PrI_3(s)) = \frac{-17102}{T} - 5.59 \log T + 29.047 \qquad (7)$$

$$\log P_{atm}(PrI_3(l)) = \frac{-14967}{T} - 7.05 \log T + 31.322 \qquad (8)$$

Since no accurate vapor pressure data are available for the erbium and thulium halides, the molar absorptivities were determined directly from a weighed amount of the respective rare-earth halides. Good results could be obtained from this method if the respective halogen, bromine, or iodine were added to the cell such that its pressure at 1000°C. was ~ 1 atm. This procedure greatly reduced the reaction of the rare-earth halide vapor with the quartz as evidenced by the fact that 80% of the rare-earth halide was recovered after a determination. In general, the average of the weights before and after was used to calculate the molar absorptivity. The values given for the molar absorptivity are probably correct to within ± 25%.

All the rare-earth halides were prepared by the ammonium halide method described by Taylor and Carter (*24*) and were used without further purification. The rare-earth oxides (Michigan Chemical) used to prepare the halides were of 99.8% purity or better.

The absolute values of the oscillator strengths may be in error by as much as ± 25%; however, the relative intensities, which determine the relative magnitudes of τ_λ, are known to within ± 5% except for the very weak transitions of the less volatile praseodymium and neodymium halides for which the errors may be as large as ± 25%.

2,2,6,6-Tetramethyl-3,5-heptanedionates. Ten millimoles of each of the rare-earth chelates were prepared by the method of Eisentraut and Sievers (*9*). H(thd) from the Pierce Chemical Co., Rockford, Ill. was used without further purification. Five mmoles of the 99.9% rare earth oxide (Michigan Chemical Corp., Saint Louis, Mich.) were dissolved in the stoichiometric amount of 6*N* HNO_3, and appropriate amounts of H_2O and 95% EtOH were added to make 50 ml. of 50% ethanol solution containing the required amount of rare-earth nitrate. The dried product was sublimed at 180°C. *in vacuo,* recrystallized from *n*-hexane *in vacuo,* and vacuum dried. Although no elemental analyses were made on the final product, the melting points were taken on a Fisher-Jones melting point apparatus, and the results obtained were compared with the literature values shown in Table XII. The products were stored in evacuated desiccators.

The general procedure for obtaining the absorption spectrum of each compound consisted of adding a weighed amount of the compound to a 10 or 20 cm. cell which had been evacuated previously and flamed out. The cell was then returned to the vacuum line, evacuated, and sealed off with a hand torch. Absorption spectra measurements were made using a Cary 14 H spectrophotometer. The unique characteristics of this instrument, which permits its use up to temperatures of 2400°K. or higher, have been described by Gruen (*10*). The cells were heated by a horizontally positioned 12″ long Marshall furnace. The furnace was maintained at the desired temperature by an automatic controller. Small, auxiliary, platinum-wound tube heaters controlled by variacs surrounded each end of the optical cell. The temperature of these furnaces was maintained at a level just sufficient to prevent condensation of the metal chelate on the cell windows.

The absorption spectrum was recorded at various temperatures until there was no further increase in the maximum of the most intense peak. At this temperature, the entire spectrum from 4000–30,000 $cm.^{-1}$ was then recorded.

The molar extinction coefficients were calculated as outlined by DeKock and Gruen (*6*). The concentration of the absorbing species was calculated from the measured volume of the cell and the known quantity of material added to the cell.

Acknowledgments

We are indebted to B. G. Wybourne and G. L. Goodman for a number of fruitful discussions.

Literature Cited

(1) Akishin, P. A., Naumov, V. A., Tatevskii, V. M., *Nauch. Doklady Vysshei Shkoly, Khim. & Khim. Tekhnol.* **1959**, 229 (1959); *Chem. Abstr.* **53**, 19493*e* (1959).
(2) Axe, J. D., Jr., *J. Chem. Phys.* **39**, 1154 (1963).
(3) Broer, L. J. F., Gorter, C. J., Hoogschagen, J., *Physica* **11**, 231 (1945).
(4) Carnall, W. T., Fields, P. R., Wybourne, B. G., *J. Chem. Phys.* **42**, 3797 (1965).
(5) Carnall, W. T., Gruen, D. M., McBeth, R. L., *J. Phys. Chem.* **66**, 2159 (1962).
(6) DeKock, C. W., Gruen, D. M., *J. Chem. Phys.* **44**, 4387 (1966).
(7) Dworkin, A. S., Bredig, M. A., *J. Phys. Chem.* **67**, 2499 (1963).
(8) *Ibid.*, p. 697.
(9) Eisentraut, K. J., Sievers, R. E., *J. Am. Chem. Soc.* **87**, 5254 (1965).
(10) Gruen, D. M., *Quart. Rev. (London)* **19**, 349 (1965).
(11) Gruen, D. M., DeKock, C. W., *J. Chem. Phys.* **45**, 455 (1966).
(12) Holleck, L., Eckardt, D., *Z. Naturforsch.* **9b**, 274 (1954).
(13) Jørgensen, C. K., Judd, B. R., *Mol. Phys.* **8**, 281 (1964).
(14) Judd, B. R., *Phys. Rev.* **127**, 750 (1962).
(15) Judd, B. R., *J. Chem. Phys.* **44**, 839 (1966).
(16) Kononenko, L. I., Poluektov, N. S., *Russ. J. Inorg. Chem. (English Transl.)* **7**, 965 (1962).
(17) Krupke, W. F., Gruber, J. B., *Phys. Rev.* **139**, A2008 (1965).
(18) Krupke, W. F., *Phys. Rev.* **145**, 325 (1966).
(19) Moeller, T., Brantley, J. C., *J. Am. Chem. Soc.* **72**, 5447 (1950).
(20) Moeller, T., Ulrich, W. F., *J. Inorg. Nucl. Chem.* **2**, 164 (1956).
(21) Ofelt, G. S., *J. Chem. Phys.* **37**, 511 (1962).
(22) Shimazaki, E., Niwa, K., *Z. Anorg. Allgem. Chem.* **314**, 21 (1962).
(23) Taketatsu, T., Banks, C. V., *Anal. Chem.* **38**, 1524 (1966).
(24) Taylor, M. D., Carter, C. P., *J. Inorg. Nucl. Chem.* **24**, 387 (1962).
(25) VanVleck, J. H., *J. Phys. Chem.* **41**, 67 (1937).
(26) Vickery, R. C., *J. Chem. Soc.* **1952**, 421 (1952).

RECEIVED October 17, 1966. This work was performed under the auspices of the U. S. Atomic Energy Commission.

9

Preparation, Structure and Spectra of Some Tetravalent Praseodymium Compounds

LARNED B. ASPREY, JAMES S. COLEMAN, and MARTIN J. REISFELD

University of California, Los Alamos Scientific Laboratory, Los Alamos, N. M.

Several fluoride complexes of tetravalent praseodymium have been prepared, and their lattice parameters and absorption spectra have been ascertained. The compounds $Na_7Pr_6F_{31}$ *and* Na_2PrF_6 *were prepared by reaction of appropriate mixtures of* PrF_3 *and NaF in the presence of fluorine gas.* PrF_4 *was prepared by extracting NaF from* Na_2PrF_6 *with liquid anhydrous HF in a fluorine atmosphere. The space groups are:* $Na_7Pr_6F_{31}$ *is rhombohedral (R$\bar{3}$);* Na_2PrF_6 *is orthorhombic (Immm); and* PrF_4 *is monoclinic (C2/c). The spectra show characteristic absorption peaks at 2893, 2873, and 2889 cm.*$^{-1}$ *for the three compounds, corresponding to the electronic transition* $^2F_{5/2} \rightarrow {}^2F_{7/2}$*, and lead to a value of* $\zeta_{4f} = 824 \pm 2$ *cm.*$^{-1}$*.*

Of all the lanthanide elements, only a few form compounds in which the lanthanide is in the plus four oxidation state. The dioxides of cerium, praseodymium, and terbium have all been prepared, as have the tetrafluorides of cerium and terbium. Complex chloride, sulfate, and nitrate compounds of Pr^{4+} have also been reported (*2*). This paper reports the preparation of pure PrF_4 along with lattice constants and spectroscopic data. The compounds $Na_7Pr_6F_{31}$ and Na_2PrF_6 have also been made, and similar data are given.

Experimental

The sodium compounds containing tetravalent Pr were prepared by heating intimate mixtures of PrF_3 and the alkali fluorides in the desired stoichiometric ratios in the presence of fluorine gas (*1*). PrF_3 was prepared by adding aqueous HF to acid solutions of Pr(III), followed by treating the air-dried solid with fluorine gas at 400°C. for several hours. Sodium fluoride was used without further treatment. The two anhydrous compounds, NaF and PrF_3, were then ground together in mullite mortars in an inert atmosphere. The fluorination reactions were carried out in a nickel reactor. Inert aluminum oxide containers were used in the fluorination. The mixtures were fluorinated in the temperature range of 300–500°C. at 1–4 atm. of fluorine for two or more hours. An alternative method for preparing Na_2PrF_6 was also employed. A mixture of Pr_6O_{11} and NaF in the desired stoichiometric proportions was placed in the reactor. The mixture was fluorinated directly at 450°C. for several hours under a fluorine pressure of 2 atm. The product obtained in this manner was Na_2PrF_6, identical to that prepared by the PrF_3 plus NaF technique.

To prepare PrF_4, a different technique was necessary (3). A sample of Na_2PrF_6 obtained by one of the previous methods was placed in a Kel-F tube connected to the gas handling system. A plug of Teflon wool was placed over the sample. In the presence of 1/2 atm. of fluorine gas, HF was condensed onto the sample. After several minutes, the tube was inverted, and the liquid was filtered off through the wool plug. The HF plus fluorine treatment was repeated three more times. This washing process which extracted the NaF from the Na_2PrF_6 proved sufficient to generate a sample whose net weight corresponded within 1% of that expected for a conversion to PrF_4.

Results

X-ray powder patterns were obtained for the three Pr(IV) compounds. For $Na_7Pr_6F_{31}$, a rhombohedral ($R\bar{3}$) structure was found, isostructural with $Na_7U_6F_{31}$. Na_2PrF_6 was found to be isostructural with orthorhombic γ-Na_2UF_6 (Immm). The material identified as PrF_4 was found to be isostructural with monoclinic UF_4 (C2/c). The derived lattice parameters and unit cell volumes are given in Table I.

Table I. Structure and Lattice Parameters for Pr^{4+} Compounds

Compound	*Structure and Space Group*	*Lattice Parameters*	*Volume (A^3)*
PrF_4	Monoclinic (C2/c)	$a =$ 12.47 A.	865.4
		$b =$ 10.54 A.	
		$\beta = 126.4°$	
		$c =$ 8.18 A.	
$Na_7Pr_6F_{31}$	Rhombohedral ($R\bar{3}$)	$a =$ 8.96 A.	583.6
		$\alpha = 107.9°$	
Na_2PrF_6	Orthorhombic (Immm)	$a =$ 5.54 A.	254.5
		$b =$ 3.97 A.	
		$c =$ 11.57 A.	

A computation was made of the nearest-neighbor distances and bond angles involving the central praseodymium ion in order to ascertain the structure and symmetry of the first coordination spheres for the three compounds. These structures are depicted in Figure 1.

In all cases the praseodymium may be considered as eight-fold coordinated. For Na_2PrF_6 the local symmetry is cubic, with eight fluorines approximately equidistant at a distance of 2.23 A. For PrF_4 the structure is that of a tetragonal antiprism again containing eight fluorines approximately equidistant from the praseodymium at distances ranging from 2.20 to 2.28 A. The situation for $Na_7Pr_6F_{31}$ is slightly more complex. The structure may be viewed as a distorted antiprism with eight fluorines at varying distances between 2.08 and 2.23 A. A ninth fluorine atom is also bonded to the praseodymium and is located on top of one of the faces of the antiprism at a distance of 3.02 A. Although we have here a true case of nine-fold coordination, the long ninth Pr–F bond still allows us to view the structure as eight-fold coordinate.

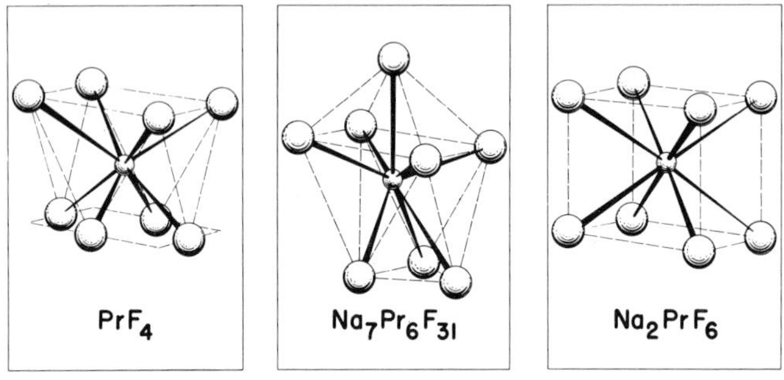

Figure 1. Structure of first coordination sphere of fluorides around tetravalent praseodymium ion

In contrast to the typically green color of Pr^{3+} compounds, the materials reported here are white, with the $Na_7Pr_6F_{31}$ showing a slight tan cast. Absorption spectra were taken on all three compounds in both the visible and infrared regions. Samples were ground in an inert atmosphere with Fluorolube oils of varying viscosities to obtain good mulls. The mulls were placed between CaF_2 flats for observation. A Cary Model 14 spectrophotometer was used for measurements in the range 2000–25000 A., and a Perkin-Elmer Model 521 spectrophotometer was utilized for the region of 1500–4000 cm.$^{-1}$. Spectra were also taken at liquid nitrogen temperatures. The low temperature spectra in the region of 2800–3000 cm.$^{-1}$ are shown in Figure 2.

Whereas the spectra of Pr^{3+} typically exhibit three bands in the region of 4000 A. arising from transitions to the $^3P_{0,1,2}$ multiplet, none of the oxidized Pr(IV) samples showed such transitions—further evidence for the existence of the plus four state of the Pr. Pr^{4+} has a $4f^1$ electronic configuration, and therefore the absorption spectrum should consist of a single line, corresponding to a $J = 5/2 \rightarrow 7/2$ transition arising from the spin-orbit coupling removing the degeneracy of the ^2F level. If a plot is made for the lanthanide ions of ζ_{4f} *vs.* $Z + I$, a straight line is obtained in the region from Ce^{3+} to Eu^{3+} (ζ_{4f} is the spin-orbit coupling constant, Z the atomic number, and I the oxidation state.) This line predicts a value of ζ_{4f} for Pr^{4+} of 820 cm.$^{-1}$. This value, under the free-ion approximation leads to an expected absorption for Pr^{4+} at 2870 cm.$^{-1}$. Experimentally, for Na_2PrF_6, $Na_7Pr_6F_{31}$, and PrF_4, strong absorptions are found at 2873, 2893, and 2889 cm.$^{-1}$, respectively. An average value of 2885 cm.$^{-1}$ is therefore taken as the energy of the $^2F_{5/2} \rightarrow {}^2F_{7/2}$ transition in Pr^{4+} with a ζ_{4f} value of 824 cm.$^{-1}$, as compared with a predicted value of 820 cm.$^{-1}$. In addition to the peaks shown in Figure 2, a number of weak bands were observed, ranging from 403 to 3910 cm.$^{-1}$. The absorption at 403 cm.$^{-1}$ probably arises from the asymmetric Pr–F stretching vibration, but the origin of the other peaks (probably crystal-field components) has not been ascertained as yet. An interesting feature of the above data may

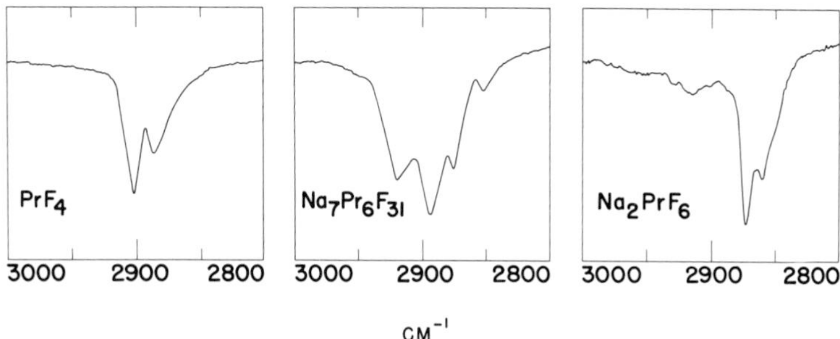

Figure 2. Infrared spectra taken at 80°K. of praseodymium-fluoride complexes

be found by examining the spectrum of Na_2PrF_6. For this structure, in which a site containing an inversion center is present, the electric dipole moment mechanism cannot be operative. In this case we would ordinarily expect a marked diminution in intensity for the transition. Although the presence of a splitting in the main peak of 12 cm.$^{-1}$ might suggest the existence of two different symmetry sites in the sample, x-ray investigation, as previously noted, gave no such indication. Utilizing the mull technique, we have no idea as to the relative oscillator strengths of the transition for the three compounds. The most likely mechanism for the apparent enhancement of the intensity of the transition in Na_2PrF_6 is a vibronic coupling of one of the fundamental infrared vibrational modes. Future work utilizing single crystals and polarization data should resolve the question.

Literature Cited

(1) Asprey, Larned B., Keenan, Thomas K., *J. Inorg. Nucl. Chem.* **16,** 260 (1961).
(2) Pajakoff, S. W., *Monatsh* **94,** 482 (1963).
(3) Soriano, J., Givon, M., Shamir, J., *Inorg. Nucl. Chem. Letters* **2,** 13 (1966).

RECEIVED October 14, 1966. This work was done under the auspices of the U. S. Atomic Energy Commission.

10

Thermodynamic Parameters of Fluoride Complexes of the Lanthanides

JEFFREY B. WALKER and GREGORY R. CHOPPIN

Florida State University, Tallahassee, Fla.

Solvent extraction, potentiometry, and calorimetry have been used to determine the thermodynamic parameters of the formation of the monofluoride complex of the trivalent lanthanide ions at 25°C. and an ionic strength of 1M ($NaClO_4$). The enthalpies were all endothermic, ranging from 4.0 to 9.5 Kcal./mole; consequently, the large, positive entropies, ranging from 25 to 48 cal./°C./mole, explain the high stability constants. This large entropy results from the decrease in overall water structure when the fluoride ion is complexed. The difference in the enthalpies of formation of LnF^{2+} and $LnAc^{2+}$ can possibly be explained by a difference in covalence for Ln-F and Ln-O bonds.

Evaluating the enthalpy and entropy changes associated with the formation of complexes of lanthanide ions has provided evidence on their structure in aqueous solutions. The halide (*10*), nitrate (*9*), and thiocyanate (*8*) complexes are weak outer-sphere ion pairs for which a small exothermic enthalpy of formation is sufficient to overcome the small negative entropy. The sulfate complexes have larger stability constants as a result of a relatively large positive entropy predominating over an endothermic enthalpy (*11*). The enthalpy and entropy values were similar to corresponding values for propionate complexes of the lanthanides (*7*). Since the latter are likely inner-sphere complexes, it is probable that the sulfate complexes are of the same nature although there may be some contribution from outer-sphere ion-pairing. Previous reports (*15, 16*) had indicated that the fluoride complexes were much stronger than any of these other lanthanide complexes with inorganic ligands. It was of interest to determine the enthalpies and entropies of complexation in order to gain insight into the fluoride complexes.

Experimental

Reagents. All reagents were analytical grade, and all aqueous solutions were prepared with distilled water.

LANTHANIDE PERCHLORATES. Stock solutions, approximately 0.3*M*, were prepared as described previously (*5*). The solutions were standardized by passing aliquots through a column of H^+-form Dowex-50 resin and titrating the liberated acid with standard sodium hydroxide.

IRON PERCHLORATE. The ferrous perchlorate and ferric perchlorate solutions were prepared as described by Kury (*15*).

SODIUM FLUORIDE. Buffered solutions of pH 3.0 ranging in sodium fluoride concentrations to 0.02*M* (0.01*M* free fluoride ion) were prepared using sodium perchlorate to obtain a total ionic strength of 1*M*.

DINONYLNAPHTHALENE SULFONATE. Solutions of this liquid cation exchanger in heptane were prepared and standardized as described elsewhere (*9*).

TRACERS. ^{144}Ce, ^{147}Pm, and $^{152-154}Eu$ were obtained from Oak Ridge National Laboratory, while ^{169}Er, ^{170}Tm, and ^{175}Yb were prepared by irradiation in the University of Florida Nuclear Reactor.

Equipment. POTENTIOMETRIC TITRATIONS. The apparatus consisted of three identical glass cells of about 25 ml. capacity, fitted with a four-hole Teflon plug (for the platinum electrode, the agar salt bridge, a buret, and an inlet for nitrogen gas). The cells were jacketed for circulating water at $25.0 \pm 0.1°C$. The interior of the cells were coated with epoxy resin to eliminate reaction between hydrofluoric acid and the glass. The solutions were agitated by magnetic stirrers, and the cells were connected electrically by agar salt bridges. The platinum electrodes were connected to a differential voltmeter of infinite impedance (Fluke model 881A). The nitrogen atmosphere above the solutions prevented aerobic oxidation of ferrous ions to ferric ions.

CALORIMETRIC TITRATIONS. The calorimeter was of about 50 ml. capacity and jacketed so it could be insulated by vacuum. The top, fitted to the calorimeter by a ground glass joint, had tubes which housed thermistor, heater and buret inlets. The solutions were stirred magnetically. The buret was attached to a 30 ml. reservoir which, together with the calorimeter, was immersed in a constant temperature water bath at $25.00 \pm 0.02°C$. More details are to be found in previous publications (*6, 23*).

Procedure. POTENTIOMETRIC TITRATIONS. The half-cells consisted of the following solutions:

(A) $NaClO_4$, $HClO_4$, $Fe(ClO_4)_2$, $Fe(ClO_4)_3$
(B) $NaClO_4$, $HClO_4$, $Fe(ClO_4)_2$, $Fe(ClO_4)_3$
(C) $NaClO_4$, $HClO_4$, $Fe(ClO_4)_2$, $Fe(ClO_4)_3$, $Ln(ClO_4)_3$

The $Fe(ClO_4)_2$ and $Fe(ClO_4)_3$ concentrations were $8 \times 10^{-4}M$; the $HClO_4$, between 0.05 and 0.10*M*; the $Ln(ClO_4)_3$, $6 \times 10^{-3}M$; the $NaClO_4$, sufficient to make the total ionic strength 1*M*. Adding aliquots of solutions of NaF ($\mu = 1M$) to cells B and C caused differences in potential because of the formation of complexes of ferric-fluoride in cell B, and of LnF^{2+} and of ferric-fluoride complexes in cell C.

SOLVENT EXTRACTION. The procedures used are described elsewhere (*9, 10*). Although preliminary experiments showed that equilibrium was established within two hours, all samples were mixed for 24 hours. Duplicate 1-ml. aliquots of the organic phase were counted either in a well counter (for gamma emission) or as dry samples in a 2π proportional counter (for beta emission).

CALORIMETRIC TITRATIONS. The procedure and calculations have been described previously (*6*).

Results

It was necessary to use the potential difference when titrating between cells B and A to calculate the stability constants for formation of FeF^{2+} (K_1), FeF_2^+ (K_2), and FeF_3 (K_3). Knowledge of the equilibrium constants for two other reactions were required:

$$HF = H^+ + F^- \qquad K_{HF} = 0.00107^{1}$$
$$Fe^{3+} + H_2O = Fe(OH)^{2+} + H^+ \qquad K_h = 0.0017^{3}$$

The following assumptions were also made:

(1) Negligible complexing of ferrous ions by fluoride ions. This had been verified previously (*4, 18*).

(2) The presence of HF_2^- could be neglected (*22*).

(3) Negligible complexing of ferrous and ferric ions by perchlorate ions (*12*).

(4) Ferrous ion hydrolysis was too small to be detected (*17*).

Considering now only cells B and A, the potential of the concentration cell B-A was given by:

$$E_{B-A} = \frac{-RT}{F} \ln \frac{(Fe^{3+})_B (Fe^{2+})_A}{(Fe^{3+})_A (Fe^{2+})_B} \qquad (1)$$

Using stoichiometric considerations:

$$(\Sigma F^-)_B = (HF)_B + (F^-)_B + (FeF^{2+})_B + 2(FeF_2^+)_B + 3(FeF_3)_B \qquad (2)$$

$$(\Sigma Fe^{3+})_B = (Fe^{3+})_B + (FeF^{2+})_B + (FeF_2^+)_B + (FeF_3)_B + (FeOH^{2+})_B \qquad (3)$$

$$(\Sigma Fe^{3+})_A = (Fe^{3+})_A + (FeOH^{2+})_A \qquad (4)$$

Another useful relation was:

$$\left\{1 + \frac{K_h}{(H^+)_A}\right\} = \left\{1 + \frac{K_h}{(H^+)_B}\right\} \qquad (5)$$

This was justified since the initial concentration of hydrogen ions in both cells B and A was the same, and the changes in hydrogen ion concentration on complexation were negligible. From these equations, it was possible to derive:

$$\left\{1 + \frac{K_h}{(H^+)_B}\right\}\left\{e^{FE/RT} - 1\right\} = K_1\left(\frac{HF}{H}\right)_B + K_1K_2\left(\frac{HF}{H}\right)^2 + K_1K_2K_3\left(\frac{HF}{H}\right)_B^3 \quad (6)$$

which can be rearranged and substituted to give:

$$\left(\frac{HF}{H}\right)_B = \frac{1}{K_h + (H^+)_B}\left\{(\Sigma F^-)_B - (\Sigma Fe^{3+})_B + (Fe^{3+})_B\,(1 + \frac{K_h}{(H^+)_B} - K_1K_2(Fe^{3+})_B\left(\frac{HF}{H}\right)_B^2 - 2K_1K_2K_3(Fe^{3+})_B\left(\frac{HF}{H}\right)_B^3\right\} \quad (7)$$

Using Equations 6 and 7, K_1, K_2, and K_3 can be calculated by an iterative procedure, as outlined previously (*15*). All calculations in the

Table I. Potentiometric Titration Data[b]

Dysprosium
$Fe^{3+} = 8.34 \times 10^{-4}M$
$Fe^{2+} = 8.34 \times 10^{-4}M$
$Dy^{3+} = 0.01076M$

Volume NaF Added (ml.)	*Fluoride (10^4M)*[a]	$E_{B\text{-}A}$ *(mV)*	$E_{C\text{-}A}$ *(mV)*
0.100	6.52	13.19	11.06
0.025	8.14	16.72	14.18
0.025	9.75	20.17	17.00
0.025	11.36	23.31	19.61
0.025	12.96	26.23	22.14
0.025	14.56	29.01	24.54
0.025	16.15	31.64	26.84
0.025	17.73	34.03	29.05
0.025	19.31	36.40	31.16

Neodymium
$Fe^{3+} = 7.28 \times 10^{-4}M$
$Fe^{2+} = 7.36 \times 10^{-4}M$
$Nd^{3+} = 0.005990M$

Volume NaF Added (ml.)	*Fluoride (10^4M)*[a]	$E_{B\text{-}A}$ *(mV)*	$E_{C\text{-}A}$ *(mV)*
0.100	6.52	13.24	13.00
0.025	8.14	16.71	16.00
0.025	9.75	20.04	19.10
0.025	11.36	23.16	21.70
0.025	12.96	26.04	24.20
0.025	14.56	28.87	27.10
0.025	16.15	31.73	29.60

[a] Accumulative concentration of fluoride.
[b] $(\mu) = 1M$, $NaClO_4$; T = 25.0 ± .02°C.; $[H^+] = 0.0908M$.

present work were performed with an IBM 709 Computer. The results for the stability constants of the successive ferric-fluoride complexes at an ionic strength of $1M$ ($NaClO_4$) at 25°C. were:

$$K_1 = 170.0$$
$$K_2 = 8.7$$
$$K_3 = 1.2$$

These values compare favorably with those reported by Kury at $\mu = 0.5$ and 25°C. The stability constants of the lanthanide fluoride complexes were obtained by comparing changes in the potential in cell C with those in that of cell B upon adding sodium fluoride solution. Owing to the insolubility of LnF_3, only a few (often only six) aliquots of sodium fluoride solution could be added to cell C before precipitation interferred. Precipitation could be observed easily since upon its occurrence, the potential between cells C and A would drift rapidly to lower values.

Two typical sets of potentiometric titration data are presented in Table I, while the data for solvent extraction measurements are given in Table II. Again, an iterative calculation procedure was used to obtain

Table II. Experimental Results of Solvent Extraction of ^{169}Er and ^{147}Pm[a]

Fluoride Concentration of Aqueous Phase (10^4M)	*Activity (Er) (counts/min.)* Organic	Aqueous	$\frac{1}{Kd}$
0	31180	13574	0.435
5.0	25155	19599	0.779
10.0	16622	28132	1.692
15.0	15789	28956	1.833
20.0	13090	31664	2.419
25.0	12408	32346	2.607
30.0	10905	33849	3.104
40.0	8700	36054	4.144
45.0	6878	37876	5.507
50.0	6613	38141	5.768
0	41500	8963	0.216
5.0	36575	13925	0.381
10.0	34253	16247	0.474
15.0	29795	20705	0.695
20.0	21780	28720	1.319
25.0	23309	27191	(1.167)
30.0	18929	31571	1.668
40.0	13732	36768	2.678
45.0	—	—	—
50.0	—	—	—

[a] $\mu = 1M$ $NaClO_4$, T = 25.0 ± 0.2°C., $[H^+] = 0.001M$.

the stability constants, which are listed in Table III. Also included in this table are the results of the solvent extraction measurements as well as the stability constants reported by Kury (*15, 16*) and others (*19, 20*). The error limits represent one standard deviation ($1 \times \sigma$).

Two typical sets of the calorimetric data are presented in Table IV. The enthalpies of complexation were calculated as described previously (*6*). The heat of dilution of the lanthanide perchlorate was checked by titrating two of the lanthanides ($\mu = 1M$, pH = 3.0) with $NaClO_4$ ($\mu = 1M$, pH = 3.0). No heat was observed. The heat of dilution of the sodium fluoride was checked by titrating 1*M* $NaClO_4$ (pH = 3.0) with NaF ($\mu = 1M$, pH = 3.0). A small heat of dilution was observed for the first two points in the titration; after this it was negligible. The heats of dilution of the sodium fluoride were accounted for in the calculations.

The resulting thermodynamic parameters for the formation of the monofluoride complexes at 25°C. in an ionic medium of 1*M* $NaClO_4$ are given in Table V. The error limits represent one standard deviation.

Table III. Stability Constants for the Reaction at 25°C.

$$Ln^{3+} + F^{-} = LnF^{2+}$$

Ion	*Potentiometry* $\mu = 1M$	*Solvent Extraction* $\mu = 1M$	*Potentiometry* $\mu = 0.5M$ (15, 17)
La	470 ± 30		480 ± 70
Ce	650 ± 80	528 ± 127	1301 ± 200
			104 < 103 (*19*)
Pr	1030 ± 80		
Nd	1220 ± 100		
Pm	—	1437 ± 244	
Sm	1310 ± 40		
Eu	1540 ± 50	1593 ± 198	
Gd	2060 ± 190		2358 ± 350
Tb	2660 ± 130		
Dy	2900 ± 260		
Ho	3320 ± 130		
Er	3460 ± 100	3669 ± 660	
Tm	3650 ± 110	3680 ± 294	
Yb	3830 ± 270	3965 ± 476	
Lu	4110 ± 290		
Y	4020 ± 360		8500 ± 1280 (*20*)

Discussion

From Table V we see that the high stability of the fluoride complexes of the lanthanide ions is attributed to a large positive entropy in contrast to the negative values found for the formation of the mono-

Table IV. Calorimetric Titration Data[a]

Praeseodymium
$Pr^{3+} = 0.03846M$
Initial vol. = 50.76 ml.
$[F^-] = 0.025M$

Fluoride Added (ml.)	*Complexed Fluoride (10^6M)*	*Q (cal.)*	Q_{acc} *(cal.)*	ΔH_1 *(kcal./M)*
0.50	238	0.06828	0.06828	5.60
0.50	471	0.06828	0.13656	5.60
0.50	700	0.07308	0.20964	5.73
0.49	918	0.07162	0.28126	5.81
0.52	1147	0.06577	0.34703	5.68
0.50	1362	0.06870	0.41573	5.68
				Average = 5.68 ± 0.06 kcal./*M*

Thulium
$Tm^{3+} = 0.0467M$
Initial vol. = 51.31 ml.
$[F^-] = 0.025M$

Fluoride Added (ml.)	*Complexed Fluoride (10^6M)*	*Q (cal.)*	Q_{acc} *(cal.)*	ΔH_1 *(kcal./M)*
0.52	249	0.11315	0.11315	8.76
0.50	484	0.11164	0.22479	8.87
0.48	706	0.10126	0.32605	8.75
0.49	927	0.10126	0.42731	8.64
0.52	1159	0.10126	0.52857	8.47
				Average = 8.70 ± 0.11 kcal./*M*

[a] $\mu = 1M$ $NaClO_4$; $T = 25.00 \pm 0.02°C.$; $[H^+] = 0.001M$.

chlorides, nitrates, and thiocyanates. The entropy values obtained in the present study are significantly larger than the corresponding values for the monoacetate, glycolate, and sulfate complexes as illustrated in Figure 1. In Figure 2, a similar comparison is presented for the enthalpies of complexation for the monoacetate, glycolate, EDTA and fluoride systems. The enthalpies for the fluoride complex are more endothermic than any of the others. The enthalpies for outer-sphere ion pairing with chlorides, nitrates, and thiocyanates are exothermic, while those for the inner sphere sulfate complexes are endothermic, corresponding roughly to the acetate values.

Considering these thermodynamic values, we suggest that fluoride forms inner-sphere complexes like the acetate and sulfate rather than ion pairs like chloride, nitrate, and thiocyanate. Similar to the other inner-sphere complexes, stability is attributed to the positive entropies which have been interpreted in the earlier studies as reflecting the disruption of the hydration zone around the lanthanide ion upon complexation.

Fluoride ion differs from most anions inasmuch as it has a strong ordering effect on water. Consequently, we would expect that dehydration of the fluoride ion upon complexation would affect the entropy values. The equation for complexation is:

$$Ln(H_2O)_x^{3+} + F(H_2O)_y^{1-} \rightarrow LnF(H_2O)_z^{2+} + (x + y - z)H_2O$$

The entropy change would be:

$$\Delta S = S°_{LnF(aq)} + (x + y - z)S°_{H_2O} - S°_{Ln(aq)} - S°_{F(aq)}$$

We can focus on the effect of the fluoride ion dehydration by rearranging to:

$$\Delta S + S°_{F(aq)} = S°_{Ln(aq)} + (x + y - z)S°_{H_2O} - S°_{LnF(aq)} = \Delta S'_F$$

Unfortunately, data on the $S°$ values are not available in solutions of $\mu = 1M$ for which the ΔS data were obtained. The values of x, y, and z are unknown. An estimate of the extent of the ordering effect of the fluoride ion can be attempted by comparing the fluoride data with the acetate data if $S°_{F(aq)}$ and $S°_{Ac(aq)}$ for $\mu = 0.00M$ are used (*21*) to obtain $\Delta S + S°_{X(aq)}$ values. $S°_{Ln(aq)}$ would have the same value in both ligand solutions (therefore, X is constant). $S°_{LnX(aq)}$ is not likely to be the same, but it is also unlikely that the difference would be large. The value reported for $S°_{F(aq)}$ is −2.3 cal./degree/mole, while $S°_{Ac(aq)}$ is

Table V. Thermodynamic Parameters at 25°C.[a]

Ion	*−ΔF(kcal./mole)*	*ΔH(kcal./mole)*	*ΔS(cal./degree/mole)*
La	3.64 ± 0.22	4.00 ± 0.07	25.6 ± 0.8
Ce	3.84 ± 0.50	4.82 ± 0.17	29.0 ± 1.8
Pr	4.11 ± 0.33	5.74 ± 0.08	33.1 ± 1.1
Nd	4.21 ± 0.34	6.83 ± 0.10	36.9 ± 1.2
Sm	4.25 ± 0.13	9.39 ± 0.10	45.8 ± 0.5
Eu	4.35 ± 0.13	9.22 ± 0.15	45.4 ± 0.7
Gd	4.52 ± 0.41	8.90 ± 0.20	45.1 ± 1.5
Tb	4.67 ± 0.23	7.51 ± 0.13	40.8 ± 0.9
Dy	4.72 ± 0.42	7.03 ± 0.05	39.4 ± 1.4
Ho	4.80 ± 0.19	7.26 ± 0.04	40.4 ± 0.7
Er	4.83 ± 0.14	7.43 ± 0.18	41.2 ± 0.8
Tm	4.86 ± 0.15	8.66 ± 0.18	45.4 ± 0.8
Yb	4.89 ± 0.34	9.56 ± 0.10	48.5 ± 1.2
Lu	4.93 ± 0.35	9.53 ± 0.20	48.5 ± 1.4
Y	4.91 ± 0.44	8.32 ± 0.08	44.5 ± 1.5

[a] $\mu = 1M$ ($NaClO_4$) for the reaction: $Ln^{3+} + F^- = LnF^{2+}$.

+20.8 cal./degree/mole. Figure 3 is a plot of the $\Delta S + S°_X$ (ΔS_X) values as a function of atomic number. The numerical agreement is fortuitous considering the assumptions involved. Nevertheless, it would seem correct to assume that, qualitatively, the agreement between $\Delta S'_F$ and $\Delta S'_{Ac}$ indicates that the greater stability of the fluoride complexes compared with the acetate complexes is caused by the increase in entropy associated with the increase in the disorder of the solvent water when fluoride ions are removed by complexation. Correspondence of the two curves in Figure 3 is further evidence for the similarity in the nature of the Ln-Ac^{2+} and Ln-F^{2+} species—*i.e.*, inner sphere complexes.

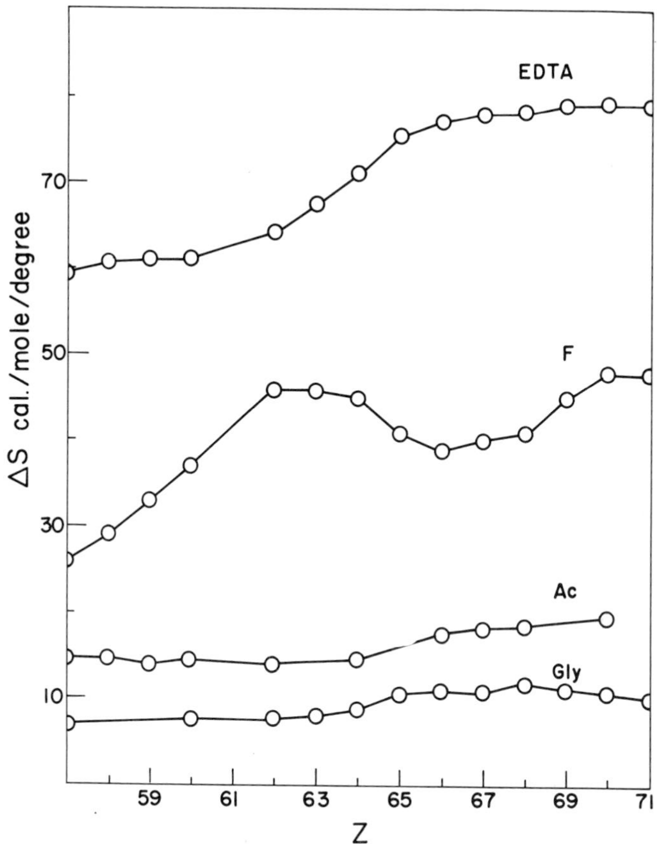

Figure 1. Entropy of formation of the monoligand complex as a function of the atomic number of the lanthanides for EDTA, fluoride, acetate, and glycolate ligands

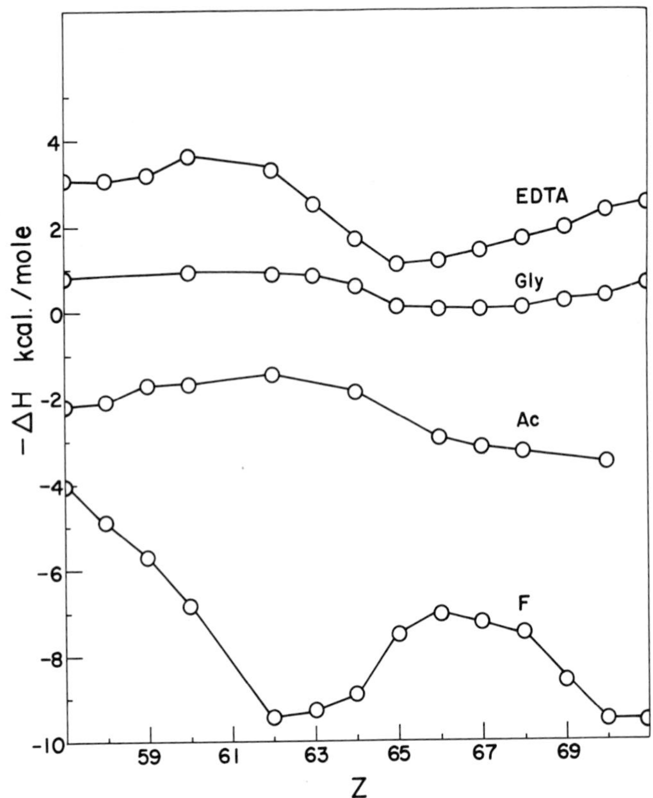

Figure 2. Enthalpy of formation of the monoligand complex as a function of the atomic number of the lanthanides for EDTA, glycolate, acetate, and fluoride ligands

A similar treatment of the enthalpies using —78.66 kcal. for the $\Delta H^\circ{}_f$ of $F^-{}_{(aq)}$ (*21*) and —116.84 kcal. for the $\Delta H^\circ{}_f$ of $Ac^-{}_{(aq)}$ (*21*) increases the difference in the enthalpies of the fluoride and acetate such that

$$\Delta H_{\mathrm{LnF(aq)}} - \Delta H_{\mathrm{LnAc(aq)}} = 40\text{-}46 \text{ kcal}$$

(ignoring the problem of standard state difference and assuming x and z are equal in both cases). There are too many possible variables to allow fruitful discussion of the results of this rough estimate. For example, since both bonds are predominantly ionic, the differences in electronegativities could result in different effective dielectric constants in the Born equation which could cause differences of this magnitude in the enthalpies. Since such an effect should be almost constant across the lanthanide series, it would not seem to account for the difference in shape of the curve for fluoride in Figure 2 compared to those of the other ligands.

The oxyanion ligands would all have larger nephelauxetic effects than would fluoride. Consequently, while the bonding in both the fluoride and acetate complexes is predominantly ionic, there will be a greater difference in the covalent contribution between these two than between acetate and other oxyligands including water. It is difficult to assess the covalent contribution in these complexes, but as a first approximation we can consider changes in charge transfer energies as reflecting the covalency changes (*13*).

Jørgensen (*14*) has shown that the variation in the wavenumber of the first electron transfer transition of lanthanide complexes can be approximately predicted by the equation

$$E = W - q(E\text{-}A) + \text{Constant } (q) \ (D/13)$$

where W is a function characteristic of the ligands, the factor $q(E\text{-}A)$ represents the monotonic decrease of the $4f$ energy across the series, q being the number of f electrons, and D representing the spin-pairing energy. The theory can be further refined giving an equation containing the Racah Parameter E^3 and the spin orbit coupling constant (*14*). He

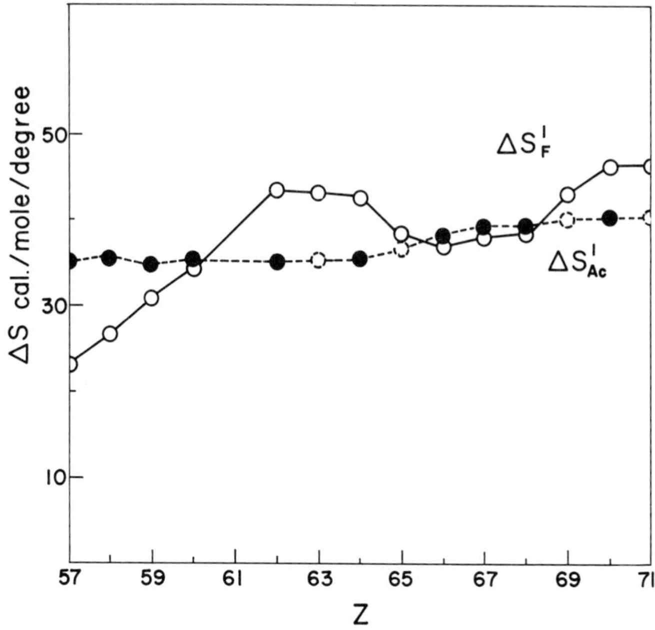

Figure 3. Comparison of the values of $\Delta S'_x$ (= $\Delta S + S°_x$) for the formation of LnF^{2+} and $LnAc^{2+}$

$\Delta S'_F$ —o—o—o—o

$\Delta S'_{Ac}$ – – ● – ● – ● – –

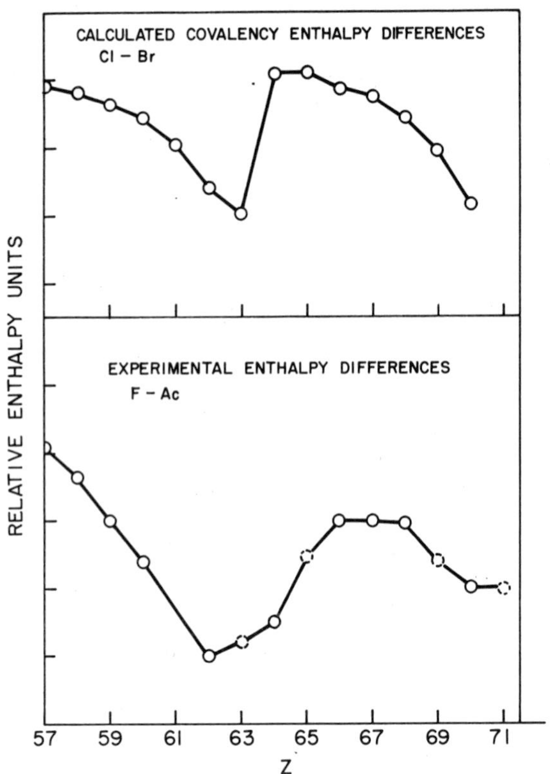

Figure 4. Comparison of the difference in enthalpies for the formation of LnF^{2+} and $LnAc^{2+}$ with the "covalence difference" between the chloride and bromide complexes in ethanol

used the above equation to predict the charge transfer energies of Ln^{3+}-Br^{-} in EtOH. From the results of Barnes (2) we have obtained the variation in the wavenumber of the chloride-to-lanthanide charge transfer bond. (*see* Table I.)

Using these results, it is possible to predict, qualitatively, the variation in the covalent contribution between the chloride and bromide complexes to ΔH complexation. We assume that the ground state energy of the complex may be written

$$E_{\text{complex}} = E(M^{3+}X^{-}) + CE(M^{2+}X)$$

and that C will vary approximately as $1/E$ (change transfer). Then the contribution $\Delta H_{\text{covalent}}$ to the observed ΔH should vary as

$$\left(\frac{1}{E_{CT}{}^{(a)}} - \frac{1}{E_{CT}{}^{(b)}}\right) = \frac{E^{(b)} - E^{(a)}}{E^{(a)}E^{(b)}}$$

Table VI. Predicted Variation in the Wavenumber of the First Electron Transfer Band of Ln^{3+}-X^- complexes in Ethanol ($X^- = Cl^-, Br^-$) Using the Equation $E = W - q(E - A) + C(q)D/13$

q	*Ion*	$C(q)$	$E(kK)Br^{-}$ (21)	$E(kK)Cl^-$	$\frac{E(Br^-) - E(Cl^-)}{E(Br^-) \times E(Cl^-)} (kK)^{-1} \times 10^3$
0	La^{3+}	0	70	71	−2.0
1	Ce^{3+}	−8	63	66	−7.2
2	Pr^{3+}	−16	56	61	−15.0
3	Nd^{3+}	−24	49 (49)*	55	−22.0
4	Pm^{3+}	−32	42	50	−38.0
5	Sm^{3+}	−40	35 (40.2)*	45 (45.7)*	−64.0
6	Eu^{3+}	−48	28 (31.2)*	36 (36.2)*	−79.0
7	Gd^{3+}	+48	73	71	+3.9
8	Tb^{3+}	+40	66	64	+4.7
9	Dy^{3+}	+32	59	61	−5.6
10	Ho^{3+}	+24	52	55	−10.0
11	Er^{3+}	+16	45	50	−22.0
12	Tm^{3+}	+8	38 (44.5)*	45	−41.0
13	Yb^{3+}	0	31 (35.5)*	40 (41.0)*	−73.0
				$W = 70$ kK $(E\text{-}A) = 3.0$ kK $D = 6.5$ kK	$W = 71$ kK $(E\text{-}A) = 2.4$ kK $D = 4.6$ kK

* Experimental values.

where the E's denote the charge transfer energies in the complexes a and b respectively. For a decrease in covalent character ($E^{(b)} > E^{(a)}$), ΔH_{cov} is positive.

In Table VI the results of this treatment are listed. Unfortunately, charge transfer data are not available for the complexes (fluoride and acetate) of interest. However, as a qualitative estimate of the manner in which ΔH_{cov} varies across the lanthanide series with change in the nature of the anion, we have plotted on relative scales the values in final column of Table VI and the differences in the enthalpies for the fluoride and acetate complexes (Figure 4). The similarity of the curves provides some evidence that the variation in enthalpy for the fluoride complexes compared with the oxyanion complexes is possibly attributed to a decrease in the covalent contribution as a result of the smaller nephelauxetic effect of fluoride compared to oxygen.

Acknowledgments

We wish to thank David Henrie for his assistance in the development of the argument on ΔH_{cov} trend.

Literature Cited

(1) Ahrland, S., Larsson, R., *Acta Chem. Scand.* **8,** 354 (1954).
(2) Barnes, J. C., *J. Chem. Soc.* **1964,** 3880 (1964).
(3) Bray, W. C., Hershey, A. V., *J. Am. Chem. Soc.* **56,** 1889 (1934).
(4) Brossett, C., Gustover, B., *Svensk. Kem. Tidskv.* **54,** 185 (1942).
(5) Choppin, G. R., Chopoorian, J. A., *J. Inorg. Nucl. Chem.* **22,** 97 (1961).
(6) Choppin, G. R., Friedman, H. G., *Inorg. Chem.* **5,** 1599 (1966).
(7) Choppin, G. R., Graffeo, A. J., *Inorg. Chem.* **4,** 1254 (1965).
(8) Choppin, G. R., Ketels, J., *J. Inorg. Nucl. Chem.* **27,** 1335 (1965).
(9) Choppin, G. R., Strazik, W. F., *Inorg. Chem.* **4,** 1250 (1965).
(10) Choppin, G. R., Unrein, P. J., *J. Inorg. Nucl. Chem.* **25,** 387 (1963).
(11) de Carvalho, R. G., Choppin, G. R., *J. Inorg. Nucl. Chem.* (to be published).
(12) Dodgen, H. W., Rollefson, G. K., *J. Am. Chem. Soc.* **71,** 2600 (1949).
(13) Henrie, D., Dissertation, Florida State University (1967).
(14) Jørgensen, C. K., *Mol. Phys.* **5,** 271 (1962).
(15) Kury, J. W., *Lawrence Radiation Lab. Rept.* **UCRL-2271** (1953).
(16) Kury, J. W., Hugus, Z. Z., Latimer, W. M., *Lawrence Radiation Lab. Rept.* **UCRL-3678** (1957).
(17) Leussing, D. L., Koltoff, I. M., *J. Am. Chem. Soc.* **75,** 2476 (1953).
(18) Low, G. W., Pryde, E. H., *J. Am. Chem. Soc.* **61,** 2237 (1939).
(19) Mayer, S. W., Schwartz, S. D., *J. Am. Chem. Soc.* **73,** 222 (1951).
(20) Paul, A. D., Gallo, L. S., Van Camp, J. B., *J. Phys. Chem.* **65,** 441 (1961).
(21) Pitzer, K. S., Brewer, L., "Thermodynamics," p. 400, McGraw-Hill, New York, 1961.
(22) Roth, W. A., *Ann.* **542,** 35 (1939).
(23) Schylter, K., *Trans. Roy. Inst. Technol., Stockholm, No.* **132** (1959).

RECEIVED October 17, 1966. Research supported by the Atomic Energy Commission [Contract AT-(40-1)-1797]. An NSF grant to the FSU Computing Center also provided support for the computations.

11

Volatile Rare Earth Chelates of β-Diketones

ROBERT E. SIEVERS, KENT J. EISENTRAUT, and CHARLES S. SPRINGER, JR.

Aerospace Research Laboratories, ARC, Wright-Patterson Air Force Base, Ohio

DEVON W. MEEK

Ohio State University, Columbus, Ohio

A number of volatile rare earth chelates containing the ligands, 1,1,1,2,2,3,3-heptafluoro-7,7-dimethyl-4,6-octanedione, [H(fod)], and 2,2,6,6-tetramethyl-3,5-heptanedione, [H(thd)] have been synthesized and investigated. The fod complexes are more volatile than other known compounds of the lanthanide elements. The fod complex of Sc(III) and the lanthanide thd compounds are anhydrous. The fod chelates of Y(III) and the lanthanides are isolated as hydrates but can easily be dehydrated in vacuo *over* P_4O_{10}. *Gas chromatographic and thermogravimetric data reveal that the volatilities of the complexes increase as the ionic radii of the metal ions become smaller.*

Gas chromatography is an effective technique in studying metal coordination compounds. It has been used in separating geometrical isomers, in kinetic and equilibrium measurements, in elucidating stoichiometry, in resolving optical isomers, in ultrapurification, in studies of metal-ligand interactions and the solvation of metal complexes, and in metal analysis at the ultra-trace level (*18*).

To be amenable to investigation by gas chromatography, metal compounds must be volatile and thermally and solvolytically stable at the temperatures necessary for reasonably rapid elution. Many metal chelates of β-diketones have been found to possess these properties and have been successfully chromatographed. Until recently, however, almost all gas chromatographic studies had been limited to complexes of the transition and representative elements because of the paucity of volatile, thermally stable, lanthanide compounds.

Among the many rare earth complexes of β-diketones that have been described (*1, 12, 15, 16*), the tris compounds generally have the most promising physical properties. Recently it has been demonstrated that the rare earth ions tend to accommodate extra donor groups easily to form complexes with coordination numbers larger than six (*1, 15*). Because of this proclivity, most of the tris bidentate complexes are isolated as hydrates. Noteworthy exceptions are the complexes of scandium(III); the acetylacetonate (*10*) and the trifluoroacetylacetonate (*18*) have been studied chromatographically. Our discussion will refer primarily to chelates of the lanthanides and yttrium.

Cunningham, Sands, and Wagner have recently reported the first x-ray crystallographic study of a tris rare earth(III) chelate (*6*). The yttrium ion in $[Y(acac)_3(H_2O)_2] \cdot H_2O$ (acac = the uninegative anion of 2,4-pentanedione), is eight-coordinate, being bonded to three acetylacetonate rings and two water molecules. The third water molecule associated with each complex is not coordinated to the metal ion but takes part in a chain of hydrogen bonds to link the molecules in pairs. The coordination polyhedron about the yttrium is a distorted square antiprism.

The presence of water has been postulated to cause the thermal instability of many of the hydrates (*3, 4, 20*), and attempts to chromatograph neodymium(III) trifluoroacetylacetonate dihydrate have failed (*23*). There is some evidence that hydrolysis occurs at elevated temperatures (*3, 4, 20*). Furthermore, there are indications that certain complexes undergo hydrolysis when allowed to stand *in vacuo*, even at room temperature (*20*). For these reasons the chelates are difficult to dehydrate by conventional means. Many of the claims in the older literature that anhydrous tris chelates were obtained must be considered questionable because the assignments of composition were either arbitrary or were based on analytical methods relatively insensitive to the amount of water present. Some investigators, however, have reported reasonably well-characterized anhydrous tris complexes (*4, 11, 15*), but most of these are not sufficiently volatile and stable to be chromatographed.

In the early stages of this research (*5, 18, 22*), it was reasoned that the nature of the ligand "shell" should greatly influence such physical properties of the complexes as volatility. This can be manifested in several ways, the most striking of which is the effect of incorporating fluorocarbon moieties in the ligand shell. A more subtle, but equally important facet of the "shell concept" is the control of the number and type of coordinated groups by judicious selection of ligands in which steric crowding becomes significant. This leads one to conclude that the most promising approach in preparing anhydrous, volatile tris complexes would be to choose ligands that are sufficiently bulky to decrease the likelihood that hydrates would be formed. A thorough investigation of the tris chelates of 15 tervalent rare earth metal ions with 2,2,6,6-tetramethyl-3,5-heptanedione, [H(thd)] (*see* Figure 4 for structure of anion), revealed that these compounds were isolated as anhydrous materials and led to the first successful separation and elution of lanthanide complexes by gas chromatography (*7*).

Incorporating fluorocarbon moieties increases the volatility of β-diketonate complexes (*18*). To retain the steric effect of the bulky thd ligands and to take advantage of the volatility effect of fluorocarbon substituents, the ligand, 1,1,1,2,2,3,3-heptafluoro-7,7-dimethyl-4,6-octanedione, [H(fod)] (*see* Figure 5 for structure of anion), was synthesized. Fifteen tris complexes of tervalent rare earth metal ions with this bulky fluorinated ligand have been prepared and studied. Their properties are compared with other rare earth complexes, principally those of thd.

Experimental

Syntheses. TRIS(2,2,6,6-TETRAMETHYL-3,5-HEPTANEDIONATO)LN(III) COMPLEXES.

The syntheses of the rare earth thd complexes have been reported earlier (*7*).

TETRAKIS(2,2,6,6-TETRAMETHYL-3,5-HEPTANEDIONATO)ZR(IV). The Zr(IV) thd complex was prepared by a ligand substitution reaction involving Zr(IV) acetylacetonate and H(thd). Zirconium(IV) acetylacetonate was freshly purified by precipitation from hot benzene upon adding low boiling petroleum ether. The melting point (195°–198°C.) agreed with the literature value (*26*). A quantity (4.88 grams, 0.01 mole) was dissolved in 120 ml. of carbon tetrachloride. An excess of H(thd) (9.21 grams, 0.05 mole) was added to the solution, which was then warmed in an evaporating dish on a steam bath under a stream of air until a powdery solid remained. After adding 2.8 grams (0.015 mole) of fresh H(thd) and 40 ml. carbon tetrachloride, the above procedure was repeated. The resulting solid was exposed to the atmosphere for four days with occasional stirring and crushing with a stirring rod. The yield of this crude product was 7.7 grams, which corresponded to 93.4% yield (based on $Zr(acac)_4$). The crude product was recrystallized from boiling ethanol upon cooling in a refrigerator. The resulting white crystalline material was collected by filtration, washed with ethanol, and dried for one hour *in vacuo* at room temperature (m.p. 336°–342°C.). The NMR spectrum in CCl_4 exhibits peaks at 1.08 [$C(CH_3)_3$, rel. area-72] and 5.69 (CH, rel. area-3.6) p.p.m. downfield from the internal standard, tetramethylsilane. The molecular weight measured in benzene was 818 (theoretical, 824). Anal. calc. for $Zr(thd)_4$, $ZrC_{44}H_{76}O_8$: Zr, 11.07; C, 64.11; H, 9.29. Found: Zr, 11.11; C, 64.16; H, 9.22.

1,1,1,2,2,3,3-HEPTAFLUORO-7,7-DIMETHYL-4,6-OCTANEDIONE. 1,1,1,2,2,-3,3-Heptafluoro-7,7-dimethyl-4,6-octanedione was prepared by a Claisen condensation (*19*). Anhydrous sodium methoxide (MCB = Matheson Coleman, and Bell) (54.03 grams, 1 mole) was suspended in approximately 400 ml. of diethyl ether. One mole (100.16 grams) of pinacolone (MCB) was added slowly to this stirred slurry. A dark red, cloudy solution resulted. To this solution, 242.11 grams (1 mole) of ethyl heptafluorobutyrate (Peninsular Chem. Research, Inc.) was added dropwise. The solution remained tomato-red. When stirring ceased, a light yellow solid settled to the bottom of the reaction vessel, leaving a clear, dark red solution. The mixture was allowed to stand overnight. A solution of 55 ml. of 18*M* H_2SO_4 in approximately 800 ml. of distilled water was added to the solution with stirring. A light yellow organic layer separated above the clear, colorless aqueous layer. Both layers were slightly acidic. The aqueous layer was washed three times with a total of approximately 250 ml. of diethyl ether. The washings were combined with the organic layer, and the whole mixture was distilled under vacuum on a 12″ Vigreaux column. After two subsequent fractional distillations a middle fraction [weighing 193.9 grams (65.5%) B.P. 33°C./2.7mm.] of clear colorless liquid with a pungent odor was obtained.

The colorless product darkened upon standing for several days (even when stored in a dark bottle) but no decomposition products could be detected in the proton NMR spectrum. [The following peaks were observed for the completely enolized neat sample: 1.23 [$C(CH_3)_3$, rel. area-9.00], 6.09 (CH, rel. area-0.96), 14.76 (OH, rel. area-0.93); (peak positions are given in p.p.m. downfield from the internal standard tetramethylsilane).] The physical properties were identical with those of an analyzed sample synthesized by a different method (*24*). The yield of this reaction was found to be fairly insensitive to the order of adding pinacolone and ethyl heptafluorobutyrate.

TRIS(1,1,1,2,2,3,3-HEPTAFLUORO-7,7-DIMETHYL-4,6-OCTANEDIONATO)-MONOAQUO LN(III) [ALSO Y(III)] COMPLEXES AND TRIS(1,1,1,2,2,3,3-HEPTAFLUORO-7,7-DIMETHYL-4,6-OCTANEDIONATO)LN(III) [ALSO Y(III) AND SC(III)] COMPLEXES. All of the rare earth fod chelates were synthesized by the following general method. The hydrated rare earth(III) nitrate was prepared as described before (7), and 0.011 mole was dissolved in the minimum amount of absolute methanol (MCB). The pH of the resulting solution was adjusted (pH paper) to a value between 4 and 6 by adding a solution of 4.12*M* aqueous NaOH. In another vessel, H(fod) (0.033 mole) was dissolved in approximately 20 ml. of absolute methanol. This solution was neutralized with 8.01 ml. of 4.12*M* NaOH solution. The two solutions were mixed with stirring. The entire mixture was added dropwise over a period of approximately two hours to *ca.* 400 ml. of distilled water which was stirred rapidly. The solid complex precipitated, and the mixture was stirred until the precipitate was in the form of fine granules. The resulting mixture was suction filtered with an aspirator and air dried for approximately one hour. The product isolated was the monohydrate [except for $Sc(fod)_3$ which was isolated as an anhydrous light yellow oil]. The yields of crude products averaged *ca.* 87% and ranged from *ca.* 74% to essentially quantitative.

The crude product was twice recrystallized from the minimum amount of methylene chloride (Baker "Analyzed" or MCB "Spectroquality") necessary to dissolve it at room temperature by cooling to a temperature $< 0°C$. The crystals were dried *in vacuo* for approximately 12 hours between each crystallization. The purified product was dehydrated in a vacuum desiccator over P_4O_{10} for one week.

EUROPIUM(III) COMPLEXES OF OTHER β-DIKETONES. The complexes, $(C_2H_5)_3NH[Eu(hfa)_4]$ and $(CH_3)_4N[Eu(hfa)_4]$, were synthesized by the methods described by Melby, Rose, Abramson, and Caris (*15*). The tris bidentate chelates, $Eu(tfa)_3 \cdot 2H_2O$, and $Eu(tta)_3 \cdot 3H_2O$, were obtained commercially (Distillation Products Industries) and were analyzed prior to use. The ligands corresponding to the various symbols are as follows: tfa—1,1,1-trifluoro-2,4-pentanedionate, hfa—1,1,1,5,5,5-hexafluoro-2,4-pentanedionate, and tta—4,4,4-trifluoro-1(2-thienyl)-1,3-butanedionate.

Characterization of thd and fod Complexes. The rare earth thd and fod chelates were characterized by the following measurements: elemental analyses, molecular weights, infrared spectra, nuclear magnetic resonance spectra on the Sc, Lu, Y, and La chelates, Karl Fischer titrations, and melting points. Detailed properties and elemental analyses have been described elsewhere (*7, 24*).

Gas Chromatography. All gas chromatographic data were obtained on an F and M Model #810 research chromatograph. All columns were constructed of Teflon (DuPont) tubing of 4.5 mm. i.d. The carrier gas used was helium which had been passed through molecular sieves. Specific conditions for a particular experiment are given under Results.

Thermogravimetric Analyses. All thermogravimetric analytical data were obtained on a DuPont Model #950 Thermogravimetric Analyzer. The atmosphere over the sample was helium gas which had been passed through molecular sieves. The helium flow rate was kept constant throughout all experiments at 60 ml./min., and the sample heating rate was 10°C./min. Attempts were made to keep the sample masses used as nearly the same as possible (10 mg.), to maximize comparability.

Results

The lanthanide thd chelates were isolated as anhydrous complexes, $M(thd)_3$ (*7*). The fod chelates (except for that of Sc) were isolated as monohydrates, $M(fod)_3 \cdot H_2O$. This stoichiometry was confirmed by Karl Fischer titrations, elemental analyses, and infrared spectroscopy.

Careful examination of thermograms obtained from hydrated fod samples reveals a 1–2% weight loss at temperatures in the vicinity of 100°C. This suggests the volatilization of the mole of water present. (Percentages of water calculated for monohydrated formulations range from 1.67 for the Lu complex to 1.81 for that of Y.) The resulting anhydrous compounds vaporize without apparent decomposition. Mass spectroscopic results for the hydrated fod chelate of lutetium show a large water peak and a parent ion mass peak ($m/e = 1057$, the theoretical mass of $Lu(fod)_3$ is 1061) (*14*). No peak is observed in the higher mass region corresponding to the parent ion of $Lu(fod)_3 \cdot H_2O$ ($m/e = 1079$), indicating that the hydrate dissociates at the temperature and pressure of the ion source. The rest of the spectrum is similar to those of the thd chelates. Also Karl Fischer titrations of $M(fod)_3$ samples stored *in vacuo* over P_4O_{10} for over a week show no detectable water. From these data, it is apparent that the $M(fod)_3 \cdot H_2O$ compounds can be dehydrated at elevated temperatures and/or reduced pressures with no appreciable hydrolysis. The anhydrous compounds are hygroscopic in the atmosphere, causing some properties such as melting point and percentage of hydrogen as determined by elemental analysis to be sensitive functions of the history of the sample. The melting points of the fod chelates given in Table I illustrate this effect; they are lowered, in some cases rather drastically, by the presence of water. The values reported in the last column of Table I are the lowest observed. This same phenomenon has been noted for different rare earth β-diketonate complexes by other investigators (*4, 11, 20*). Hydration and dehydration of the fod complexes appear to be totally reversible processes; the melting points of the hydrated and anhydrous states of a particular fod chelate can be reproduced by drying or exposing to the atmosphere as necessary. The rather wide melting range exhibited by any particular fod compound in either state is further indicative of the sensitivity of the compounds to moisture.

The molecular weight data obtained for the fod chelates in chloroform (Table II) show that the species present are discrete monomers. No evidence of polymeric species in solutions of the thd compounds was found (*7*).

Both series of compounds can be vacuum sublimed between 100 and 200°C.; however, sublimation should be viewed as a fairly stringent purification method for the fod compounds because of their relatively lower thermal stability as compared with the thd complexes. While the thd chelates are thermally stable to *ca.* 300°C., the fod compounds decompose at temperatures only slightly above 200°C.

The results of a gas chromatographic study are shown in Figure 1. The logarithms of the absolute retention times and the retention volumes relative to the hydrocarbon, eicosane (n-$C_{20}H_{42}$), are plotted against the ionic radii of the six coordinate, terpositive metal ions (*25*) for most of the thd and fod chelates. The following conditions were employed: column, 14 cm. long, packed with 10% (w/w) SE-30 (a polydimethylsiloxane supplied by General Electric) on Chromosorb W (Johns-Manville, 60/80 mesh); carrier gas flow rate, 100 ml./min.; column temperature, 171°C.; thermal conductivity detector temperature, 227°C.; injection port temperature, 230°C. The anhydrous fod chelates were dissolved in benzene which had been dried over molecular sieves #13X (Linde), and these samples were injected with a microsyringe. Sample sizes of saturated solutions ranged from 0.1 to 2 μliters. Similar results were obtained for the thd chelates on a column containing 10% (w/w) Apiezon N (a mixture of high molecular weight hydrocarbons supplied by The J. G. Biddle Co.) on Gas-Pack F (*7*).

Table I. Melting Points of thd and fod Rare Earth Complexes

Metal Ion (M)	*Melting Point (°C.)* $M(thd)_3$ [a]	$M(fod)_3$ [b]	$M(fod)_3 \cdot H_2O$ [c]
Sc	152–155	<25	<25
Lu	172–174	118–125	111–115
Yb	166–169	125–132	112–115
Tm	171.5–173.5	140–146	110–115
Er	179–181	158–164	104–112
Y	169–172.5	162–167	108–112
Ho	180–182.5	172–178	103–111
Dy	180–183.5	180–188	103–107
Tb	177–180	190–196	92–97
Gd	182–184	203–213 [d]	60–65
Eu	187–189	205–212 [d]	59–67
Sm	195.5–198.5	208–218 [d]	63–67
Nd	215–218 [e]	210–215 [d]	210–215 [d]
Pr	222–224 [e]	218–225 [d]	218–225 [d]
La	238–248 [e]	215–230 [d]	215–230 [d]

[a] As isolated (7).
[b] Stored *in vacuo* over P_4O_{10} for at least one week.
[c] Exposed to the atmosphere for at least one day, after dehydration as in *b*.
[d] Sample melted with decomposition.
[e] Taken in a sealed, evacuated capillary tube.

Table II. Molecular Weights of fod Rare Earth Complexes

Metal Ion	*Theoretical* [a]	*Found* [b]
Y	992	990
La	1042	1052
Pr	1044	1050
Nd	1048	1042
Sm	1054	1049
Eu	1056	1050
Gd	1061	1060
Tb	1062	1058
Dy	1066	1054
Ho	1068	1060
Er	1071	1059
Tm	1072	1060
Yb	1077	1065
Lu	1079	1070

[a] Calculated for the monohydrated species, $M(fod)_3 \cdot H_2O$.
[b] Measured in chloroform solutions of samples which had been dried *ca.* 4 hours *in vacuo* over silica gel (not P_4O_{10} as in the foregoing).

A chromatogram showing the elution of $Yb(thd)_3$ and the hydrocarbon, tetracosane (n-$C_{24}H_{50}$), is illustrated in Figure 2. This column was 15 cm. long, contained an Apiezon liquid phase and was thermostated at 185°C.

The thermogravimetric curves of several europium compounds and tetracosane are shown in Figure 3. The thermograms of some of the tris rare earth thd chelates and the tetrakis zirconium compound are presented in Figure 4, and those of the tris fod chelates are shown in Figure 5.

Discussion

The thermograms of $Eu(tfa)_3 \cdot 2H_2O$ and $Eu(tta)_3 \cdot 3H_2O$ (Figure 3) show clearly the thermal instability problems which have been attributed to water of hydration in some rare earth β-diketonate hydrates. It will be noted that large percentages of residues still remain at temperatures above 450°C. Charles and Ohlmann (*3*) showed a similar curve for $Eu(tta)_3 \cdot 2H_2O$ and postulated the following equations to explain the two major breaks in the curve. Equation 1 is

$$Eu(tta)_3 \cdot 2H_2O \xrightarrow{\sim 100^\circ C.} Eu(tta)_3 \cdot H_2O + H_2O \quad (1)$$

$$Eu(tta)_3 \cdot H_2O \xrightarrow{\sim 250^\circ C.} Eu(tta)_2OH + H(tta) \quad (2)$$

the simple dissociation of 1 mole of water while Equation 2 involves the hydrolysis by the remaining mole of water to produce the nonvolatile basic compound. Pope, Steinbach, and Wagner (*20*) have shown that such reactions occur in the acetylacetonate cases.

In contrast with the unstable complexes, the tris complexes of thd and fod, even though the latter are isolated as hydrates, are completely volatilized with no apparent decomposition. In the light of the obvious ease of dehydration of the fod complexes, there is some doubt that the water is coordinated to the metal ion. An alternate possibility is that in the case of the bulky fod complexes the water molecule may instead be hydrogen-bonded to an electronegative site on the ligand shell. If this is true, it would appear that the bulky thd and fod ligands have effectively blocked the access to additional coordination sites on the metal ion.

It has been suggested that the bulky *tert*-butyl groups in thd complexes prevent more than three ligands from approaching the lanthanide ion (*1*). This hypothesis was advanced to account for unsuccessful attempts to synthesize tetrakis complexes of thd with trivalent lanthanides. The synthesis of $Zr(thd)_4$ reported here demonstrates that it is possible to introduce a fourth thd group and indicates that there is still a significant amount of room available in the tris lanthanide complexes. Crowding must be considered only in relative terms, however, and this observation does not affect the earlier contention that steric crowding decreases the likelihood of hydrate formation. The thermodynamics of steric repulsion must be weighed against the thermodynamics of ligand-metal bond formation. Steric factors would be expected to be more readily manifested for the association of a neutral ligand with the neutral tris complex of a tervalent ion than for an anionic ligand satisfying the charge requirements of quadrivalent zirconium. Furthermore, the hydrophobic character of the ligand shell, as manifested in $M(thd)_3$, may well minimize the likelihood of hydrate formation.

The apparent volatility of the triethylammonium tetrakis (hexafluoroacetylacetonato)europate(III) complex (*21*) (Figure 3) is especially interesting when compared with the nonvolatile tetramethylammonium analog. One could conceive of the following equilibrium

$$Et_3NH[Eu(hfa)_4] \rightleftharpoons Et_3N + Eu(hfa)_3 + H(hfa) \qquad (3)$$

as explaining these observations. It is expected that increasing the temperature would continually drive the equilibrium toward the side favored

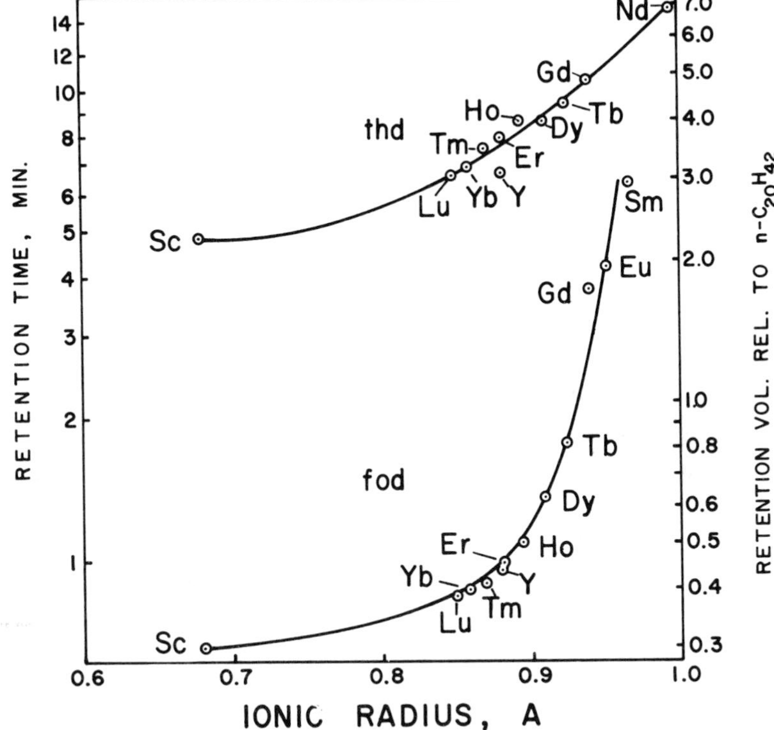

Figure 1. Gas chromatographic retention data as a function of ionic radius (25). Column temperature: 171°C. Liquid phase: SE–30, Helium flow rate: 100 ml./min. For detailed conditions, see Results section

by the removal of the more volatile products by the carrier gas. Because the tetramethylammonium analog cannot enter a similar equilibrium, it shows no tendency to vaporize under comparable conditions, and at considerably higher temperatures it eventually decomposes. However, Lippard has recently reported the sublimation, at temperatures between 180° and 230°C., of $Cs[Y(hfa)_4]$, which apparently can exist in the gas phase as a stable ion pair (*13*). Consequently, the mode of vaporization of the triethylammonium compound is not presently known with certainty.

Of greater interest are the orders of elution of the tris complexes evidenced in Figure 1. The trend of lower retention time with decreasing ionic radius reported by Eisentraut and Sievers (*7*) is reaffirmed for both the thd and the fod systems. It will be noted that the retention data cannot be correlated with mass. The retention times of the yttrium points are correlative in the ionic radius plots but are anomalous in the analogous atomic number or mass curves.

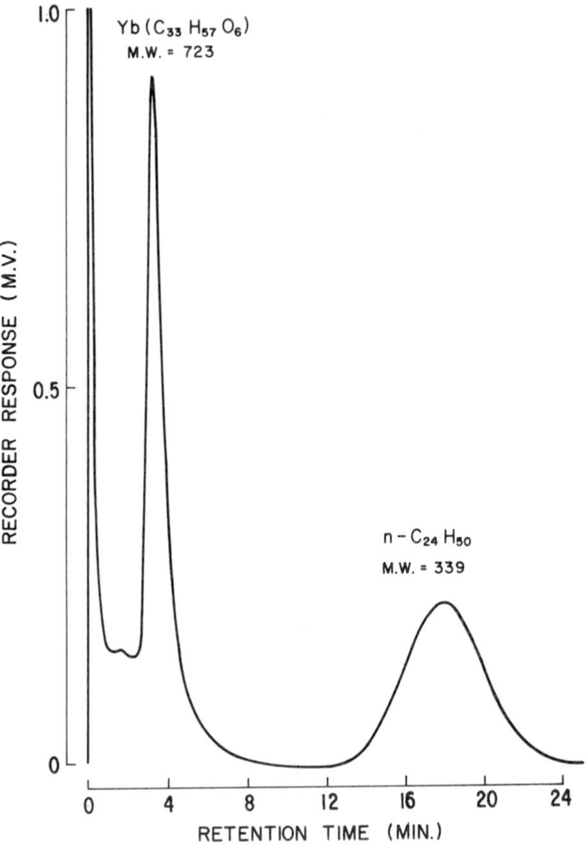

Figure 2. Gas chromatographic elution of Yb(thd)₃ and tetracosane. Column temperature: 185°C.

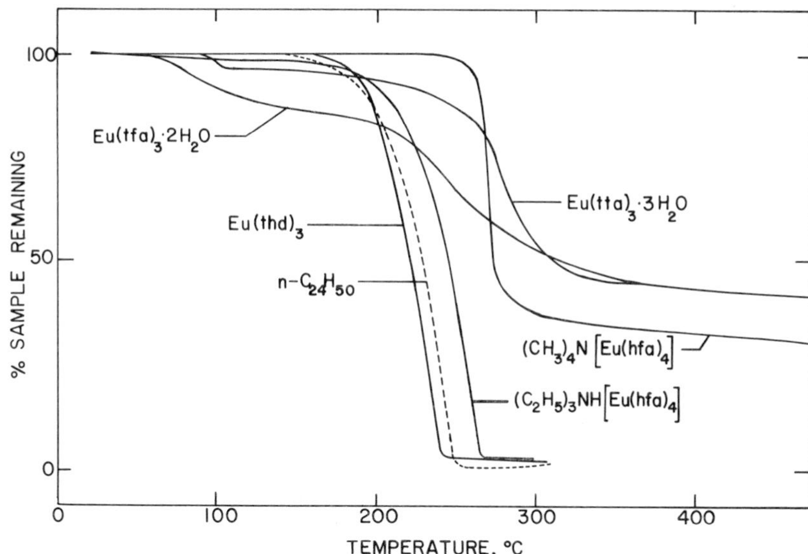

Figure 3. Thermogravimetric curves of some europium(III) β-diketonate complexes

The thermogravimetric analytical data exhibited in Figures 4 and 5 show that the trend in volatility arising from the lanthanide contraction is real and not a specific solution effect (*17*). The chelates of the larger metal ions are vaporized at higher temperatures than those of smaller radius. The only exception to this trend is the thermogram of $Sc(fod)_3$ which is not shown in Figure 5 but is almost coincidental with the curve for $Tm(fod)_3$. It is interesting to observe in the chromatographic experiment (Figure 1) that the $Sc(fod)_3$ retention time occupies its predicted position in the radii plot.

The reasons for the correlation of volatility with size of metal ion are not entirely clear, but we wish to offer the following hypotheses. One might assume that in going from the larger lanthanides to the smaller members the local dipoles present in the molecules either become smaller or are more efficiently shielded, so as to cause a decrease in intermolecular attractive forces.

An alternate explanation assumes that variations in the position of possible monomer $\rightleftharpoons$ polymer equilibria with ionic radius cause the observed trend in volatility. There is longstanding evidence that acetylacetonate chelates of the lanthanides tend to polymerize in solution (*2*, *9*), the molecular weight values (*2*) being anomalously high. Filipescu, Hurt, and McAvoy (*8*) have recently found other examples of what appear to be monomer-dimer equilibria. Considering the trend in volatility one can image that monomer $\rightleftharpoons$ polymer transformations could take

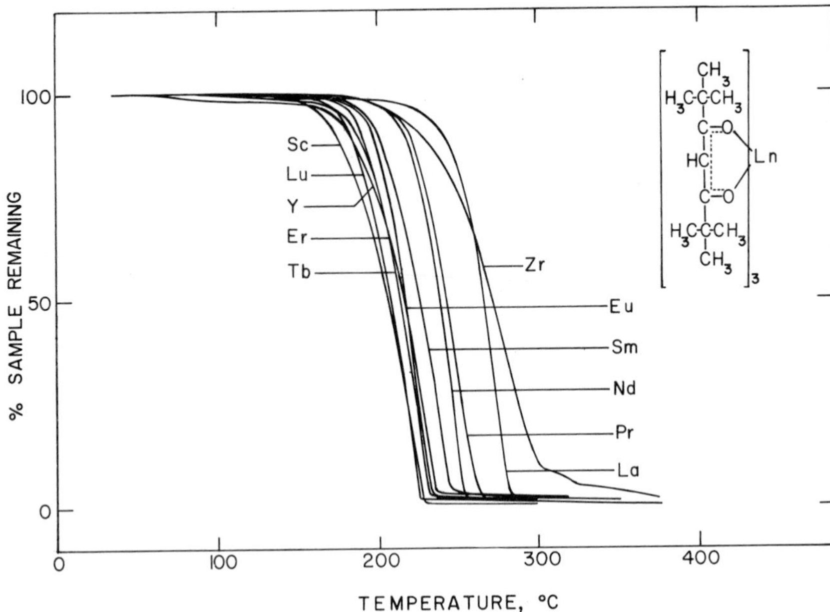

Figure 4. Thermogravimetric curves of some rare earth thd complexes

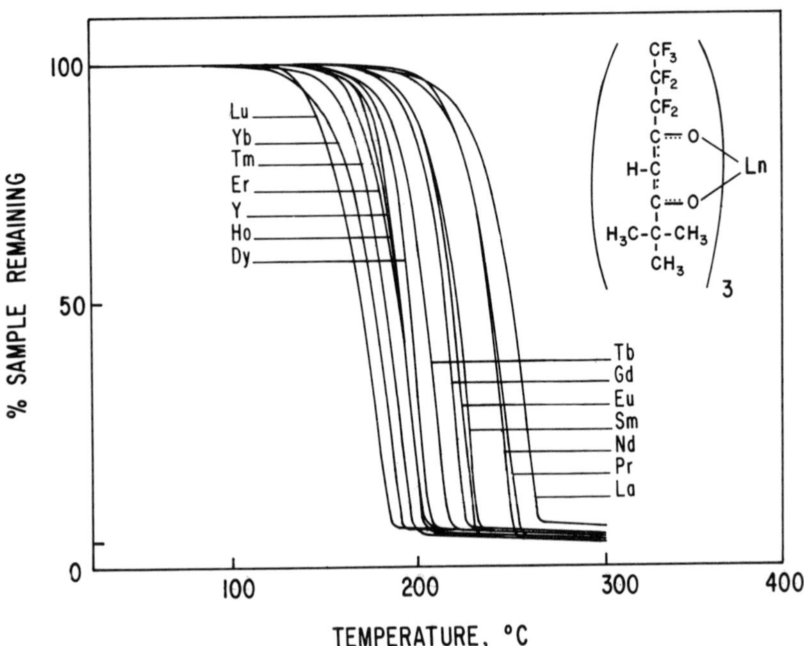

Figure 5. Thermogravimetric curves of the rare earth fod complexes

place in the condensed phase (solid, liquid, or solution as in the chromatographic experiments) in equilibrium with the monomeric gaseous species. If, for example, the lanthanum complex were to polymerize more extensively than the more compact lutetium compound, it could exhibit a lower apparent vapor pressure. We have concluded that this hypothesis is in all probability incorrect, on the basis of the molecular weight data discussed in the Results section and presented in Table II. There is no evidence for polymer formation in any of the complexes examined in the present study.

Most of the fod chelates are eluted before eicosane (Figure 1). Figure 2 shows that even in the less volatile thd system, where the presence of fluorine does not complicate matters, $Yb(thd)_3$ is eluted before tetracosane. This is shown to be the true order of volatilities of these compounds by the thermograms in Figures 3 and 4. Figure 3 shows that $Eu(thd)_3$ vaporizes at lower temperatures than tetracosane under identical conditions, while Figure 4 indicates the volatilization at lower temperatures of $Yb(thd)_3$ as compared with $Eu(thd)_3$.

Figure 1 also confirms the well established fact that fluorinating the β-diketonate ligand increases the ease of elution of the corresponding metal complex from gas chromatographic columns (*18*). Any particular $M(fod)_3$ chelate is eluted well before its thd analog. Similarly, a comparison of Figures 4 and 5 indicates the increased volatility of the fluorocarbon compounds relative to their equivalent hydrocarbon analogs. The fod chelates are the most volatile rare earth compounds yet reported. The occurrence of a number of highly electronegative fluorine atoms in the coordination shell of the metal ion apparently reduces the intermolecular forces.

Literature Cited

(1) Bauer, H., Blanc, J., Ross, D. L., *J. Am. Chem. Soc.* **86**, 5125 (1964).
(2) Biltz, W., *Ann.* **331**, 334 (1904).
(3) Charles, R. G., Ohlmann, R. C., *J. Inorg. Nucl. Chem.* **27**, 255 (1965).
(4) Charles, R. G., Perrotto, A., *J. Inorg. Nucl. Chem.* **26**, 373 (1964).
(5) *Chem. Eng. News* **40**, 50 (April 2, 1962).
(6) Cunningham, J. A., Sands, D. E., Wagner, W. F., *Inorg. Chem.* **6**, 499 (1967).
(7) Eisentraut, K. J., Sievers, R. E., *J. Am. Chem. Soc.* **87**, 5254 (1965).
(8) Filipescu, N., Hurt, C. R., McAvoy, N., *J. Inorg. Nucl. Chem.* **28**, 1753 (1966).
(9) Freed, S., Weissman, S. I., Fortess, F. E., *J. Am. Chem. Soc.* **63**, 1079 (1941).
(10) Fujinaga, T., Kuwamoto, T., Ono, Y., *Nippon Kagaku Zasshi* **86**, 1294 (1965).
(11) Halverson, F., Brinen, J. S., Leto, J. R., *J. Chem. Phys.* **40**, 2790 (1964).
(12) Hammond, G. S., Nonhebel, D. C., Wu, C. S., *Inorg. Chem.* **2**, 73 (1963).
(13) Lippard, S. J., *J. Am. Chem. Soc.* **88**, 4300 (1966).

(14) Margrave, J. L., Rice University, Houston, Tex. (private communication).
(15) Melby, L. R., Rose, N. J., Abramson, E., Caris, J. C., *J. Am. Chem. Soc.* **86**, 5117 (1964).
(16) Moeller, T., Martin, D. F., Thompson, L. C., Ferrús, R., Feistel, G. R., Randall, W. J., *Chem. Rev.* **65**, 1 (1965).
(17) Moshier, R. W., Gere, D. R., "Abstracts of Papers," 152nd Meeting, ACS, Sept. 1966, p. B 60.
(18) Moshier, R. W., Sievers, R. E., "Gas Chromatography of Metal Chelates," Pergamon Press, Oxford, 1965.
(19) Park, J. D., Brown, H. A., Lacher, J. R., *J. Am. Chem. Soc.* **75**, 4753 (1953).
(20) Pope, G. W., Steinbach, J. F., Wagner, W. F., *J. Inorg. Nucl. Chem.* **20**, 304 (1961).
(21) Rose, N. J., University of Washington, Seattle, Wash. (private communication).
(22) Sievers, R. E., Ponder, B. W., Moshier, R. W., "Abstracts of Papers," 141st Meeting, ACS, March 1962, p. 35M.
(23) Sievers, R. E., Wheeler, Jr., G., Ross, W. D., "Advances in Gas Chromatography, 1965," A. Zlatkis, L. Ettre, eds., Preston Technical Publishing Co., Evanston, Ill., 1966.
(24) Springer, Jr., C. S., Meek, D. W., Sievers, R. E., *Inorg. Chem.* **6**, 1105 (1967).
(25) Topp, N. E., "The Chemistry of the Rare Earth Elements," p. 12, Elsevier Publishing Co., New York, 1965.
(26) Young, R. C., Arch, A., "Inorganic Syntheses, Vol. II, p. 121, McGraw-Hill, New York, 1946.

RECEIVED October 17, 1966. Abstracted in part from a thesis submitted by Charles S. Springer, Jr. to the Graduate School of The Ohio State University in partial fulfillment of the requirements for the degree of Doctor of Philosophy. This research was supported in part by the A.R.L. In-House Independent Laboratory Research Funds, Office of Aerospace Research, U. S. Air Force.

12

Europium Chelates as Laser Materials

DANIEL L. ROSS and JOSEPH BLANC

RCA Laboratories, Princeton, N. J.

A variety of lasers based on tetrakis β-diketonates of Eu^{3+} have been developed over the last few years. A summary of the chemistry and energy transfer in these laser systems is presented, with particular attention to the salts of tetrakis benzoyltrifluoroacetone chelates of europium. Chemical effects attributed to solvents, benzene ring substitutions in the ligand, differing cations, and deuteration are considered. These effects manifest themselves most markedly in the variability of laser thresholds from compound to compound and solvent to solvent. The thresholds reflect association-dissociation equilibria, as well as energy transfer processes in the ligand and throughout the manifold of Eu^{3+} states.

Considerable work over the past few years has been stimulated by Weissman's observation (*35*) that ultraviolet excitation of organic chelates of europium brings about efficient intramolecular energy transfer from ligand excited states to europium emissive levels and by the suggestions of Whan and Crosby (*36*) and Schimitschek (*34*) that europium chelates could be the basis of laser systems. This research has resulted in the demonstration of laser action by solutions of chelates of europium with benzoylacetone (*20*), dibenzoylmethane (*30*), trifluoroacetylacetone (*31*), thenoyltrifluoroacetone (*31*), and benzoyltrifluoroacetone and its ring-substituted derivatives (*25, 28, 31, 33*). Laser activity was observed initially at temperatures near −140°C. Recently, room temperature operation (*28*) of europium chelate lasers has been observed, and the possibility of a circulating, room temperature liquid chelate laser, a feature which should permit long term, repetitive flashing by externally cooling the solution, has been demonstrated (*32*).

One significant advance in the field of lanthanide chemistry resulting from research in this area is the unequivocal demonstration that the trivalent lanthanides prefer to show a coordination number of eight in their reaction with bidentate ligands such as β-diketones and ortho phenanthroline (*1, 22*). All of the successful laser systems have required the use of compounds of the type C^+ $[(\beta\text{-diketono})_4Eu]^-$ as the active species, where C^+ is a cation, either substituted ammonium, or, in one case, Na^+ (*27*). In the case of the benzoylacetonates and dibenzoylmethides, the tris chelates have been shown to be inactive and to have quite different spectroscopic properties (*2, 23, 30*).

Several articles (*29*) point out that the most significant property of these compounds which limits their usefulness as laser materials is their high ultraviolet extinction coefficients, necessitating the use of extremely thin sections of liquid (*ca.* 1-6 mm.) to achieve uniform excitation of the solutions containing the concentration of chelate required (*ca.* $10^{-2}M$) for laser action. At present, it appears that no attempts to overcome this fundamental limitation by using other europium derivatives with lower extinction coefficients or by different energy transfer paths (*12, 16*) have met with success. The wide range of spectroscopic and chemical behavior to be found within this general class of compounds suggests that fruitful work can be done toward optimizing those properties which are required for efficient laser performance of the tetrakis β-diketono europium chelates (*9, 21*).

We shall discuss the results of investigating the effects of chemical changes on the performance and spectroscopic properties of europium chelate laser materials. Much of our work has been done with the salts of tetrakis chelates of europium with benzoyltrifluoroacetone (BTFA). These materials were chosen for study because the high room temperature photoluminescent quantum efficiency of europium fluorinated diketone derivatives, and the fact that several of them had been observed to lase at room temperature (in acetonitrile) suggested that, by working at low temperatures, we might be allowed considerable freedom in investigating the effect of varying a number of the chemical properties of this system without its being prevented, *via* excessive nonradiative energy losses, from exhibiting laser action. The chemical effects to be considered here are those of solvent, ligand benzene-ring substitution, the cation, and deuteration.

For the work discussed in the following sections, we have used as low temperature laser solvents for BTFA chelates a 2:1:1 mixture of β-ethoxypropionitrile, β-ethoxyethanol, and acetonitrile, (EEA), which forms a clear medium to about 135°K., and a mixture, reported by Samelson, Lempicki, and Brecher (*26*), of equal parts of propionitrile, butyronitrile, and isobutyronitrile ("nitrile solvent") which seems to remain clear at lower temperatures.

Effect of Solvent

The dissociation of tetrakis chelates into mixtures of nonlasing tris chelates (and possibly lower forms) and free diketonate anion in solution has been discussed extensively by Brecher, Samelson, and Lempicki (*5, 26*). These workers have shown that the degree of dissociation of a given compound is markedly affected by the nature of the solvent. For example, the piperidinium salt of europium tetrakis benzoylacetonate was found to be 37% dissociated into tris or lower forms in a 3:1 ethanol-methanol solution at 93°K., while adding dimethyl formamide to this system increased the dissociation to 82%. Similarly, the dibenzoylmethane derivative showed a change from 43 to 51% dissociation for the two solvent mixtures. In this latter case, however, the reduction in efficiency caused by the increase in dissociation is more than compensated for by a different effect—that of an interaction between the dimethylformamide and the remaining tetrakis chelate ions (possibly to form a nine-coordinate complex), which results in a change in the symmetry about the europium ion and thus the emission spectrum. The net effect is a considerable decrease in the laser threshold of the alcohol-dimethylformamide solution. [By the term "laser threshold" we mean that amount of energy (in these cases, the ultraviolet light provided by a xenon flash tube) which must be delivered to the laser device to bring it to the point at which the onset of laser action is observed.]

The piperidinium benzoyltrifluoroacetone derivative shows even more interesting behavior. In the alcohol mixture, it is completely dissociated. Adding dimethylformamide decreases the degree of dissociation to 47%, while a solution of this compound in nitrile solvents (in which the benzoylactonate is found to be completely dissociated) even at room temperature, is less than 10% dissociated. The high inherent quantum efficiency of this and closely related fluorinated chelates (*15*), and the specific beneficial effect of nitrile solvents has permitted laser action to occur at room temperature with, for example, piperidinium $(BTFA)_4Eu$ in acetonitrile (*28*).

It appears that dissociation of tetrakis chelates in solution to give free ligand anions (which show phosphorescence lifetimes long with respect to those of ion fluorescence) (*4*) is responsible for reports of the observation of both molecular phosphorescence and ion fluorescence from solutions of certain europium β-diketonates, the unequal lifetimes of which led to the suggestion that energy transfer to the europium ion came from a different triplet level (or a higher triplet level) than that from which phosphorescence is observed.

In some cases, solvent molecules take part in a chemical reaction with the chelate. Fry and Pirie (*14*) have shown that both heat and ultraviolet light brought about the formation of acetophenone and ethyl acetate (reverse Claisen condensation of the ligands) in a solution of europium tris benzoylacetonate in 3:1 ethanol-methanol and that this reaction, probably the cause of the "aging" of these solutions noted by Lempicki and Samelson (*19*), was accelerated by adding piperidine.

Besides influencing the proportion of tetrakis chelate present in solution, solvents can also play a role in the nonradiative deactivation of the excited states of the chelate molecule especially at higher temperatures. Before intramolecular energy transfer takes place, the ligand singlet and triplet states are vulnerable to quenching. If the solvent molecules have energy levels below those of the ligands, simple quenching by energy transfer from ligand triplet to quencher triplet can occur as demonstrated by Bhaumik and El-Sayed (*3*) who observed that *cis*-piperylene quenched the fluorescence of europium thenoyltrifluoroacetone and trifluoroacetylacetone derivatives.

Vibrational interactions of the solvent with the electronic states of the chelate may also be expected to be a source of deactivation. This may partially account for the shorter lifetimes and lower quantum efficiencies reported for tris chelates which, lacking the fourth ligand, are less well shielded from the solvent. This process should increase in importance as the gap increases between the triplet energy level and the upper ion level which receives this energy (*see* discussion below). We have observed (Table III) that while the quantum yield of fluorescence from $(BTFA)_4Eu$ chelates increases by about 40% in EEA on cooling from room temperature to 165°K. it changes only 10% in the "nitrile solvent," and the lifetime change is about 10% in either solvent. Part of this difference may be caused by greater dissociation at room temperature in EEA (possibly caused by the presence of the β-ethoxyethanol), but there is a small but measurable difference in the triplet levels (as determined by measuring the phosphorescence of the gadolinium chelates) in the two solvents. In EEA, the triplet lies slightly below the $^5D_2$ Eu level, but in the nitrile solvent there is an essentially exact match of these two levels.

The Effect of Ring Substituent

We prepared a number of derivatives of benzoyltrifluoroacetone bearing substituents on the meta and para positions of the benzene ring and converted these to the corresponding europium tetrakis chelates. Schimitschek (*33*) has studied the nine BTFA derivatives obtained by substituting fluorine, chlorine, or bromine at the ortho, meta, or para position of the ring. Table I shows that substituents can have a considerable effect on the laser threshold of these compounds although the quantum yields and lifetimes are less sensitive, and the effects (*cf.* 4-fluoro) may be smaller at low temperature.

Table I. Effect of Ring-Substituent on Properties of Eu[BTFA]$_4$ Chelates

Substituent	*Cation*	*Laser Threshold*[a]	$\tau_{^5D_0}$ *msec.*	Φ[e]	*Reference*
4-CH_3O-	Piperidinium	>4.00[b]	—	0.56	present work
3,4-Cl_2-	Piperidinium	3.31[b]	0.75[d]		present work
H	2,4,6-trimethylpyridinium	1.00[b]	0.70[d]	0.63	present work
4-CF_3	2,4,6-trimethylpyridinium	3.14[b]	0.70[d]		present work
4-I	2,4,6-trimethylpyridinium	2.53[b]	0.70[d]	0.58	present work
4-F	2,4,6-trimethylpyridinium	1.51[b]	0.74[d]		present work
4-F	Dimethylammonium	1.0[c]	0.67[c]	0.63	*33*
4-Cl	Dimethylammonium	1.2[c]	0.67[c]	0.63	*33*
3-Cl	Dimethylammonium	1.2[c]	0.67[c]	0.63	*33*
2-Cl	Dimethylammonium	0.5[c]	0.67[c]	0.54	*33*

[a] Normalized to [BTFA]$_4$ Eu pip = 1.00 with each combination of solvent and temperature.
[b] At 168°K. in EEA.
[c] At 294°K. in acetonitrile.
[d] At 145°K. in EEA.
[e] Φ is the quantum yield of $^5D_0 \rightarrow {}^7F_2$ Eu fluorescence with the chelate irradiated in its ultraviolet absorption band; these values were obtained at room temperature in acetonitrile by comparison with the "standard" of Ref. *15*.

There appear to be three principal ways that ring substituents can affect the over-all efficiency of energy transfer from ligand to europium ion. First, the substituents can influence the position of the triplet level of the ligand. It has been emphasized (*6, 7, 8*) that a good match of the triplet level with an upper level of the europium ion (in these cases $^5D_2$) is important for efficient energy transfer. Secondly, by resonance and inductive effects, the substituent can change the electron density at the keto-enol oxygen atoms and thus affect the degree of covalency of the metal-to-oxygen bond and the ease of transmission of energy through these bonds. By the same mechanism, the electronic effects of the substituents can influence the chemical stability of the chelate and affect the position of the dissociation equilibrium in solution. Ortho substituents can presumably play an additional role owing to their steric effects. The larger the ortho substituent, the more it could be expected to influence the relative positions of the four ligands around the europium atom. Ortho substituents, by some combination of these mechanisms, seem to show the most pronounced effects on laser performance of BTFA chelates.

Schimitschek (*33*) has shown that by introducing an ortho halogen atom into the benzene ring of these compounds the room-temperature laser threshold can be markedly lowered, even though the quantum efficiencies of the resulting compounds are lower than that of the unsubstituted BTFA derivative. He interprets the lower quantum efficiency of these compounds as caused in part by a shift of the energy of the ligand triplet state and suggests that the lower laser threshold may be explained by the observation that of the two principal $^5D_0 \rightarrow {}^7F_2$ emission bands found at ~ 6120 and 6140A. at low temperature, the relative intensity of the lasing, shorter wavelength transition is increased markedly in the ortho substituted chelates. Such a subtle change in the details of the emission spectrum is exactly what one would expect as a result of a minor repositioning of the ligands around the europium ion brought about by steric effects.

The interplay of the various effects of substituent is poorly understood at present and deserves further study.

The Effect of Cation

We have reported (*1*) that the emission spectra of solid C^+ [diketono)$_4$Eu]$^-$ salts can be influenced by the nature of the cation. Inasmuch as each tetrakis chelate anion must have a cation as its near neighbor in the crystal lattice, it would be expected that the size and other steric features of the cation could affect the preferred geometric arrangement of the four ligands around the europium ion so as to minimize cation-anion interactions. Since the structural details of the europium fluorescence are determined by the symmetry at the europium ion site, slight rearrangements of the relative positions of the ligands will change these features of the emission spectrum.

We were led to the conclusion that in solution as well, at least at low temperature, there is significant interaction between the cation and the chelate anion, perhaps by way of some sort of ion pairing. Although it showed only about 10% more dissociation and no appreciable difference in its usual spectroscopic properties from the piperidinium salt, the tetrapropylammonium salt of the benzoylacetone chelate did not undergo laser action. A cation effect is shown by the data listed in Table II where the tetrapropylammonium ion shows an adverse effect on the laser behavior of BTFA chelates as well.

A possible way in which changes in the cation might influence the chelate solutions, other than by an ion pairing mechanism, is by changing the position of the equilibrium:

$$C^+[L_4Eu]^- \rightleftharpoons L_3Eu + C^+L^-;$$

if C^+ is R_3NH^+:

$$R_3NH^+L^- \rightleftharpoons R_3N + LH$$

where C^+ is the cation, L^- is the diketonate anion, and LH is the neutral β-diketone.

The thermodynamic stability of C^+L^- could clearly influence the position of this equilibrium. The importance of this effect is shown by the work of Reidel and Charles (23) who prepared salts of $[(BTFA)_4Eu]^-$ with 15 different substituted ammonium cations and observed a more than threefold change in laser threshold at 0°C. on going from piperidinium through quinolinium. The increase in threshold roughly parallels an increase in the pK_b of the amine from which the cation is derived for those compounds with other than quaternary ammonium ions, and for the quinolinium salt these workers showed that the extent of dissociation to tris chelate is about 40%, as compared with 10% or less for the piperidinium compound.

Table II. Effect of Cation on Threshold of C^+ $[BFTA]_4$ Eu^-

Cation	*Threshold*[a]	*Reference*
Piperidinium	1.00[b]	24; present work
2,4,6-Trimethylpyridinium	1.00[b]	present work
Imidazolium	1.09[b]	present work
Tetramethylammonium	1.16[c]	24
n-Butylammonium	1.33[c]	24
Pyridinium	1.50[c]	24
Triethylammonium	1.83[c]	24
Tetraethylammonium	3.00[c]	24
Tetrapropylammonium	3.00[d]	24
Tetrapropylammonium	1.62[b]	present work
Quinolinium	>3.0[c]	24

[a] These thresholds fall into two groups: the set reported in ref. 24, measured in acetonitrile at 273°K. and those of the present work, done in EEA at 140°K.; within each group, the values are normalized to $[BTFA]_4$ Eu pip = 1.00 although the absolute value of the threshold is, of course, different under the two experimental conditions.
[b] At 140°K. in EEA.
[c] At 273°K. in acetonitrile.
[d] At 243°K. in acetonitrile; presumably the figure compared with the piperidinium salt at the same temperature will be higher.

In one case, a change of the cation has been observed to shift the frequency of the laser emission. Lempicki and co-workers (27) observed that adding sodium acetate to a solution of piperidinium tetrakis (benzoylacetono) europium in an alcoholic solution changed the laser frequency from 6131 to 6114A. and suggested that here, a new species, "an adduct of the tetrakis chelate and the cation," is formed with a different symmetry.

In order to test for the possibility of ion pairing in solution, we wished to change the cation in a way that would not disturb the dissociation equilibrium. By substituting the deuterated piperidinium ion, in which the piperidine carbon-bound hydrogen atoms are replaced by deuterium, for normal piperidinium, gives a new compound ("[BFTA]$_4$Eu d_{10} pip") in which the steric effects, base strength, and degree of solvation of the cation should be as nearly as possible the same as in the undeuterated salt. If direct interactions of the chelate electronic states with the cation were to be important, a change in the spectroscopic properties or laser behavior should be noted.

Table III. Effect of Deuteration on Properties of Piperidinium [BFTA]$_4$ Eu Chelates

Chelate	*Solvent*	$\tau_{^5D_0}$, *msec.* 298°	168°	Φ^d 298°	168°	*Relative Laser Threshold (168°K.)*
[BTFA]$_4$Eu pip	EEA[b]	0.62	0.68	0.35	0.59	1.00
[BTFA]$_4$Eu pip	"nitrile"[c]	0.63	0.70	—	—	—
[BTFA]$_4$Eu pip	CH_3CN	0.66	0.64	0.63	—	—
[BTFA]$_4$Eu pip	CD_3CN	0.70	0.66	0.63	—	—
[BTFA]$_4$Eu d_{10} pip	EEA	0.63	0.70	0.36	0.59	0.64
[d_5BTFA]$_4$ Eu pip	EEA	0.65	0.68	0.40	0.59	0.59
[d_5BTFA]$_4$Eu d_{10} pip	EEA	0.63	0.66	0.41	0.59	0.47
[d_5BTFA]$_4$Eu d_{10} pip	CH_3CN	0.69	0.66	0.63	—	—
[d_5BTFA]$_4$Eu d_{10} pip	"nitrile"	0.62	0.72	—	—	—
[d_5BTFA]$_4$Eu d_{10} pip	CD_3CN	0.69	0.71	0.63	—	—
[TFTBD[a]]$_4$Eu pip	EEA	—	0.73	—	—	1.62
[TFTBD[a]]$_4$ d_{10} pip	EEA	—	0.70	—	—	0.99

[a] Thenoyltrifluoroacetone.
[b] See text.
[c] 1:1:1 Butyronitrile, isobutyronitrile, propionitrile.
[d] Obtained by comparison to "standard" of Ref. *15*.

The Effect of Deuteration

As can be seen in Table III, deuteration of the piperidium ion in the BTFA chelate did lower the threshold of laser action at low temperature although no significant change was noted in the emission spectrum, quantum yield, or lifetime of ion fluorescence (*25*). This clearly demonstrates that, at least at low temperatures, the piperidium ion is sufficiently near the europium chelate cation to affect significantly some portion of the energy transfer scheme at high illumination intensities. This finding prompted us to prepare the corresponding compounds with the five ligand benzene ring hydrogen atoms also substituted by deuterium. The resulting materials ("d_5BTFA" derivatives) also showed a significant decrease in laser threshold at low temperature (Table III) although at these temperatures the pertinent quantum yields and lifetimes were, within experimental error, the same throughout the series of four compounds (*25*). These threshold reductions were especially surprising. Although

Freeman, Crosby, Lawson (*13*), Kropp, and Windsor (*17, 18*) had reported that hydrated europium chloride crystals and aqueous solutions of europium salts, respectively, showed considerable enhancement of ion fluorescence and lifetimes upon substitution of H_2O by D_2O, the latter workers have reported (*37*) that "wet" hydrocarbon solutions of the thenoyltrifluoroacetone chelate of europium showed no enhancement of quantum yield and lifetime upon replacing the H_2O present by D_2O. They suggested that whereas deuteration enhanced the fluorescent properties of the free ions by inhibiting nonradiative deactivation of the $^5D_0$ level, the quantum efficiency of $^5D_0$ luminescence obtained upon direct excitation of this level (*10, 11*) is already so high in the fluorinated diketone chelates (*e.g.* thenoyltrifluoroacetone) that deuteration of the environment should have little further enhancing effect.

Additional evidence which shows that the deuterium enhancement of laser performance is not principally caused by an increased efficiency of the transfer of energy from ligand to europium ion is provided by the data in Table IV which show that the already short lifetime of the triplet state in the gadolinium chelate is not at all changed by deuteration of the ligand or solvent.

As discussed below, the lack of differences in absorption, quantum yield, fluorescence risetime and lifetime, or emission spectrum between "normal" and deuterated BTFA chelates at low temperature, suggests that deuteration of the ligands influences the energy transfer scheme at some point subsequent to the $^5D_0 \rightarrow {}^7F_2$ radiative step.

Having completed our survey of the "chemical" aspects of the chelate laser, we now proceed to examine the energy transfer and loss mechanisms in these systems.

Table IV. Phosphorescence Lifetimes of Piperidinium $[BFTA]_4$ Ln Chelates at 77°K.

Ln	*Ligand*	*Solvent*	τ[c] *msec.*
—	BTFA[a]	EEA[b]	170
La	BTFA	"	79
Gd	BTFA	"	3.7 (1.0)
Gd	d_5BTFA	"	3.7 (1.3)
Gd	BTFA	CH_3CN	2.7 (0.89)
Gd	BTFA	CD_3CN	2.6 (0.87)
Gd	4-I-BTFA	EEA	2.6 (1.5)
Lu	BTFA	EEA	95

[a] Piperidinium salt of benzoyltrifluoroacetone.
[b] *See* text.
[c] The plots of log intensity *vs.* time of the phosphorescence of the Gd chelates were resolvable into two components; the slow one dominates in EEA and the fast one dominates in (crystalline) CH_3CN. In EEA, this behavior is independent of concentration over the range 10^{-2} to $10^{-4}M$.

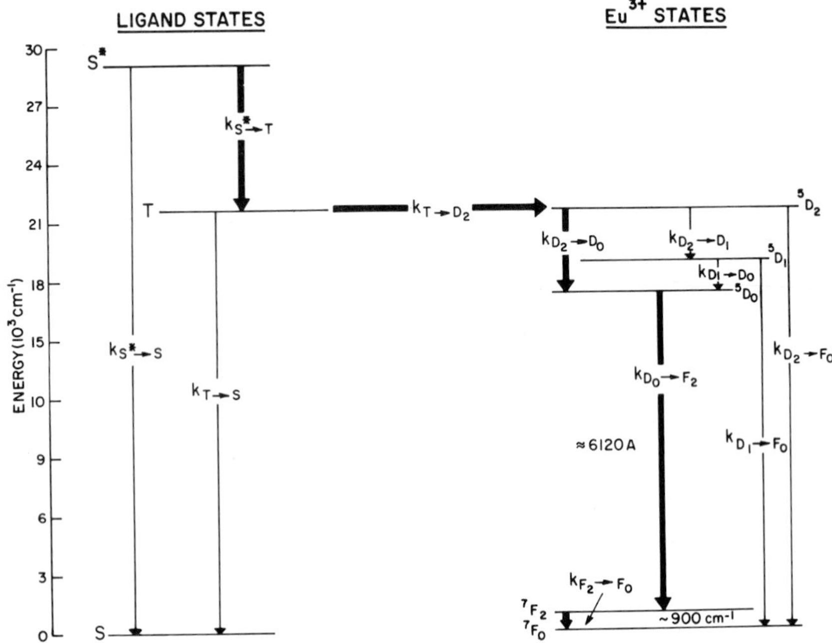

Figure 1. Energy level diagram for BTFA chelates of Eu^{3+}. The arrows show the principle possible paths of energy migration in the system occurring at rates k. The dark arrows indicate the population and depopulation routes for the laser transition, $^5D_0 \rightarrow {}^7F_2$ of Eu^{3+}. Vibrational levels of the ligand and ligand field splittings in Eu^{3+} have been omitted for simplicity

The Energy Transfer Scheme

The efficiency of fluorescence and laser action of europium chelates depends in turn on the over-all efficiency with which the energy initially absorbed from a quantum of ultraviolet light by the ligand ground state → excited singlet transition is transferred to the $^5D_0$ level of the europium ion. This multistep process, indicated by heavy lines in Figure 1, will be influenced by competition at each step with a number of other processes resulting in energy losses. It should be remembered that in this simplified diagram, each process shown with rate constant k is in principle a combination of radiative and nonradiative processes.

Through the efforts of several workers in this field, it is possible to develop a reasonably cogent assessment of the roles played by these various processes in europium BTFA chelates.

Energy in the ligand excited singlet state, S* can either return to the ground state ($k_{S^* \rightarrow S}$) or undergo intersystem crossing to the triplet state T ($k_{S^* \rightarrow T}$). We do not consider here direct transfer of energy from S* to the europium manifold, for Bhaumik and El-Sayed (3) have energy is transferred to the europium ion. The radiative portion of the deactivation of S* to the ground state can be estimated from the absorption coefficient to be *ca.* 10^8 sec.$^{-1}$, and Bhaumik and El-Sayed (*3*) have estimated the intersystem crossing rate ($k_{S^* \rightarrow T}$) to be 10^{11} sec.$^{-1}$ in two [illegible] ...hed that no more than 10% of the europium fluorescence arrives [illegible] and the work of Crosby and co-workers (*6, 7, 8*), [illegible] (*16*) and El-Sayed and Bhaumik (*12*) have all [illegible] that the ligand triplet is the source from which fluorinated europium chelates, which allows estimation of $\frac{k_{S^* \rightarrow T}}{k_{S^* \rightarrow S}}$ as *ca.* 10^3. The fact that the ligand triplet state in europium chelates competes successfully with the ground state for S* energy is supported by considering the luminescence spectra of other lanthanide chelates. In our study of $(BTFA)_4Ln$ chelates we have confirmed the observations made initially by Yuster and Weissman (*38*) that chelates of La and Lu show, at low temperatures, both molecular fluorescence and phosphorescence, while Gd chelates show only phosphorescence. Since $k_{S^* \rightarrow S}$ should not be significantly changed on changing the lanthanide ion, this suggests that $k_{S^* \rightarrow T}$ is increased in the Gd compound, an effect attributed by Yuster and Weissman to the fact that Gd^{3+} is paramagnetic, (as is Eu^{3+}) which leads to an increase in the mixing of the singlet and triplet wave functions in the Gd compounds and thus to an increase in the transition probabilities between them. This interpretation receives further support from the effect of the lanthanide ion on the phosphorescence lifetimes (in this case, intersystem crossing between triplet and ground state singlet, $1/k_{T \rightarrow S}$) of these compounds (Table IV). The decrease in lifetime on going from the free $BTFA^-$ anion to $[(BTFA)_4La]^-$ and $[(BTFA)_4Lu]^-$ is presumably attributed to a normal "heavy atom" effect, while the further decrease on going to the Gd chelate can again be explained as a result of the paramagnetism of Gd.

This enhancement of intersystem crossing by combining heavy atom and paramagnetic effects explains the relative insensitivity of the Gd phosphorescence lifetime (Table IV) to any additional heavy atom effect (as in the chelate with iodo-BTFA), or to deuteration of solvent or ligand which, by inhibiting nonradiative deactivation, usually increases the lifetime of organic phosphorescence. This insensitivity of the lifetime of the Gd chelate permits us to assign the value of *ca.* 3×10^2 sec.$^{-1}$ as the intrinsic radiative rate for the triplet state for Gd BTFA chelates, and a similar value should apply for the Eu compounds.

There are two pathways available to the ligand triplet state energy. It can decay to the ground state ($k_{T \rightarrow S}$) or it can be transferred to the europium ion. Crosby and co-workers showed that the fluorescence efficiency of europium chelates, or in other words $k_{T \rightarrow {}^5D}$, increases as the ligand triplet state more closely matches one of the ^5D ion levels. While data on the value of $k_{T \rightarrow {}^5D}$ are not available for BTFA chelates, Bhaumik and El-Sayed have shown that for thenoyltrifluoroacetone and hexafluoroaceacetylacetone chelates of europium at room temperature, $k_{T \rightarrow {}^5D}$ is *ca.* 10^{10} sec^{-1}. Of these two highly efficient chelates, the former has a triplet level slightly below the europium $^5D_2$ level while that of the latter is slightly above. Since in BTFA chelates, the triplet closely matches $^5D_2$, we can reasonably assume the same value for $k_{T \rightarrow {}^5D}$ in these compounds. This rate is sufficiently high to preclude any significant direct depopulation of the triplet level to the ground state at low temperatures.

Since we have argued that both $k_{S^* \rightarrow T}$ and $k_{T \rightarrow {}^5D}$ are much faster than any competing processes, we conclude that, at low temperature in undissociated europium $(BTFA)_4$ chelates, the over-all quantum efficiency of population of the $^5D_2$ level is nearly unity. Tables I and III show, however, that even under the most favorable combinations of solvent, temperature, and chemical structure, the over-all quantum efficiency for $^5D_0 \rightarrow {}^7F_2$ emission, which comprises more than 95% of the total luminescence for these compounds, never exceeds about 60%.

Windsor and his co-workers (*10, 11*) have shown, by direct excitation of the ^5D levels in a number of europium compounds, that the quantum yield of $^5D_0$ fluorescence decreases progressively as one successively excites $^5D_0$, $^5D_1$, and $^5D_2$. While the yield on direct excitation of $^5D_0$ is quite dependent on the particular compound and medium (the value is 0.82 for the thenoyltrifluoroacetone chelate in acetone solution), the proportion of the energy lost between *e.g.* $^5D_2$ and $^5D_0$ within a given compound is rather insensitive to changes in the environment. These nonradiative processes from $^5D_2$ and $^5D_1$, whose nature is not understood, would appear to be responsible for most of the *ca.* 40% energy loss in these materials.

Once the energy arrives at $^5D_0$, it is emitted to $^7F_2$ with high efficiency. Nonradiative processes from $^5D_0$ are almost completely lacking in $(BTFA)_4Eu$ chelates in nitrile solvents as is indicated by the relative insensitivity of the lifetime of the $^5D_0 \rightarrow {}^7F_2$ emission to changes in environment and temperature.

The last step we consider is the return of the europium ion to the ground state, $^7F_2 \rightarrow {}^7F_0$. The rate, $k_{F_2 \rightarrow F_0}$, does not influence the quantum yield or lifetime of $^5D_0 \rightarrow {}^7F_2$ emission, but it can be of paramount importance in determining laser performance. Even without detailed mathematical analysis, it is clear that if $k_{F_2 \rightarrow F_0}$ is much slower than $k_{D_0 \rightarrow F_2}$, no net inversion of $^5D_0$ can be obtained under steady state conditions since the energy will tend to pile up in the $^7F_2$ level. There is no direct experimental evidence dealing with the magnitude of $k_{F_2 \rightarrow F_0}$, but the only way we have been able to rationalize the decreases in laser threshold brought about by deuteration of $(BTFA)_4Eu$ pip is to assume that it is this rate which is controlling the over-all process. The separation between $^7F_2$ and $^7F_0$ is 900 cm.$^{-1}$. It is not unreasonable to expect $k_{F_2 \rightarrow F_0}$ to be significantly affected by the availability of molecular vibrational modes with this energy. In the case of the d_5BTFA chelates, we have observed the appearance of new absorptions in the infrared spectrum at 875, 842, and 830 cm.$^{-1}$ shifted to these values from aromatic C-H in-plane deformations seen at 1105, 1082, and 1070 cm.$^{-1}$ in the undeuterated compounds.

We have not been able to arrive at theoretical values for $k_{F_2 \rightarrow F_0}$, but if our interpretation is correct, then for the undeuterated compound it must be of the same order as $K_{D_0 \rightarrow F_2}$, and larger (by a factor of two or more) in the d_5BTFA chelates.

In conclusion, although a detailed outline of both the chemistry and energy transfer processes in β-diketonates of Eu^{3+} has emerged in the last few years, it is clear that much experimental and theoretical work needs to be done, especially on chelate-solvent interactions and energy loss mechanisms within the europium ion manifold.

Literature Cited

(1) Bauer, H., Blanc, J., Ross, D. L., *J. Am. Chem. Soc.* **86**, 5125 (1964).
(2) Bhaumik, M. L., *et al.*, *J. Phys. Chem.* **68**, 1490 (1964).
(3) Bhaumik, M. L., El-Sayed, M. A., *J. Chem. Phys.* **42**, 787 (1965).
(4) Bhaumik, M. L., Ferder, L., El-Sayed, M. A., *J. Chem. Phys.* **42**, 1843 (1965).
(5) Brecher, C., Samelson, H., Lempicki, A., *J. Chem. Phys.* **42**, 1081 (1965).
(6) Crosby, G. A., Whan, R. E., *Naturwiss.* **47**, 276 (1960).
(7) Crosby, G. A., Whan, R. E., *J. Chem. Phys.* **32**, 614 (1960).
(8) Crosby, G. A., Whan, R. E., Alire, R. M., *J. Chem. Phys.* **34**, 743 (1961).
(9) Crosby, G. A., *Mol. Crystals* **1**, 37 (1966).
(10) Dawson, W. R., Kropp, J. L., *J. Opt. Soc. Am.* **55**, 822 (1965).
(11) Dawson, W. R., Kropp, J. L., Windsor, M. W., *J. Chem. Phys.* **45**, 2410 (1966).
(12) El-Sayed, M. A., Bhaumik, M. L., *J. Chem. Phys.* **39**, 2391 (1963).
(13) Freeman, J. J., Crosby, G. A., Lawson, K. E., *J. Mol. Spectry.* **13**, 390 (1964).
(14) Fry, F. H., Pirie, W. R., *J. Chem. Phys.* **43**, 3761 (1965).
(15) Gudmundsen, R. A., Marsh, O. J., Matovich, E., *J. Chem. Phys.* **39**, 272 (1963).
(16) Heller, A., Wasserman, E., *J. Chem. Phys.* **42**, 949 (1965).
(17) Kropp, J. L., Windsor, M. W., *J. Chem. Phys.* **39**, 2769 (1963).
(18) Kropp, J. L., Windsor, M. W., *J. Chem. Phys.* **42**, 1599 (1965).
(19) Lempicki, A., Samelson, H., "Proceedings of the Symposium on Optical Masers," p. 347, Polytechnic Press, Brooklyn, N. Y., 1963.
(20) Lempicki, A., Samelson, H., *Phys. Letters* **4**, 133 (1963).
(21) Levine, A. K., ed., "Lasers, a Series of Advances," Chap. 3, Marcel Dekkar, Inc., New York, 1966.
(22) Melby, L. R., Rose, N. J., Abramson, E., Caris, J. C., *J. Am. Chem. Soc.* **86**, 5117 (1964).

(23) Metlay, M., *J. Chem. Phys.* **39,** 491 (1963).
(24) Riedel, E. P., Charles, R. G., *J. Appl. Phys.* **36,** 3954 (1965).
(25) Ross, D. L., Blanc, J., Pressley, R. J., *Appl. Phys. Letters* **8,** 101 (1966).
(26) Samelson, H., Brecher, C., Lempicki, A., *Proc. Rare Earth Conf. 5th, Ames, Iowa,* **1,** 41 (1965).
(27) Samelson, H., Brophy, V. A., Brecher, C., Lempicki, A., *J. Chem. Phys.* **41,** 3998 (1964).
(28) Samelson, H., Lempicki, A., Brecher, C., Brophy, V. A., *Appl. Phys. Letters* **5,** 173 (1964).
(29) Samelson, H., Lempicki, A., Brophy, V. A., Brecher, C., *J. Chem. Phys.* **40,** 2553 (1964).
(30) Schimitschek, E. J., Nehrich, R. B., *J. Appl. Phys.* **35,** 2786 (1964).
(31) Schimitschek, E. J., Nehrich, R. B., Trias, J. A., *J. Chem. Phys.* **42,** 788 (1965).
(32) Schimitschek, E. J., Nehrich, R. B., Trias, J. A., *Appl. Phys. Letters* **9,** 103 (1966).
(33) Schimitschek, E. J., Nehrich, R. B., Trias, J. A., *J. Chim. phys.* **64,** 673 (1967).
(34) Schimitschek, E. J., Schwarz, E. G. K., *Nature* **196,** 832 (1962).
(35) Weissman, S. I., *J. Chem. Phys.* **10,** 214 (1942).
(36) Whan, R. E., Crosby, G. A., *J. Mol. Spectry.* **8,** 315 (1962).
(37) Windsor, M. W., TRW Systems, Redondo Beach, California (private communication).
(38) Yuster, P., Weissman, S. I., *J. Chem. Phys.* **17,** 1182 (1949).

RECEIVED October 18, 1966.

13

Complexes of the Rare Earths

N-Substituted Iminodiacetic Acids

LARRY C. THOMPSON, BARBARA L. SHAFER, JOHN A. EDGAR, and KATHLEEN D. MANNILA

University of Minnesota, Duluth, Minn.

The solution stabilities of the rare earth complexes with N-*methyliminodiacetic acid,* N-*benzyliminodiacetic acid,* N-*phenyliminodiacetic acid,* N-*methoxyethyliminodiacetic acid, and* N-*methylmercaptoethyliminodiacetic acid have been measured at 25°C. and $\mu = 0.1$ (KNO_3). The linear relationship between the pk values for the ionization of the ammonium proton and the log K_1 values for terdentate iminodiacetate ligands is demonstrated. This relationship is used to provide a measure of the free energy of formation of the third chelate ring in quadridentate iminodiacetates. The relative affinities of the HO—, CH_3O—, CH_3S—, and groups for the rare earth ions in this type of compound have been determined.*

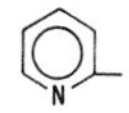

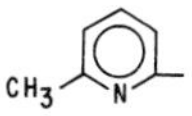

During the past several years a significant research effort has been applied to the aqueous coordination chemistry of the rare earth ions. Much data have been obtained concerning the affinity of these ions for a variety of ligands (9). We have been concerned with the stability constants for the simple aminopolycarboxylic acid chelates built upon the iminodiacetate structure and containing a fourth potentially bonding group substituted on the nitrogen atom (*14, 15*). Various evidence indicates strongly that these species in aqueous solution use metal coordination numbers larger than six. It has also been found that the hydroxy and pyridyl groups possess large affinities for the rare earth ions, and the latter might possibly be the stronger donor group, at least in this type of compound.

To obtain a semiquantitative estimate for this enhancement, we decided to use the approach of Schwarzenbach in a similar study with divalent metal ions (*12*). This approach is based on the assumption that for ligands of essentially the same structure a linear relationship should exist between the acid dissociation constants of the ligands and the stability constants of the metal chelates which they form with a single metal ion. The ligands used to establish this linear relationship are *N*-substituted iminodiacetic acids in which the *N*-substituent is not capable of bonding to the metal ion. When the *N*-substituent contains a group which can form an additional bond to the metal, it is found that the relationship between the acid dissociation constant and the stability constant is such that a positive deviation from the base line is obtained (*12*). The magnitude of this deviation should be related to the free energy of forming this additional chelate ring (*i.e.*, it is related to the affinity of the bonding group for the metal ion in this particular structure). In this way, semiquantitative estimates of the affinities of various donor groups (or atoms) for a given metal ion can be obtained.

The structural formulas for the ligands which are discussed in this paper are given below.

$$R-N\begin{matrix} \diagup CH_2COOH \\ \diagdown CH_2COOH \end{matrix}$$

$R = H-$	(iminodiacetic acid)	I
$= CH_3-$	(*N*-methyliminodiacetic acid)	II
$= C_6H_5-CH_2-$	(*N*-benzyliminodiacetic acid)	III
$= C_6H_5-$	(*N*-phenyliminodiacetic acid)	IV
$= HOCH_2CH-$	(*N*-hydoxyethyliminodiacetic acid)	V
$= CH_3OCH_2CH_2-$	(*N*-methoxyethyliminodiacetic acid)	VI
$= CH_3SCH_2CH_2-$	(*N*-methylmercaptoethyliminodiacetic acid)	VII
= 2-pyridyl$-CH_2-$	(*N*-(2-picolyl)iminodiacetic acid)	VIII
= 6-CH_3-2-pyridyl$-CH_2-$	(*N*-(6-methyl-2-picolyl)iminodiacetic acid)	IX

The experimental results for ligands I, V, VIII, and IX have been given in previous communications in this series of papers.

Experimental

Preparation of Ligands. The ligands used in this study were prepared by methods given in the literature: *N*-methyliminodiacetic acid (*4*); *N*-benzyliminodiacetic acid (*4*); *N*-phenyliminodiacetic acid (*7*);

N-methoxyethyliminodiacetic acid (*12*) and *N*-methylmercaptoethyliminodiacetic acid (*12*). The latter two acids were prepared by direct action of chloroacetate on the amine eliminating the preparation of the dimethyl ester. The preparation of the free acid was then carried out as described by Schwarzenbach. The products were checked for purity either by determining their melting points, by elemental analysis or by a satisfactory agreement between the pk_2 values in Table II with those in the literature. (For ligands II, IV, VI, and VII Schwarzenbach reported pk_2 values at 20°C. and $\mu = 0.1$ as 9.65, 4.96, 8.96, and 8.91. For ligand III Ando reported pk_2 at 25°C. and $\mu = 0.1$ as 8.90.)

Table I. Experimental Data for Ligand VI and Lanthanum
25°C., $\mu = 0.1M$ (KNO_3)

C_L	$C_{La^{3+}}$	a[a]	pH
1.957 × 10^{3-}	0.979 × 10^{3-}	1.100	4.18
1.955	0.978	1.150	4.32
1.952	0.976	1.225	4.55
1.951	0.976	1.250	4.62
1.950	0.975	1.275	4.68
1.949	0.975	1.300	4.77
1.947	0.974	1.350	4.93
1.946	0.973	1.400	5.09
1.944	0.972	1.450	5.24
1.942	0.971	1.500	5.41
1.940	0.970	1.550	5.58
1.938	0.969	1.600	5.77
1.936	0.968	1.650	5.95
1.934	0.967	1.700	6.15
1.933	0.967	1.725	6.24
1.932	0.966	1.750	6.38
1.931	0.966	1.775	6.49
1.931	0.966	1.800	6.62
1.929	0.965	1.850	6.93
1.927	0.964	1.900	7.32

[a] The value of *a* is moles of base added per mole of ligand.

Solutions. The solutions were prepared and standardized as described previously (*13*).

Procedure. The direct pH method described previously was used to determine the stability constants (*13*). The solutions used had a ligand to metal ratio of about 2:1 and the concentration level was about 0.001*M* rare earth ion. All solutions were made up to ionic strength 0.1*M* using potassium nitrate. Experimental data for one system are given in Table I.

Calculations. Data for ligands II, III, IV, VI and VII, which are reported for the first time, were reduced to stability constants using the program Gauss G modified for the IBM 1620 computer (*17*). The input data for the computer program have been deposited as Document Number 9694 with the ADI Auxiliary Publications Project, Photoduplication

Table II. Formation Constants for
with Rare

$T = 25°C.,$

Metal Ion	*I*	*II*		*III*		*IV*
	log K_1	*log* K_1	*log* K_2	*log* K_1	*log* K_2	*log* K_1
	$pk_1 =$ 2.60, $pk_2 =$ 9.33	$pk_1 =$ 2.33	$pk_2 =$ 9.63	$pk_1 =$ 2.04	$pk_2 =$ 8.89	$pk_1 =$ 2.15, $pk_2 =$ 5.05
La^{3+}	5.89	6.23	4.70	5.42	3.99	2.6
Ce^{3+}	6.19	6.46	4.89	5.75	4.26	2.5
Pr^{3+}	6.41	6.70	5.22	5.84	4.51	2.5
Nd^{3+}	6.51	6.71	5.13	5.99	4.44	2.73
Sm^{3+}	6.67	6.85	5.41	6.06	4.64	2.79
Eu^{3+}	6.73	6.92	5.40	6.07	4.60	2.81
Gd^{3+}	6.69	6.90	5.37	6.09	4.60	2.85
Tb^{3+}	6.75	7.11	5.63	6.33	4.85	2.98
Dy^{3+}	6.88	7.18	5.68	6.36	4.85	2.81
Ho^{3+}	6.97	7.21	5.69	6.35	4.90	2.87
Er^{3+}	7.04	7.40	5.94	6.54	5.09	2.94
Tm^{3+}	7.20	7.47	6.00	6.59	5.15	2.82
Yb^{3+}	7.40	7.59	6.14	6.69	5.26	2.84
Lu^{3+}	7.58	7.60	6.20	6.70	5.32	2.70
Y^{3+}	6.76	7.02	5.54	6.18	4.75	2.64
Zn^{2+}		7.74	6.25	7.06		3.52
Cd^{2+}		6.71	5.43			
Cu^{2+}			6.62			
Ni^{2+}						3.70
Ca^{2+}				3.21		

[a] The 95% confidence levels for the log K_1 values is ± 0.02 and for the log K_2 values lanthanum, cerium, and praseodymium and ± 0.04 for the remainder.

$$k_1 = \frac{[H][HA]}{[H_2A]} \; ; \; k_2 = \frac{[H][A]}{[HA]}$$

Service, Library of Congress, Washington 25, D.C., 20540. A copy may be secured by citing the document number and by remitting $3.75 for photoprints, or $2.00 for 35 mm. microfilm. Advance payment is required. Make checks or money orders payable to: Chief, Photoduplication Service, Library of Congress.

Results

The results which were obtained for the acid dissociation constants and the formation constants for the rare earth chelates are given in Table II along with the log K_1 values for the ligands which were studied earlier. We have included the measured values for some other ions which were

N-Substituted Iminodiacetic Acids
Earth Ions[a]

$\mu = 0.1$ (KNO_3)

V	VI		VII		VIII	IX
log K_1	*log* K_1	*log* K_2	*log* K_1	*log* K_2	*log* K_1	*log* K_1
$pk_1 =$ 1.91					$pk_1 =$ 2.6	$pk_1 =$ 3.46
$pk_2 =$ 8.72	$pk_1 =$ 2.18	$pk_2 =$ 8.95	$pk_1 =$ 2.00	$pk_2 =$ 8.89	$pk_2 =$ 8.21	$pk_2 =$ 8.30
8.00	7.14	5.94	5.59	4.09	7.80	5.72
8.46	7.54	6.48	5.92	4.54	8.30	6.00
8.64	7.75	6.89	6.08	4.57	8.53	6.18
8.80	7.84	7.10	6.19	4.91	8.64	6.28
9.10	7.98	7.59	6.31	4.99	8.92	6.57
9.10	7.99	7.59	6.24	5.03	8.92	6.76
9.01	7.88	7.63	6.18	4.96	8.76	6.71
9.08	7.97	7.68	6.24	5.04	8.87	7.16
9.08	8.06	7.48	6.41	5.09	9.00	7.23
9.18	8.06	7.23	6.38	5.13	9.07	7.30
9.24	8.16	7.02	6.63	5.27	9.25	7.42
9.35	8.27	6.69	6.60	5.40	9.40	7.54
9.38	8.39	6.54	6.70	5.43	9.60	7.65
9.50	8.42	6.52	6.71	5.47	9.72	7.60
9.22	7.70	6.96	6.18	4.87	8.63	6.84
	8.38		8.34	4.44		
	4.66		3.41			

is ± 0.04 or better in all cases except for ligand IV where the values are ± 0.1 for

; $K_1 = \frac{[MA]}{[M][A]}$; $K_2 = \frac{[MA_2]}{[MA][A]}$

used to check our experimental procedure and our procedure for calculating the stability constants. A comparison of our results for these ions with those in the literature (given in Table III) shows satisfactory agreement in all cases (*1, 12*). Values for log K_1 and log K_2 for the rare earth complexes of ligands II and III have appeared previously (*5*), but there is a serious discrepancy between our values and these. We feel that our results are the correct ones for the following reasons: (1) our values for the control ions (Ca^{2+} and/or Zn^{2+}) are in excellent agreement with the literature. (2) The values reported for ligand III by Hering are greater than the values for ligand II, even though the latter is more basic by 0.7 p*K* units. For all the other metals with which these ligands have

Table III. Formation Constants for *N*-Substituted Iminodiacetic Acids With Metal Ions Used to Check Experimental Procedure

M^{n+}	*Ligand*	*T, °C.*	μ	*log* K_1	*log* K_2	*Ref.*
Zn^{2+}	II	20	0.1	7.66	6.43	*12*
Cd^{2+}	II	20	0.1	6.77	5.75	*12*
Cu^{2+}	II	20	0.1		6.83	*12*
Zn^{2+}	III	25	0.1	6.97		*1*
Ca^{2+}	III	25	0.1	3.13		*1*
Zn^{2+}	IV	20	0.1	3.22		*12*
Ni^{2+}	IV	20	0.1	3.53		*12*
Zn^{2+}	VI	20	0.1	8.43		*12*
Ca^{2+}	VI	20	0.1	4.53		*12*
Zn^{2+}	VII	20	0.1	8.28	4.50	*12*
Ca^{2+}	VII	20	0.1	3.34		*12*

been studied, the reverse, as expected, has been found. Our results for the rare earths are consistent with this trend.

In order to determine the extra stability caused by the bonding groups in the fourth position, it was necessary to construct a base line using ligands I, II, III, and IV. This base line, log $K_1 = a\ pk_2 + b$, for La^{3+} and for Zn^{2+}, using data determined in our laboratory, is plotted in Figure 1. The extra stability of the other ligands was obtained by measuring the deviation from this line. The values which were obtained are listed in Table IV. This extra stability for zinc and the CH_3O— and CH_3S— groups at 25°C. compares well with Schwarzenbach's values at 20°C. (1.6 and 1.4 respectively).

Discussion

The trends in the formation constants of the complexes reported here are much the same as reported previously for similar ligands. The over-all behavior of the chelates of *N*-benzyliminodiacetic acid and *N*-methyliminodiacetic acid is virtually identical to that of iminodiacetic acid itself (*13*). The only major difference is attributed to the different basicities of the ligands which determines the absolute magnitude of the log K_1 values but has little affect on the trends from one metal ion to another. For both ligands, the position of yttrium is in the heavy earths for both log K_1 and log K_2, although the actual value is slightly less than the "normal" value.

The ligand *N*-phenyliminodiacetic acid is a relatively weak complexing agent for the rare earths, being about as effective as the simple hydroxycarboxylic acids having approximately the same pk value (*9*). This ligand was previously shown to be a weak chelating agent for divalent metal ions (*12*).

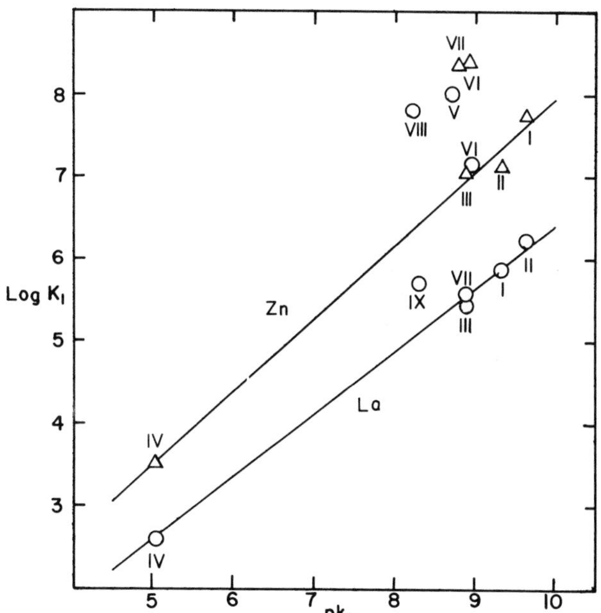

Figure 1. Plots of log K_1 vs. pk_2 *for* Zn^{2+} (Δ) *and* La^{3+} (O)

Table IV. Values of Δ (log K_1 Experimental—K_1 Interpolated) for Potentially Quadridentate Ligands

Metal Ion	V (HO—)	VI (CH_3O—)	VII (CH_3S—)	VIII (2-pyridyl)	IX (6-methyl-2-pyridyl)
La^{3+}	2.6	1.6	0.0	2.8	0.6
Ce^{3+}	2.8	1.7	0.1	3.1	0.7
Pr^{3+}	2.8	1.7	0.1	3.2	0.8
Nd^{3+}	2.9	1.7	0.1	3.2	0.7
Sm^{3+}	3.1	1.7	0.1	3.3	0.9
Eu^{3+}	3.0	1.7	0.0	3.3	1.1
Gd^{3+}	3.0	1.6	0.0	3.2	1.0
Tb^{3+}	2.9	1.5	−0.1	3.1	1.3
Dy^{3+}	2.8	1.6	0.0	3.2	1.4
Ho^{3+}	2.9	1.5	−0.1	3.2	1.4
Er^{3+}	2.8	1.5	0.0	3.3	1.4
Tm^{3+}	2.8	1.5	−0.1	3.4	1.4
Yb^{3+}	2.7	1.5	−0.1	3.5	1.5
Lu^{3+}	2.8	1.5	−0.1	3.5	1.3
Y^{3+}	3.1	1.4	−0.1	3.0	1.5
Zn^{2+}		1.4	1.4	3.7 [b]	

Ligand [a]

[a] The values are considered to be reliable to about ± 0.2 log *K* units.
[b] This was determined from the value of log K_1 reported by Irving and da Silva (6).

N-methoxyethyliminodiacetic acid forms rare earth complexes which are much more stable than those formed by *N*-benzyliminodiacetic acid even though the p*k* values are nearly the same. This suggests that the methoxy group is coordinated in the 1:1 complexes (*15*). The over-all trend in the formation constants is much the same as has been reported for *N*-hydroxyethyliminodiacetic acid (*14*). The 2:1 constants essentially parallel those of ligand V, including the region of marked decrease from terbium to lutetium. (With ligand V this maximum comes one element later at dysprosium.) This would seem to suggest that the methoxy group is coordinated in the 2:1 complex as well. Since the methoxy group is somewhat bulkier than the hydroxy group, it would be expected that any steric effect would be greater in the former complexes. The decrease in log K_2 values in the heavy rare earths is much larger for the methoxy compound, in agreement with the postulate of a coordination number larger than six and participation of the methoxy group in both the 1:1 and 2:1 complexes.

The final ligand which was studied, *N*-methylmercaptoethyliminodiacetic acid, has a p*k* value identical to that of *N*-benzyliminodiacetic acid, and the two ligands form rare earth complexes of almost the same stability. This would indicate that the thioether group is not bonding to the rare earth ion. The general trend in the log K_1 values for this potentially quadridentate ligand thus follows that of ligands I, II, and III, all of which are terdentate only. Log K_2 values follow the same regular trend as log K_2 values of these terdentate ligands. Since for all other potentially quadridentate ligands which have been studied, there is a maximum followed by a sharp decrease in the values of log K_2, this is additional confirmation that the thioether group is not an effective donor for the rare earths in aqueous solution.

Examining the data in Table II shows some interesting relationships among various types of donor atoms. The rare earth ions are typical Class A metal cations (*11*) [or "hard" acids in the Pearson sense (*10*)] and should complex in aqueous solution strongly to oxygen donors. The extra stability caused by closing the third chelate ring should then be larger for the HO— and CH_3O— groups than for the CH_3S— group. The values of Δ (0.1 to −0.1) indicate that the CH_3S— group essentially does not coordinate to the rare earth ions and confirms the previous studies in which such behavior was indicated for simple acids such as S-ethylthioglycolic acid (*3*). It is also of interest to note that whereas with the transition metals which were studied by Schwarzenbach (*12*) the CH_3S—, HO—, and CH_3O— groups were of nearly the same effectiveness as donors, there is much more selectivity in the rare earths. A comparison of the Δ values for the CH_3O— group indicates that only lead ($\Delta = 2.3$) and copper ($\Delta = 1.9$) are stabilized to a greater extent than the rare earth ions. For all the divalent metal ions studied previously there is essentially no discrimination between the HO— and CH_3O— groups. For the rare earth ions, there is a large difference in the effectiveness of these two groups as donors, which amounts to an additional stabilization of between 1 and 1.7 log K units for the HO— group.

A logical explanation for these observations with regard to the HO—, CH_3O—, and CH_3S— groups can be obtained using the usual electrostatic arguments for the interactions between these groups and the trivalent rare earth ions (*8*). The increased stability with the HO— group could possibly be related to the smaller steric interaction in complexes which have the large coordination number apparently characteristic of the rare earths.

The most surprising and puzzling observation is the large value of Δ for ligands VIII and IX which contain the pyridyl group as the fourth donor atom. The difference between the values for the two ligands is explicable on the basis of steric hindrance of the methyl group in ligand IX as discussed previously (*15*). The absolute values of Δ for ligand VIII with the rare earth ions are only slightly less than for Zn^{2+}, Co^{2+}, and Pb^{2+} ($\Delta \sim 3.5$–4.0) and considerably larger than for some of the other metal ions which have been investigated (*6*). The reason for this is still obscure, particularly in view of the observation that on this basis the pyridyl group, in the type of compound under consideration, is a more effective donor toward the rare earth ion than is the HO— group. Previous studies have shown that the pyridyl group does coordinate to the rare earth ions (*16*), but it would be expected that the HO— group should bond more strongly.

Irving and da Silva (*6*) point out that comparisons using the relationship log $K = a$ p$k + b$ are misleading since for different ions the slopes can be quite different and cause a reversal in the order of stabilities. Although this is unquestionably true for the diverse metals which they were considering, it is not true when the metal ions are quite similar. The two ligands under consideration have close pk_2 values so that the uncertainties are minimized. We are more inclined to consider that this enhancement is real and does reflect the greater affinity of the pyridyl group for the rare earth ion in this type of compound.

One possible explanation for this observation could be the unique properties of the HO— group. As a result of the drain of electrons from the O—H bonding region when this group coordinates to the metal ion, the hydrogen atom acquires a larger partial positive charge than in the free ligand. When this HO— group bonds to the metal ion, some of the water molecules in the hydration sphere of the metal ion are released.

Under normal circumstances it would be expected that these water molecules would escape from the vicinity of the complex and as a result, there would be a significant entropy contribution to the stability of the complex. This partial charge on the hydrogen atom of the HO— group could have the effect of ordering those water molecules which were released from the hydration sphere of the metal ion and, consequently, result in a decrease in the entropy term. Such an effect is not possible with the pyridyl ligand, and it would be expected that there would be the normal entropy contribution to the stability constant.

If this explanation is correct, then it would be reasonable to expect quite different contributions of ΔH and ΔS to the stabilities of the complexes of the two ligands. The preliminary calorimetric data which we have obtained seem to support this.

The nature of the interaction between ligands of this type and the rare earth ions are still somewhat unclear and must await more definitive structural and spectral studies. Such studies are now in progress, and we expect that they will serve to clarify some of the questions considered above.

Acknowledgment

This work was supported in part by PHS Research Grant GM-08394 from the Division of General Medical Studies, Public Health Service, by the Graduate School of the University of Minnesota, and by the National Science Foundation through its Undergraduate Research Participation Program. The rare earth materials were generously supplied by Lindsay Chemical Division, American Potash and Chemical Corp., West Chicago, Ill.

Literature Cited

(1) Ando, T., *Bull. Chem. Soc. Japan* **35**, 1395 (1962).
(2) Ando, T., Ueno, K., *Inorg. Chem.* **4**, 375 (1965).
(3) Bear, J. L., Choppin, G. R., Quagliano, J. V., *J. Inorg. Nucl. Chem.* **25**, 513 (1963).
(4) Chase, B. H., Downes, A. M., *J. Chem. Soc.* **1953**, 3874 (1953).
(5) Hering, R., Krüger, W., Kühn, G., *Z. Chem.* **2**, 374 (1962).
(6) Irving, H., da Silva, J. J. R. F., *J. Chem. Soc.* **1963**, 945 (1963).
(7) Johnson, T. B., Bengis, R., *J. Am. Chem. Soc.* **33**, 745 (1911).
(8) Livingstone, S. E., *Quart. Revs.* **19**, 386 (1965).
(9) Moeller, T., Martin, D. F., Thompson, L. C., Ferrús, R., Feistel, G. R., Randall, W. J., *Chem. Rev.* **65**, 1 (1965).
(10) Pearson, R. G., *J. Am. Chem. Soc.* **85**, 3533 (1963).
(11) Schwarzenbach, G., *Advan. Inorg. Chem.-Radiochem.* **3**, 257 (1961).
(12) Schwarzenbach, G., Anderegg, G., Schneider, W., Senn, H., *Helv. Chim. Acta* **38**, 1147 (1955).

(13) Thompson, L. C., *Inorg. Chem.* **1**, 490 (1962).
(14) Thompson, L. C., Loraas, J. A., *Inorg. Chem.* **2**, 594 (1963).
(15) Thompson, L. C., *Inorg. Chem.* **3**, 1015 (1964).
(16) Thompson, L. C., *Inorg. Chem.* **3**, 1319 (1964).
(17) Tobias, R. S., Yasuda, M., *Inorg. Chem.* **2**, 1307 (1963).

RECEIVED October 10, 1966.

14

Electronic Structure of the Actinide Elements

MARK FRED

Argonne National Laboratory, Argonne, Ill.

The 5f, 6d, *and* 7s *electrons of the elements from actinium to curium, all having about the same energy, produce many low levels. The spectra are complex, and analysis is complicated by the existence of two sets of low parent terms built on* f^N *and* $f^{N-1}d$, *having opposite parities and responsible for two almost independent sets of transitions. Within the past several years considerable progress has been made in the analysis with the aid of new data, especially Zeeman data, and the further help of theoretical predictions. It is now possible to describe the variation of binding energies of different types of electrons as a function of atomic number and degree of ionization, which can be correlated with chemical behavior.*

Interest in the electronic structure of the actinides existed before the transuranic elements became available. This was stimulated by the hope that knowledge of the structure could lead to predictions about chemical behavior. Since the structure was difficult to establish, the chemical behavior was established first and deductions were then made about the structure. These deductions about actinide atoms were vague because chemical behavior is also influenced by neighboring atoms. First, it would be desirable to know the structure of isolated atoms. The most precise information about this comes from atomic spectroscopy. However, actinide spectra are very complex, and each element can produce tens of thosands of different lines. Hence, it is difficult both to determine the energy levels which cause the transitions and to identify the levels in terms of quantum numbers and electron configurations. After 20 years of effort we have been able to analyze many of these spectra and extract definite information about the relative binding energies of the valence electrons.

Energy Levels

Levels are identified from the following considerations. Each kind of electron configuration gives rise to a certain number of levels for each value of J, the total angular momentum. The value of the energy for each level is given in principle by the solution of Schrödinger's equation, expressed as a combination of powers of r integrated over the electron density. Since an exact solution is impossible in practice, it is customary to fit the levels empirically using the angular parts of the integrals (which can be determined exactly) as coefficients for the radial integrals which are treated as parameters. The parameters can be divided into electrostatic interactions (electron-nucleus and electron-electron) and spin-orbit interactions, which are magnetic. The LS level scheme corresponds to the case in which the electrostatic parameters are large compared with the spin-orbit parameters. This scheme is a good approximation for light elements. The spin-orbit interaction increases rapidly with atomic number, and the actinides are more appropriately described by the jj coupling scheme, in which the electrostatic interaction is small compared with the spin-orbit.

In the general case (intermediate coupling) the different parameters are comparable. Levels with the same J interact, and the wavefunctions mix. The properties which depend on the wavefunctions are consequently intermediate, particularly the g-factors and the relative intensities of transitions to these levels. It is an important point that the g's and intensities can be calculated from the same parameters which determine the energies, so no additional parameters are required.

Configuration. If we find experimentally a set of levels whose energies can be described by the right number of parameters, and these parameters also give the right g-factors and relative intensities, we can be confident in assigning them to a given configuration. The assignment would be doubtful if it required more parameters for this configuration because we can fit any set of levels with enough parameters. We could obtain corroboration if the g's fit and the parameters are consistent with the systematics of these configurations. This is valuable because often configurations are perturbed by other configurations (configuration interaction) and do not give an exact fit but a close fit. Sometimes the fit is not close if the configuration interaction is large, in which case both configurations must be considered together.

Even though a proper description of a configuration must be made in intermediate coupling, it is often useful experimentally to identify the levels according to the nearest pure coupling scheme because the level separations, g-values, and intensities approximately correspond.

The levels of various configurations can be identified from the appropriate secular equations. This identification was made in the early

Table I. Number of Levels of Each

Conf.	Spectrum	J ½	1½	2½	3½	4½	5½	6½	7½
f^1	Ac III			1	1				
f^3s^2	Pa I	2	6	7	7	7	5	3	3
f^5s^2	Pu II	10	21	28	30	29	26	20	16
f^7s^2	Am I	17	31	42	50	46	42	35	26
f^2ds^2	Pa I	8	15	19	19	17	13	9	5
f^5ds	Pu II	184	342	457	516	517	466	390	305
f^2d^2s	Pa I	61	110	141	149	139	113	83	52
f^2dsp	Pa I	88	160	203	212	192	154	109	66
f^7dp	Am I	825	1548	2085	2386	2443	2285	1971	1576
		J 0	1	2	3	4	5	6	7
f^2s^2	Pa II	2	1	3	1	3	1	2	
f^2ds	Pa II	8	23	34	38	36	30	22	14
$f^2d^2s^2$	U I	21	40	70	71	78	61	52	31
f^4s^2	U I	6	7	17	13	19	14	13	7
f^3ds^2	U I	14	36	50	59	60	54	44	31
f^5ds^2	Pu I	48	136	206	251	265	252	220	176
f^6s^2	Pu I	14	19	37	37	46	37	38	24
f^7dsp	Cm I	825	2373	3633	4471	4829	4728	4256	3547

days of spectroscopy on an empirical basis without explicit knowledge of the energy equations, in much the same way that the early organic chemists established molecular structure apparently by intuition. Comparison with theory is essential for spectra arising from a number of valence electrons. This is particularly necessary for the lanthanides and actinides because of the presence of *f*-electrons, which results in many levels. Instead of solving high order secular equations for these, it is more appropriate to use the formalism of matrix mechanics. For each value of *J* the levels are described by the eigenvalues and eigenvectors of the Hamiltonian operator, the matrix elements being expressed by the same Slater parameters according to the tensor algebra of Racah (*15, 16, 17, 18*). Racah's methods, although appearing abstract, permit a great simplification in calculating the coefficients appearing in each matrix element and make it feasible to calculate them by computer. Computer calculation is usually necessary because there are still many calculations to perform.

Some typical configurations which are found in actinide spectra are shown in Table I, which lists the number of levels to be expected for each *J*-value. In most cases the number of levels is large and in some cases enormous. For the f^N configurations the situation is not formidable, and

J for Some Actinide Configurations

J									
8½	*9½*	*10½*	*11½*	*12½*	*13½*	*14½*	*15½*	*16½*	*Total*
									2
1									41
9	5	3	1						198
18	11	5	3	1					327
2									107
216	139	79	40	18	5	1			3675
29	12	4							893
32	11	2							1229
1170	803	505	288	147	66	25	7	1	18131

J										
8	*9*	*10*	*11*	*12*	*13*	*14*	*15*	*16*	*17*	*Total*
										13
7	2									214
21	8	4								457
7	2	2								107
19	11	5	1							384
129	87	52	27	13	5	1				1868
20	11	8	2	2						295
2746	1973	1308	793	435	213	91	32	8	1	36230

it will be instructive to consider these first. These configurations are observed in solid compounds and in solutions of the 3^+ ions, and the same levels also occur in the neutral atoms in the configurations f^Ns^2 since the *s*-electrons form a closed shell and do not contribute to the structure. The $4f^N$ configurations have been studied for a long time in the lanthanide elements and are now well established. The same term structure is found in the $5f^N$ configurations of the actinides, although the spacings are different because the electrostatic parameters are smaller and the spin-orbit parameter larger. The low terms are shown schematically in Figure 1. The number of terms increases with the number of *f*-electrons up to a half-closed shell and then decreases symmetrically. The maximum multiplicity also increases and then decreases, so that both factors contribute in the same direction to the distribution of levels shown in Table I. For each configuration the lowest term, which is the most important, is given by Hund's rule that the lowest term is the term of highest multiplicity (*S*-value) having the largest *L*-value (orbital angular momentum). The *LS* designation for the lowest term, in fact for all the terms, is an approximation because the coupling is intermediate. Each term consists in general of a number of levels, and a given level interacts with the levels of other terms having the same *J*-value. The terms mix and each is impure.

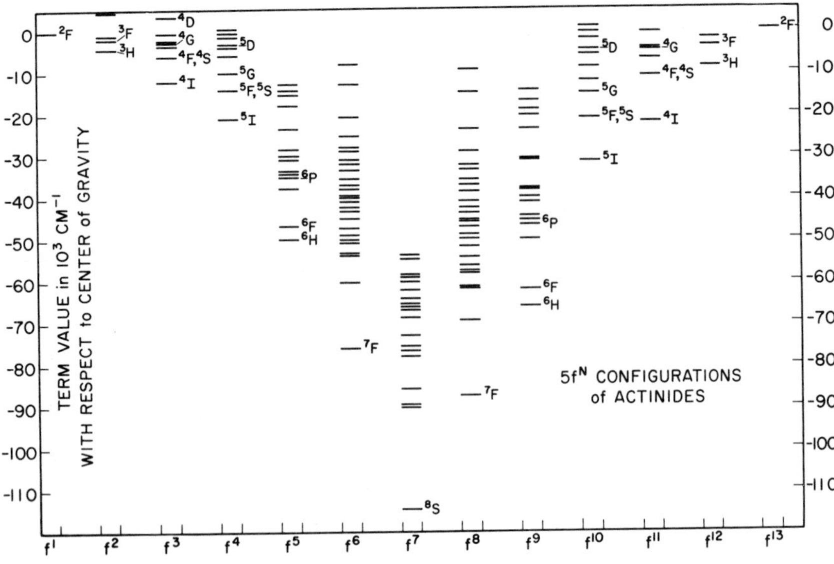

Figure 1. Low terms of the f^N *configurations of the actinides*
Parameters from Reference 4

Matrix Elements

As an example of this process we show in Table II the energy matrix elements for the $J=O$ levels of the configuration f^6s^2, using a set of parameters appropriate for Pu (also appropriate for f^6s^2, which includes the

Table II. Numerical Energy Matrix

Eigen-value	*0*	*51430*	*31405*	*20922*	*86414*	*77288*	*58542*
Term	^{7}F	$^5D1$	$^5D2$	$^5D3$	$^3P1$	$^3P2$	$^3P3$
^{7}F	7703	7004	–1872	–3585			
$^5D1$	7004	37401	3093	17595	–8579	–195	645
$^5D2$	–1872	3093	33866	6468		3640	345
$^5D3$	–3585	17595	6468	26890			–6485
$^3P1$		–8579			76031	–1170	10724
$^3P2$		–195	3640		–1170	68300	–3939
$^3P3$		645	345	–6485	10724	–3939	48392
$^3P4$		–435	814		–3723	–6578	–2430
$^3P5$		456	1341	–1146	1775	–9858	5886
$^3P6$		4936	–1319	–4133	19200	2612	–18548
^{1}S1					–9906		
^{1}S2					–5194	–707	1066
^{1}S3						–1651	
^{1}S4						–5953	

lowest level $^7F_0$ of Pu I). There are 14 levels, and the energies are given by the eigenvalues of a 14 × 14 matrix. In the *LS* coupling scheme there is one level belonging to the ^7F term, there are three different ^5D terms which are designated $^5D1$, $^5D2$, and $^5D3$ by Nielson and Koster (*14*), there are six different ^3P terms, and four ^1S terms. If we had a fairly pure coupling scheme, each level could be considered independently, and its energy in zero'th approximation would be given by the value of the corresponding diagonal matrix element. Each such element is given by a combination of parameters. There are formulas for the off-diagonal elements which represent the interaction between the two different terms which each one connects. If the off-diagonal elements are small (more accurately if they are small compared with the difference between the diagonal elements) then according to first-order perturbation theory the levels are repelled, and each is changed in energy by an amount given by the square of the off-diagonal element divided by the separation between the diagonal elements. This amounts to treating each pair of terms as a 2 × 2 matrix. By appropriate matrix multiplication the eigenvectors of a matrix are able to produce a diagonal matrix whose elements are the eigenvalues. If the original 2 × 2 matrix is nearly diagonal, each eigenvector consists of a large component and a small component, and the fractional composition of each level is given by the squares of these components. The eigenvector components are a measure of the mixing produced by the perturbation. For Table II there are many off-diagonal elements. Some are pushing up on a state, and others are pushing down.

for J = 0 Levels of f^6s^2 for Pu I

46233	*42712*	*9178*	*131005*	*67757*	*62196*	*35881*
$^3P4$	$^3P5$	$^3P6$	$^1S1$	$^1S2$	$^1S3$	$^1S4$
–435	456	4936				
814	1341	–1319				
	–1146	–4133				
–3723	1775	19200	–9906	–5195		
–6578	–9858	2612		–707	–1651	
–2430	5886	–18548		1066		–5953
50500	1058	–1861		–1581	–3692	
1058	45127	–1548		754		–4209
–1861	–1548	40370		8151		–3502
			121739	–23334		
–1581	754	8151	–23334	56183	–3175	17260
–3692				–3175	61439	–2942
–4209	–3502			17260	–2942	47022

Table III. Percentage Composition (Columns)

Eigenvalue	0	*51430*	*31405*	*20922*	*86414*	*77288*	*58542*
Term	^7F	$^5D1$	$^5D2$	$^5D3$	$^3P1$	$^3P2$	$^3P3$
^7F	36.5						
$^5D1$	18.0	43.5					
$^5D2$			58.6	10.4			
$^5D3$	22.3	22.3		38.2			
$^3P1$					75.5		
$^3P2$						57.5	
$^3P3$						12.1	15.2
$^3P4$		13.1					16.9
$^3P5$							
$^3P6$	11.1			10.9			
$^1S1$							
$^1S2$							19.3
$^1S3$							17.0
$^1S4$			10.8				16.8

The total effect is complicated and must be described by the eigenvalues of the whole matrix. Some of the off-diagonal elements are large. Consider, for example, the states called $^3P3$ and $^3P6$. The diagonal elements are about 8000 cm.$^{-1}$ apart, but they are connected by an element of over 18,000 which would produce a first-order perturbation of over 40,000. This would push the $^3P6$ state below the ^5D states at around 30,000. But the ^5D states also interact with $^3P6$, and the result of pushing the $^3P6$ state through the ^5D states can be thought of as an exchange, the $^3P6$ becoming a ^5D. However, the ^5D's also interact with the ground state ^7F, and the final result is a large mixing of $^3P6$ and ^7F, even though there is no off-diagonal element directly connecting them.

The compositions of the levels are given in Table III. None of the levels except the highest is pure in terms of *LS* basis states. The level called $^3P6$ actually contains more of the ^7F state than does the ground state. Since the *LS* designations have little meaning, it seems best to retain the label $^7F_0$ for the ground state because it then corresponds better with the other ^7F levels of different *J*. In the same way the $^3P3$ state which is pushed up becomes mixed up with the ^1S states and is quite impure. For the remaining levels the largest component agrees with the *LS* designations, but the impurities are still appreciable. The level properties are not strictly those implied by the designation. For example, the *LS* selection rule $\Delta L = 0, \pm 1$ forbids transitions from *P* states to *F* states, but since the $^7F_0$ level of Pu I contains a large amount of *D* state it can combine with a *P* state with considerable intensity.

for J = 0 Levels of f^6s^2 for Pu I

46233	*42712*	*9178*	*131005*	*67757*	*62196*	*35881*
$^3P4$	$^3P5$	$^3P6$	$^1S1$	$^1S2$	$^1S3$	$^1S4$
		52.0				
						13.7
	11.3			15.9		
		11.1			20.5	
48.8						
	52.1					18.2
		19.4			11.6	
			87.4			
				20.3		13.3
				18.3	54.9	
10.5				19.8		19.0

Another property which is affected by impurities is the g-value, which is given by the sum of the squares of the eigenvector components each multiplied by the LS g-factor for that component. In general, the g-value is not that of a pure LS state but an intermediate state. This is valuable in identifying experimental levels with calculated levels, especially where there are a number of close levels which can change order with small changes in the parameters. The converse is not necessarily true: if a measured g-value is near a pure LS g-value, it does not necessarily imply that the level is nearly pure. An example of this is the lowest nonzero level of Pu I, $^7F_1$, which has an LS g-factor of 1.5012 and was measured to have a g-value of 1.4975 (9). Despite this close agreement the level called $^7F_1$ is only 65% pure. Most of the remainder is $^5D_1$ and $^3P_1$, both of which have LS g-factors of 1.5012. Any mixture of $^7F_1$, $^5D_1$, and $^3P_1$ has a g-value of 1.5012, and so the g-value in this case gives no information about the composition of the level. The measured g-value of a level gives evidence for the interpretation which is often necessary but sometimes insufficient and does not replace calculation.

There will be a separate energy matrix for each J-value, similar to Table II, involving the same set of electrostatic and spin-orbit parameters but with different coefficients for each matrix element. For the middle range of J there are many levels. For example, there are 46 levels for f^6, $J = 4$, which means that the energies for $J = 4$ are given by the eigenvalues of a 46×46 matrix, and the eigenvectors have up to 46 components. An average level in the configuration f^6 has many components with no especially dominant component, and it is meaningless to try to call the level by an *LS* term symbol. It can only be described by its energy and a string of numbers specifying the magnitudes of the components. There is nothing ambiguous about this description, and one can calculate properties of the configuration such as *g*-values and intensities of transitions. It would be useful and convenient to have a physically more meaningful description for each level, and it is of interest to see if another coupling scheme might be better—*i.e.*, having an energy matrix which is more diagonal.

The energy matrix shown in Table II can be divided into sub-matrices as indicated in Figure 2. There are square sub-matrices along the diagonal containing states of the same *S* and *L* having diagonal and off-diagonal elements determined by both the electrostatic parameters and the spin-orbit parameter. There are rectangular sub-matrices having only off-diagonal elements connecting terms of adjacent *S* and *L*, determined only by the spin-orbit parameter, and there are rectangular sub-matrices which are further off-diagonal and contain only zeros. Since the electrostatic parameters are in general larger than the spin-orbit parameter, the large off-diagonal elements lie within the square sub-matrices, as in the case of the $^3P3$-$^3P6$ interaction mentioned above. In looking for another coupling scheme for the configuration f^N one is handicapped by the difficulty that the configuration contains only identical particles which must be treated equivalently. Hence, the only other coupling possibility is *jj*—*i.e.*, the zero-order states are considered as made up of various combinations of $f_{5/2}$ and $f_{7/2}$ electrons. The matrix elements of these states lie along the diagonal with magnitudes given by various multiples of the spin-orbit splitting of one *f*-electron. Then the electrostatic interactions between the electrons must be added, which will contribute off-diagonal elements not restricted to small sub-matrices near the diagonal. The result for $5f^N$ is an energy matrix in which the diagonal elements are smaller and the off-diagonal elements larger than for *LS* coupling. This matrix is a transformation of the *LS* matrix and has the same eigenvalues, but because of the larger and more numerous off-diagonal elements the eigenvectors will be spread over more components, which is not what we are looking for. It must be concluded that the *LS* scheme is the best that can be done with the $5f^N$ configurations of the actinides.

For configurations which involve several different types of electrons added to the f^N core, such as $5f^67s7p$, the general approach is similar but more complicated. There are more interactions and more levels and also more coupling possibilities. The outer electrons can be added to the f^N core one at a time, or first, they can be combined together, and the resultant added to the core. In any case there are large energy matrices whose elements are given by various combinations of the electrostatic and spin-orbit parameters. The problem of interpretation is to find a set of parameters giving eigenvalues which agree as closely as possible with the experimental energy levels and agree in other properties such as g-values, hyperfine structure, and so on. If there is good agreement, the levels can be identified with the configuration, and the values of the parameters then describe the configuration. The first problem is to find the experimental levels.

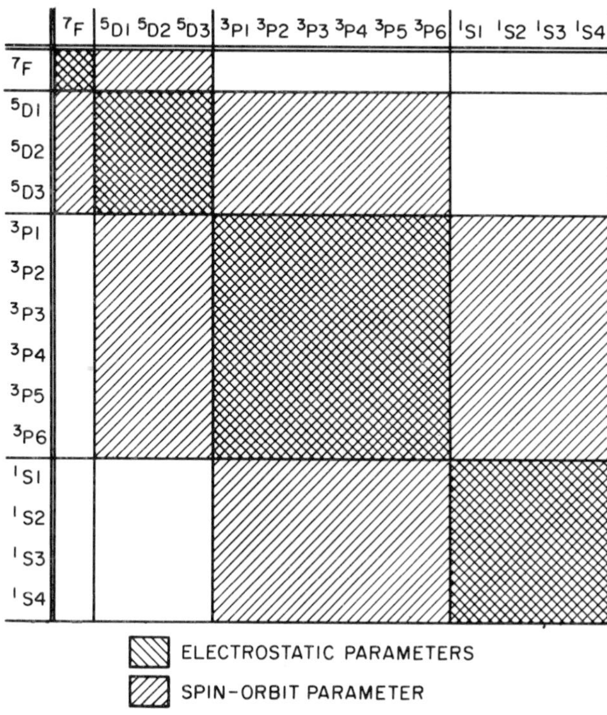

Figure 2. Schematic algebraic energy matrix of f^6, $J = O$

Actinide Spectroscopy

The spectroscopy of the actinides is difficult because these elements are usually hazardous, reactive, scarce, and have complex spectra. A suitable light source which has been developed is shown in Figure 3. It consists of a short length of quartz tubing into which is sublimed about 200 micrograms of the element as iodide, after which the tube is sealed off under vacuum. Microwave excitation produces a bright source which lasts for many hours, gives sharp spectrum lines, and can also be operated in a magnet for Zeeman exposures. Because there are many lines, requiring high resolving power and also high accuracy in wavelength measurements, a large grating spectrograph is most suitable. The Argonne spectrograph is convenient, because it covers a large range in one exposure. Most wavelength measurements have been made manually with the aid of a digital computer. Existing equipment can be said to be adequate in the photographic region, but there is a need for better facilities in the infrared, which is an important region for the actinide

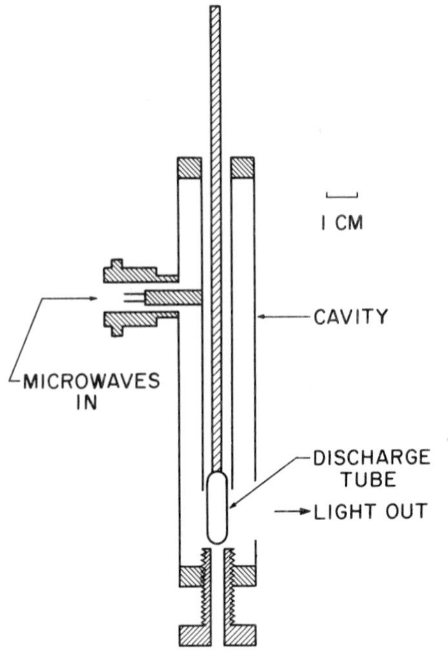

Figure 3. Light source commonly used to excite actinide spectra

In the empirical term analysis of a spectrum, the lines are organized into an array in which the rows are characterized by the term values of odd parity and the columns by the term values of even parity (or vice versa). Each element of the array is defined by the difference between an odd and an even term and thus represents the wavenumber of a transition. The problem is: given the observed wavenumbers, find the term values. For spectra of only moderate complexity this was done by looking for constant differences—*i.e.*, pairs of lines for which the difference in wavenumber is constant within experimental error. If a given difference is repeated a number of times, it cannot be attributed to chance but must represent a term difference—*i.e.*, the pairs of transitions all end on the same pair of terms. In very complex spectra containing thousands of lines there are millions of possible differences forming a practically continuous distribution, and any difference is repeated many times by chance within experimental error. Hence, the real differences cannot be distinguished above the noise. More information than just wavenumbers is needed, and in addition to the labor of extensive wavelength measurements the analysis of actinide spectra requires data on the Zeeman effect, hyperfine structure, isotope shift, temperature classification, intensities, absorption or self-reversal behavior, and theoretical predictions.

Zeeman Effect. The Zeeman effect is the most useful single source of information. Typical patterns are shown in Figure 4. In most cases these provide the J-value and g-value for each level involved in a transition. For example, one sees immediately that the U line λ6392 is a $J = 6 \rightarrow J = 6$ transition, while the line λ6395 is a $J = 6 \rightarrow J = 7$ transition, with g's as determined by measuring the patterns. It turns out that the g-value for the $J = 6$ level of λ6395 is identical with one of the g-values for λ6392 ($g = 0.751$) which strongly suggests that both lines end on the same $J = 6$ level. It is the lowest level $^5L_6$ of U I. None of this could be guessed from just looking at the two no-field lines shown in the center of the patterns. In addition to indicating possible relationships between various lines, the Zeeman effect shows whether a line belongs to the neutral atom or the first ion. This is because the J-values may be integral, implying an even number of electrons, or they may be half-integral, implying an odd number of electrons. The microwave source gives both types, but the excitation is not high enough for third spectra.

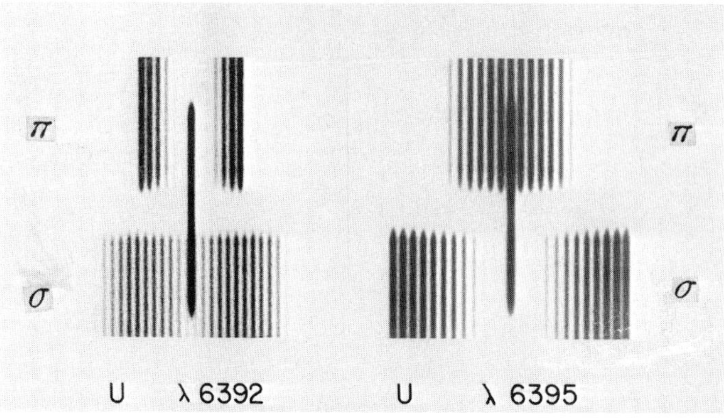

Figure 4. Zeeman patterns for two lines of U I
The no-field lines are shown in the middle

Hyperfine Structure. Another source of information is hyperfine structure. Figure 5 shows two lines from the spectrum of singly ionized Am originating from a common upper level and ending on the two lowest levels. It will be seen that from well-resolved patterns the level splittings can be derived, and the J-values can then be deduced. Other transitions to the same levels must give the same level splittings and *J*-values, and so the hyperfine structure can be used in the same way as Zeeman data to find related lines. This approach was used to make a partial term analysis of Am I and Am II (7). The method is restricted to lines showing hyperfine structure in the odd Z elements.

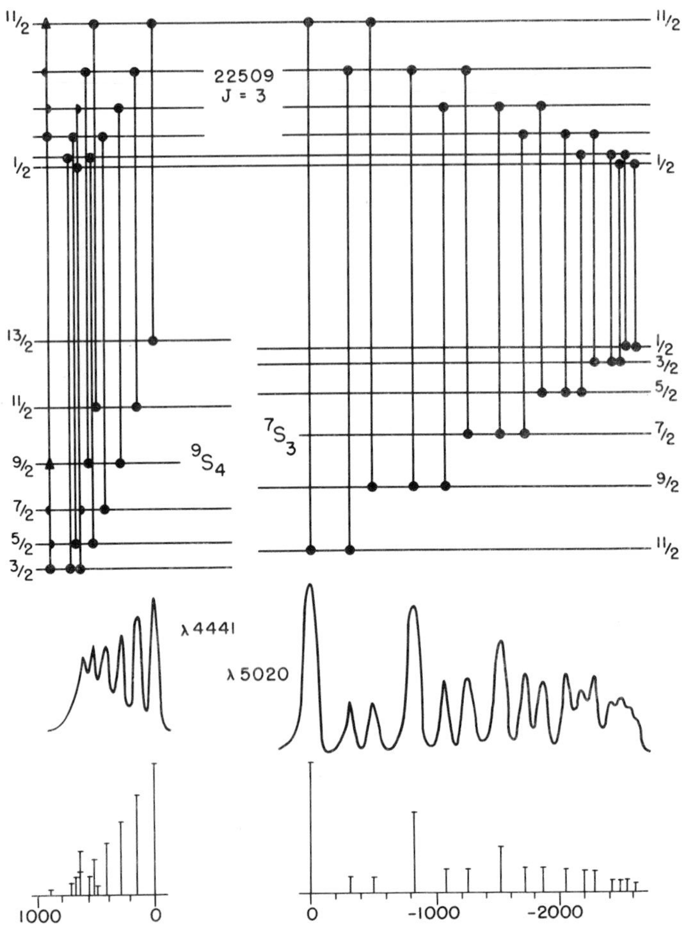

Figure 5. Hyperfine structure of two lines of Am II

The bar diagram at the bottom (scale in 10^{-3} cm.$^{-1}$) has been calculated from the level splittings averaged from a number of lines

Isotope Shift. Further information comes from isotope shift, illustrated in Figure 6 for a line of U I. In an empirical term analysis the isotope shift of a level can be considered a characteristic property in the same way as the *g*-value or hyperfine splitting. One cannot determine the isotope shifts of the two levels involved in a transition from the one line alone, in contrast to g-values and hyperfine splittings, but only the difference in shifts between the levels. The situation is the same as determining energy levels from a transition, which gives only the energy difference between the levels. Isotope shifts present another independent property with which to test for constant differences—*i.e.*, the difference in isotope shifts for pairs of lines ending on the same pair of levels must be constant, just like the pairs of wavenumbers of the lines. Moreover, the isotope shift of a level is important in interpreting the level, as discussed below.

Intensities. Finally, there are intensities and the way they vary under different conditions. The strong lines tend to involve low levels, but the correlation is not close. In addition the strong lines tend to lie along the diagonal of a multiplet so that they do not show many constant differences. For these reasons it is not fruitful to attempt an analysis with just the strong lines. A better approach is to begin with lines which must involve low levels because they appear in absorption in a furnace or are self-reversed in a hot electrodeless discharge tube. The number of such lines is usually large, and one still requires the other information.

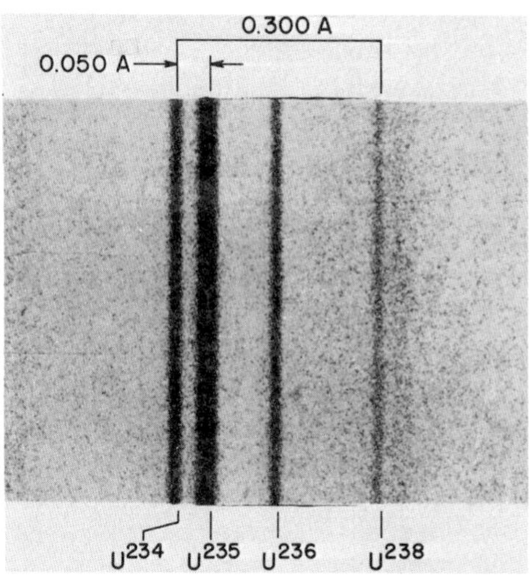

Figure 6. Isotope shift in λ 4244 of U I

Assigning Configuration

With the aid of all these data and much tedious work one makes an analysis, ending up with most of the strong lines classified and perhaps half of the weak lines. This empirical analysis gives the positions of some hundreds of levels with J-values and other properties, the latter usually far from complete. The problem then becomes one of interpretation. Of course, on the basis of previous experience and theoretical predictions one knows what configurations to expect and has a rough idea of the order in which they will lie. However, the complexity of the levels is so great that these expectations are little help in assignments. The Zeeman data, which are indispensable in the analysis, give the *J*-values and *g*-values, but they say nothing about configurations. It is impossible to assign configurations from the Zeeman data alone since each configuration has many levels, the configurations overlap, and they often interact.

The most useful information for assigning configurations comes from isotope shifts. In the heavy elements isotope shift is purely a nuclear volume effect. While the size of the nucleus is small compared with the size of an atom, the Coulomb attraction between the nucleus and an electron becomes enormous at small distances, and deviations from a Coulomb potential near the center of the atom have a measurable effect on the average energy of the electron. This will be effective only for those electrons having a probability distribution which remains finite as $r \to 0$, that is, *s*-electrons. The effect is additive and is about twice as much for the configuration $7s^2$ as for $7s$. (The effect for the inner *s*-electrons is much larger but unobservable since these remain undisturbed during an optical transition.) The magnitude of the effect also depends on what other outer electrons are present because of shielding. If two $7s$ electrons are present, each shields the other, increasing the probability distribution per electron for large r and decreasing it at small r. Hence, the isotope shift for $7s^2$ is only about 1.6 that of a single $7s$ electron. The $5f$ electrons are also effective in shielding the $7s$ electron since the $5f$'s stay inside the radon core and tend to squeeze the $7s$ further outside, thereby reducing the $7s$ charge density at the nucleus. The amount of this shielding is proportional to the number of $5f$ electrons present. The other outer electrons which may be present also contribute to the shielding of the $7s$ electron but to a lesser extent than the $5f$'s because they extend further out. Hence, if a $5f$ electron is changed to a $6d$ electron, the net shielding is decreased, and if the $6d$ is changed to a $7s$ or $7p$, it is still further reduced. Hence, the isotope shift is increased in this process: $5f^67s^2 < 5f^56d7s^2 < 5f^57s^27p$. The shifts are the same for each level of the configuration. If two configurations interact, the levels mix (by differing amounts), and the observed shifts are intermediate between the two configurations exactly as in the effect on the *g*-value in the mixing of two levels with different *g*-factors.

Hyperfine structure is another kind of electron-nuclear interaction and so also indicates the presence of an *s*-electron. In this case, the effect is not additive—the configuration s^2 gives no hyperfine structure. Hyperfine structure and isotope shift are somewhat complementary.

Plutonium. The most fully known actinide spectrum is that of neutral plutonium and is represented in Figure 7 as an example (*6*). Each

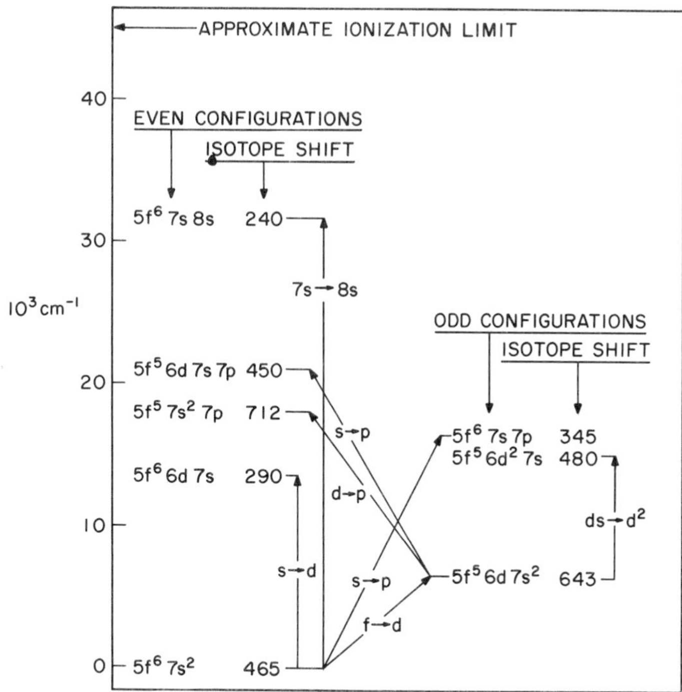

Figure 7. Lowest levels of various configurations in Pu I, with isotope shifts in 10^{-3} cm.$^{-1}$

The electrons which change between configurations are indicated

configuration has levels spread over a range of more than 100,000 cm.$^{-1}$; hence, only the position of the lowest level for each configuration is shown. At present 323 even levels and 436 odd levels are known, and most of them have been identified as to configuration on the basis of isotope shifts. While the shifts deduced for each configuration are reasonable, one can be sure of a configuration only if its levels conform to expectations. Further identification of the levels within any one configuration in terms of composition according to quantum numbers is much less complete. For purposes of chemistry, one is tempted to say that this is sufficient, that the important thing to know is the energy required to go from the lowest level of one configuration to the lowest level of another, and this we know now. These numbers, however, are a function of the Slater parameters and in order to systematize the chemistry of the actinide elements one needs to know how these parameters change in going from one element to the next. The parameters can be said to be more fundamental than the levels, just as the levels are more fundamental than the spectrum lines.

For each configuration the levels are given by the eigenvalues of a large matrix similar to that of Table II. Each matrix element is given by a linear combination of the parameters. General expressions for the coefficients of each parameter based on Racah's tensor algebra have been developed by Judd (*10, 11*), and Wybourne (*20*). Thousands of coefficients are required for a configuration involving hundreds of levels. These are so tedious to evaluate that they are not yet available for all the configurations of interest. A computer program for evaluating the coefficients has been developed by Cowan (*3*) and applied to some actinide configurations.

Even with all the theoretical apparatus available, the practical comparison with the experimental levels is still a formidable task. For example, for the configuration f^5ds^2, the lowest odd configuration in Pu I, Table I gives over 250 levels for each of the middle J-values. After adopting a particular set of parameters to produce a numerical matrix for each J, the matrix must be diagonalized, which requires a large computer. The eigenvalues of the matrix must be compared with the experimental levels, and the parameters must be adjusted to give as close a fit as possible. Since there are many more levels than parameters, it is customary to make the fit by least squares. The least-squares fitting procedure also requires a large computer. Besides these technical difficulties one must correlate the eigenvalues with the corresponding experimental levels. The experimental levels are always more or less incomplete, but one does not usually know just which ones are missing. With small changes in the parameters another set of eigenvalues can be produced which seems to fit almost as well. Under these circumstances the parameters become somewhat indeterminate. There is the further difficulty that the levels are perturbed by configuration interaction, not only by nearby configurations but also by configurations far away in energy and still unobserved.

Because of these difficulties it must be said that few of the experimental actinide configurations have been fitted with theory. The low terms are the ones most easily observed and recognized, but their positions usually depend only on some of the parameters, and the remaining parameters are thus not determined. An example of this is the lowest configuration in Pa I, f^2ds^2. The terms can be considered as produced by the addition of a d electron to each of the terms of the f^2 core. The configuration f^2 produces the following set of terms: ^1S, ^3P, ^1D, ^3F, ^1G, ^3H, ^1I. The triplets lie lowest according to Hund's rule. Racah showed that the relative positions of the terms of f^N are simplified if one uses certain linear combinations of the Slater electrostatic parameters called E^0, E^1, E^2, and E^3 instead of the parameters F_0, F_2, F_4, and F_6. For example, $E^3 = (5F_2 + 6F_4 - 91F_6)/3$. It then turns out that the relative positions of the triplet terms of f^2 depend only on E^3. The ^3F term is above the ground ^3H term by $9E^3$ and the ^3P term is at $42E^3$. The parameters E^1 and E^2 enter only in the energies of the singlet terms, and if the singlet terms are unknown, then E^1 and E^2 cannot be determined. This is the case for Pa I. The Pa spectrum has been analyzed by Giacchetti (8), and the levels were fitted to Slater parameters (5). However, all the observed levels of f^2ds^2 were found to be based on ^3H and ^3F parents of f^2, and independent values of F_2, F_4, and F_6 could not be determined—only one linear combination of them.

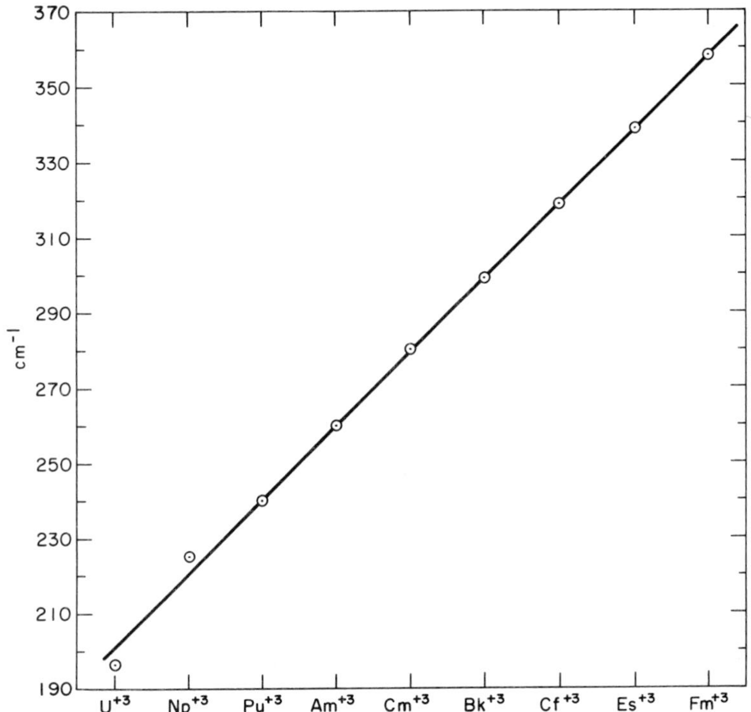

Figure 8. Values of the Slater Parameter F_2 for the ions U^{3+} to Fm^{3+} The points are Cm^{3+} are extrapolated

The same relationship generally holds for the terms of highest multiplicity in the configuration f^N. For example, for f^3 there are three intervals among the quartet terms; they do not give three parameters but only E^3. This fact has been used to interpret the levels of various f^N configurations observed in solution or crystals. Since the observed spectra tend to involve the terms of highest or next to highest multiplicity, they depend mostly on just one or two electrostatic parameters. It is convenient to

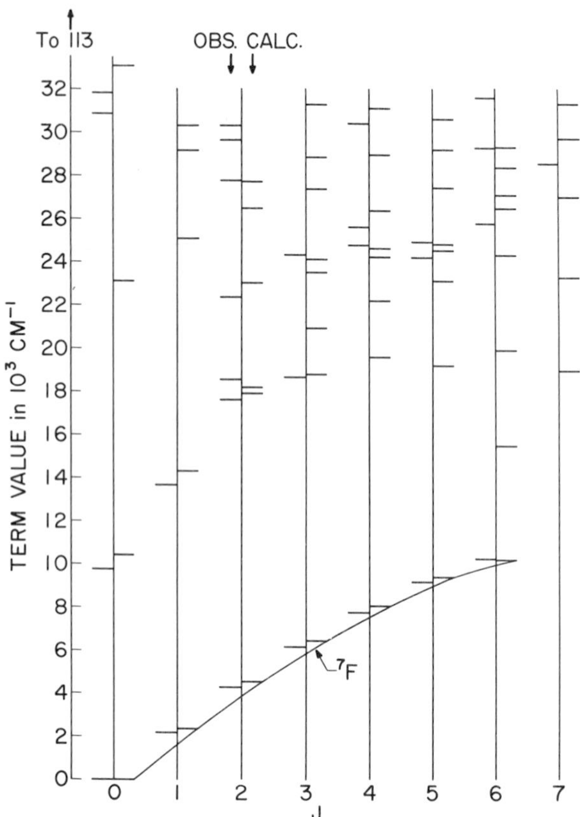

Figure 9. Comparison of observed and calculated levels of f^6s^2 *for Pu I*

take F_2 as the independent parameter and to fix F_4 and F_6 in a constant ratio to F_2. For the $5f$ electron in hydrogen $F_4/F_2 = 0.142$ and $F_6/F_2 = 0.0161$. If one uses the F's in this ratio, one can fit the observed spectra fairly well (of course, it is necessary to add the spin-orbit energy as well). The values of F_2 derived by Fields, Wybourne, and Carnall (*4*) are shown in Figure 8. The linear dependence on atomic number is striking and is the kind of relationship one generally hopes to obtain for the actinides. However, these values of F_2 are based on the assumption of hydrogenic ratios for F_4 and F_6. The good fit does not prove the hydrogenic ratio but just the insensitivity of the observed terms to the ratio. The higher terms observed in the neutral atoms for f^Ns^2 do not fit those calculated for these ratios. Figure 9 shows the comparison for Pu I. It is still too early to give better values for F_4 and F_6 in most cases. The hydrogenic approximation shows that Hund's rule is obeyed for f^Ns^2, which is sufficient to identify the lowest term of the configuration.

Because of the difficulty in identifying observed levels with calculated levels in the configurations $f^N s^2$, it is instructive to consider the configurations $f^N ds^2$. In these configurations there are more levels to be fitted and more parameters to be determined, but one has the advantage of a model which is a fairly good approximation. This model is $J_1 j$ coupling, treated by Judd (*10*). It is assumed that the spin-orbit interaction of the d-electron is larger than the electrostatic f-d interaction. Then one has two levels, $d_{3/2}$ and $d_{5/2}$ separated by the ^2D interval, coupled to each level of the f^N core. The core or parent levels are characterized by angular momentum J_1, which combines with the j of the d-electron to produce a total angular momentum J having values from $|J_1 - j|$ to $J_1 + j$.

Figure 10 shows the low odd levels of Pu I arranged according to this coupling scheme. The f^5 parent terms ^6H and ^6F are known from crystal spectra (*2*), and the positions of these terms should be similar in the free atom. The observed levels of Pu I appear in two groups about each parent level. The lowest set consists of a $d_{3/2}$ electron coupled to a $^6H_{5/2}$ parent, giving J-values of 1 to 4. The levels within each set are split by the electrostatic f-d interaction, which is seen to be smaller than the mean $d_{3/2}$-$d_{5/2}$ separation. The advantage of this model for the actinides is that the energy matrix is more diagonal, the eigenvectors purer, and the g-values closer to the $J_1 j$ limit than for the same levels described in LS coupling. This is a real advantage in attempting to correlate observed and calculated levels. It is true that in practice the coupling is intermediate, but in the process of changing the parameters to provide

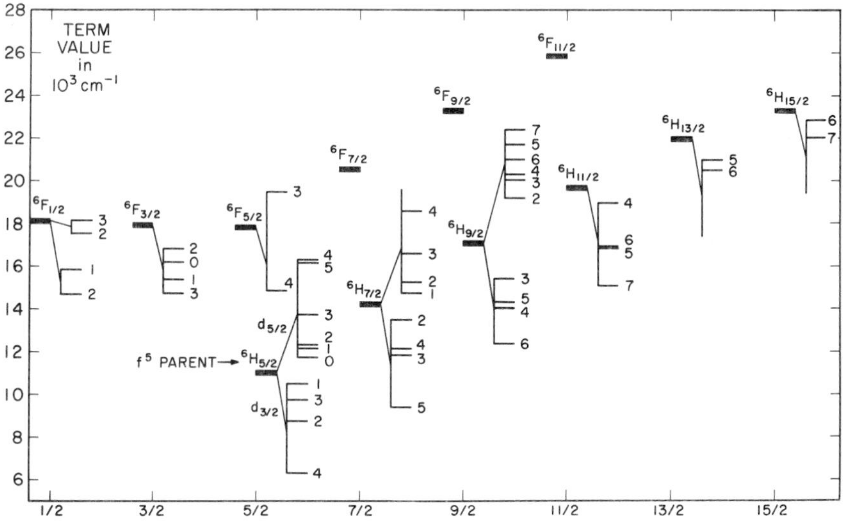

Figure 10. The configuration f⁵ds² *of Pu I in $J_1 j$ coupling*

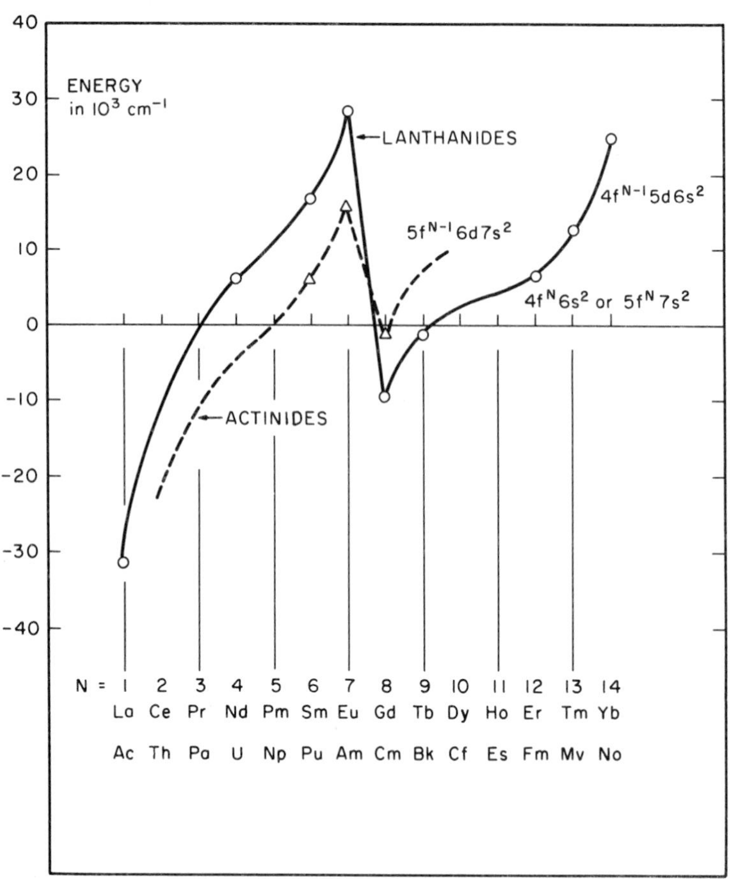

Figure 11. Approximate relative positions of f^Ns^2 *and* $f^{N-1}ds^2$ *configurations of neutral lanthanides and actinides*

a better fit between calculated and observed levels one has a better insight into how the levels should be organized. In the case of the configuration f^Ns^2, where only *LS* coupling applies, the correlation is more difficult.

The J_1j coupling scheme is most applicable for configurations having one electron outside the f^N core (other than s^2). In Pu I, for instance, one can recognize the levels of f^5s^2p in the same way as in Figure 10, from the existence of groups because of the addition of a $p_{1/2}$ or $p_{3/2}$ electron coupled to the f^N core. For most elements the levels are still too incomplete at present to assign many of them with confidence according to J_1j quantum numbers for the appropriate configuration, and the parameters remain undetermined. In these cases without either a J_1j or an *LS* assignment of the existing levels one cannot be certain that they belong to a given configuration. There is one fortunate circumstance which makes the identification of the lowest term of a configuration quite probable, namely the fact that for most configurations Hund's rule is valid. In the case of f^5ds^2 of Pu I shown in Figure 10 in J_1j coupling, the lowest level resulting from coupling a $d_{3/2}$ electron to each level of the lowest parent term, ${}^6H_{5/2\text{-}15/2}$, is also a member of the lowest f^5ds^2 term expressed in *LS* coupling, ${}^7K_{4\text{-}10}$. Thus, in spite of the fact that for most levels J_1j coupling is closer than *LS*, for the lowest term the two descriptions are equivalent. The purity is high for each level of the Hund's rule term, and the observed *g*-value is close to the pure *LS* *g*-factor. The lowest term of a configuration can usually be recognized, and the relative positions of different configurations established.

For the physical and chemical properties of atoms the electron configurations of most interest are the lowest. In the neutral actinide atoms there is a competition between $5f^N7s^2$ and $5^{N-1}6d7s^2$. Some actinides have one of these as the lower and some have the other. An analogous situation exists for the configurations $4f^N6s^2$ and $4^{N-1}5d6s^2$ in the neutral lanthanides, as shown in Figure 11 (*1*). For some time the choice of lowest lanthanide configuration appeared to be capricious, but as more spectra have been analyzed, a regularity appears. A similar regularity exists in the lanthanide ions, where f^N-$f^{N-1}d$ separation appears as the wavenumber of the lowest allowed transition in the absorption spectrum. McClure and Kiss (*13*) have discussed the divalent lanthanides in terms of Slater parameters, and they show that the increasing separation is caused by the fact that F_2 increases with atomic number and also the coefficient of F_2 in each half of the series. The break in the middle is attributed to a sudden decrease in the coefficient for F_2 and to the fact that the coefficients for the *f*-*d* parameters change sign beyond the half-closed shell. Low (*12*) gives the corresponding relation for the trivalent lanthanides.

Pu, Am, and Cm. Figure 11 shows the f^Ns^2-$f^{N-1}ds^2$ separation for the three actinides Pu, Am, and Cm. For the other actinides either one of the configurations is unknown or the separation is unknown. The separation is more difficult to establish for the actinides because it is smaller and the transitions connecting the two configurations are at long wavelengths beyond the region of observation. The first two observed points indicate a separation about 12,000 cm.$^{-1}$ smaller than for the corresponding lanthanides, as suggested by the dashed curve. The relationship of Figure 11 between f^Ns^2 and $f^{N-1}ds^2$ for the neutral atoms holds approximately for the f^Ns-$f^{N-1}ds$ separation for the first ions, and for f^N-f^{N-1}d for the second and higher ions. The energy of a 5*f*-electron is lowered relative to 7*s* as a given atom is increasingly ionized. The same also applies to the 6*d*-electron but to a lesser extent, so that the f^N configuration lies lower relative to $f^{N-1}d$ with degree of ionization.

For the elements in the first half of the *f*-shell Figure 11 indicates that less energy is required to promote a 5*f* electron to 6*d* than for the 4*f*-5*d* promotion in the lanthanides. There is a greater tendency in the actinides to form more bonding electrons, and higher valencies are more common. This also applies to Th and suggests the reason Th is not trivalent like Ce.

Recently the f^8s^2-f^7ds^2 separation has been established for Cm I (*19*) and furnishes a third point which should be added to Figure 11. The Cm separation is of interest because instead of lying 12,000 cm.$^{-1}$ below the corresponding separation in Gd, it is found to be about 8,000 above. This reversal presumably corresponds to the change in sign for the coefficients of the *f*-*d* parameters, which are smaller in the actinides. It also corresponds with the chemistry of the later actinides, which more resemble the lanthanides than the earlier actinides do.

Acknowledgment

I am indebted to Jean Blaise for supplying data for the lanthanide spectra, and to Earl F. Worden, Jr., for the Cm separation.

Literature Cited

(1) Blaise, J. (private communication).
(2) Conway, J. G., Rajnak, K., *J. Chem. Phys.* **44,** 348 (1966).
(3) Cowan, R. G., Opt. Soc. Am. Meeting, Oct. 15-17, 1966.
(4) Fields, P. R., Wybourne, B. G., Carnall, W. T., Argonne Natl. Lab. Rept., **ANL-6911**.
(5) Fred, M. (unpublished).
(6) Fred, M., Blaise, J., Gutmacher, R. S., Opt. Soc. Am. Meeting, Oct. 15-17, 1966.
(7) Fred, M., Tomkins, F. S., *J. Opt. Soc. Am.* **47,** 1076 (1957).
(8) Giacchetti, A., *J. Opt. Soc. Am.* **56,** 653 (1966).
(9) Hubbs, J. C., Marrus, R., Nierenberg, W. A., Worcester, J. L., *Phys. Rev.* **109,** 390 (1958).
(10) Judd, B. R., *Phys. Rev.* **125,** 613 (1962).
(11) Judd, B. R., "Operator Techniques in Atomic Spectroscopy," McGraw-Hill, 1963.
(12) Low, E., *Phys. Rev.* **147,** 332 (1966).
(13) McClure, D. S., Kiss, Z., *J. Chem. Phys.* **39,** 3251 (1963).
(14) Nielson, C. W., Koster, G. F., "Spectroscopic Coefficients for the p^n, d^n, and f^n Configurations," The M.I.T. Press, Cambridge, 1963.
(15) Racah, G., *Phys. Rev.* **61,** 186 (1942).
(16) Racah, G., *Phys. Rev.* **62,** 438 (1942).
(17) Racah, G., *Phys. Rev.* **63,** 367 (1943).
(18) Racah, G., *Phys. Rev.* **76,** 1352 (1949).
(19) Worden, E. F., Jr., Conway, J. G., Gutmacher, R. S. (private communication).

RECEIVED October 18, 1966. This work was performed under the auspices of the U. S. Atomic Energy Commission.

15

Optical and Electron Paramagnetic Resonance Spectroscopy of Actinide Ions in Single Crystals

N. EDELSTEIN, W. EASLEY, and R. McLAUGHLIN

Lawrence Radiation Laboratory, University of California, Berkeley, Calif.

The formation and stabilization of various oxidation states of actinide positive ions in CaF_2 crystals are described. Paramagnetic resonance and optical spectra are reported for divalent Am and trivalent Cm in these crystals. Tetravalent Cm and Pu, formed as a consequence of the intense alpha radiation, are identified by their optical spectra.

Rare earth ions are stabilized in the divalent state in crystals of alkaline earth halides (*14*). This oxidation state is usually formed by reduction of the trivalent rare earth ion to the divalent form by one of three methods—gamma irradiation of the crystals (*14*), solid state electrolysis (*4, 7*), or alkaline earth metal reduction (*10*). The last two techniques are more efficient since under some conditions all of the trivalent rare earth ions can be reduced. Recently we reported the stabilization of divalent Am in CaF_2, the first well characterized divalent actinide (*3*). In this paper we will briefly review the Am work and summarize our further attempts to find other divalent actinides. We will also report on the paramagnetic resonance (PMR) spectra of Cm^{3+} in CaF_2.

Experimental

The actinide-doped single crystals of CaF_2 were grown by the Bridgman–Stockbarger technique. A concentrated solution of the actinide in 10–50λ of dilute HNO_3 solution was pipeted onto a powder of CaF_2 containing 2 wt.% PbF_2, which had been placed in a carbon crucible. The crucible and sample were then placed in a furnace, melted under vacuum, and then the crucible was lowered slowly through the hot zone of the furnace. PMR measurements were taken at 4.2°K. and

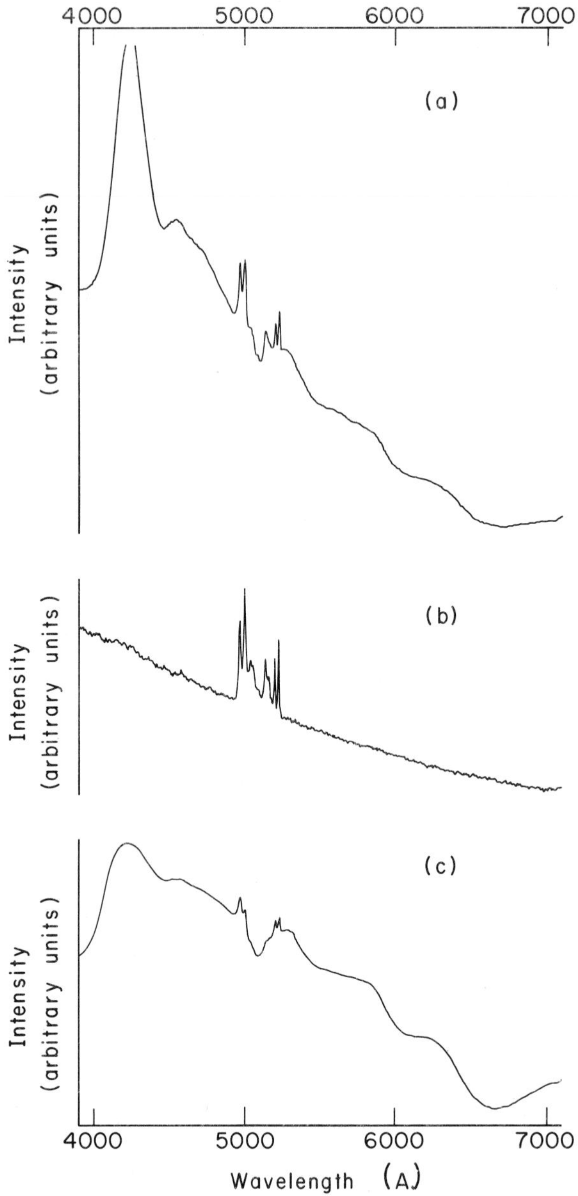

Figure 1. (a) Optical spectrum of a radiation reduced Am^{2+}-CaF_2 crystal. (b) Optical spectrum of Am-CaF_2 crystal after annealing. (c) Optical spectrum of an electrolytically reduced Am^{2+}-CaF_2 crystal

1°K. at a frequency of approximately 9.0 Gc/sec. with a superheterodyne spectrometer. Optical measurements were made at room temperature and 77°K. with a Cary Model No. 14 spectrometer and a Jarrell-Ash F-6 spectrometer using photographic plates.

Results and Discussion

Am in CaF_2. Crystals grown with Am are initially light pink. On standing for weeks to months they darken to a brown color. The initial absorption spectrum shows lines characteristic of trivalent Am (Figure 1b). As the crystal darkens because of radiation damage, new broad bands grow in as shown in Figure 1a. Figure 1c shows the spectrum obtained from an electrolytically reduced crystal. The origin of these new broad bands is probably attributed to *f* to *d* transitions of divalent Am. The crystals which have darkened show at 4° and 1°K. a six-line isotopic PMR spectrum which is assigned to the Γ_6 crystal field state of the $^8S_{7/2}$ (f^7) electronic configuration of divalent Am in cubic symmetry. Since both ^{241}Am and ^{243}Am have nuclear spins of I=5/2, the line is split into six hyperfine components. The measured parameters of the spin Hamiltonian

$$\mathcal{H} = g\beta\vec{H}\cdot\vec{S'} + \vec{AI}\cdot\vec{S'}$$

for Am^{2+} in CaF_2 are given in Table I. The *g* value calculated for the Γ_6 crystal field state of Am^{2+} using wavefunctions given by Lea, Leask, and Wolf (*12*) and the Lande *g* value taken from atomic beam data on atomic Am (*13*) is 4.517. The agreement between experiment and theory is satisfactory.

Table I. Am^{2+} in CaF_2 ($S' = 1/2, I = 5/2$)

	$g = 4.490 \pm 0.002$
	$A \times 10^2$ (cm.$^{-1}$)
^{241}Am	1.837 ± 0.002
^{243}Am	1.821 ± 0.002
$\frac{A\,(^{241}\text{Am})}{A\,(^{243}\text{Am})}$	$= 1.009 \pm 0.001$

Spin Hamiltonian parameters of Am^{2+}-CaF_2.

After the crystals have aged for several weeks or longer, on heating to about 500°C. they emit an intense green thermoluminescence, characteristic of trivalent Am in noncubic sites. Figure 2 shows the emission spectrum of this thermoluminescence photographed at 500°C. and the absorption spectrum of trivalent Am taken at 77°K. There is a shift in the centers of the lines caused by different crystal fields at the two temperatures, but the emission clearly arises from ions in sites that are the same as those which cause the absorption spectrum. This type of thermoluminescence has been observed in rare earth-doped CaF_2, and a reaction mechanism has been given (*9, 15*).

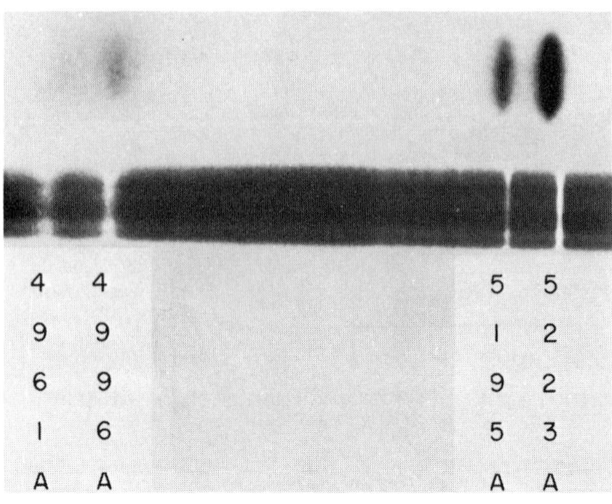

Figure 2. (Top) Emission spectrum of a radiation reduced Am^{2+}-CaF_2 crystal at ~500°C. (Bottom) Absorption spectrum of Am^{3+}-CaF_2 at 77°K.

Cm^{3+} in CaF_2. Crystals grown with Cm are initially pale yellow or almost colorless after annealing. Because of the damage from the high radiation level they are rose colored after one hour. After 3–4 hours the color has changed to burgundy, and in about 15 hours the crystals are black. At all temperatures the characteristic orange glow of Cm^{3+} is present which is attributed to emission from crystal field levels of the first excited electronic state down to the ground electronic state. The change in color of the crystal is caused by the growth of a broad absorption band centered at 5000A. with about 2000A. half-width. Besides this broad absorption band which grows in with time, there are a number of relatively sharp lines which start to appear after annealing. These lines have been assigned to Cm^{4+} in the CaF_2 crystal. Figure 3 shows the energy level diagram of Cm^{3+} and Cm^{4+} in the CaF_2 crystal. For comparison we show the data of Gruber and Conway on Cm^{3+} in $LaCl_3$ (*6*), and the data obtained by Keenan on CmF_4 (*8*).

Trivalent rare earth or actinide ions can be incorporated in the alkaline earth halides in sites of various symmetries. Since the crystal as a whole must be electrically neutral, charge-compensating ions must also

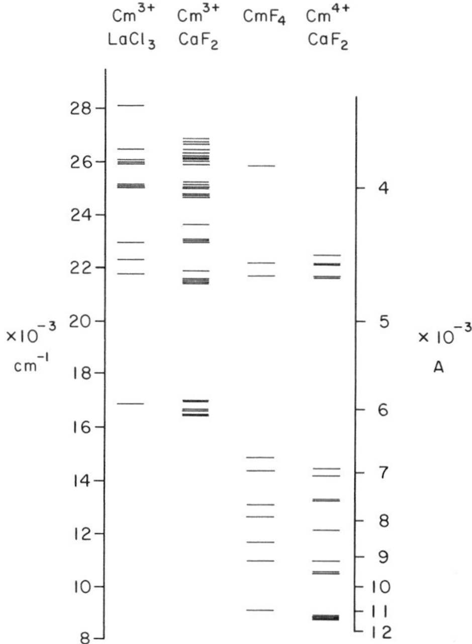

Figure 3. Energy level diagram of Cm^{3+} and Cm^{4+} in various matrices

be present. The arrangement of these charge-compensating ions about the rare earth (or actinide) ion determines the symmetry site of the impurity ion and its crystal field splittings. The most common symmetry sites present in these types of crystals are cubic, tetragonal, and trigonal (*16*). The sites present depend on the way the crystals are grown and annealed (*5*). In our Cm-CaF_2 crystals we find trivalent Cm in the cubic site and in two different trigonal sites.

Preliminary values of the *g* tensor in the two trigonal sites are given in Table II. Also included is the value for the cubic site. In all three sites the crystal field splitting is large, and at 4°K. and 1°K. we see only resonance lines from the ground crystal field state. The *g* value for the cubic site is, within experimental error, the same as divalent Am in CaF_2, and therefore the Γ_6 crystal field state is the lowest for this ion also. This *g* value also agrees with the work of Abraham, Judd, and Wickman on Cm^{3+} in $LaCl_3$ (*1*).

The number of absorption lines we obtain from the Cm^{4+} depends on the temperature at which radiation damage takes place. If, after annealing, the crystal is kept at room temperature, more absorption lines are found than when the crystal is placed at 77°K. More diffusion of charge-compensating ions takes place in the crystal at the higher temperature with the consequence that more symmetry sites appear.

Table II. Cm^{3+} in CaF_2 ($S' = 1/2$)

Cubic Site	
$g = 4.492 \pm .002$	
Trigonal Site I	
$g_{\|\|} = 3.41 \pm .02$	$g_{\perp} = 6.88 \pm .02$
Trigonal Site II	
$g_{\|\|} = 2.69 \pm .02$	$g_{\perp} = 5.91 \pm .02$

Spin Hamiltonian parameters of Cm^{3+}-CaF_2.

Pu in CaF_2. Crystals grown with ^{239}Pu are light blue in appearance and gradually change to a deeper blue in periods of months. Crystals with ^{238}Pu changed to a deep, dark blue in a few days. Optical spectra of the trivalent ^{239}Pu-CaF_2 crystals shows three groups of sharp lines and a number of groups of diffuse lines. This result is similar to that of Lämmermann and Conway (*11*) who found in the spectra of trivalent Pu in La ethyl sulfate only three groups of sharp lines. The center of the three groups of sharp lines of Pu in CaF_2 agree with the centers of the three sharp line groups in the ethyl sulfate crystal within 300 cm.$^{-1}$. In the ^{238}Pu-CaF_2 crystal, two types of absorption lines appeared with time after annealing the crystal; broad bands of ~100A. half-width and sharp lines of ~1A. half width. We have considered the sharp line spectrum separately from the other structure and assign it to Pu^{4+} in the crystal.

Figure 4 shows an energy level diagram of Pu^{4+} in various diluents. The first column is the data of Cohen (*2*) on Pu^{4+} in 1*M* $HClO_4$. Because we felt the agreement with our data on the Pu^{4+} in CaF_2 crystal (column 3 in Figure 3) was not conclusive, we co–precipitated approximately 10 wt.% Pu^{4+} with CaF_2 and took the optical spectrum of the precipitate in a mineral oil mull. These data are shown in column 2. The agreement of the mull data with the crystal data is quite satisfactory. The broad bands are likely caused by color centers formed in the crystal or associated with Y^{3+} impurities. The broad bands formed in the ^{238}Pu-CaF_2 system show no correspondence with the broad band formed in the Cm-CaF_2 system.

If the ^{238}Pu-CaF_2 crystal after annealing is kept at 77°K., no sharp lines appear, indicating that no Pu^{4+} is formed at this temperature. The broad bands do appear which give the crystal a different shade of blue than that which appears at room temperature. Again this result must be attributed to the diffusion of various species which can or cannot take place in the crystal, depending on the temperature.

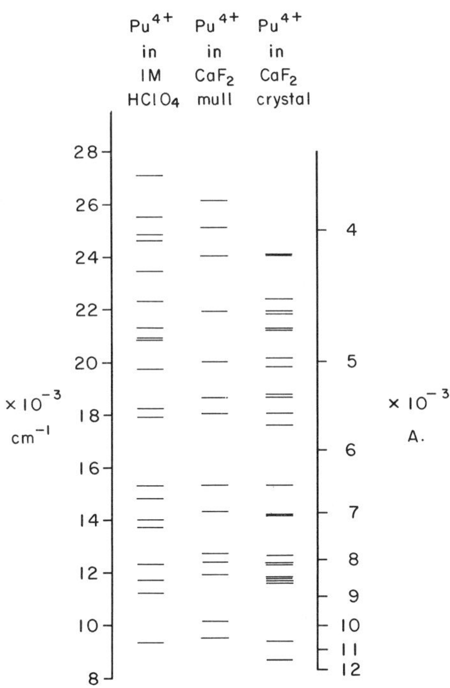

Figure 4. Energy level diagram of Pu^{4+} in various matrices

Conclusion

Our results show that as expected Am is the actinide element which forms the divalent oxidation state most easily. In our attempts to form divalent Pu and Cm we found instead sharp line spectra caused by the tetravalent state. Our experiments do not exclude the possibility that divalent ions of these elements are formed because we do not have an unambiguous method of detection. In our attempts to make divalent ions we have found interesting solid-state chemical effects attributed to the high level of radiation in the crystals.

Acknowledgments

We wish to thank B. B. Cunningham, B. R. Judd, J. G. Conway for many valuable comments, and R. White for collaboration with the Pu experiments.

Literature Cited

(1) Abraham, M., Judd, B. R., Wickman, H. H., *Phys. Rev.* **130,** 611 (1963).
(2) Cohen, D., *J. Inorg. Nucl. Chem.* **18,** 211 (1961).
(3) Edelstein, N., Easley, W., McLaughlin, R., *J. Chem. Phys.* **44,** 3130 (1966).
(4) Fong, F. K., *J. Chem. Phys.* **41,** 2291 (1964).
(5) Friedman, E., Low, W., *J. Chem. Phys.* **33,** 1275 (1960).
(6) Gruber, J. B., Cochran, W. R., Conway, J. G., Nicol, A., *J. Chem. Phys.* **45,** 1423 (1966).
(7) Guggenheim, H., Kane, J. V., *Appl. Phys. Letters* **4,** 172 (1964).
(8) Keenan, T. K., *J. Am. Chem. Soc.* **83,** 3719 (1961).
(9) Kiss, Z. J., Staebler, D. L., *Phys. Rev. Letters* **14,** 691 (1965).
(10) Kiss, Z. J., Yocom, P. N., *J. Chem. Phys.* **41,** 1511 (1964).
(11) Lämmermann, H., Conway, J. G., *J. Chem. Phys.* **38,** 259 (1963).
(12) Lea, K. R., Leask, M. J. M., Wolf, W. P., *J. Phys. Chem. Solids* **23,** 1381 (1962).
(13) Marrus, R., Nierenberg, W. A., Winocur, J., *Phys. Rev.* **120,** 1429 (1960).
(14) McClure, D. S., Kiss, Z., *J. Chem. Phys.* **39,** 3251 (1963).
(15) Merz, J. L., Pershan, P. S., *Bull. Am. Phys. Soc.* **11,** 364 (1966).
(16) Weber, M. J., Bierig, R. W., *Phys. Rev.* **134,** A1492 (1964).

RECEIVED October 14, 1966.

16

Some Uranium-Transition Element Double Oxides

HENRY R. HOEKSTRA

Chemistry Division, Argonne National Laboratory, Argonne, Ill.

ROBERT H. MARSHALL

Department of Chemistry and Physics, Memphis State University, Memphis, Tenn.

The preparation and properties of some double oxides of uranium with the seven transition elements from chromium through zinc are described. Thirteen compounds with the composition MUO_4 or MU_3O_{10} were prepared by heating mixed oxides in air or in sealed silica tubes, by hydrothermal methods, and by high pressure techniques. Four of these compounds, ($FeUO_4$, FeU_3O_{10}, $NiUO_4$ (20) and $ZnUO_4$) have not been previously reported. $NiUO_4$ has been prepared in two crystal forms. The thermal stability, crystal structure, and infrared spectrum (from 1000–200 cm.$^{-1}$) of each of the 13 compounds has been investigated. The structure of $FeUO_4$ and α–$NiUO_4$ is similar to $CrUO_4$, while β–$NiUO_4$ and $ZnUO_4$ crystallize in the $MgUO_4$ structure. FeU_3O_{10} has the pseudo-hexagonal lattice characteristic of the transition element triuranates.

Recent investigations have shown that chromium, manganese, cobalt, nickel, copper, and zinc oxides react with uranium oxides at elevated temperatures to form double oxides with the formulas MUO_4 and MU_3O_{10}. Table I lists eight compounds for which some structural and thermal stability information has been reported.

The double oxides are sometimes referred to as mono- and triuranates of the transition metals, even though the existence of U(VI) in some of the compounds is questionable. This is particularly true for $CrUO_4$ since divalent chromium is readily oxidized. When the double oxides are referred to as uranates in this paper, it should be borne in mind that the term is used for convenience and does not necessarily indicate the existence of U(VI) in these compounds.

Table I. Transition Metal Uranates

Compound	*Lattice Parameters*			*Decomp. T*	*References*
	a	*b*	*c*		
$CrUO_4$	4.868	5.048	11.785	>1200°C.	*3, 8*
$MnUO_4$	6.645	6.983	6.749	1200°C.	*2, 4*
$CoUO_4$	6.497	6.952	6.497	1200°C.	*2, 4*
MnU_3O_{10}[a]	3.79	—	4.14	1000°C.	*5*
CoU_3O_{10}	3.79	—	4.08	940°C.	*5*
NiU_3O_{10}	3.78	—	4.04	960°C.	*5, 9*
CuU_3O_{10}	3.77	—	4.17	910°C.	*5, 10*
ZnU_3O_{10}	7.56	—	16.418	900°C.	*15*

[a] Data on Mn, Co, Ni, and Cu triuranates refer to the α-UO_3 type pseudo-cell.

Among the 1:1 oxides, $CrUO_4$ is orthorhombic, space group Cmmc, and is believed to be isostructural with $BiVO_4$ (*7*), while $MnUO_4$ and $CoUO_4$ in space group Imma have the $|(UO_2)O_2|^{2-}$ chains characteristic of the $MgUO_4$ structure (*22*). A monouranate of copper, thermally stable to 900°C. has also been prepared (*5*), but its cell dimensions and symmetry are unknown. The complex pseudo-hexagonal lattice of the 1:3 double oxides appears to be closely related to hexagonal α-UO_3 (*21*). Since there is little evidence for solid solution in these compounds, the true unit cell of the triuranates must be a multiple of the small pseudo-cell which contains only 1/4 formula weight. The large hexagonal cell reported for ZnU_3O_{10} was obtained by single crystal x-ray methods. In addition to the dry preparative method, a hydrothermal synthesis has been reported for NiU_3O_{10} and CuU_3O_{10} (*9, 10*). Synthesis of hexagonal forms of $CuUO_4$ and $ZnUO_4$ (*18*) has been claimed, but based on the reported cell dimensions, the compounds obtained were probably the corresponding 1:3 double oxides.

Among the transition metals from chromium through zinc, iron remains the only element for which no double oxide formation with uranium oxide has been reported. Both the 1:1 and 1:3 compounds of manganese, cobalt, and copper have been prepared, while only the 1:1 compound of chromium, and the 1:3 compound of nickel and zinc are known.

Experimental

The starting materials employed in these syntheses were reagent grade compounds; they were used without further purification except for a preliminary dehydration of some of the oxides: U_3O_8, Cr_2O_3, Fe_2O_3, NiO, CuO, and ZnO were dried at 800°C.; γ-UO_3 at 500°C. The composition of MnO_2 and Co_2O_3 was verified by chemical analysis and by thermogravimetric analysis (TGA).

Preliminary TGA and differential thermal analysis (DTA) curves were obtained on individual oxides and on the mixed transition metal-uranium oxides to ascertain the reaction characteristics of the individual systems. The TGA data were obtained on an Ainsworth BR balance equipped with an AU recorder. Samples of 1 gram each were heated to 1100°C. at 10°C. per minute. DTA information was obtained on a Tempres Research Model DT-4A instrument. Samples weighing approximately 50 mg. were heated at 5°C. per minute to 1250°C. Differential temperatures were measured with a platinum-platinum 10% rhodium thermocouple at a recorder sensitivity of 20 microvolts per inch.

Synthetic Procedures

Dry Method. Thoroughly ground mixtures of U_3O_8 with each of the transition element oxides were heated in air at appropriate temperatures for uranate synthesis as indicated by the DTA and TGA results. The heating process was interrupted several times to permit regrinding of the samples. Progress of the reactions was followed by measuring weight change, by x-ray diffraction methods, and by infrared analyses. Powder patterns were obtained with a Philips 114.59 mm. camera using Ni-filtered Cu radiation. Infrared spectra were obtained on KBr disks containing ~1% of the double oxide, or on Nujol mulls which were spread on KBr plates for the high frequency portion of the spectrum, and on polyethylene disks for the low frequency region. The spectra were recorded on a Beckman IR-12 spectrophotometer.

Synthesis of nine uranates discussed in the introductory material was confirmed in the air-ignited samples of the mixed oxides. Each compound was identified by its characteristic x-ray diffraction pattern. Some evidence was found for an additional double oxide in the copper-uranium oxide system. Thermal decomposition of $CuUO_4$ or CuU_3O_{10} in the temperature interval between 900° and 1000°C. appears to give a rhombohedral structure resembling that of $Na_2U_2O_7$. Measurement of oxygen loss suggests a formula of $Cu_2O_2O_7$ for the new compound, but its restricted stability range has prevented isolation of a pure phase to confirm the postulated formula. No evidence was obtained in these experiments for the formation of any double oxide in the iron-uranium oxide system nor for the existence of CrU_3O_{10}, $NiUO_4$, or $ZnUO_4$.

$CrUO_4$, $MnUO_4$, and $CoUO_4$ can be synthesized conveniently by heating the mixed oxides for a day at 1000°–1100°C. The corresponding copper compound should not be heated above 875°C. since oxygen loss becomes appreciable above this temperature. The oxygen content of monouranate samples prepared at the temperatures indicated is within 1% of the theoretical value. The manganese and cobalt compounds cannot be prepared below 1000°C. since the 1:3 compound will be formed rather than the desired 1:1 oxide. In some instances annealing of $MnUO_4$ or $CoUO_4$ at ~800°C. has led to disproportionation to the 1:3 double oxide and Mn_2O_3 or Co_3O_4.

The five triuranates can be prepared at 875°C. Nickel, copper, and zinc triuranates are readily obtained as stoichiometric compounds (± 0.05 atom oxygen), but the corresponding manganese and cobalt compounds tend to remain oxygen deficient. After three days at 900°C. the compositions calculated for typical preparations were $MnU_3O_{9.57}$ and $CoU_3O_{9.46}$. Oxygen was absorbed slowly with continued heating and remained more than 1% low even after three months at 900°C.

Sealed Tube Method. No evidence for compound formation was observed when mixtures of iron and uranium oxides were heated in air to temperatures as high as 1200°C. Substituting ferric and uranyl nitrates for the oxides as starting materials also proved unsuccessful. Ferric oxide and $UO_{2.64}$ were the only product phases, thus giving an empirical formula of $FeUO_{4.14}$ in the 1:1 mixture, and $FeU_3O_{9.42}$ in the 1:3 mixture. Unlike the situation encountered in the other double oxide systems, the iron uranates do not appear to have sufficient thermodynamic stability to be synthesized at ambient oxygen pressure.

To achieve the required oxygen composition, the calculated amounts of iron and uranium oxides (Equation 1, 2)

$$FeO + UO_3 \xrightarrow{1050°C.} FeUO_4 \quad (1a)$$

or

$$2Fe_2O_3 + U_3O_8 + UO_2 \xrightarrow{1050°C.} 4FeUO_4 \quad (1b)$$

$$Fe_2O_3 + U_3O_8 + 3UO_3 \xrightarrow{880°C.} 2FeU_3O_{10} \quad (2)$$

were sealed into evacuated silica tubes and heated at the indicated temperatures for two weeks. Under these conditions reaction did occur to give the desired products. Complete reaction was difficult to achieve, particularly with the 1:3 mixture. Traces of residual U_3O_8 were identifiable in the x-ray films of every product. Oxygen analysis of FeU_3O_{10} was obtained by heating the sample at 1000°C. for 8 hrs. to decompose the double oxide, then at 750°C. for several hours to give Fe_2O_3 and U_3O_8 as final products. The observed weight loss corresponded to a formula of $FeU_3O_{10 \pm 0.1}$ for the starting material.

Hydrothermal Method. The hydrothermal experiments were carried out in a 20 cc. platinum-lined Morey bomb (*17*). The experimental conditions were approximately those used by Gill and Marshall (*8*) to synthesize CuU_3O_{10}. The transition element oxide (Cr_2O_3, Mn_3O_4, FeO, CoO, NiO, CuO, or ZnO) and γ-UO_3 were placed in the bomb with 10 ml. 0.06*M* H_2SO_4. The mixed oxide samples weighed approximately 2.5 grams in a 1*M*:4U molar ratio. The excess uranium was added to attain complete reaction of the transition element oxide. The sealed vessel was heated 5 days or longer at 350°C. The resulting solid product was then purified with several treatments of 0.06*M* H_2SO_4. Excess uranium present as $H_2U_2O_7$ was dissolved by this procedure to leave the pure triuranate for x-ray and infrared analysis.

These experiments indicate that the hydrothermal method can be used to prepare manganese, cobalt, and zinc triuranates as well as the nickel and copper compounds. No evidence was obtained for a reaction between either Cr_2O_3 or Fe_2O_3 and UO_3 under the experimental conditions used. When FeO was heated with UO_3, the principal reaction observed was an oxidation of FeO to Fe_2O_3 by hexavalent uranium.

Hydrothermal experiments with 1:1 mixtures of the transition element oxide and uranium trioxide with a single exception, did not give the desired MUO_4 compounds. The CuO–UO_3 experiment gave a mixture of $CuUO_4$, CuU_3O_{10}, and a basic copper sulfate. All attempts to prepare 1:1 double oxides of the four remaining members of the series led to the formation of the corresponding triuranate phase mixed with unreacted transition element oxide.

High Pressure Method. Sometimes, certain solid phases or compounds which defy synthesis at ambient pressure can be prepared at high pressures. Conditions are particularly favorable if the product molar volume is appreciably less than that of the reactants. Since the other techniques failed to produce either $NiUO_4$ or $ZnUO_4$, the preparation of these compounds was attempted by a high pressure method.

The high pressure equipment used in these experiments was a 2,000–8,000 ton tetrahedral anvil apparatus obtained from Barogenics, Inc. The sample assembly and the procedure used have been described elsewhere (*13*) and will not be repeated in detail here. Briefly, 1:1 mixtures of NiO + UO_3 and ZnO + UO_3 weighing approximately 1 gram each were wrapped in platinum foil envelopes, and inserted into the sample cavity of a pyrophyllite tetrahedron (Figure 1). The oxides were then heated for 30 minutes at 1000°C. while exposed to a pressure of 40 kbar. After being returned to ambient conditions, the samples were investigated by x-ray and infrared techniques. The synthesis of $NiUO_4$ and $ZnUO_4$ was confirmed in every instance.

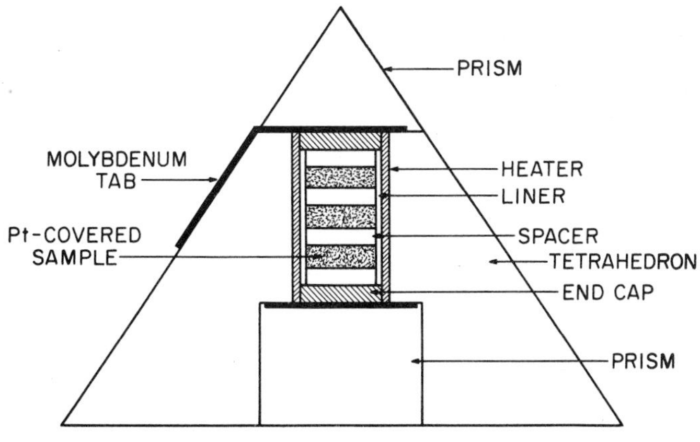

Figure 1. High pressure sample assembly

An attempt to prepare $FeUO_4$ at 1000°C. and 30 kbar. proved unsuccessful, but $CoUO_4$ and $MnUO_4$ were synthesized under similar conditions. Attempts to prepare 1:3 double oxides were unsuccessful, presumably because these compounds do not possess a close-packed structure (See discussion of MU_3O_{10} structure).

Results and Discussion

Crystal Structure. With the synthesis of $FeUO_4$, $NiUO_4$ and $ZnUO_4$, the 1:1 double oxide series is complete from chromium through zinc. Three structure types are formed among the seven compounds: (a) $CrUO_4$, $FeUO_4$, and $\alpha NiUO_4$, (b) $MnUO_4$, $CoUO_4$, β-$NiUO_4$, $ZnUO_4$, and (c) $CuUO_4$.

Our x-ray powder data on $CuUO_4$ are in accord with the "*d*" values published by Brisi (5); the symmetry appears to be monoclinic, but the space group and unit cell parameters have not been resolved. The cell dimensions calculated from our preparations of $CrUO_4$, $MnUO_4$, and $CoUO_4$ are in excellent agreement with those given in Table I and need not be repeated here. Powder diffraction data on $FeUO_4$, $ZnUO_4$, and the two $NiUO_4$ phases are given in Table II. The cell parameters calculated from these data are:

$FeUO_4$	$a = 4.883 \pm 0.009$	$b = 5.099 \pm 0.009$	$c = 11.879 \pm 0.022$A.
α–$NiUO_4$	4.820 ± 0.006	5.188 ± 0.006	11.627 ± 0.012A.
β–$NiUO_4$	6.472 ± 0.012	6.870 ± 0.012	6.472 ± 0.012A.
$ZnUO_4$	6.492 ± 0.012	6.994 ± 0.012	6.574 ± 0.012A.

It should be noted that $c/a = 1$ in the pseudo-tetragonal unit cell of $CoUO_4$ and β-$NiUO_4$, while the larger Mn and Zn ions form monouranates with $c/a > 1$.

Both forms of $NiUO_4$ have been synthesized under similar conditions, and one high pressure preparation consisted of a mixture of the two phases. No tendency could be discerned for converting α to β, or the reverse, during annealing experiments. At present no means is known to determine which phase will be obtained in any single experiment. The molar volumes at atmosphere pressure are similar but suggest that the β–form should be preferred as the pressure is increased. In September 1966, Young reported the synthesis of the β phase of $NiUO_4$ at high pressure (*20*).

The lattice parameters of the five triuranates prepared in the dry way are in excellent agreement ($\pm$0.01A.) with the data given in Table I. A comparison of powder patterns obtained from hydrothermal and dry preparations indicates that only MnU_3O_{10} shows any appreciable dependence upon the preparative method employed. The pseudo-cell dimensions are a = 3.80A. and c = 4.14A. when the dry synthesis is used, a = 3.73A. and c = 4.12A. when the hydrothermal procedure is followed. Analytical results have confirmed the manganese-to-uranium ratio in the hydrothermal compound (1.02 Mn: 3.00 U). An identical ratio was found for the dry method double oxide.

It is apparent from the powder diffraction data on FeU_3O_{10} given in Table II that the iron compound closely resembles the other five members of the triuranate series. Dimensions of the hexagonal pseudo-cell obtained from these data are a = 3.76A. and c = 4.03A. Traces of U_3O_8 persist in the triuranate preparations even after the reactants have been heated for several weeks at 900°C. Diffraction patterns free of lines caused by residual U_3O_8 were obtained by using a slight excess of iron oxide in the reactant mixture. No shift in FeU_3O_{10} line positions was noted in these experiments.

Since x-ray diffraction data on the triuranate powders did not appear to afford promise for determining the true crystal structure of these compounds, efforts were made to prepare materials suitable for single crystal studies. Several crystals of the desired size were obtained in one hydrothermal NiU_3O_{10} preparation. In addition, crystals of CuU_3O_{10} and ZnU_3O_{10} were prepared by the reaction of UO_3 with the molten anhydrous transition element chloride in evacuated and sealed silica tubes at 600°–650°C. for several weeks. These crystals of the triuranates were invariably twinned about the "c" axis. This twinning gives an apparent hexagonal symmetry to the crystal, although the true symmetry is lower. Several crystals which contained relatively large untwinned segments were cut so as to isolate the untwinned portion. Preliminary single crystal data obtained on these pieces gave the following cell parameters for NiU_3O_{10}: a = 7.525A., b = 6.545A., c = 16.126A., $\beta \cong$ 91°C. and for CuU_3O_{10}: a = 7.575A., b = 6.473A., c = 16.679A., $\beta \cong$ 91°C.

The MU_3O_{10} Structure. Ippolitova, *et al.* (*15*) concluded from single crystal and powder x-ray work that the ZnU_3O_{10} crystal lattice is hexagonal and that its pseudo-cell dimensions indicate a close structural similarity to α-UO_3. Zachariasen (*11*) showed that the α phase can be written as $UO(O)_2$ since two types of oxygen sites occur in the crystal. Two of every three oxygen atoms are located in $U(O)_2$ layers along the "a" direction. The layers are joined by the remaining oxygen atom to form U–O–U–O chains in the "c" direction. Each uranium is bonded to six oxygen atoms in the layer and to two oxygen atoms in the chain.

Conversion of α-UO_3 to MU_3O_{10} involves the replacement of one-fourth of the uranium atoms by divalent metal ions. As a result the oxygen–metal ratio is decreased to 2.5:1, and oxygen "vacancies" are created in the chains or in the sheets. Ippolitova *et al.* reported that the "a" dimension of the true triuranate cell is twice that of α-UO_3, owing to the ordered distribution of uranium and zinc atoms in the lattice, and that the true "c" dimension of ZnU_3O_{10} is four times that of α-UO_3

Table II. Powder Diffraction Element-Uranium

$FeUO_4$			α-$NiUO_4$		
I	*d*	*hkl*	*I*	*d*	*hkl*
F	5.900	002	VVW	5.773	002
W	3.863	012	F	4.426	101
M	3.366	111	W	3.865	012
MW	3.070	103	S	3.367	111
F	2.975	004	M	3.006	103
F	2.629	113	F	2.905	004
VVW	2.571	014	W	2.586	020
F	2.546	020	W	2.533	014
VVW	2.433	200	VW	2.402	200
F	2.346	022	F	2.365	022
F	2.254	202	B-F	2.233	121, 202
F	2.218	121	VW	2.094	105
F	2.143	105	W	2.034	212
VW	2.064	212	M	1.9627	123
W	1.9620	123	VW	1.9369	024, 115
F	1.9323	024	F	1.8515	204
F	1.8870	204	F	1.8034	016
MW	1.7686	214, 220	M	1.7612	220
F	1.6892	222	M	1.7424	214
VVW	1.6365	125, 032	F	1.6859	222
F	1.6082	301	F	1.6564	032
VVW	1.5902	131	VVW	1.6281	125
F	1.5678	026	W	1.6085	131
W	1.5348	206, 311, 117	F	1.5505	026
F	1.5187	224	W	1.5182	311
F	1.5048	303	B-W	1.5004	117, 133
F	1.4897	133, 008	M	1.4810	303
VVW	1.4774	034	F	1.4509	008, 216
F	1.4299	018	F	1.3987	018
VVW	1.3590	232, 127	VW	1.3637	232
F	1.3441	305	F	1.3424	127
F	1.3321	135	F	1.3333	135

F = faint, W = weak, M = medium, S = strong, B = broad.

because the layers are superposed so that the first layer is not repeated until the fifth layer—*i.e.*,

Zn	U–O–U–O–U			Zn	U–O–U	
1	2	3	4	5	6	7

Each metal atom is bonded to six oxygen atoms within its layer, each uranium is bonded to a total of seven or eight oxygen atoms, and each zinc to six oxygen atoms. This structure is derived from the α-UO_3 lattice by removing oxygen atoms from the chains.

Data on Transition Oxides

β-$NiUO_4$			$ZnUO_4$			FeU_3O_{10}	
I	*d*	*hkl*	*I*	*d*	*hkl*	*I*	*d*
F	4.679	011	W	4.568	101	VVW	5.005
VW	4.548	101	F	3.473	020	VVW	4.639
VVW	3.411	020	M	3.272	200	VVW	4.100
M	3.218	200, 002	M	3.226	002	MS	4.009
M	2.736	121	M	2.780	121	F	3.625
F	2.665	211, 112	F	2.683	112	VW	3.414
VW	2.351	022, 220	W	2.374	022		
VW	2.282	202	W	2.301	202	MS	3.238
VW	2.054	013	W	2.067	301, 013	F	2.922
VW	2.045	103, 301	VVW	2.051	103		
VVW	1.9013	222	VVW	1.9217	222		
F	1.7926	231, 132	F	1.8139	132	M	2.544
M	1.7556	321, 123	M	1.7825	321	M	2.514
F	1.7354	312, 213	M	1.7697	123	VW	2.014
VVW	1.7159	040	VW	1.7476	040	VVW	1.9478
VVW	1.6157	400, 004	W	1.6394	400	VW	1.8831
VVW	1.6092	141	W	1.6195	004	VW	1.8686
F	1.5680	033	VW	1.5814	033	F	1.7904
VVW	1.5303	411, 114	W	1.5383	303, 240 042, 114	VVW	1.7648
VW	1.5144	240, 042	F	1.4839	420	W	1.7193
F	1.4618	420	VVW	1.4639	402	W	1.7045
VVW	1.4456	204, 402	VVW	1.4547	204	F	1.6436
F	1.4115	332, 233	VW	1.4079	323	F	1.6245
VVW	1.3929	323	VVW	1.3940	242	VVW	1.5821
VVW	1.3714	242	F	1.3508	422	VVW	1.5533
F	1.3323	422, 224	F	1.3365	341	VVW	1.5175
F	1.3153	341, 143	F	1.3045	134	F	1.4202
F	1.2943	431, 134	F	1.2839	413, 314	F	1.3809
VW	1.2720	413, 314, 015	F	1.2765	015	F	1.3457
F	1.2409	152, 251	VVW	1.2075	521	F	1.3206
VVW	1.1905	521, 125	VVW	1.1968	440, 125	B-F	1.2768
F	1.1844	215, 512	VVW	1.1894	044, 215	B-F	1.2407

Our preliminary single crystal data on the corresponding copper double oxide indicate that the CuU_3O_{10} lattice contains oxygen vacancies in the sheets, rather than the chains. Figure 2 depicts the atomic arrangement within each layer of the crystal. The rectangular base of the true unit cell, and the near-hexagonal pseudo-cell are outlined. One-fourth of the oxygen atoms within each layer are missing. The remaining oxygens are arranged so that every copper atom is bonded to four oxygens in a square-planar configuration. In addition, two weaker bonds are formed with oxygens situated above and below the plane. Two different uranium sites can be distinguished; one is bonded to four "layer" oxygens, the other to five. In each instance two of the U–O bonds (indicated by double lines in Figure 2) are shorter than the remaining bonds. These paired, virtually linear, short bonds can be considered to form uranyl groups in the CuU_3O_{10} lattice. The uranyl bond lengths are approximately 1.8A., while the longer U–O bonds in the sheets range from 2.25 to 2.45A. The chain U–O bond lengths (2.08A.) are virtually identical with the corresponding bonds in α-UO_3.

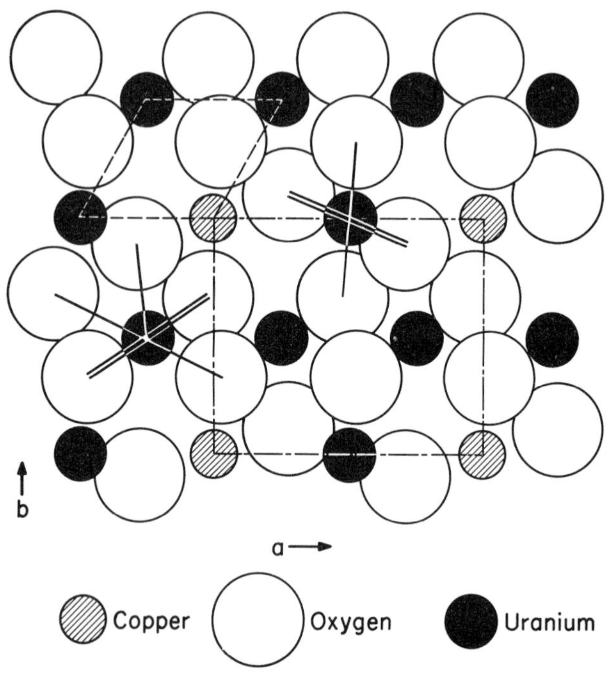

Figure 2. CuU_3O_{10} Structure

Although our results indicate that the CuU_3O_{10} oxygen "vacancies" occur in the layers rather than along the chains, it cannot be assumed that a similar configuration occurs in the remaining triuranates. Based on the transition element ionic radii given by Ahrens (*1*), one notes that the "*c*" dimension of the nickel, cobalt, zinc, and manganese double oxides unit cells follow in the same order as the respective transition element ionic radii, but that the CuU_3O_{10} "*c*" dimension is abnormally long. This fact suggests that directional covalent bonding governs the atomic arrangement in this compound since covalently bonded copper(II) frequently forms four strong bonds in a plane with two weak bonds at right angles to the plane.

Thermal Stability. DTA and TGA studies have been made on the 13 double oxides synthesized in this investigation. The decomposition temperatures listed in Table III are those temperatures at which the DTA trace first showed a deviation from its base line. Supplementary experiments have shown that thermal decomposition at constant temperature occurs 20–30°C. below the DTA temperatures given in Table III.

Table III. Thermal Decomposition of Transition Element-Uranium Double Oxides

Compound	*Dec. T,°C.*	*Products*	*Compound*	*Dec. T,°C.*	*Products*
$CrUO_4$	>1250°C.	No decomposition	MnU_3O_{10}(I)	900	MnU_3O_{10}(II)
$MnUO_4$	1110°C.	Cubic phase + Mn_3O_4	MnU_3O_{10}(II)	1015	$MnUO_4 + UO_{2.6}$
$FeUO_4$	840°C.	$UO_{2.6} + Fe_2O_3$	FeU_3O_{10}	910	$Fe_2O_3 + UO_{2.6}$
$CoUO_4$	1190°C.	Cubic phase + CoO	CoU_3O_{10}	965	$CoUO_4 + UO_{2.6}$
$NiUO_4$	920°C.	NiU_3O_{10} + NiO	NiU_3O_{10}	980	$NiO + UO_{2.6}$
$CuUO_4$	900°C.	CuU_2O_7(?)	CuU_3O_{10}	900	$Cu_2U_2O_7$(?) + $UO_{2.6}$
$ZnUO_4$	925°C.	$UO_{2.6}$ + ZnO	ZnU_3O_{10}	930	$ZnO + UO_{2.6}$

All decomposition reactions are endothermal except that of $FeUO_4$, presumably because this is the only reaction which involves oxidation of the double oxide. No significant difference was noted in the DTA or TGA curves of the two $NiUO_4$ phases. It is interesting to note the alternating pattern in the decomposition reactions of the uranates. The iron, nickel, and zinc double oxides tend to decompose directly into their constituent oxides, while the manganese, cobalt, and copper compounds decompose to other double oxides. The pattern is not carried over into the decomposition temperatures. In this instance, the thermal stability of the double oxides appears to vary directly with the characteristic transition element oxidation states: Cr(III) > Mn, Co(III, II) > Ni, Zn(II) > Cu(II, I). The iron compounds constitute a definite exception to this pattern.

The two forms of MnU_3O_{10} show differences in their decomposition behavior as well as in their cell dimensions. The hydrothermal triuranate(I) loses ~0.6 atom of oxygen at 900°C. as it is converted to the dry method oxide(II). The final two decomposition steps (1) to $MnUO_4 + UO_{2.6}$ and (2) to a cubic phase ~$MnU_3O_{8.5}$, are identical in the two forms. It was noted earlier that MnU_3O_{10}(II) is somewhat oxygen-deficient; the TGA data suggest that the hydrothermal compound may contain some oxygen in excess of the triuranate formula. There does not appear to be an appreciable solid solution region about the MnU_3O_{10}(I) composition.

Infrared. Representative spectra of the double oxides are shown in Figures 3, 4, and 5, and the absorption maxima of all fifteen phases are listed in Tables IV and V. As is evident from the spectra, the infrared results on the 1:1 oxides are in agreement with the x-ray diffraction data. Three spectral types can be distinguished. Qualitatively, the $CoUO_4$-type spectrum appears to represent a form intermediate between the $CrUO_4$ and $CuUO_4$ spectral types.

The triuranate spectra are rather complex, as could be predicted from their composition and their crystal structure. While the powder diffraction data indicate that the heavy atomic framework is substantially identical in the six triuranates, the infrared results indicate that this is not true for the oxygen atom locations. The cobalt, nickel, and zinc spectra are virtually identical, but substantial differences appear in the spectra of the three remaining compounds. The exact significance of these variations can only be interpreted after complete structural information is available on the compounds, but they probably arise from differences in transition element-oxygen bonding and the resulting adjustment in uranium-oxygen bonding.

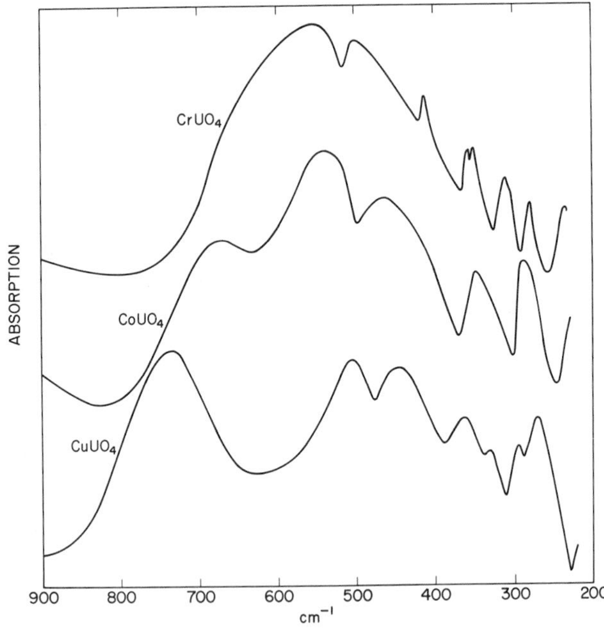

Figure 3. Absorption spectra for $CuUO_4$, $CoUO_4$, and $CrUO_4$

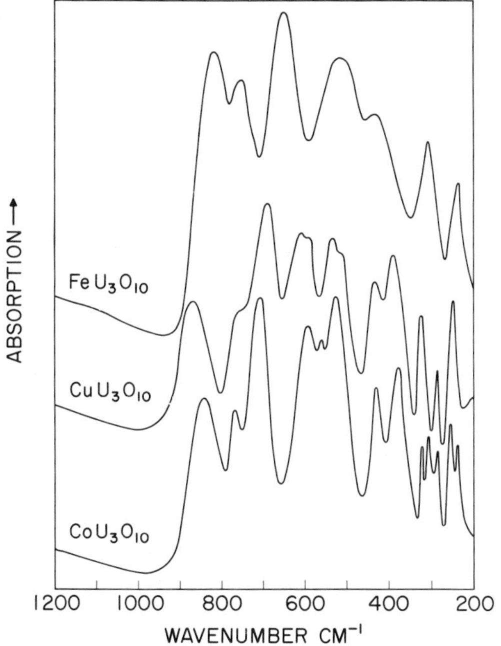

Figure 4. Absorption spectra for CoU_3O_{10}, CuU_3O_{10}, and FeU_3O_{10}

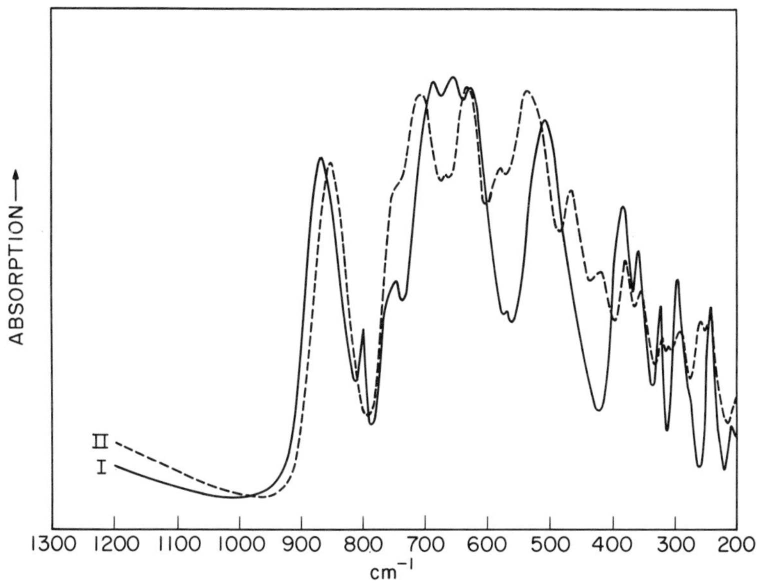

Figure 5. Comparison of MnU_3O_{10} spectra: I. Hydrothermal and II. Air Ignited

Table IV. Infrared Data on Monouranates

$CrUO_4$	*$FeUO_4$*	*α-$NiUO_4$*	*$MnUO_4$*	*$CoUO_4$*	*β-$NiUO_4$*	*$ZnUO_4$*	*$CuUO_4$*
							757 S
			655 M	680 M	685 M	690 M	
552 S	565 S	560 S					
			525 S	535 S	550 S	550 S	
500 S	500 sh						515 S
			448 M	455 M	460 sh	455 S	456 S
412 W	432 W	430 M					
358 W	370 W		350 W	345 W	345 W	340 W	358 M
350 W		342 M					
310 W	330 W						
280 W	278 W	264 M	292 W	290 W	298 M	300 W	292 W
			250 W	277 W	265 sh	268 W	268 M
238 W	235 W	220 W	223 W	221 W	220 W	222 sh	226 W

In general, the spectra of hydrothermal and dry MU_3O_{10} preparations are essentially indistinguishable. The highest frequency absorption maximum tends to occur at a slightly higher frequency (10–20 cm.$^{-1}$) in the hydrothermal samples. This small difference could reflect a slight oxygen deficiency in the high temperature samples. Manganese triuranate is an exception to this rule since changes in band location as well as intensity are observed (*see* Table V and Figure 5).

Table V. Infrared

MnU_3O_{10}(I) Hydrothermal	*MnU_3O_{10}(II) Air*	*FeU_3O_{10} Sealed tube*	*CoU_3O_{10} Hydrothermal*
868 S	849 S	825 S	842 M
801 W	794 VW		
748 M	750 Sh	760 S	768 W
684 S	701 S		
652 S	665 VW	660 S	705 S
630 S	628 S		
570 W	573 M		592 S
	531 S	530 S	
510 S	462 M		525 S
	418 W	440 S	430 S
387 M	380 W		380 S
362 W	353 VW		
327 W	320 W	313 M	323 W
	305 W		307 W
300 W	288 W		290 W
	258 W		257 W
243 W	240 W	240 W	240 W

Although detailed structural information is not available for most of the double oxides, correlations which have been established between infrared and x-ray data permit a qualitative interpretation of the spectral results. The arrangement of oxygen atoms about U(VI) is usually unsymmetrical, with two short primary bonds and four, five, or six longer secondary bonds. The primary bonds form the linear uranyl group, while the secondary bonds lie in or near a plane normal to the uranyl axis (*23*). Primary bond lengths vary from 1.7A. (bond strength = 2) to 2.08A. (bond strength = 1). The double bond is found in uranyl salts such as UO_2F_2, UO_2CO_3, or $NaUO_2(OCOCH_3)_3$, while the single bond is encountered in the chain structure of α-UO_3. Modified uranyl bonds having bond strengths between one and two and bond lengths of 1.8 to 2A. are found in some uranyl salts and in the alkali and alkaline earth uranates. The secondary bonds (bond strength < 1) vary from 2.08 to 2.5A. in length.

The asymmetric U–O stretching vibration of the uranyl groups (bond strength = 2) is found at 950 ± 50 cm.$^{-1}$, while the symmetric vibration, normally inactive in the infrared, can be shown to occur near 870 cm.$^{-1}$ (*11, 16*). The uranyl bending frequency is ~200 cm.$^{-1}$ As the uranyl bond length increases in complex or hydrated uranyl salts and in the metal uranates, the asymmetric stretching frequency decreases—*e.g.*, to 865 cm.$^{-1}$ in $K_3UO_2F_5$, to 820 cm.$^{-1}$ in the alkali diuranates, to 740 cm.$^{-1}$

Data on Triuranates

NiU_3O_{10} *Hydrothermal*	CuU_3O_{10} *Air*	ZnU_3O_{10} *Hydrothermal*
865 M	848 S	852 M
769 W		772 W
	735 Sh	
705 S	690 S	703 S
	610 M	
585 M	588 M	565 S
	538 M	532 S
515 S	513 M	
430 Sh	438 M	415 Sh
375 S	390 M	380 S
	366 Sh	
323 W	326 W	319 W
310 W	318 W	300 W
290 W	283 W	286 W
	265 W	
258 W	255 W	250 M
240 W	240 W	236 W

in the monouranates and to 590 cm.$^{-1}$ in Na_4UO_5 (*12*). The strong absorption at 700 cm.$^{-1}$ in α-UO_3 is attributed to the asymmetric stretching vibration in the uranium–oxygen chain (*19*). The anomalously high frequency observed for the U–O single bond apparently stems from the existence of a continuous chain rather than individual uranyl groups.

The inverse relationship between uranyl bond length and asymmetric stretching frequency has been shown to agree reasonably well over a rather substantial range with the predictions of Badger's rule. The form of the rule proposed by Jones (*16*) is

$$R_{UO}\ (\text{A.}) = \frac{1.08}{F_{UO}^{1/3}} + 1.17 \qquad (3)$$

in which R_{UO} is the primary bond length in A., F_{UO} is the stretching force constant in millidynes per A., and 1.08 and 1.17 are constants.

More recently Carnall, *et al.* (*6*) have pointed out that the symmetric stretching frequency cannot be determined in many uranyl compounds, thus preventing the calculation of F_{UO}. Since the error introduced by neglecting bond-bond interactions should be only several percent, they suggest use of the asymmetric stretching frequency only, thus permitting modification of the equation to

$$R_{UO}\ (\text{A.}) = \frac{53.3}{v_A^{2/3}} + 1.17 \qquad (4)$$

where v_A is the asymmetric stretching frequency.

Based on the preceding discussion, the transition metal uranate infrared spectra can be divided into three portions. The absorption maxima in the 1000 to 650 cm.$^{-1}$ frequency range are attributable to the primary uranium-oxygen stretching vibrations. The intermediate region, from 650 to 350 cm.$^{-1}$, contains stretching vibrations of the secondary uranium-oxygen bonds, and the low frequency region contains the bending modes. These limits are not rigid and may show some variation from one compound to another, but they do serve to indicate the approximate frequency ranges.

While the modified uranyl stretching vibration is readily discernible in $CuUO_4$, it is less apparent in the cobalt type 1:1 compounds, and seems to be missing entirely in $CrUO_4$, $FeUO_4$, and α-$NiUO_4$. The spectrum of $CrUO_4$ appears to support the suggestion of Felten *et al.* (*8*) that pentavalent uranium is present in $CrUO_4$. Their alternative suggestion—the presence of equal amounts of U(IV) and U(VI)—is not compatible with the infrared data unless one assumes the existence of U(VI) without uranyl type bonding in this compound. It should be remembered that Li_4UO_5 and Na_4UO_5 have four primary bonds and only two secondary bonds; the primary bond stretching frequency is found at 590 cm.$^{-1}$ in these compounds (*14*). Thus, uranyl groups are not always present in metal uranates. Uranyl bond lengths calculated from Equation 4 are 1.81A. for $CuUO_4$, and 1.86A. for the $CoUO_4$-type structure. The latter distance can be compared with 1.92 ± 0.03A. reported by Zachariasen (22) for the isostructural $MgUO_4$.

Uranyl bond lengths in the seven triuranate phases are expected to show relatively little variation since the observed range of the stretching frequency (868–842 cm.$^{-1}$) is only 26 cm.$^{-1}$ The U–O distance calculated from Equation 4 is 1.76A.—only .04A. less than the preliminary x-ray value obtained on CuU_3O_{10}.

Acknowledgment

We are indebted to S. Siegel for permission to include the preliminary single crystal x-ray work on CuU_3O_{10}, and to F. Gallagher for the experimental results at high pressures.

Literature Cited

(1) Ahrens, L. H., *Geochim. Cosmochim. Acta* **2,** 155 (1954).
(2) Bertaut, E. F., Delapalme, A., Forrat, F., Pauthenet, R., *J. Phys. Rad.* **23,** 477 (1962).
(3) Borchardt, H. C., *J. Inorg. Nucl. Chem.* **12,** 113 (1959).
(4) Brisi, C., *Atti. Accad. Torino: I Classe Sci. Fis. Mat. Nat.* **95,** 534 (1960).
(5) Brisi, C., *Ann. Chim.* **53,** 325 (1963).
(6) Carnall, W. T., Neufeldt, S. J., Walker, A., *Inorg. Chem.* **4,** 1808 (1965).
(7) de Jong, W. F., de Lange, J. J., *Am. Mineralogist* **21,** 809 (1936).
(8) Felten, E. J., Juenke, E. F., Bartram, S. F., *J. Inorg. Nucl. Chem.* **24,** 839 (1962).
(9) Gill, J. S., Marshall, W. L., *J. Inorg. Nucl. Chem.* **26,** 277 (1964).
(10) Gill, J. S., Marshall, W. L., *J. Inorg. Nucl. Chem.* **20,** 85 (1961).
(11) Hoekstra, H. R., *Inorg. Chem.* **2,** 492 (1963).
(12) Hoekstra, H. R., *J. Inorg. Nucl. Chem.* **27,** 801 (1965).
(13) Hoekstra, H. R., *Inorg. Chem.* **5,** 754 (1966).
(14) Hoekstra, H. R., Siegel, S., *J. Inorg. Nucl. Chem.* **26,** 693 (1964).
(15) Ippolitova, E. A., Simanov, I. P., Kovba, L. M., Polunina, G. P., Bereznikova, I. A., *Radiokhimiya* 660 (1959).
(16) Jones, L. H., *Spectrochim Acta* **11,** 409 (1959).
(17) Morey, G. W., Ingerson, E., *Am. Mineralogist* **22,** 1121 (1937).
(18) Neufeldt, S. J., Ph.D. Dissertation, München (1963).
(19) Tsuboi, M., Terada, M., Shimanouchi, T., *J. Chem. Phys.* **36,** 1301 (1962).
(20) Young, A. P., *Science* **153,** 1380 (1966).
(21) Zachariasen, W. H., *Acta Cryst.* **1,** 265 (1948).
(22) *Ibid.,* **7,** 788 (1954).
(23) *Ibid.,* p. 795.
(24) Zachariasen, W. H., Plettinger, H. A., *Acta Cryst.* **12,** 526 (1959).

RECEIVED October 17, 1966. Based on work performed under the auspices of the U. S. Atomic Energy Commission.

17

The Solid-State Chemistry of Americium Oxides

C. KELLER

University of Karlsruhe and Nuclear Research Centre, Karlsruhe, Germany

Ternary and polynary oxides of trivalent to hexavalent americium are obtained by solid-state reactions of Am_2O_3 and AmO_2 with the oxides of various elements. Compounds of pentavalent and hexavalent americium, which are isostructural with the corresponding ternary oxides of Pa, U, Np, and Pu, are formed only with the oxides of alkali metals and alkaline earth metals. By reaction of AmO_2 with oxides of tetravalent elements—e.g., *SiO_2, GeO_2, ZrO_2, HfO_2 or ThO_2—ternary oxides or oxide phases with tetravalent americium are stabilized. The solid-state reaction of AmO_2 with most group V elements yields compounds with trivalent americium which are isostructural with the analogous rare earth compounds. In the last types of reactions americium exhibits a typical actinide behavior.*

In accordance with its electronic configuration and the resulting position in the periodic system of elements the actinide element americium is the heavy homolog of the rare earth element europium (*14*):

$$\text{Americium: } 5s^2p^6d^{10}f^7\ 6s^2p^67s^2\,(^8S_{7/2})$$

$$\text{Europium: } 4s^2p^6d^{10}f^7\ 6s^2p^67s^2\,(^8S_{7/2}).$$

Despite this formal relationship a comparison of the chemical properties of the two elements shows considerable differences, not only of a qualitative but also of a fundamental nature. All experiments to date have failed to prepare bivalent americium in analogy with Eu(II). (Compounds such as AmO and AmH_2 contain bivalent americium only in a formal sense). In contrast to the rare earth elements, americium is able to exist in solution as well as in solid compounds in the oxidation states +4, +5, and +6. This shows a close relation to the elements preceding it in the periodic system of elements—*i.e.*, uranium, neptunium, and plutonium.

The 3+ valence of americium is the most stable in solution as well as in solid compounds, as shown by its behavior as a typical actinide element. Because of the similar ionic radii of Am^{3+} ($r = 0.99$ A.) and Nd^{3+} ($r = 0.995$ A.), there is a close relationship in the chemical behavior of these elements in the 3+ valence state.

Two oxides of americium are known so far: AmO_2 and Am_2O_3 (*40*). AmO_2, which crystallizes in the fluorite lattice ($a = 5.377 \pm 0.001$ A.), is formed by annealing the oxalate, hydroxide, or other easily decomposing compounds of americium in oxygen at 800°–1100°C. Reduction of AmO_2 with hydrogen at 600°C. yields the cubic modification of Am_2O_3 (Mn_2O_3-type, rare earth C-type oxide, $a = 11.03$ A.), at 800°C. the hexagonal modification (La_2O_3-type, rare earth A-type oxide, $a = 3.817$ A., $c = 5.971$ A.). The system Am-O has not been investigated systematically as yet.

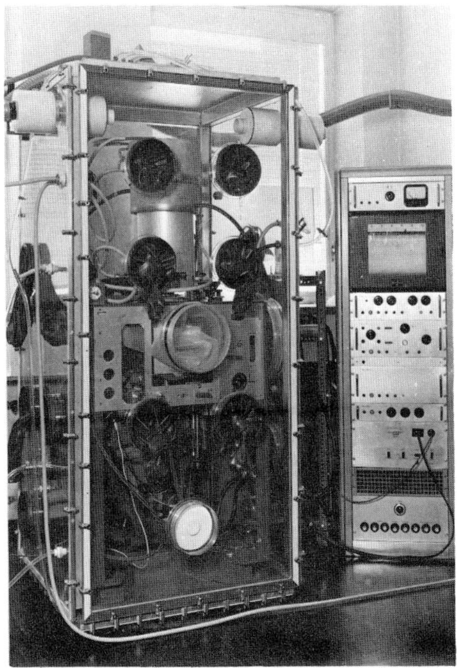

Figure 1. Glove-box with thermomicrobalance (type Mettler) installed

This paper briefly surveys the solid-state reactions of AmO_2 and Am_2O_3 in the presence of second or third metal oxides at higher temperatures. The main interest is focused upon three types of reactions:

(a) Reaction with the oxides of alkali metals and alkaline earth metals with the aim of producing ternary oxides of pentavalent and hexavalent americium.

(b) Reaction with oxides of the group IV elements. It was to be expected that in this reaction the 4+ valence of americium would be maintained with compounds of the general type $A^{IV}B^{IV}O_4$, and in solid solutions of the AO_2-BO_2 type.

(c) Thermal behavior of AmO_2 in the presence of oxides of group III and V elements. It was to be expected that americium would behave as a typical actinide element—*i.e.*, that the majority of the ternary oxides to be expected contain Am(III). This assumption is based upon the analogous behavior of CeO_2, Pr_6O_{11}, and Tb_4O_7 found in reactions with oxides of group V elements as well as upon the excellent thermal stability and the high lattice symmetry of compounds like $Me^{III}X^{III}O_3$ and $Me^{III}X^{V}O_4$.

Methods of Investigation

All investigations were carried out in glove boxes with quantities of 5–20 mg. $^{241}AmO_2$. The experimental results were evaluated mainly by x-ray analysis. In special cases, differential thermal analysis (DTA) and the thermogravimetric analysis (TGA) (Figure 1) were employed, respectively. The valence of americium in the ternary oxides with Am(V) and Am(VI), after dissolution of the reaction product in diluted $HClO_4$, was determined by recording an absorption spectrum of the solution obtained.

Table I. Ternary Oxides of Tri- to Hexavalent

System	*Composition*	*Reaction Conditions*
Li_2O/AmO_3	Li_4AmO_5	$2Li_2O + 2AmO_2/450°C./O_2/4$ hrs.
	Li_6AmO_6	$3.5Li_2O + AmO_2/360°C./O_2/12$ hrs.
$Li_2O/AmO_{2.5}$	Li_3AmO_4	$1.5Li_2O + AmO_2/700°C./O_2/6$ hrs.
	Li_7AmO_6	$Li_3AmO_4 + Li_2O/900°C./N_2/12$ hrs.
$LiLi_2O/AmO_2$	Li_2AmO_3	$Li_2O + AmO_2/600°C./$vacuum/16 hrs.
	Li_8AmO_6	$4Li_2O + AmO_2/600°C./$vacuum/16 hrs.
$Li_2O/AmO_{1.5}$	$LiAmO_2$	$Li_2O + Am_2O_3/600°C./H_2/30$ hrs.
Na_2O/AmO_3	Na_4AmO_5	$2.5Na_2O_2 + AmO_2/< 300°C./O_2/4$ hrs.
	Na_6AmO_6	$3.5Na_2O_2 + AmO_2/400°C./O_2/6$ hrs.
$Na_2O/AmO_{2.5}$	Na_3AmO_4	$2Na_2O_2 + AmO_2/650°C./O_2/4$ hrs.
Na_2O/AmO_2	Na_2AmO_3	$Na_2CO_3 + AmO_2/750°C./N_2/6$ hrs.
BaO/AmO_3	Ba_3AmO_6	$BaO_2 + AmO_2/1100°C./O_2/8$ hrs.
BaO/AmO_2	$BaAmO_3$	$1.5BaO + AmO_2/1250°C./O_2/30$ hrs.
$BaO/AmO_{1.5}$	$BaO \cdot Am_2O_3$	$BaAmO_2/1250°C./H_2$
SrO/AmO_2	$SrAmO_3$	$1.5SrO + AmO_2/1250°C./O_2/30$ hrs.

Results and Discussion

The reaction conditions and the lattice constants of the americium compounds described in the following sections are listed in Tables I and II.

Ternary Oxides of Trivalent to Hexavalent Americium with Lithium and Sodium. Solid-state reactions of AmO_2 with Li_2O in oxygen at 350°–450°C., depending on the molar ratio of $Li_2O:AmO_2$, result in the compounds Li_4AmO_5 and Li_6AmO_6 with hexavalent americium (*4, 20*). The blackish-brown Li_4AmO_5 has the tetragonal structure of Li_4UO_5 discovered by Kovba (*26*), and Hoeckstra and Siegel (*12*), respectively, which is a lattice derived from α-UF_5 closely related to the rocksalt structure. In adherence to the hexagonal indexing of x-ray powder patterns of the compounds Li_7BiO_6 and Li_8PbO_6 given by Blasse (*5*), and Scholder and Huppert (*38*), respectively, it was also possible to determine the lattice constants of $Me_6Am^{VI}O_6$ (Li, Na), $Li_7Am^{V}O_6$, and $Li_8Am^{IV}O_6$. Despite the different Am:Li ratio and the different valence of americium the compounds of the type Li_xAmO_6 ($x = 6, 7, 8$) are isostructural among each other.

The analogous solid-state reaction of Na_2O_2 with AmO_2 in oxygen always results in α-Na_4AmO_5 of the rocksalt structure below 300°C., but in the temperature range between 300° and 500°C., one obtains Na_6AmO_6

Americium with Alkaline and Alkaline Earth Elements

Type of Structure	*Lattice Constants (A.)* *a*	*c*	*Isostructural Compounds*
Li_4UO_5 (*12, 26*), tetrag.	6.666 ± 0.001	4.415 ± 0.002	Np, Pu
Li_6ReO_6 (*38*), hexag.	5.174 ± 0.005	14.59 ± 0.05	Tc, Np, Pu
Li_3UO_4 (*5*), tetrag.	4.459 ± 0.005	8.355 ± 0.01	Pa, U, Np, Pu
Li_7BiO_6 (*5*), hexag.	5.54 ± 0.02	15.65 ± 0.05	Sb, Nb, Ta, Os, Pa, U, Np, Pu
Li_2PrO_3, unknown			
Li_8PbO_6 (*5*), hexag.	5.62 ± 0.02	15.96 ± 0.05	Sn, Zr, Ce, Pr, Tb, Ir, Pt, Pu
α-$LiEuO_2$ (*3*), monoklin			La, Pr, Nd, Sm, Gd, Eu
α-Na_4UO_5, cubic			U, Np, Pu
Li_6ReO_6, hexag.	5.76 ± 0.03	16.10 ± 0.1	Re, Tc, Np, Pu
Na_3UO_4 (*38*), cubic	4.757 ± 0.005		U, Ru
Li_2SnO_3 (*27*), monoklin	5.92 ± 0.01	11.23 ± 0.02	Ti, Tc
	b = 10.26 ± 0.02	β = 100°7′	
Ba_3WO_6, cubic	8.81 ± 0.01		U, Np, Pu, Mo
$CaTiO_3$, cubic	4.365 ± 0.005		Pa, U, Np, Pu, Tc, Zr
$CaFe_2O_4$, orthorhomb.			R.E., Y, Sc
$CaTiO_3$, pseudocubic	4.23 ± 0.05		

Table IIa. Ternary and Polynary Oxides of Tetra-

System	*Composition*	*Reaction Conditions*
Am_2O_3/B_2O_3	$AmBO_3$	$AmO_2 + H_3BO_3$/900°C./12 hrs.
Am_2O_3/Al_2O_3	$AmAlO_3$	$Am(OH)_3 + Al(OH)_3$/1250°C./16 hrs.
Am_2O_3/V_2O_3	$AmVO_3$	$AmVO_4 + H_2$/1200°C./8 hrs.
AmO_2/SiO_2	$AmSiO_4$	$Am(OH)_4 + SiO_2 \cdot aq$/230°C./7d
AmO_2/GeO_2	$AmGeO_4$	$Am(OH)_4 + GeO_2 \cdot aq$/230°C./7d
$BaO/AmO_{1.5}/Nb_2O_5$	Ba_2AmNbO_6	$BaO + AmNbO_4$/1300°C./8 hrs.
$BaO/AmO_{1.5}/Ta_2O_5$	Ba_2AmTaO_6	$BaO + AmTaO_4$/1300°C./8 hrs.
$TiO_2/AmO_{1.5}/Nb_2O_5$	$AmNbTiO_6$	$TiO_2 + AmNbO_4$/1150°C./24 hrs.
$TiO_2/AmO_{1.5}/Ta_2O_5$	$AmTaTiO_6$	$TiO_2 + AmTaO_4$/1150°C./24 hrs.

Table IIb. Ternary and Polynary Oxides of Tetra-

System	*Composition*	*Reaction Conditions*
$AmO_{1.5}/ZrO_2$	$Am_2Zr_2O_7$	$AmO_2 + ZrO_2$/1200°C./20 hrs./H_2
$AmO_{1.5}/HfO_2$	$Am_2Hf_2O_7$	$AmO_2 + HfO_2$/1400°C./20 hrs./H_2
$AmO_{1.5}/P_2O_5$	$AmPO_4 \cdot$ 0-0.5H_2O	$Am^{3+} + HPO_4^{2-}$/80°C./4 hrs.
	$AmPO_4$	$AmO_2 + (NH_4)_2HPO_4$/800°C./6 hrs.
$AmO_{1.5}/As_2O_5$	$AmAsO_4$	$Am(NO_3)_3 + (NH_4)_2HAsO_4$/1000°C.
$AmO_{1.5}/V_2O_5$	$AmVO_4$	$2AmO_2 + V_2O_5$/1000°C./10 hrs.
$AmO_{1.5}/Nb_2O_5$	α-$AmNbO_4$	$2AmO_2 + Nb_2O_5$/1200°C./24 hrs.
	β-$AmNbO_4$	660°C.
	$Am_{0.33}NbO_3$	$2AmO_2 + 3Nb_2O_5$/1200°C./24 hrs.
$AmO_{1.5}/Ta_2O_5$	α-$AmTaO_4$	$2AmO_2 + Ta_2O_5$/1200°C./24 hrs.
	$Am_{0.33}TaO_3$	$2AmO_2 + 3Ta_2O_5$/1200°C./24 hrs.
$AmO_{1.5}/Pa_2O_5$	$(Am_{0.5}^{III}, Pa_{0.5}^{V})O_2$	$2AmO_2 + Pa_2O_5$/1100°C./8 hrs.

independently of the Na:Am ratio. Quantitative oxidation of Am(IV) to Am(VI) takes a surplus of about 0.3–0.5 moles Na_2O_2. If there is a sodium shortage, part of the AmO_2 is present after the reaction without having undergone conversion to Am(VI).

The compounds of hexavalent americium with alkali metals have little thermal stability. At 550°C. (Me = Li) and 700°C. (Me = Na) there is a loss of oxygen, and compounds with pentavalent americium are formed (*31*). The continued thermal decomposition in the system Li_2O-AmO_2-O_2 results directly in AmO_2 above 900°–1000°C.; whereas the decomposition of Na_3AmO_4 leads to AmO_2 *via* Na_2AmO_3. The indi-

and Trivalent Americium with Group III-V Elements

Type of Structure	Lattice Constants (A.) *a*	*b*	*c*	Isostructural Compounds
Aragonite, orthorhomb.	5.053	8.092	5.738	R.E.
$LaAlO_3$, hexagonal	5.336		12.91	Pr, Nd, Pu
$GdVO_3$, orthorhomb.	5.45	5.85	7.76	R.E., Pu
$ZrSiO_4$, tetragonal	6.87		6.20	Th-Pu
$CaWO_4$, tetragonal	5.04		11.03	Zr, Ce, Th-Pu
Ba_3WO_6, cubic	8.520			R.E.
Ba_3WO_6, cubic	8.518			R.E.
$CaTa_2O_6$, orthorhomb.	5.34	11.00	7.53	La-Eu (-Lu)
$CaTa_2O_6$, orthorhomb.	5.33	10.95	7.49	La-Dy

and Trivalent Americium with Group III-V Elements

Type of Structure	Lattice Constants (A.) *a*	*b*	*c*	Isostructural Compounds
Pyrochlor, cubic	10.565			R.E.
Pyrochlor, cubic	10.650			R.E.
$CePO_4 \cdot 0\text{-}0.5H_2O$, hexag.	6.99		6.39	R.E., Cm, Ac
$ThSiO_4$, monoklin	6.73	6.93	6.41 $\beta = 103°50'$	R.E., Pu, Cm
$ThSiO_4$, monoklin	6.89	7.06	6.62 $\beta = 105°30'$	La-Nd, Pu
$ZrSiO_4$, tetragonal	7.31		6.42	Ce-Lu
$YTaO_4$, monoklin	5.444	11.25	5.141 $\beta = 95°57'$	R.E., Pu
$ZrSiO_4$, tetragonal	5.30		11.34	R.E.
$La_{0.33}NbO_3$	3.819		7.835	R.E.
$YTaO_4$, monoklin	5.489	11.21	5.115 $\beta = 95°22'$	R.E.
$La_{0.33}NbO_3$	3.889		7.820	La-Nd, Cm
Fluorite, cubic	5.458			La-Er, Y, Cm

vidual modes of decomposition and the temperatures of decomposition are indicated in Figures 2 and 3.

The simplest way to prepare the alkali metal americates (V) Li_3AmO_4, Li_7AmO_6, and Na_3AmO_4 is by allowing AmO_2 and Li_2O (Na_2O_2) to react in a stream of N_2 + some 1% O_2 at the temperatures quoted in Figures 2 and 3. The thermal stability of Li_7AmO_6 extends up to some 1000°C.; *via* Li_3AmO_4 the decomposition finally yields AmO_2. While Na_3AmO_4, as Na_3UO_4 (*37*) crystallizes in the undistorted NaCl-lattice, Li_3AmO_4 has the tetragonally distorted rocksalt structure of Li_3UO_4 (*5*), which is caused by a larger difference in the ionic radii of Li^+ and Am^{5+}.

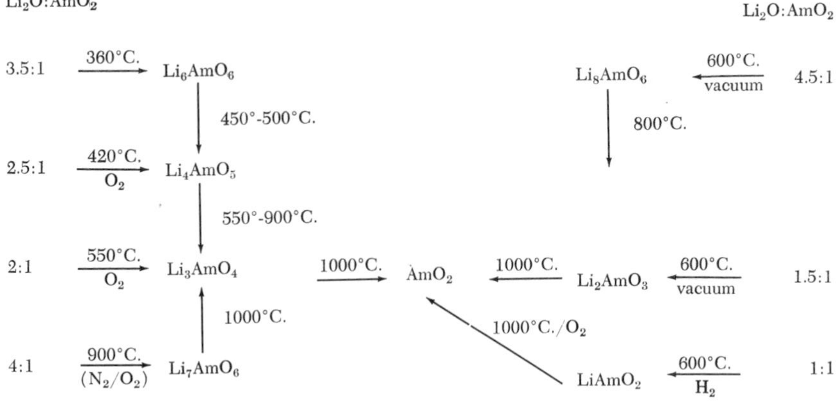

Figure 2. Preparative conditions and thermal stability of compounds in the system Li-Am-O

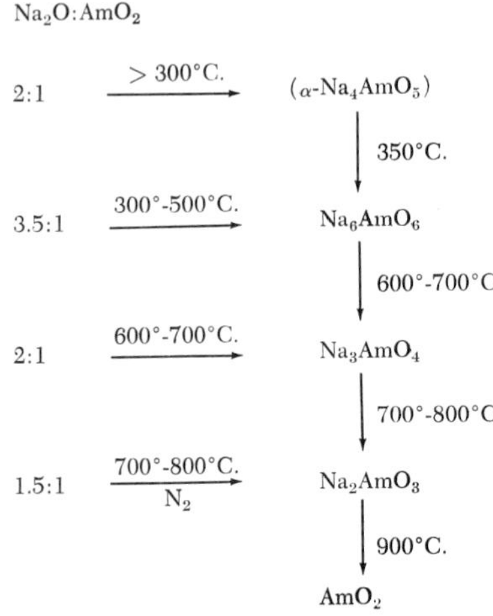

Figure 3. Preparative conditions and thermal stability of compounds in the system Na-Am-O

Although above 700°C. the thermal decomposition of the Am(V) and Am(VI) compounds with sodium passes through Na_2AmO_3—of the monoclinic structure of Li_2SnO_3 (*27*)—it was not possible to obtain an intermediate compound with Am(IV) for Li-compounds. Double oxides in the system LiO_2-AmO_2 were obtained by direct reaction of Li_2O with AmO_2 in an evacuated quartz tube. At 600°C. one obtains for $Li_2O:AmO_2$ = 1.5:1 the substance Li_2AmO_3 which is isostructural with Li_2PrO_3 (*36*); in the case of $Li_2O:AmO_2$ = 4.5:1, the compound Li_8AmO_6. The Li_2O-surplus is necessary to compensate for the volatilization of Li_2O.

By solid-state reactions of Am_2O_3 with Li_2O in hydrogen at 600°C., it was possible to prepare $LiAmO_2$ which is isostructural with the monoclinic α-$LiEuO_2$ the lattice constant of which has been determined by Bärnighausen (3). Probably, another high temperature modification may be expected for $LiAmO_2$ which, as β-$LiEuO_2$ (2) or $LiGdO_2$, has an orthorhombic structure.

Most of the compounds of tetravalent to hexavalent americium described here were obtained for uranium, neptunium, and plutonium (Table III). The decomposition temperatures of the americium compounds are considerably below (200°–300°C.) those of the corresponding temperatures of the analogous neptunates and plutonates (*4, 25*).

Compounds of Americium with Alkaline Earths Metals. While the system americium oxide—alkali metal oxide, at least for Me^I =Li and Na were worked on in detail, only a few attempts have been made to characterize the ternary oxides expected in the system americium oxide—alkaline earth oxide.

In the solid-state reaction of 3.5 BaO + 1 AmO_2 at 800°–900°C. the compound $Ba(Ba_{0.5}{}^{II}, Am_{0.5}{}^{VI})O_3$ (*17*) with ordered perovskite structure is formed. At higher temperatures there is a loss of oxygen, transforming $Ba(Ba_{0.5}, Am_{0.5})O_3$ into $BaAm^{IV}O_3$ with the cubic perovskite lattice in such a way that no intermediate stages of this transition can be recognized. $BaAmO_3$ and $SrAmO_3$ are obtained in a simpler way by direct reaction of BaO_2 (or $BaCO_3$) and AmO_2 (air, 30 hrs., 1250°C.) (*4, 19*). To achieve a quantitative reaction of AmO_2, a molar ratio of Am:Me^{II} = 1:1.5 is required; there is no solid solution in the system MeO-$MeAmO_3$ in contrast to the system $BaUO_3$/BaO. The dark brown $BaAmO_3$ and $SrAmO_3$ are soluble in strong acids along with disproportionation of Am(IV).

Table III. Schematic Representation of Lithium and Sodium Uranates (VI) and Transuranates (VI)

	U		*Np*		*Pu*		*Am*	
Composition	*Li*	*Na*	*Li*	*Na*	*Li*	*Na*	*Li*	*Na*
$Me_2X_3O_{10}$	+	—	—	—	—	—	—	—
$Me_2X_2O_7$	+	+	—	+	—	—	—	—
α-Me_2XO_4	+	+	—	+	—	—	—	—
β-Me_2XO_4	+	+	—	+	—	—	—	—
α-Me_4XO_5	—	+	—	+	—	+	—	+
β-Me_4XO_5	+	+	+	+	+	+	+	—
Me_6XO_6	—	—	+	+	+	+	+	+

+ = *existent*
— = *none-existent*

The reduction of $BaAmO_3$ and $SrAmO_3$ with hydrogen results in compounds which most probably have the formula $BaAm_2O_4$ and $SrAm_2O_4$ (*16*) and the structure of $CaFe_2O_4$. A more detailed investigation has not been made.

The System Am_2O_3/B_2O_3 and Am_2O_3/Al_2O_3. The solid-state reaction of AmO_2 with H_3BO_3 or B_2O_3 (1:1) at 900°C. results in the formation within 12 hours of $AmBO_3$ along with the thermal decomposition of Am(IV) into Am(III). X-ray analysis shows that $AmBO_3$ is isostructural with the low temperature modifications of $LaBO_3$ and $NdBO_3$ (*29*) crystallizing in the orthorhombic aragonite lattice.

By solid-state reactions of AmO_2 with Al_2O_3 at 1250°C. in H_2 no compound formation could be observed. In order not to increase the reaction temperature, a 1:1 mixed hydroxide precipitation of americium and aluminium reacted in H_2 for 2–8 hrs. at 1250°C. This resulted in the quantitative formation of rose-colored $AmAlO_3$ having the hexagonal distorted perovskite structure of the aluminates of La, Pr, Nd (*11*), and Pu (*17, 35*).

The Reaction of AmO_2 with Oxides of the Group IV Elements. The dioxides of the elements thorium, protactinium, uranium, neptunium, and plutonium react directly with SiO_2 and GeO_2 either thermally or hydrothermally to form ternary oxides of the type $A^{IV}B^{IV}O_4$ which, depending upon the actinide element and the conditions of preparation, possess a zircon ($ZrSiO_4$), scheelite ($CaWO_4$), or huttonite ($ThSiO_4$) structure (*16*). Corresponding reaction products could be expected for AmO_2 even if the low thermal stability of AmO_2 at the required high reaction temperatures causes difficulties. The solid-state reaction of AmO_2 with SiO_2 at 1250°C. in all cases resulted in an extensive oxygen loss of AmO_2 along with the formation of Am(III). The hope of forming an Am(IV) silicate by a solid-state reaction was poor because in the series of tetravalent actinides only silicates of Th(IV) and Pa(IV), but not of U(IV), Np(IV), and Pu(IV) could be obtained by thermal methods.

An Am(IV) silicate, $AmSiO_4$, having the structure of zircon (α-form of the actinide(IV) silicates) was obtained by hydrothermal synthesis out of a mixed hydroxide precipitation of $Am(OH)_4 + SiO_2 \cdot aq$. The Am fraction, after precipitation by the method of Pennemann *et al.* (*31*), was oxidized with NaOCl in an alkaline solution to form $Am(OH)_4$. After 5–7 days at 230°C. and a pH of 8.2–8.6, the components reacted to form crystalline $AmSiO_4$, which is isostructural with the silicates of the other tetravalent actinides prepared the same way.

Attempts to prepare $AmGeO_4$ by a solid-state reaction of $AmO_2 + GeO_2$ resulted in a partial decomposition of AmO_2 in all cases also at 1000°C. in O_2. The nondecomposed part of AmO_2 reacts by forming

$AmGeO_4$ with scheelite structure (α-form of the actinide(IV) germanates). Pure $AmGeO_4$ is obtained again by hydrothermal reaction of $Am(OH)_4$ + $GeO_2(aq)$ under the same experimental conditions as quoted for $AmSiO_4$. The thermal decomposition of $AmGeO_4$ starts at about 1050°C.

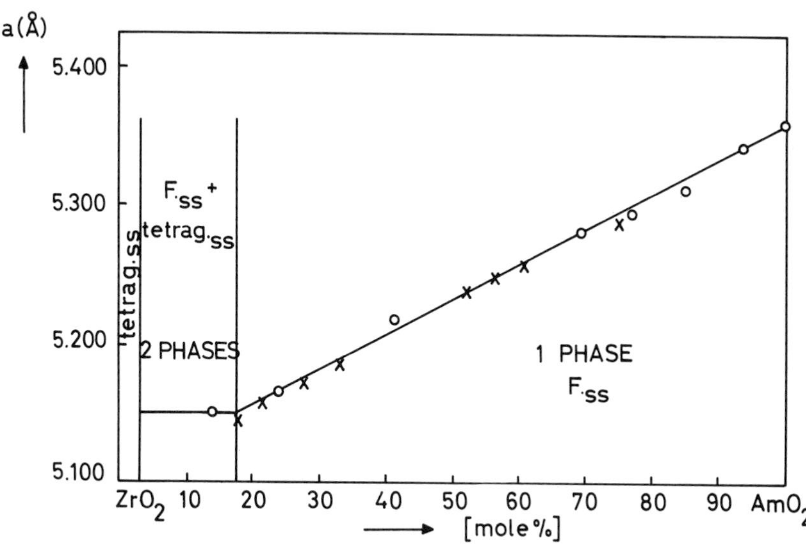

Figure 4. Lattice constants and extension of solid solutions in the system AmO_2-ZrO_2

O = *1200°C.*
X = *1400°C.*

It has been known for a long time that ThO_2 and UO_2 form extensive series of mixed crystals with ZrO_2 above 1000°C. which have a tetragonal fluorite structure at low ThO_2 and UO_2 content and a cubic fluorite structure at higher content [*e.g.* (*6, 9, 26, 42*)]. Figure 4 shows that the corresponding series of mixed crystals exist also in the system AmO_2-ZrO_2. A one-phase solid solution of fluorite structure extends above 18 mole% AmO_2 up to pure AmO_2. The lattice constants of these oxide phases increase proportionally with the AmO_2 content, which must be explained as an indication of the presence of pure Am(IV). The corresponding experiments in the system AmO_2-HfO_2 did not show quantitative results, but here too a fluorite phase of a large but undetermined extension is found.

Reduction of the AmO_2-ZrO_2 and AmO_2-HfO_2 fluorite phases results in the corresponding ternary oxides and oxide phases of trivalent americium. In the system $AmO_{1.5}$-HfO_2 there is a 1:1 compound $Am_2Hf_2O_7$ of a pyrochlore structure which has a nearly stoichiometric composition

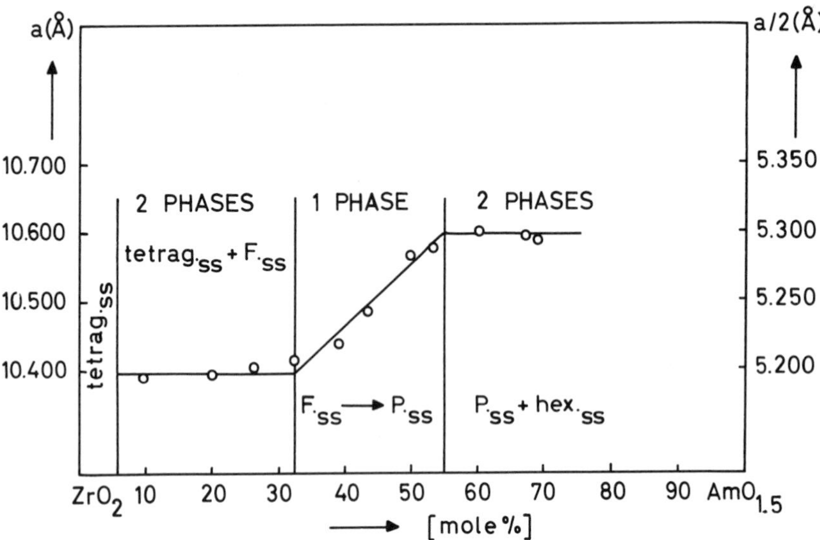

Figure 5. Lattice constants and extension of solid solutions in the system $AmO_{1.5}$-ZrO_2, 1200°C.

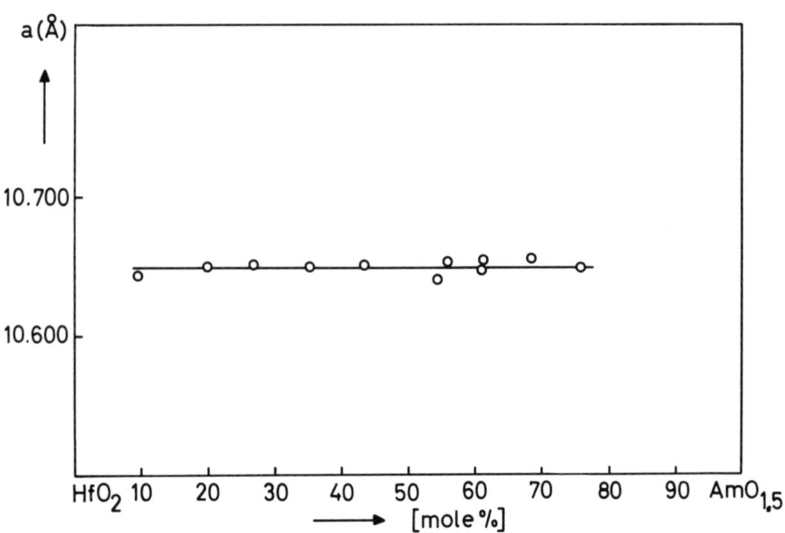

Figure 6. Lattice constants in the system $AmO_{1.5}$-HfO_2, 1400°C.

(Figure 5). More complicated are the results in the system $AmO_{1.5}$-ZrO_2. Besides the pure starting components, two one-phase areas can be observed at 1200°C.: a tetragonal solid solution of 0–6 mole% $AmO_{1.5}$ and a cubic solid solution of about 32–55 mole% $AmO_{1.5}$ (Figure 6). In the cubic solid solution, in whose region exists $Am_2Zr_2O_7$ with the pyrochlore-type structure, a continuous transition from the fluorite phase to the pyrochlore phase can be observed. In this respect the system $AmO_{1.5}$-ZrO_2 fits excellently into the series of rare earth zirconates investigated by French authors—*e.g.*, (*7, 8, 32*); for the corresponding Hf systems there are, as yet, no comprehensive investigations reported in the literature. The striking difference in the systems $AmO_{1.5}$-ZrO_2 and $AmO_{1.5}$-HfO_2 cannot be explained, however.

As expected, ThO_2 forms a complete series of mixed crystals with AmO_2, whose lattice constants follow Vegard's rule (Figure 7).

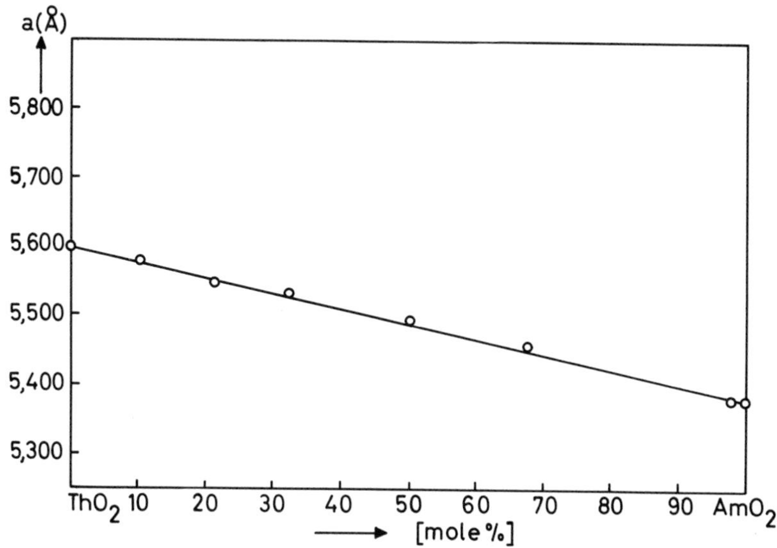

Figure 7a. Lattice constants in the system AmO_2-ZrO_2, 1300°C.

The solubility of $AmO_{1.5}$ in ThO_2 at 1300°C. is about 50 mole%. In this case the pure fluorite structure remains; the lack of oxygen is balanced by the formation of statistically distributed oxygen holes. An exact determination of the solubility of $AmO_{1.5}$ in ThO_2 is possible in practice only by quoting a large margin of error because the lattice constants of ThO_2 ($a = 5.599$ A.) and those of the cubic $AmO_{1.5}$ ($a/2 = 5.515$ A.) are relatively close to each other; and moreover, the quality of x-ray powder patterns of samples above 50 mole% $AmO_{1.5}$ leaves much to be desired.

The Reaction of AmO_2 and Am_2O_3 with the Oxides of Group V Elements. In its reactions with group V elements americium behaves like a typical rare earth element. When using AmO_2 as the americium component there is always loss of oxygen and the formation of ternary oxides of Am(III). This is shown most clearly in the reaction of the actinide dioxides with Nb_2O_5 and Ta_2O_5 in a molar ratio of 1:2. ThO_2, PaO_2, UO_2, NpO_2, and PuO_2 form ternary oxides of the composition $MeO_2 \cdot 2X_2O_5$ with Nb_2O_5 and Ta_2O_5 in a ratio of 1:2 (*22*) whose structure, in accordance with the nomenclature $Me_{0.25}{}^{IV}X^{V}O_4$ may be taken as an intermediate state of transition from the primitive cubic ReO_3 lattice to the bcc $CaTiO_3$-lattice. Ternary oxides of a similar structure are also produced in the reaction of the sesquioxides of the light lanthanides (Me^{III} = La-Nd for X = Nb and Me^{III} = La-Er for X = Ta) with Nb_2O_5 and Ta_2O_5 (*23, 34*). These compounds must be given the formula $MeO_{1.5} \cdot 1.5X_2O_5 \equiv Me_{0.33}{}^{III}XO_3$.

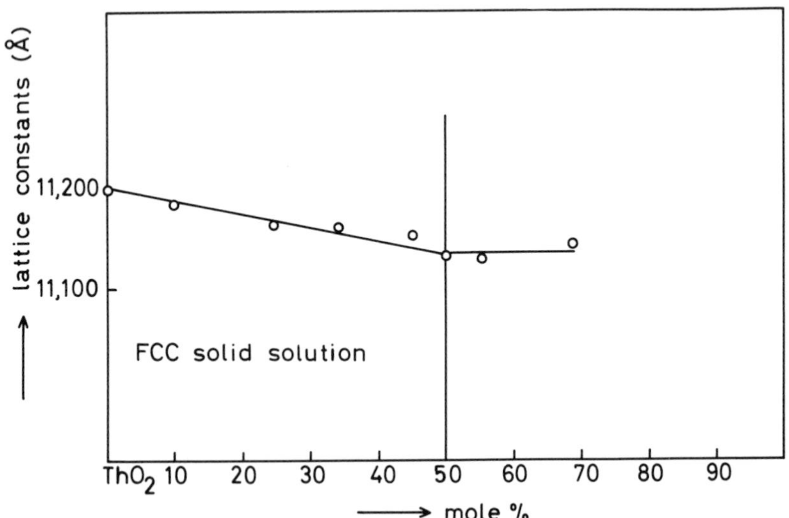

Figure 7b. Lattice constants and extension of fcc solid solutions in the system $AmO_{1.5}$-ThO_2, 1300°C.

In the solid-state reaction of AmO_2 with Nb_2O_5 and Ta_2O_5, respectively, (1:1.5 and 1:2 respectively) the result in all cases consisted of substances of a pale rose color which fit well into the series of rare earth compounds and whose lattice constants showed the same values, independent of their preparation in H_2 or O_2 (for X = Ta) or their preparation from $AmO_{1.5}$ and X_2O_5 in the evacuated tube or in air. The x-ray powder patterns of starting mixtures Am:X = 1:4 always contained the reflexes of X_2O_5 which were no longer observed for the starting ratio of 1:3. This permits the unequivocal conclusion that these compounds contain Am(III) and should be formulated as $Am_{0.33}NbO_3$ and $Am_{0.33}TaO_3$.

While the compounds quoted of the tetravalent actinides show a tetragonally distorted perovskite structure, the symmetry of the Me(III) compounds is orthorhombic-pseudotetragonal.

The reaction of AmO_2 with Pa_2O_5 results in a double oxide $(Am_{0.5}^{III}, Pa_{0.5}^{V})O_2$ of fluorite-type structure with a statistical distribution of the metal ions (*18*). $(Am_{0.5}^{III},Pa_{0.5}^{V})O_2$, like the analogous compounds of the rare earth elements, forms a double oxide with BaO, $Ba(Am_{0.5},Pa_{0.5})O_3$ with an ordered perovskite-type of structure (*19*).

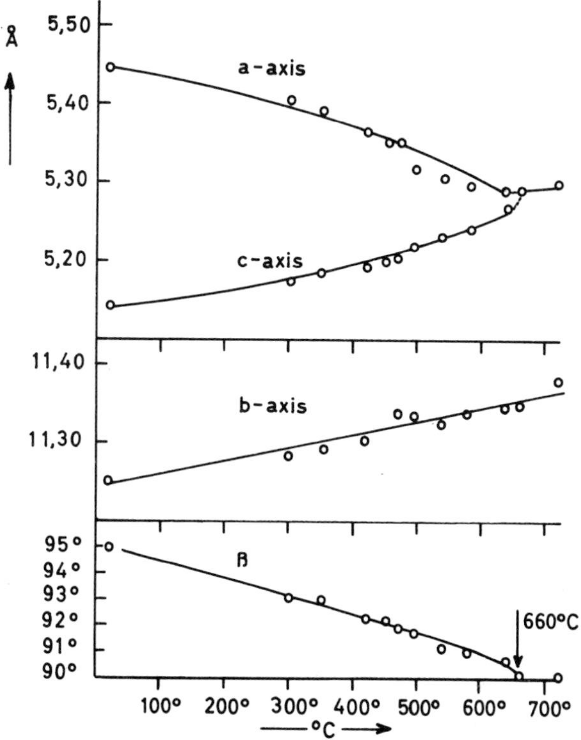

Figure 8. Structural transformation of monoclinic $AmNbO_4$

Analogous solid-state reactions of AmO_2 with the corresponding secondary components result in the compounds $AmPO_4$ ($CePO_4$ structure), $AmAsO_4$ (huttonite structure), $AmVO_4$ ($CaWO_4$ structure), $AmNbO_4$ and $AmTaO_4$ (β-fergusonite type), $AmTaTiO_6$ and $AmNbTiO_6$ (priorite type) as well as $Ba(Am_{0.5},Nb_{0.5})O_3$ and $Ba(Am_{0.5},Ta_{0.5})O_3$ (ordered perovskite structure) (*19, 24*). $AmNbO_4$ and $AmTaO_4$ have two modifications. The low temperature modification, which has a monoclinic distorted scheelite lattice, changes into the tetragonal scheelite

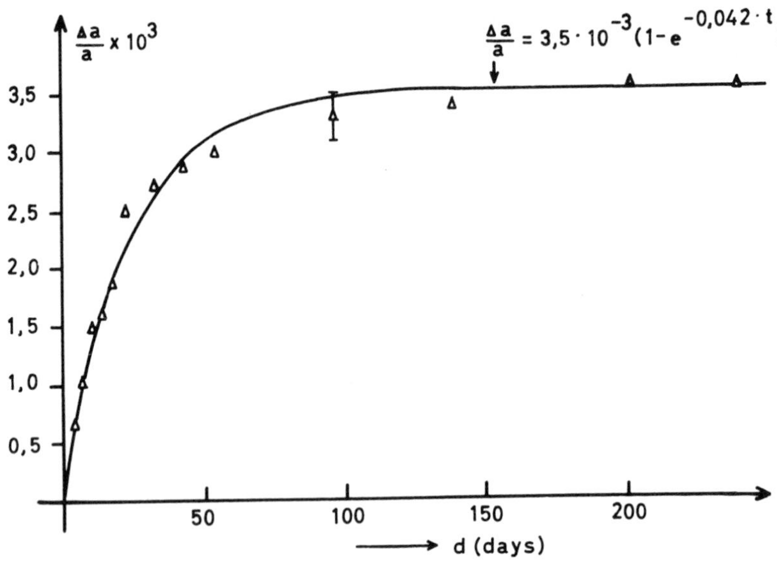

Figure 9. Changes in lattice parameters for AmO_2

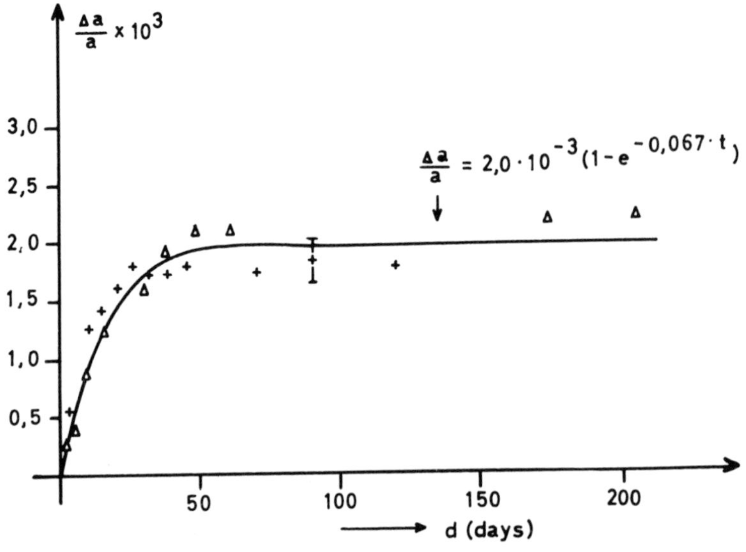

Figure 10. Changes in lattice parameters for $Am_2Hf_2O_7$

structure with increasing temperatures. The high temperature form of $AmNbO_4$ and $AmTaO_4$ cannot be retained in the metastable state even by fast quenching; this also holds for the corresponding compounds of the rare earths (*35, 36*). The point of crystal transformation for $AmNbO_4$ is 660 ± 20°C. (Figure 8).

The reduction of $AmVO_4$ with hydrogen at 1200°C. results in light brown-colored $AmVO_3$ which, like all vanadates(III) of the rare earths crystallizes in an orthorhombic-deformed perovskite lattice.

Like the orthophosphates of actinium (*39*), plutonium (*4*), and the light rare earths (*30*) $AmPO_4$ exists in two modifications. The precipitate obtained in a precipitation reaction of an Am^{3+} solution out of a weakly acid solution by adding $(NH_4)_2HPO_4$ has a hexagonal structure. As shown by Mooney (*30*), this lattice is able to take up a maximum of 0.5 molecules of water zeolytically so that the precipitated substance should have the formula $AmPO_4 \cdot 0\text{–}0.5\ H_2O$. The low thermal stability of this phosphate modification makes it plausible that the presence of zeolytically bound water is necessary to stabilize the lattice. The best crystallized preparations of hexagonal $AmPO_4$ were obtained by hydrothermal synthesis at 150°C. By heating hexagonal $AmPO_4$ to $>$ 200°C., there is a structural transformation into a second modification of a huttonite ($ThSiO_4$) type of structure which is also formed in the thermal reaction. The structural transformation of $AmPO_4$ is accompanied by an unusual increase in density of about 20%. The precipitated Am phosphates are easily dissolved in diluted acids; the annealed $AmPO_4$ can be dissolved only in boiling acids.

Self-Irradiation Damage of Am Compounds

If a solid is exposed to irradiation by heavy particles (n, p, alphas, fission fragments), a change in the lattice constants of the elementary cell will be found after a specified period of time. As a rule, this will be an expansion caused by the dislocation of lattice elements to interstitial positions. If radionuclides build up such a solid, a similar effect must be expected because of the "internal" irradiation—i.e., the radioactive decay. This is particularly true of radionuclides decaying under alpha emission. In addition to the dislocation of lattice elements because of this "inner" alpha activity there is also the dislocation by the recoil atom in this case. If a recoil atom or an alpha particle traverses an area where there has already been a radiation damage, there will be no further damage (*1*); hence, the relative lattice change goes towards a limiting value. The relative increase in lattice constants in this case can be expressed by the equation:

$$\frac{\Delta x}{x} = a\ (1 - e^{-bt})$$

Radiation damage arising in crystals with alpha-active nuclides were investigated by Hurley and Fairbairn (*13*) using natural zirconia containing up to 0.1% uranium and by Rand, Fox, and Street (*33*) using several plutonium compounds.

Experimental results obtained for the cubic compounds AmO_2(CaF_2

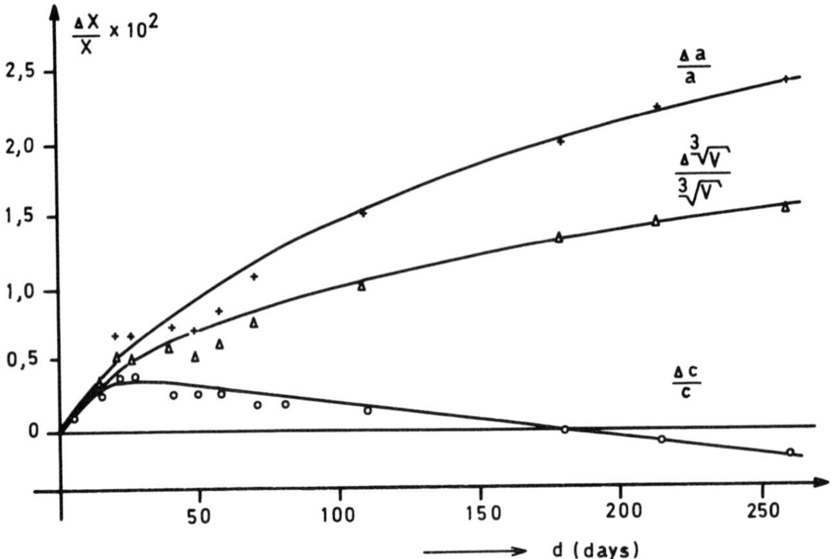

Figure 11. Changes in lattice parameters for $Li_4{}^{241}AmO_5$

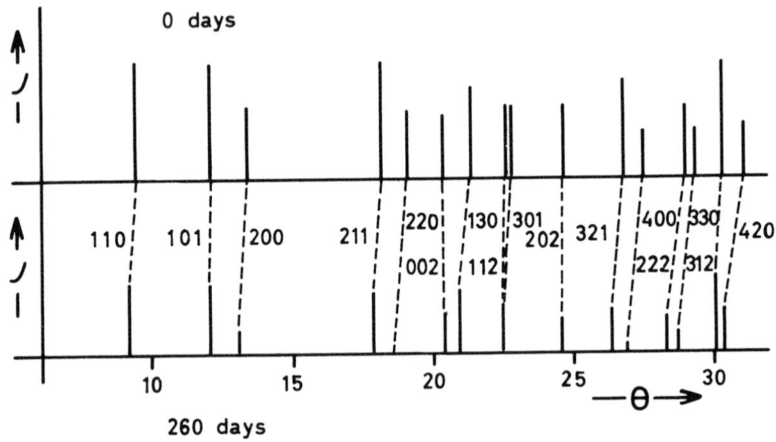

Figure 12. X-Ray powder patterns for $Li_4{}^{241}AmO_5$ vs. storage time

lattice) and $Am_2Hf_2O_7$ (pyrochlore type) and for tetragonal Li_4AmO_5 are shown in Figures 9–12. After an initial continuous increase in the lattice constants with storage time, the limit of the relative lattice expansion was reached for AmO_2 and $Am_2Hf_2O_7$ after some 150 and 70 days. The experimental values of $\frac{\Delta a}{a}$ for AmO_2 can be represented with sufficient accuracy by the equation $\frac{\Delta a}{a} = 3.5 \times 10^{-3} (1 - e^{-0.042t})$, for $Am_2Hf_2O_7$ by $\frac{\Delta a}{a} = 2.0 \times 10^{-3} (1 - e^{-0.067t})$ (t = time in days). The lattice constant of AmO_2 on the whole changes from $a_o = 5.377$ A. to $a = 5.395$ A., corresponding to an increase of 0.35%. The Debye-Scherrer powder patterns, even after long storage times of the samples (about 400 days), showed little change with respect to intensity and clarity of the individual lines. The results of an investigation of tetragonal Li_4AmO_5 are slightly different. Cell volume as well as the a-axis increase with storage time; for both quantities it was impossible to obtain a limit during the period of observation. The increase in the a-axis was one order of magnitude larger than in the compounds discussed above. Within 260 days the lattice constant increased from $a_o = 6.666$ A. to $a_t = 6.827$ A. which corresponds to an increase of 2.4%. After an initial increase a subsequent decrease was found for the c-axis; after about 180 days the lattice constant decreased even below the value obtained originally. The quality of the x-ray powder patterns experienced a considerable decrease with storage time in regard to line intensities as well as line clarity, so that after about 300 days of storage time no evaluation was possible. Probably the damage to the crystal lattice in this case is caused by the dislocation of the lattice points to interstitial positions and also by a reduction of Am(VI) to Am(V).

Conclusion

Investigations of the solid-state chemistry of the americium oxides have shown that americium has properties typical of the preceding elements uranium, neptunium, and plutonium as well as properties to be expected of a typical actinide element (preferred stability of the valence state 3+). As the production of ternary oxides of trivalent plutonium entails considerable difficulties, it may be justified to speak of a discontinuity in the solid-state chemical behavior in the transition from plutonium to americium. A similar discontinuous change in the solid-state chemical behavior is certainly expected in the transition Am → Cm. Americium must be attributed an intermediate position among the neighboring elements which is much more pronounced in the reactions of the oxides than in those of the halides or the behavior in aqueous solution.

Acknowledgment

The author thanks W. Seelmann-Eggebert for his continuous support of these investigations, and K. H. Walter and H. Radzewitz for their cooperation in the chemical investigations.

Literature Cited

(1) Adam, J., Rogers, M. D., *Reactor Sci. Techol.* **14,** 51 (1961).
(2) Bärnighausen, H., *Acta Cryst.* **16,** 1073 (1963).
(3) Bärnighausen, H., *Acta Cryst.* **19,** 1048 (1965).
(4) Bjorklund, C. W., *J. Am. Chem. Soc.* **79,** 6347 (1957).
(5) Blasse, G., *Z. Anorg. Allgem. Chem.* **331,** 44 (1964).
(6) Cohen, I., Schaner, B. E., *J. Nucl. Mater.* **9,** 18 (1963).
(7) Collongues, R., Lefévre, J., Perez Y Jorba, M., Queyroux, F., *Bull. Soc. Chim., France* **1962,** 149 (1962).
(8) Collongues, R., Queyroux, F., Perez Y Jorba, M., Gilles, J., *Bull. Soc. Chim., France* **1965,** 1141 (1965).
(9) Duwez, P., Loh, E., *J. Am. Ceram. Soc.* **40,** 321 (1957).
(10) Fried, S., Hageman, F., Zachariasen, W. H., *J. Am. Chem. Soc.* **72,** 771 (1950).
(11) Geller, S., Bala, V. B., *Acta Cryst.* **9,** 1019 (1956).
(12) Hoeckstra, H. R., Siegel, S., *J. Inorg. Nucl. Chem.* **26,** 693 (1964).
(13) Hurley, P. M., Fairbairn, H. W., *J. Appl. Phys.* **23,** 1408 (1952).
(14) Katz, J. J., Seaborg, G. T., "The Chemistry of the Actinide Elements," p. 464, Methuen and Cie, 1957.
(15) Keller, C., *Z. Anorg. Allgem. Chem.* **318,** 89 (1962).
(16) Keller, C., *Nukleonik* **5,** 41 (1963).
(17) Keller, C., Kernforschungszentrum Karlsruhe Institut für Radiochemie, Germany **Report KFK-225** (1964).
(18) Keller, C., *J. Inorg. Nucl. Chem.* **26,** 2069 (1965).
(19) Keller, C., *J. Inorg. Nucl. Chem.* **27,** 321 (1965).
(20) Keller, C., Koch, L., Walter, K. H., *J. Inorg. Nucl. Chem.* **27,** 1205 (1965).
(21) Keller, C., Koch, L., Walter, K. H., *J. Inorg. Nucl. Chem.* **27,** 1225 (1965).
(22) Keller, C., *J. Inorg. Nucl. Chem.* **27,** 1233 (1965).
(23) Keller, C., Walter, K. H., *J. Inorg. Nucl. Chem.* **27,** 1247 (1965).
(24) Keller, C., Walter, K. H., *J. Inorg. Nucl. Chem.* **27,** 1253 (1965).
(25) Koch, L., Kerforschungszentrum Karlsruhe Institut für Radiochemie, Germany Report **KFK-196** (1964).
(26) Kovba, L. M., *Zhur. Strukt. Khim.* **3,** 159 (1962).
(27) Lang, G., *Z. Anorg. Allgem. Chem.* **276,** 77 (1954).
(28) Lambertson, W. A., Mueller, M. H., *J. Am. Ceram. Soc.* **36,** 361 (1953).
(29) Levin, E. M., Roth, R. S., Martin, J. B., *Am. Mineral.* **46,** 1030 (1961).
(30) Mooney, R. C. L., *Acta Cryst.* **3,** 337 (1950).
(31) Penneman, R. A., Coleman, J. S., Keenan, T. K., *J. Inorg. Nucl. Chem.* **17,** 138 (1961).
(32) Perez Y Jorba, M., Fayard, M., Collongues, R., *Bull. Soc. Chim. France* **1962,** 155 (1962).
(33) Rand, M. H., Fox, A. C., Street, R. S., *Nature* **195,** 567 (1962).
(34) Rocksby, H. P., White, E. A. D., Langston, S. A., *J. Am. Ceram. Soc.* **48,** 447 (1965).
(35) Russel, L. E., Harrison, I. P. L., Brett, N. H., *J. Nucl. Mater.* **2,** 310 (1960).
(36) Scholder, R., *Angew. Chem.* **70,** 583 (1958).

(37) Scholder, R., Glaeser, H., Z. *Anorg. Allgem. Chem.* **327,** 15 (1964).
(38) Scholder, R., Huppert, K. L., Z. *Anorg. Allgem. Chem.* **334,** 209 (1964).
(39) Stubican, V. S., *J. Am. Ceram. Soc.* **47,** 55 (1964).
(40) Templeton, D. H., Dauben, C. H., *J. Am. Chem. Soc.* **75,** 4560 (1953).
(41) Walter, K. H., Kerforschungszentrum Karlsruhe Institut für Radiochemie, Germany Report **KFK-280** (1965).
(42) Wolten, G. M., *J. Am. Chem. Soc.* **80,** 4772 (1958).

RECEIVED October 5, 1966.

18

Tetra- and Pentavalent Actinide Fluoride Complexes

Protactinium to Curium

ROBERT A. PENNEMAN, THOMAS K. KEENAN, and LARNED B. ASPREY

University of California, Los Alamos Scientific Laboratory, Los Alamos, N. M.

X-ray data are given for tetragonal LiF · XF_4 and for rhombohedral 7NaF · $6XF_4$, X = Th, Pa, U, Np, Pu, Am, and Cm. Hydrogen reduction of alkali fluoride-Pa(V) fluoride complexes yields LiF · PaF_4 and 7MF · $6PaF_4$ (where M = Na, K, Rb). When 3NaF · PaF_5 is treated with H_2 at 450°C., its absorption spectrum shows Pa(IV) to be present but its x-ray structure is not changed. Pentavalent compounds include MF · PaF_5, MF · UF_5 (M = Li through Cs), as well as CsF · NpF_5, CsF · PuF_5, 2RbF · NpF_5, 2RbF · PuF_5, and 3RbF · PaF_5. Fluorination of UF_4 in liquid anhydrous HF yields UF_5. When alkali fluoride and UF_4 are present in liquid HF, fluorination forms blue, soluble UF_6^-. Fluorine oxidation of NpF_4 in a melt of CsF · 2HF yields magenta colored NpF_6^-.

In this paper emphasis is given to recent results obtained at the Los Alamos Scientific Laboratory rather than to a complete survey. References to the current literature will give some idea of the scope of such work.

Tetravalent Actinide Fluoride Complexes

Complexes of Protactinium(IV). PREPARATION AND X-RAY PROPERTIES. A number of complex fluorides containing other tetravalent actinides are known (*1, 8, 9, 13–15, 20, 22, 24, 25, 26, 27, 29*), but few fluoride compounds of Pa(IV) have been described—*e.g.*, the preliminary communications on $7RbF \cdot 6PaF_4$ (*3*) and $4NH_4F \cdot PaF_4$ (*4*). (Formulas of the complex fluorides are written $MF \cdot XF_4$ or $MF \cdot XF_5$ for ease of displaying the valence of the actinide.) Our previous work on $4NH_4 \cdot UF_4$ and $4NH_4F \cdot AmF_4$ (*1, 8, 22*) plus the extensive work at the Oak Ridge National Laboratory (*9, 13, 14, 15, 24, 25, 26, 27*) and by Zachariasen (*29*) on compounds in the alkali fluoride-uranium tetrafluoride systems provided x-ray data for the U(IV) fluoride complexes. In most cases, the x-ray properties of the Pa(IV) compounds are similar to those of their U(IV) analogs.

Table I. Alkali Fluoride Complexes of Tetravalent Protactinium

Ratio MF:PaF$_4$	*M*	*Structure*	*Lattice Parameter, A*
1:1	Li	Tetragonal[a]	$a_o = 14.96$, $c_o = 6.58$
7:6	Na	Rhombohedral[b]	$a_o = 9.16$, $\alpha = 107°54'$
	K	Rhombohedral[b]	$a_o = 9.44$, $\alpha = 107°09'$
	Rb	Rhombohedral[b]	$a_o = 9.64$, $\alpha = 107°0'$
	Cs	(Unknown)	
2:1	All unknown[c]		
3:1	Na	Prob. tetragonal	Existence inferred from absorption spectrum, amount Pa(IV) and of Pa(V) unknown.[d]
	K	Prob. fcc	Existence inferred from absorption spectrum, amount Pa(IV) and of Pa(V) unknown.[d]
	Rb	Prob. fcc	Existence inferred from absorption spectrum, amount Pa(IV) and of Pa(V) unknown.[d]
4:1	NH_4	Monoclinic	Isostructural with $(NH_4)_4XF_8$ (X = U, Np, Pu, and Am)

[a] Isostructural with $LiF \cdot UF_4$ (*13, 14*).
[b] Isostructural with $7NaF \cdot 6UF_4$ (*13, 15*).
[c] Hydrogen reduction of $2KF \cdot PaF_5$ powder resulted in the formation of $7KF \cdot 6PaF_4$ as the major solid phase, and not $2KF \cdot PaF_4$.
[d] The x-ray structures of the 1:1 alkali fluoride:PaF_5 fluoride complexes are quite distinct from those of the 1:1 and 7:6 alkali fluoride:PaF_4 complexes. At the 3:1 stoichiometry, the $3KF \cdot UF_3$, $3KF \cdot UF_4$, and $3KF \cdot UF_5$ compounds are all face-centered cubic and of nearly identical cell size (*28*). Absorption spectrum rather than x-ray was the criterion used to detect hydrogen reduction of $3KF \cdot PaF_5$ to $3KF \cdot PaF_4$, and of $3NaF \cdot PaF_5$ to $3NaF \cdot PaF_4$.

Complex fluorides containing tetravalent protactinium and the alkali fluorides (Li, Na, K, Rb, and NH_4) were prepared from MF + PaF_4 starting mixtures and by reducing MF-PaF_5 compounds at 400°–500°C. using pure hydrogen, obtained from UH_3. The x-ray results on compounds obtained by these methods are presented in Table I.

ABSORPTION SPECTRUM OF $7RbF \cdot 6PaF_4$. Tetravalent protactinium should have a $5f^1$ electron and show discrete optical absorption. This is demonstrated in Table II which shows the absorption spectrum characteristic of tetravalent protactinium. The spectrum was obtained from a mull in a Fluorocarbon oil, held between CaF_2 flats. A Cary 14 MR spectrophotometer was used.

Table II. Absorption Spectrum of Tetravalent Protactinium Fluoride

Compound	*Peak Maxima, A*	
$7RbF \cdot 6PaF_4$	2580	M
	2920	W
	3500	M
	12600	S
	14700	W, Br
	16000	VW, Br
	17400	VW
	18270	VS, Narrow[a]
	18510	W

[a] For $7RbF \cdot 6PaF_4$, $3NaF \cdot PaF_4$, and PaF_4, an intense infrared absorption band is observed at ~5485 cm.$^{-1}$, giving a value for ζ_{5f} of Pa(IV) = 1567 cm.$^{-1}$.

Preparation and Lattice Constants of the $LiF \cdot XF_4$ and $7NaF \cdot 6XF_4$ (X = Th — Cm) Series. The two series of 1:1 lithium-actinide(IV) fluorides (*18*) and 7:6 sodium-actinide(IV) fluorides (*18*) have now been completed for all actinides, thorium through curium (*i.e.*, those available actinides which exhibit a tetravalent state). Berkelium would undoubtedly form similar compounds, but sufficient quantities were not yet available. Although the compounds $LiF \cdot ThF_4$ (*13*), $7NaF \cdot 6ThF_4$ (*13*), $LiF \cdot PaF_4$ (*7*), $7NaF \cdot 6PaF_4$ (*7*), $LiF \cdot UF_4$ (*13, 14*), and $7NaF \cdot 6UF_4$ (*13*) had been known previously, data for the lithium and sodium double fluorides of neptunium, plutonium, americium, and curium were lacking. These compounds have now been prepared. Starting mixtures of either 1:1 Li:X or 7:6 Na:X were prepared by evaporation from aqueous HCl solution. Hydrogen reduction of the neptunium at 350°C. in the presence of HF formed $LiF \cdot NpF_4$ and $7NaF \cdot 6NpF_4$.

Treatment of the starting mixtures of plutonium, americium, or curium with elemental fluorine at 350°C. for ~ 16 hours was necessary to form good x-ray samples of $LiF \cdot XF_4$ or $7NaF \cdot 6XF_4$ (X = Pu, Am, Cm). No oxidation to pentavalent plutonium was observed under these conditions. When heavier alkalis are present (Rb or Cs), fluorination of such mixtures yields Pu(V) fluorides.

Recent single crystal studies on $LiF \cdot UF_4$ (*14*) and $7NaF \cdot 6ZrF_4$ (*15*) established the space group assignments and stoichiometry so that powder diffraction data on the new actinide compounds could be more readily interpreted. The 1:1 $LiF \cdot XF_4$ compounds are tetragonal, space group $I4_{1/a}$, with 16 molecules per unit cell. The $7NaF \cdot 6XF_4$ are rhombohedral, space group $R\bar{3}$, with three molecules per hexagonal unit cell. In both series, a steady decrease in molecular volume is noted from thorium to curium which is evidence for the actinide contraction in the tetravalent state. Figure 1 shows this contraction for the two types of compounds. Cell constants for these two series are given in Table III.

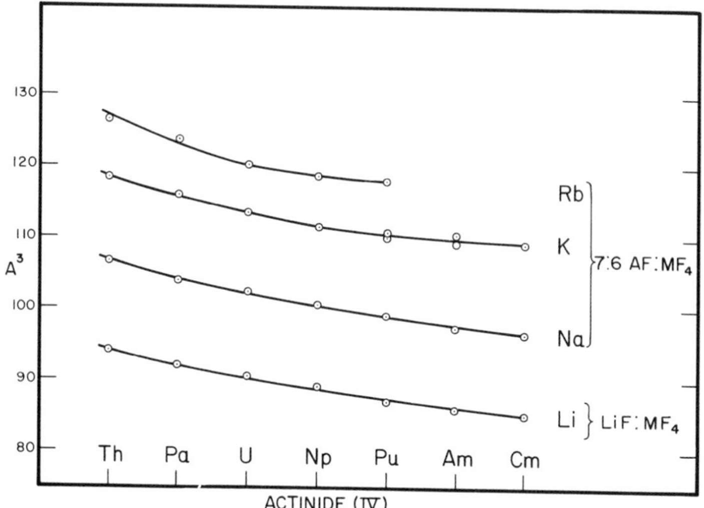

Figure 1. Molar volumes of rhombohedral $Na_7M_6F_{31}$ and tetragonal $LiMF_5$ on the basis of 1M atom/molecule

Pentavalent Actinide Fluoride Complexes

Protactinium(V). A new series of complex fluorides containing pentavalent protactinium and alkali fluorides was synthesized; the compounds $KF \cdot PaF_5$, $RbF \cdot PaF_5$, $NH_4F \cdot PaF_5$, and $CsF \cdot PaF_5$ were shown to be isostructural (*2, 6*). Other complexes with the ratio of one alkali to one protactinium were also prepared but these compounds, $LiF \cdot PaF_5$ and $NaF \cdot PaF_5$, were not isostructural with the preceding group nor with each other (*6*). Complexes of the 2:1 type, $2MF \cdot PaF_5$ (M = K, Rb, Cs but not Li or Na) form readily. The 3:1 type ($3MF \cdot PaF_5$) were also prepared, and $3RbF \cdot PaF_5$ was indexed as *fcc*, a_o = 9.6 A (*6*). These latter two classes of higher complexes were studied to a lesser extent at Los Alamos since it was found that the English group at Harwell was investigating them (*10, 11, 12*). One of their interesting findings was the coordination of nine for Pa(V) in $2KF \cdot PaF_5$ rather than seven as occurs in the tantalum analog.

Table III. $LiXF_5$; Tetragonal, Space Group I $4_{1/a}$, Z = 16

Compound	a_o, *A.*		c_o, *A.*		*Mol. Vol., A.*^{3}	*Reference*
$LiThF_5$	15.10		6.60		94.1	*13*
$LiPaF_5$	14.97	± 0.02	6.576	± 0.003	92.0	*7*
$LiUF_5$	14.8592	± 0.0096	6.5433	± 0.0009	90.3	*15*
$LiNpF_5$	14.80	± 0.02	6.516	± 0.005	89.2	*18*
$LiPuF_5$	14.67	± 0.02	6.479	± 0.005	87.1	*18, 19*
$LiAmF_5$	14.63	± 0.02	6.449	± 0.005	86.3	*18*
$LiCmF_5$	14.57	± 0.02	6.437	± 0.005	85.4	*18*
$Na_7X_6F_{31}$; Hexagonal (Rhombohedral), Space Group $R\bar{3}$, Z = 3						
$Na_7Th_6F_{31}$	14.96		9.912		640.4	*13*
$Na_7Pa_6F_{31}$	14.81	± 0.02	9.850	± 0.003	623.7	*7*
$Na_7U_6F_{31}$	14.72		9.84		615.5	*13*
$Na_7Np_6F_{31}$	14.64	± 0.02	9.785	± 0.003	605.4	*18*
$Na_7Pu_6F_{31}$	14.55	± 0.02	9.741	± 0.003	595.3	*18*
$Na_7Am_6F_{31}$	14.48	± 0.02	9.665	± 0.003	585.0	*18*
$Na_7Cm_6F_{31}$	14.41	± 0.02	9.661	± 0.003	579.1	*18*

The 1:1 complexes between the heavier alkali fluorides and protactinium pentafluoride are especially interesting since they are not like their tantalum analogs but more closely resemble those of pentavalent uranium. We find them to be orthorhombic (*see* Table IV). Systematic absences of reflections indicate the space group to be Abm2 or Abmm (Cmma). Reflections of the type h k l for which k and l are odd are extremely weak, while those with k and l even are generally quite strong. The intensity distribution of the strong reflections suggest that at least the actinide atoms are in such special positions as to produce a pseudo-cell of one quarter the volume of the true cell.

Uranium(V). In the case of uranium, gaseous fluorine will normally take UF_4 on past UF_5 to UF_6. In contrast, we find that fluorine oxidation of UF_4 in liquid anhydrous HF proceeds readily to UF_5 and then goes only slowly to UF_6. If alkali fluoride is also present, the method is especially useful in the preparation of $MF \cdot UF_5$ compounds free from traces of U(IV) or U(VI). The technique is given below:

(1) We prepared UF_5 by stirring a suspension of high surface area UF_4 in liquid anhydrous HF at 25°C. under 10 p.s.i.g. of F_2. The oxidation can be readily halted at β-UF_5 which is also insoluble in liquid HF.

(2) A stirred slurry of CsF and UF_4 (1:1 mole ratio) in liquid HF was treated with F_2 at 10 p.s.i.g., resulting in smooth oxidation of U(IV) to U(V), giving a clear blue solution of $CsF \cdot UF_5$. On evaporation of HF, blue crystals of pure $CsF \cdot UF_5$ were deposited. With RbF, light yellow $RbF \cdot UF_5$ crystals were deposited from the blue solution of $RbF \cdot UF_5$ in liquid HF. In these latter reactions, UF_4 need not be of high surface area since the $MF \cdot UF_5$ reaction products are soluble.

Neptunium(V) and Plutonium(V). Although UF_4, UF_5, and UF_6 are well known compounds, evidence for NpF_5 and PuF_5 is lacking. Using the method which proved successful in preparing UF_5, we found that at 25°C., NpF_4 (0.17 grams) as a slurry in HF was not oxidized to NpF_5 by 10 p.s.i.g. of F_2. However, when 10 grams of CsF were added and HF pumped off, fluorine then caused oxidation to Np(V). The green NpF_4 dissolved in the residual warm (50°–70°C.) CsF · 2HF mixture and was oxidized by F_2 to a soluble, magenta Np(V) fluoride complex; CsF· NpF_5 (isostructural with CsF · UF_5) was deposited from this solution (*5*). When liquid HF was recondensed on this material, disproportionation took place, as deduced from the observation that green NpF_4 remained behind and orange, volatile NpF_6 condensed in the connecting trap. CsF · NpF_5 is best prepared by the dry techniques listed below for plutonium; data for this compound are given in Table IV.

Table IV. Some Alkali Fluoride:Protactinium(V), Uranium(V), Neptunium(V), Plutonium(V) Fluoride Complexes[a]

(1:1) Isostructural Orthorhombic Compounds	a_o, A.	b_o, A.	c_o, A.
KF · PaF_5	5.64	11.54	7.98
KF · UF_5	5.61	11.46	7.96
NH_4F · PaF_5	5.84	11.90	8.03
NH_4F · UF_5	5.83	11.89	8.03
RbF · PaF_5	5.86	11.97	8.04
RbF · UF_5	5.82	11.89	8.03
CsF · PaF_5	6.14	12.56	8.06
(1:1) Isostructural Rhombohedral Compounds			
CsF · UF_5	8.04		8.39
CsF · NpF_5	8.017		8.386
CsF · PuF_5	8.006		8.370
(2:1) Isostructural Monoclinic Compounds			
2RbF · NpF_5	6.26	13.42	8.90 ($\beta = 90°$)
2RbF · PuF_5	6.27	13.41_6	8.84 ($\beta = 90°$)

[a] A complete structure determination of $RbPaF_6$ is being made by Burns, Levy, and Keller (*16*).

The compounds $2RbF \cdot PuF_5$ and $CsF \cdot PuF_5$ were the first fluoride complexes to be characterized in which a transuranium element in the pentavalent state occurs without the "yl" type of oxygen bonding (*23*). Fluorine gas was used to oxidize anhydrous solid mixtures of rubidium fluoride or cesium fluoride-plutonium(IV) fluorides in 2:1 and 1:1 mole ratio. The mixtures were contained in sapphire boats and were exposed to 6 p.s.i.g. F_2 gas at 350°–400°C. for times varying from 4 to 16 hours. The compound $2RbF \cdot PuF_5$ is monoclinic, $a_o = 6.27$, $b_o = 13.42$, $c_o = 8.84$, $\beta = 90°$; it is isostructural with $2KF \cdot TaF_5$ (*17*) and $2RbF \cdot NpF_5$ (*5*). $CsF \cdot PuF_5$ is rhombohedral, isostructural with $CsF \cdot UF_5$ (*21*). Data on these 1:1 complexes are listed in Table IV.

Literature Cited

(1) Asprey, L. B., Penneman, R. A., *Inorg. Chem.* **1,** 134 (1962).
(2) Asprey, L. B., Penneman, R. A., *Science* **145,** 924 (1964).
(3) Asprey, L. B., Kruse, F. H., Penneman, R. A., *J. Am. Chem. Soc.* **87,** 3518 (1965).
(4) Asprey, L. B., Penneman, R. A., *Centre Natl. Rech. Sci. (Paris) Colloq. Intern. Phys. Chem.* **154,** 109 (1966).
(5) Asprey, L. B., Keenan, T. K., Penneman, R. A., Sturgeon, G. D., *Inorg. Nucl. Chem. Letters* **2,** 19 (1966).
(6) Asprey, L. B., Kruse, F. H., Rosenzweig, A., Penneman, R. A., *Inorg. Chem.* **5,** 659 (1966).
(7) Asprey, L. B., Kruse, F. H., Penneman, R. A., *Inorg. Chem.* **6,** 544 (1967).
(8) Benz, R., Douglass, R. M., Kruse, F. H., Penneman, R. A., *Inorg. Chem.* **2,** 799 (1963).
(9) Barton, C. J., et al., *U. S. At. Energy Comm. Oak Ridge Natl. Lab. Rept.* **ORNL-2548** (Nov. 2, 1959).
(10) Brown, D., Smith, A. J., *Chem. Commun.* 554 (1965).
(11) Brown, D., Easey, J. F., *Nature* **205,** 589 (1965).
(12) Brown, D., Easey, J. F., *J. Chem. Soc.* **1966,** 254.
(13) Brunton, G. D., Insley, H., McVay, T. N., Thoma, R. E., *U. S. At. Energy Comm. Oak Ridge Natl. Lab. Rept.* **ORNL-3761,** (Feb. 1965).
(14) Brunton, G. D., *U. S. At. Energy Comm. Oak Ridge Natl. Lab. Rept.* **ORNL-3913,** 10 (1966); *Acta Cryst.* **21,** 814 (1966).
(15) Burns, J. H., Ellison, R. D., Levy, H. A., *U. S. At. Energy Comm. Oak Ridge Natl. Lab. Rept.* **ORNL-3913,** 17 (1966); *Acta Cryst.* (to be published).
(16) Burns, J. H., Levy, H. A., Keller, O. L., Oak Ridge Natl. Lab. (private communication).
(17) Hoard, J. L., *J. Am. Chem. Soc.* **61,** 1252 (1939).
(18) Keenan, T. K., *Inorg. Nucl. Chem. Letters* **2,** 153, 211 (1966).
(19) Keller, C., Schmutz, H., *Inorg. Nucl. Chem. Letters* **2,** 355 (1966).
(20) Kruse, F. H., Asprey, L. B., *Inorg. Chem.* **1,** 137 (1962).
(21) Penneman, R. A., Sturgeon, G. D., Asprey, L. B., *Inorg. Chem.* **3,** 126 (1964).
(22) Penneman, R. A., Kruse, F. H., George, R. S., Coleman, J. S., *Inorg. Chem.* **3,** 309 (1964).
(23) Penneman, R. A., Sturgeon, G. D., Asprey, L. B., Kruse, F. H., *J. Am. Soc.* **87,** 5803 (1965).

(24) Thoma, R. E., Barton, C. J., Friedman, H. A., Grimes, W. R., Insley, H., Moore, R. E., *J. Am. Ceram. Soc.* **41,** 63 (1958).
(25) Thoma, R. E., Insley, H., Landau, B. S., Friedman, H. A., Grimes, W. R., *J. Am. Ceram. Soc.* **41,** 538 (1958).
(26) Thoma, R. E., *Inorg. Chem.* **1,** 220 (1962).
(27) Thoma, R. E., Insley, H., Herbert, G. M., Friedman, H. A., Weaver, C. F., *J. Am. Ceram. Soc.* **46,** 37 (1963).
(28) Thoma, R. E., Friedman, H. A., Penneman, R. A., *J. Am. Chem. Soc.* **88,** 2046 (1966).
(29) Zachariasen, W. H., *J. Am. Chem. Soc.* **70,** 2147 (1948).

RECEIVED October 18, 1966. This work was sponsored by the U. S. Atomic Energy Commission.

19

Actinide Chemistry in Saturated Potassium Fluoride Solution

CONRAD E. THALMAYER and DONALD COHEN

Argonne National Laboratory, Argonne, Ill.

Absorption spectra have been obtained for certain actinide ions which are soluble in saturated KF solution: U(IV), Np(IV), Np(V), Np(VI), and Am(III). Oxidation-reduction reactions of neptunium have been studied. Four new complex fluorides have been prepared and identified by x-ray powder patterns: α*–*K_2NpF_6*,* β_1*–*K_2NpF_6*,* $KNpO_2F_2$*, and* $K_3NpO_2F_5$*. Three additional complex fluorides, of Np(III), Np(V), and U(VI), have been prepared but not identified.*

Concentrated salt solutions are a class of solvent whose properties have hardly begun to be appreciated. The ratio of water to salt in these media is so low that the primary hydration number (the number of water molecules about each ion) must be far lower than in dilute solutions. A saturated D_2O solution of KF, for example, which is 12.4*M* with a density of 1.563, has only 3.4 moles of D_2O per mole of KF while perhaps eight moles of water per mole of KF (*4*) are required for the primary hydration sphere in a dilute solution. The enhanced complex formation which necessarily results may lead to a chemistry different from aqueous chemistry. Asprey and Penneman (*3*) have reported that Am^{4+} is both stable and soluble in saturated NH_4F, RbF, and KF.

This study is concerned with the chemistry of the actinides in saturated KF solution. The areas examined are solubilities, absorption spectra, oxidation-reduction reactions, and solid compounds that can be produced in this medium. This paper reports work with neptunium which is essentially complete, and also includes work with uranium and americium.

Experimental

The fluoride solvent was prepared by dissolving Baker and Adamson reagent grade KF in 99.8% D_2O for the neptunium studies and in H_2O

for the uranium and americium work. As each new bottle of KF was used, the absorption spectrum of its solution was measured. Some bottles of KF had to be discarded because of an impurity which caused an ultraviolet absorption. D_2O solutions were used to enable spectral measurements to be made in the near infrared region. The saturated KF solution in D_2O is 12.4*M* and in H_2O is 12.6*M*.

The neptunium was purified by an anion column, and alpha pulse analysis revealed no other species than Np^{237}. The uranium solutions were prepared from reagent grade uranium nitrate hexahydrate. Alpha pulse analysis of the americium showed it to contain 47% Am^{243} and 53% Am^{241} by activity.

The reactions were carried out in borosilicate glass, quartz, and polycarbonate containers. There was very little attack upon the glass by fluoride ion. NaF was found as an impurity in only one or two preparations, and this probably was caused by a high hydrogen ion concentration.

Spectra were measured with a Cary 14 spectrophotometer or a Beckman IR-10. The x-ray studies were made with a 9-cm. Bradley-Jay camera with copper K_α radiation and a nickel filter.

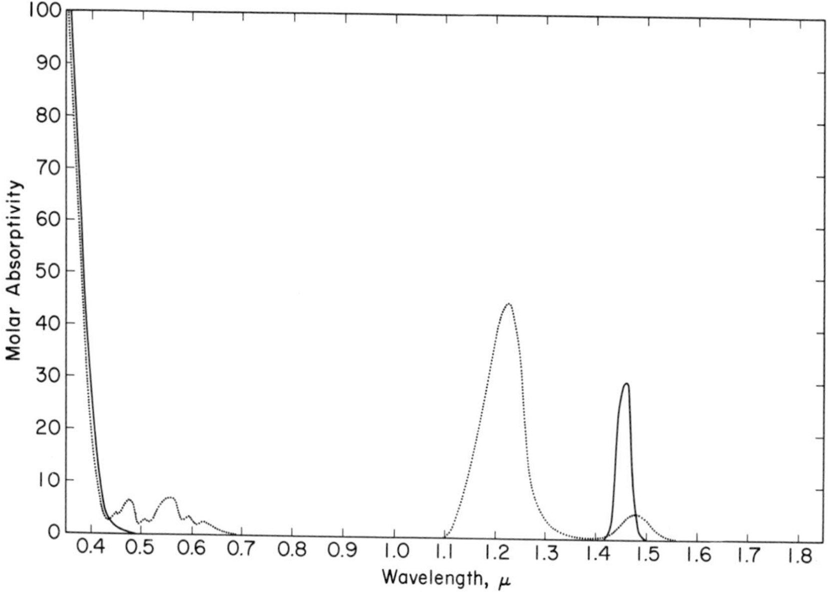

Figure 1. Absorption spectra of Np(VI) in saturated KF solution and in 1M $HClO_4$ (10, 13)

——— *in saturated KF*
. . . . *in aqueous acid*

Neptunium

Absorption Spectra. The absorption spectra of the various oxidation states of neptunium in saturated KF are given in Figures 1, 2, and 3.

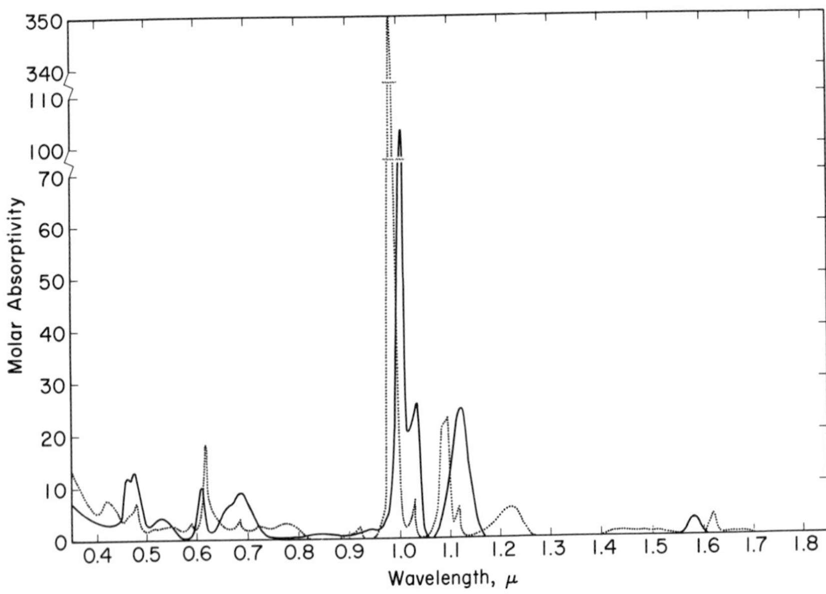

Figure 2. Absorption spectra of Np(V) in saturated KF solution and in 1M $HClO_4$ (10, 13)

——— *in saturated KF*
. . . . *in aqueous acid*

Each spectrum is compared with the aqueous dilute acid spectrum taken from Sjoblom and Hindman (*10*) and Waggener (*13*). The absorption spectrum of Np(VI) is characterized by a single peak at 1.46μ. It also exhibits the characteristic large absorption in the ultraviolet region, but it does not show any vibrational fine structure. The spectrum of Np(V) is similar to the aqueous spectrum, with the peaks usually smaller in intensity. The major Np(V) peak at 0.983μ, $\epsilon = 370$, is shifted to 1.004μ and reduced in intensity to a molar absorptivity of 104. The Np(IV) spectrum is similar to the aqueous spectrum, showing many sharp peaks.

Table I lists the molar absorptivities of the major peaks for the three oxidation states of neptunium in saturated KF in D_2O solutions. We consider the molar absorptivity for the Np(VI) peak accurate to 10%, and the values for the Np(V) and Np(IV) peaks accurate to 5%.

Solubilities. The solubilities of the several oxidation states of neptunium were determined by α-assay and absorption spectra. A concentrated solution of neptunium in each oxidation state in dilute DCl was added to a large volume of the saturated KF solution. This solution was heated and cooled to insure equilibrium, and then centrifuged. The spectrum of the solution was measured to check on the valence state, and an α-assay was made to measure the neptunium concentration.

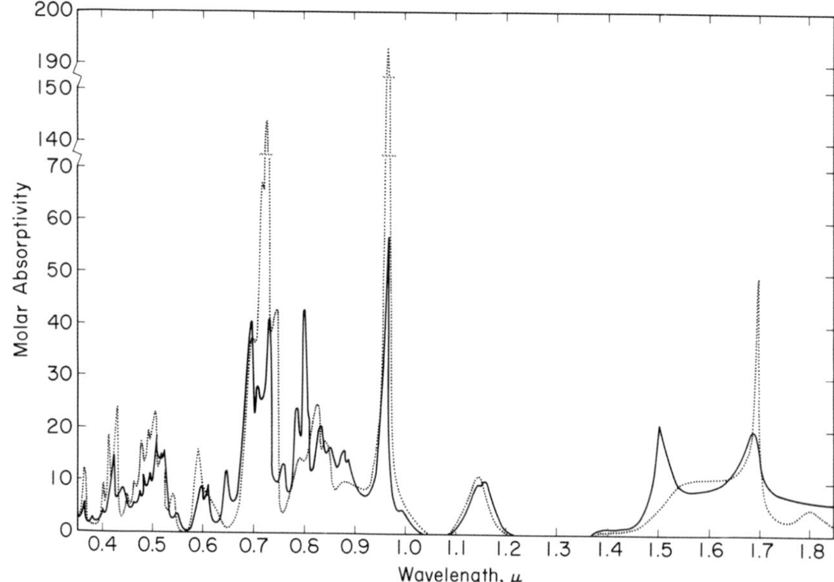

Figure 3. Absorption spectra of Np(IV) in saturated KF solution and in 1M $HClO_4$ (10, 13)

——— *in saturated KF*
. . . . *in aqueous acid*

Table I. Molar Absorptivities for the Major Absorption Peaks of Neptunium Ions in Saturated KF Solution

Oxidation State	*Wavelength, microns*	ϵ
Np(VI)	1.460	30
Np(V)	1.004	104
	1.034	26
	1.122	25
Np(IV)	0.9661	57
	0.7987	43
	0.7282	41
	0.6936	40

Np(III) is not sufficiently soluble to permit observation of its spectrum. If one assumes a molar absorptivity of 25 for the 0.790μ Np(III) peak then the solubility must be less than 0.0002*M*. Np(IV), with a solubility of 0.02*M* is the most soluble oxidation state. The next most soluble species is Np(V) with a solubility of 0.009*M*. The solubility of Np(VI) is almost a factor of ten less, being 0.001*M*.

The solubility for a freshly prepared solution of the Np(V) species is 0.009*M*. Sometimes the solubility decreased with time, and in two weeks a solution would be at only one-tenth the original concentration. Since this decrease in solubility did not always occur, it cannot be attributed to supersaturation. This phenomenon may be correlated with the hydrogen ion concentration of the solution, which was not carefully controlled.

Oxidation-Reduction Reactions. The various oxidation states of neptunium in the KF solution were obtained by adding the neptunium, which had been adjusted to the desired valence state in dilute acid, to the KF solution. Observations were made of the effect of a number of potentially useful oxidizing and reducing agents upon the oxidation state of the neptunium. The valence states of the neptunium ions, IV, V, and VI, were determined by absorption spectra. During the reduction to the III state, the solution color disappeared, and a purple solid was produced.

Table II. Oxidation-Reduction Reactions of Neptunium Ions in Saturated KF Solution

Reaction / Reagent	Conditions
Np(VI) → Np(V)	
$NaBH_4$	Room temperature
H_2O_2	Slow, even with heating
Na_2SO_3	Rapid, with heating
$NaNO_2$	Slow
$NH_2OH \cdot HCl$	Rapid
$H_2(Pt)$	Rapid
Np(V) → Np(IV)	
$NH_2OH \cdot HCl$	With heating
$H_2(Pt)$	Slow, with heating
$NaNO_2$	Slow, even with heating
SO_2	Rapid
Np(IV) → Np(III)	
Li(Hg)	
Mg(Hg)	With heating
Np(IV) → Np(V)	
H_2O_2	Rapid
NaOCl	
Na_4XeO_6	Rapid, with heating
Np(V) → Np(VI)	
O_3	Rapid, with heating
$KMnO_4$	With heating
Na_4XeO_6	Slow, even with heating
$(NH_4)_2S_2O_8$	With heating
NaOCl	With heating

The results of this study, given in Table II, show a behavior quite different from that in aqueous acid. H_2O_2 was found to reduce Np(VI) and to oxidize Np(IV) to Np(V). SO_2 rapidly reduced Np(V) to Np(IV), but a large amount of KF salted out, and a yellow addition compound (*7*) was formed which severely limited this reaction's usefulness.

The stability of each oxidation state is greater in KF solution than in aqueous acid. In aqueous solution Np(IV) is easily oxidized to Np(V), and care is necessary in storing a Np(IV) solution, but this is not true in saturated KF. We found that disproportionation of Np(V) occurred only upon adding the aqueous Np(V) to the KF solution. At most, 10% of the Np(V) would disproportionate. However, once prepared, the Np(V) in the KF solution was very stable.

Solid Compounds. The literature (*2, 5, 8, 9, 12*) on solid actinide fluoride complexes is extensive, and many new compounds are being prepared. For example, Thoma, Friedman, and Penneman (*12*) reported the first preparation of complex fluorides formed between UF_3 and the alkali fluorides KF, RbF, and CsF. This section summarizes the work which was performed concerning the solid compounds resulting from neptunium in saturated KF solution.

Table III. X-Ray Powder Pattern for x(KF) · y(NpF_3)

Intensity	$Sin^2\theta$
VW	0.0373
VS	0.0565
VS	0.0613
VVW	0.1120
M	0.1185
VS	0.1725
M	0.2249
VVW	0.2425
VVW	0.2863
VW	0.3404
W	0.3972
VVW	0.5112
VVW	0.5658
VVW	0.6249

Np(III). A purple solid was produced when Np(III) in dilute DCl (which had been prepared by hydrogen reduction) was added to a saturated KF solution. This solid was very sensitive to oxidation and changed to a green solid after two water washes. The absorption spectrum of the purple compound showed that the neptunium is in the III state. The x-ray powder pattern for this compound, given in Table III, has not yet been indexed. It is not isomorphous with the recently prepared 3KF · UF_3 (*12*).

Np(IV). Two solid compounds containing neptunium in the IV state have been prepared. If the purple Np(III) compound is oxidized by washing, the color changes to grey or dull green. Three such preparations of this solid have given the same x-ray diffraction pattern. As shown in Table IV, this pattern is indexed as face-centered cubic α-K_2NpF_6, isomorphous with fluorite-type α-K_2ThF_6 and α-K_2UF_6 (*14*). From an A *vs.* $\sin^2\theta$ plot $a = 5.905$A., which is in excellent agreement with the value extrapolated from the isomorphs.

Table IV. Partial[a] X-Ray Powder Pattern for α-K_2NpF_6, Face–Centered Cubic, $a = 5.905$A.

hkl	*Intensity*	$Sin^2\theta_{obs.}$	$Sin^2\theta_{calc.}$
111	VS	0.0525	0.0512
200	S	0.0698	0.0682
220	VS	0.1379	0.1364
311	VS	0.1898	0.1876
222	W	0.2068	0.2046
331	W	0.3264	0.3240
420	W	0.3434	0.3410
422	W	0.4121	0.4092
333, 511	W	0.4632	0.4604
531	W	0.5986	0.5968

[a] The complete pattern is in the ASTM X-Ray Powder Data File.

Table V. Partial[a] X-Ray Powder Pattern for β_1–K_2NpF_6, Hexagonal, $a = 6.56$A., $c = 3.73$A.

hkl	*Intensity*	$Sin^2\theta_{obs.}$	$Sin^2\theta_{calc.}$
100	VS	0.0192	0.0190
110	VS	0.0562	0.0562
101	VS	0.0622	0.0622
201	VS	0.1179	0.1176
300	S	0.1673	0.1671
211	VS	0.1739	0.1730
311	S	0.2834	0.2835
302, 401	S	0.3397	0.3381, 0.3387
222, 321	S	0.3936	0.3932, 0.3939
412, 421	S	0.5592	0.5585, 0.5591

[a] The complete pattern is in the ASTM X-Ray Powder Data File.

A second Np(IV) compound is prepared by adding solid KF to a Np(IV) solution in dilute DCl. Two such preparations have produced a green solid (*see* Table V for the x-ray pattern.) This pattern is indexed as hexagonal β_1-K_2NpF_6, isomorphous with β_1-K_2UF_6 (*14*) with $a =$

6.56A. and $c = 3.73$A., determined by a least-squares fitting with absorption correction.

NP(V). Adding Np(V) in a dilute acid solution to saturated KF produces either of two compounds but not a mixture. Five preparations gave the pattern shown in Table VI. This pattern is indexed as rhombohedral $KNpO_2F_2$, isomorphous with $KAmO_2F_2$ (*1*). A least-squares fitting of the high angle part of the pattern gives $a = 6.80$A. and $\alpha = 36.32°$.

Table VI. Partial[a] X-Ray Powder Pattern for $KNpO_2F_2$, Rhombohedral, $a = 6.80$A., $\alpha = 36.32°$

hkl	*Intensity*	$Sin^2\theta_{obs.}$	$Sin^2\theta_{calc.}$
1 1 1	VVS	0.0149	0.0148
1 0 0	VVS	0.0459	0.0457
1 1 0	VVS	0.0508	0.0507
2 2 2	VS	0.0595	0.0590
2 1 1	VVS	0.0708	0.0703
2 2 1	S	0.0852	0.0851
3 3 3	VVS	0.1330	0.1329
3 3 2	VVS	0.1484	0.1491
3 2 1	VS	0.1918	0.1914
4 3 2	S	0.2656	0.2652
5 4 3	S	0.3678	0.3685
4 3 1	S	0.4124	0.4137
7 3 3	S	0.9785	0.9812

[a] The complete pattern is in the ASTM X-Ray Powder Data File.

Table VII. Partial[a] X-Ray Powder Pattern for x(KF) · y(NpO_2F)

Intensity	$Sin^2\theta$
VS	0.0195
VS	0.0299
VVS	0.0598
M	0.1204
W	0.1271
W	0.1481
S	0.1785
W	0.2966

[a] The complete pattern is in the ASTM X-Ray Powder Data File.

Six preparations resulted in a light blue or green powder of which the x-ray powder pattern, which has not yet been indexed, is given in Table VII. Analyses of the samples of this solid for K, Np, and F gave KF:NpO_2F ratios ranging from 7:6 to 4:1.

Np(VI). Ozone will oxidize a hot Np(IV) or Np(V) solution in saturated KF to give a bright green water-soluble solid. The powder pattern of this $K_3NpO_2F_5$ is presented in Table VIII. It is indexed as body centered tetragonal, isomorphous with $K_3UO_2F_5$ (*15*). From a fit of the low angle lines $a = 9.12$A. and $c = 18.12$A.

Table VIII. Partial[a] X-Ray Powder Pattern for $K_3NpO_2F_5$, Body–Centered Tetragonal, $a = 9.12$A., $c = 18.12$A.

hkl	*Intensity*	$Sin^2\theta_{obs.}$	$Sin^2\theta_{calc.}$
1 1 2	VS	0.0214	0.0215
2 0 0 0 0 4	VS	0.0285	0.0286 0.0290
2 2 0 2 0 4	VS	0.0573	0.0571 0.0575
3 1 2 1 1 6 3 0 3 2 1 5	VS	0.0793	0.0786 0.0794 0.0806 0.0810
4 0 0 0 0 8	S	0.1148	0.1142 0.1158
4 2 0 4 0 4 2 0 8	M	0.1434	0.1428 0.1432 0.1444
4 1 5	M	0.1668	0.1666
4 2 4 2 2 8	M	0.1717	0.1718 0.1730
3 0 11 6 2 0 6 0 4	M	0.2851	0.2833 0.2856 0.2860

[a] The complete pattern is in the ASTM X-Ray Powder Data File.

Uranium

Only the IV state of uranium is soluble in saturated KF. Its spectrum, shown in Figure 4, is quite similar to the aqueous spectrum (*6*). In contrast, the spectrum of the UF_2^{2+} ion (*11*) is different, the sharp peaks no longer being present.

An attempt to prepare U(V) in this medium by reducing U(VI) was not possible because of the insolubility of U(VI). Reducing U(IV) to obtain U(III) was not successful. Although Li(Hg) did remove the U(IV) from solution, it was not possible to identify the resulting dark solid. The material was amorphous; it did not yield an x-ray powder pattern.

The U(IV) solid which was formed by adding solid KF to a U(IV) aqueous solution was identified by its x-ray pattern as α-K_2UF_6 (*14*). Ozone oxidized U(IV) when heated to give a green solid which was

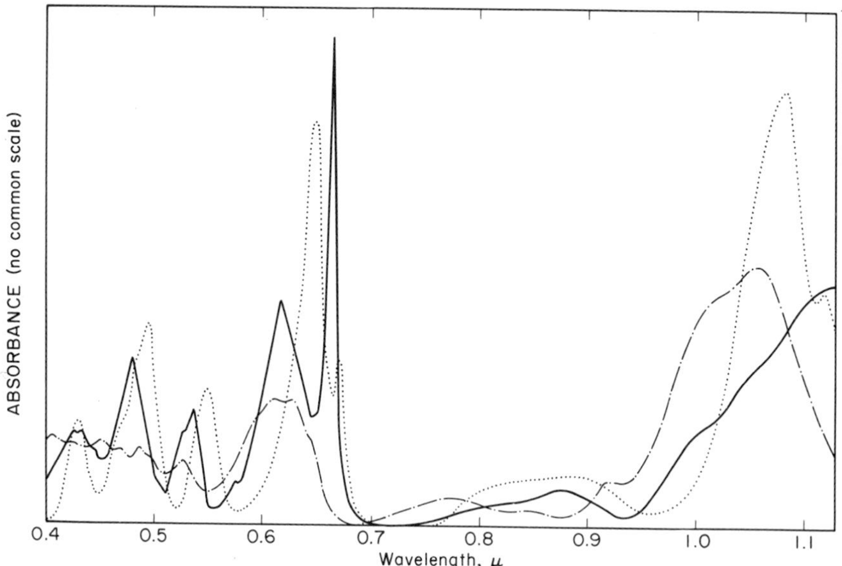

Figure 4. Absorption spectra of U(IV) in saturated KF solution, in 1M $HClO_4$ (6) and in 1M $HClO_4$, 0.08M HF (11)

——— *in saturated KF*
. . . . *in 1M $DClO_4$*
· - · - · - · - *in 1M $DClO_4$, 0.08M HF*

Table IX. Partial[a] X-Ray Powder Pattern for x(KF) · y(UO_2F_2), Cubic, a = 9.96A.

hkl	*Intensity*	$Sin^2\theta_{obs.}$	$Sin^2\theta_{calc.}$
2 0 0	S	0.0270	0.0240
2 2 0	MW	0.0508	0.0479
2 2 2	MS	0.0726	0.0719
4 1 1 } 3 3 0 }	MS	0.1088	0.1078
4 2 2	MS	0.1448	0.1438
6 0 0 } 4 4 2 }	MW	0.2165	0.2156
6 2 0	MW	0.2432	0.2396
4 4 4	M	0.2879	0.2875
8 4 2	MW	0.5035	0.5032

[a] The complete pattern is in the ASTM X-Ray Powder Data File.

found to be soluble in H_2O. The x-ray powder pattern of the first preparation is given in Table IX. This pattern was tentatively indexed as cubic with a = 9.96A., but it was necessary to ignore three weak lines. The second ozone oxidation resulted in a water-soluble green solid whose x-ray powder pattern was different and corresponded to tetragonal $K_3UO_2F_5$ (*15*). The third preparation resulted in a mixture of the two compounds, $K_3UO_2F_5$ and the cubic compound. This was the first time in which a mixture of two compounds was produced.

As yet the cubic compound has not been identified. Table X gives the infrared spectra of the cubic compound, $K_3UO_2F_5$, $K_3NpO_2F_5$, and UF_4. The bands at 480 cm.$^{-1}$ and 370 cm.$^{-1}$ are attributed to the metal-fluorine bond, and the bands at 850 cm.$^{-1}$ and 740 cm.$^{-1}$ result from the metal-oxygen bond. Thus, these data indicate a similarity in structure between the unknown cubic compound and the $K_3UO_2F_5$.

Table X. Infrared Spectra of Solids[a]

Compound	*Wavenumber, cm.$^{-1}$*			
$K_3UO_2F_5$	855 s	740 w	480 w	370 s
Cubic cmpd.		740 s	480 s	370 w
$K_3NpO_2F_5$	865 s	730 s	480 s	365 s
UF_4			480 sh	390 s

[a] s, strong; w, weak; sh, shoulder.

Americium

A study of the chemistry of americium in saturated KF solution has just been started. It is interesting that Am(III) is soluble. The spectrum of Am(III), shown in Figure 5, is surprisingly similar to the normal aqueous spectrum. The major peak at 0.5012μ has a molar absorptivity of 170. Since neither U(III) nor Np(III) is sufficiently soluble for spectral measurements, it will be of interest to try Pu(III). No attempt has been made to oxidize the Am(III) ion, and attempts to reduce Am(III) were unsuccessful.

Future plans are to complete this study with americium and to study plutonium and curium in this solvent.

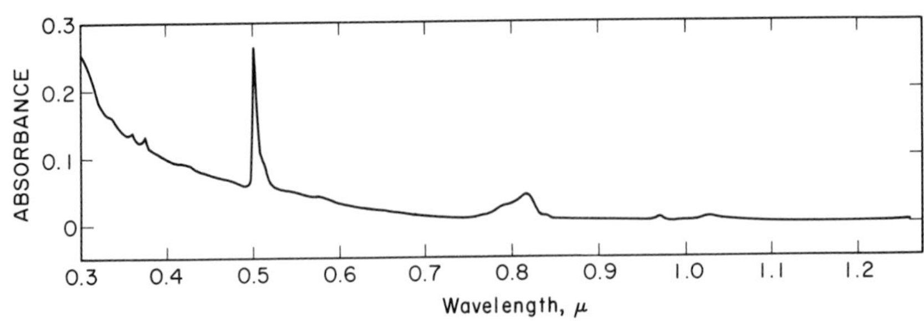

Figure 5. Absorption spectrum of Am(III) in saturated KF solution

Acknowledgment

We are grateful to the following members of the Argonne Chemistry Division: K. Jensen and I. Fox for the analyses, and S. Siegel, E. Gebert, and J. Whitaker for their valuable help in taking and interpreting the x-ray diffraction patterns.

Literature Cited

(1) Asprey, L. B., Ellinger, F. H., Zachariasen, W. H., *J. Am. Chem. Soc.* **76,** 5235 (1954).
(2) Asprey, L. B., Keenan, T. K., Penneman, R. A., Sturgeon, G. D., *Inorg. Nucl. Chem. Letters* **2,** 19 (1966).
(3) Asprey, L. B., Penneman, R. A., *J. Am. Chem. Soc.* **83,** 2200 (1961).
(4) Bockris, J. O'M., *Quart. Rev.* **3,** 173 (1949).
(5) Brown, D., Easey, J. F., *J. Chem. Soc.* (A), 254 (1966).
(6) Cohen, D., Carnall, W. T., *J. Phys. Chem.* **64,** 1933 (1960).
(7) Gmelin, L., "Handbuch der anorganischen Chemie," 8th ed., vol. 9 B-3, p. 1287, Verlag-Chemie, Berlin, 1963.
(8) Penneman, R. A., Sturgeon, G. D., Asprey, L. B., *Inorg. Chem.* **3,** 126 (1964).
(9) Penneman, R. A., Sturgeon, G. D., Asprey, L. B., Kruse, F. H., *J. Am. Chem. Soc.* **87,** 5803 (1965).
(10) Sjoblom, R., Hindman, J. C., *J. Am. Chem. Soc.* **73,** 1744 (1951).
(11) Stein, L., Williams, C. W., Fox, I. M., Gebert, E., *Inorg. Chem.* **5,** 662 (1966).
(12) Thoma, R. E., Friedman, H. A., Penneman, R. E., *J. Am. Chem. Soc.* **88,** 2046 (1966).
(13) Waggener, W. C., *J. Phys. Chem.* **62,** 382 (1958).
(14) Zachariasen, W. H., *J. Am. Chem. Soc.* **70,** 2147 (1948).
(15) Zachariasen, W. H., *Acta Cryst.* **7,** 792 (1954).

RECEIVED October 20, 1966. Based on work performed under the auspices of the U. S. Atomic Energy Commission.

20

Aqueous Oxidation-Reduction Reactions of Uranium, Neptunium, Plutonium, and Americium

T. W. NEWTON and F. B. BAKER

University of California, Los Alamos Scientific Laboratory, Los Alamos, N. M.

The experimental observations on the actinide oxidation-reduction reactions are described, and the empirical results are tabulated. The rate laws have been interpreted in terms of net activation processes, and these have been tabulated togther with the associated activation parameters—ΔF^*, ΔH^*, *and* ΔS^*. *An electrical analog is described which has been useful in interpreting complicated rate laws. Empirical correlations have been found between the formal entropies of the activated complexes and their charges, and for sets of similar reactions, between the hydrogen ion dependence and* ΔF°, *between* ΔF^* and ΔF°, *and between* ΔH^* *and* ΔH°. *The kinetic and physical evidence for binuclear species is discussed.*

Uranium, neptunium, plutonium, and americium are reasonably stable in aqueous solutions as ions with oxidation states ranging from 3+ to 6+. In acid solutions the 3+ and 4+ states exist as hydrated cations such as U^{3+} and U^{4+}. Am^{4+} has not been detected, presumably because it is too unstable with respect to disproportionation. The higher oxidation states exist as oxygenated "-yl" ions such as UO_2^{+} and UO_2^{2+}. This situation leads to many possible reactions among the actinide ions and with other oxidizing or reducing agents. The study of the kinetics of these reactions is important because it aids in understanding the mechanisms of oxidation-reduction reactions and the factors which determine their rates. In addition, information is provided which is useful in the design of separation processes and analytical procedures.

This subject, or parts of it, has been reviewed previously by Katz and Seaborg (*35*), Hindman (*26*), Rabideau *et al.* (*69*), and Newton and Rabideau (*52*). The present review is justified by the large amount of work which has appeared since 1959.

The literature has been surveyed to September 1966. The recent work (since 1959) is discussed in this section and organized according to the elements involved. The quantitative observations are summarized in Table I.

Reactions of Uranium Ions

Exchange Reactions. Masters and Schwartz (*43*) studied the U(IV)-U(VI) exchange in acid perchlorate solutions. At low U(IV) concentrations it was concluded that the exchange involves the U(IV) + U(VI) = 2U(V) equilibria, while at higher U(IV) concentrations, in agreement with an earlier suggestion by Rona (*75*), a path higher order in U(IV) is involved. A quantum yield of about 0.01 was estimated for the exchange induced by ultraviolet light. This exchange has also been studied in aqueous HCl-ethanol solutions (*44*) and in sulfate solutions (*2*). Gordon and Taube (*17*) have shown that the slow UO_2^{2+}-solvent oxygen exchange is catalyzed by U(V).

Oxidations of U(IV). The reactions of Pu(IV) (*53*) and of Ce(IV) (*3*) with U(IV) were found to be similar in that both appear to involve an activated complex of the composition $[U(OH)_2M]^{6+}$ where M is Ce or Pu) in spite of the fact that Ce(IV) is predominantly $CeOH^{3+}$ and Pu(IV) is Pu^{4+} in 1-2*M* $HClO_4$ solutions.

The reaction of Tl(III) with U(IV) has given anomalous results. It was first reported by Harkness and Halpern (*25*) to be first order in both U^{4+} and Tl^{3+} and between inverse first and inverse second order in H^+. It was proposed that a 2-electron oxidation produced U(VI) and Tl(I) in a single step. It was also noted that the reaction is moderately inhibited by Ag(I), and that the usual second-order plots did not pass through the origin. Jones and Amis (*33*), in connection with their study of the reaction in methanol-water mixtures, report that their data in water solution check acceptably those of Harkness and Halpern. However, Love *et al.* (*41*), in connection with the effect of tartaric acid on the reaction, report rate constants which are less than half those of Harkness and Halpern under identical conditions. They have also shown catalysis by Fe, but since the earlier results were independent of the initial reactant concentrations, iron contamination cannot account for the discrepancy. Wear (*96*) has studied the reaction over extended ranges of reactant concentrations but reports rate laws which are inconsistent with his observations.

Shastri *et al.* (*79*) report that the oxidation of U(IV) by Np(V) is complicated by further reaction between U(IV) and Np(IV). Preliminary results using the analogous oxidizing agent, Pu(V), also showed complicated kinetics (*62*). Np(VI), on the other hand, was shown by Sullivan *et al.* (*87*) to give well-behaved kinetics; the rate is first power in the reactant concentrations and inverse first power in the hydrogen ion concentration.

The oxidation of U(IV) by H_2O_2 (*4*), like that by O_2 (*24*), is most probably a chain reaction since it is inhibited by Cu(II) and Co(II). Plausible chain carriers are U(V) and OH. Sobkowski (*82*) reported significantly higher rate constants but suggested that a chain is not involved. His mechanism requires that U(V) disproportionation be faster than its reaction with H_2O_2.

Federova and Kanevskii (*15*) have reported rates of oxidation of U(IV) by $S_2O_8^{2-}$, ClO_2^-, and ClO_3^-, and the effects of Fe(II) and V(V) on the latter reaction (*14*). Gordon and Feldman (*19*) have also given rate constants for various U(IV)-halogenate reactions. Gordon and Andrews (*20*) have determined the rate law, but not the activation energy for the U(IV)–Br_2 reaction. This reaction is catalyzed by Fe(III) and by Mn(II), but not affected by Pb(II), Cu(II), Ni(II), nor Co(II). Rykov and co-workers (*77*) give rate laws and activation parameters for the U(IV) bromate reaction in perchlorate solutions.

Disproportionation of U(V). This reaction was reinvestigated (*59*) when it was observed that it is greatly inhibited by U(VI). A moderately stable U(V)–U(VI) complex was found with an absorption band at 7370A. ($\epsilon = 27M^{-1}$cm.$^{-1}$). Rate data were extrapolated to zero U(VI) concentrations, and activation parameters were determined which are believed to be more reliable than the polarographically previously determined ones (*32*). A more recent, controlled potential method (*63*) gives results at 25°C. in better agreement with the spectrophotometric ones.

Reductions of U(VI). Cr(II) was found to react rapidly with U(VI) to give a green binuclear intermediate (*55*) which is probably analogous to the substance which forms when Cr(II) and Np(VI) or Cr(III) and Np(V) are mixed (*89, 90*). The intermediate decomposes to U(VI), U(IV), and Cr(III) with an apparent half-time at 0°C. ranging from 4 to 8 min. Gordon (*18*) has shown that transfer of oxygen from UO_2^{2+} to $Cr(H_2O)_6^{3+}$ is efficient in this reaction.

U(VI) has been found to catalyze the V(II)–V(IV) and the V(III)–Fe(III) reactions (*58, 60*). The catalysis is caused by the reduction of U(VI) by V(II) or by V(III), followed by the rapid oxidation of the U(V) produced by V(IV) or by Fe(III) respectively. The V(II)–U(VI) reaction shows simple second-order kinetics essentially independent of the hydrogen ion concentration. The V(III) reaction, depends on the hydrogen ion concentration approximately to the −1.8 power. Detailed analysis of this dependence indicates consecutive rate determining reactions and a binuclear intermediate.

Reactions of Neptunium Ions

Reductions of Np(V). Shastri *et al.* (*78*) have studied the Np(V)–I^- reaction in aqueous HCl solutions of *ca.* 3*M*. The empirical rate law was reported to be $-d[Np(V)]/dt = k[Np(V)]^{0.86}[I^-]^{1.55}[H^+]^{2.61}$. The unexpected Np(V) dependence might be caused in part by the fact that the ionic strength apparently was not constant.

Appelman and Sullivan (*1*) found a two-term rate law to be necessary to describe the reduction of Np(V) by V(III). The proposed mechanism: V(III) + Np(V) → V(IV) + Np(IV), V(III) + Np(IV) ⇄ V(IV) + Np(III), and Np(III) +Np(V) → 2Np(IV) is not in strict accordance with the data. A misprint in the authors' Table IV has been noted: values for k_N should be multiplied by 100.

The reduction of Np(V) by Cr(II) has been studied recently by Thompson and Sullivan (*94*). The reaction is complicated by the consecutive-competitive reaction between Cr(II) and product Np(IV). This latter reaction has been studied separately (*93*).

Oxidations of Np(V). Dukes and Siddall (*12, 81*) have used solvent extraction techniques to study the kinetics of the oxidation of Np(V) by HNO_3 catalyzed by HNO_2, and by V(V), in HNO_3 solutions. The former reaction is interesting in that the rate is independent of HNO_2 concentration above $5 \times 10^{-5}M$ and of NO_3^- concentration above 2.4*M*. A highly protonated Np(V) is suggested as the active intermediate. The V(V) reaction approaches equilibrium at rates first power in Np(V) and V(V) and about second power in HNO_3.

Sullivan (*91*) found the rate law for the Np(V)–Cr(VI) reaction to show inhibition by Np(VI) and to require two consecutive rate-determining steps. It appears that Cr(V), formed in the first step, can react with either Np(VI) to regenerate the reactants or with Np(V) to give Cr(IV), which reacts rapidly to give final products. The temperature dependence of the rates was found not to agree with the Arrhenius equation.

Reductions of Np(VI). The rate law found by Zielen *et al.* (*100*) for the H_2O_2–Np(VI) reaction is analogous to that mentioned above for the Np(V)–Cr(VI) reaction. In this case, the radical HO_2 probably forms in the first step and reacts with either Np(V) to regenerate the reactants or with Np(VI) to give products.

Sheppard (*80*) has studied the reduction of Np(VI) by V(III) and found the kinetics to be complicated by the subsequent V(IV)–Np(VI) reaction. To minimize complications from this source, rate constants were estimated using data from the initial 20–30% of reaction. Our calculations show that the error in such an estimate can range from 4% for an initial V(III)/Np(VI) ratio of 2 and 20% completion up to 15% for an initial ratio of 1 and 30% completion. The reported rate constants are in poor agreement with the Arrhenius equation.

Hindman *et al.* (*28, 29, 30*) have investigated the effect of D_2O on the Np(IV)–Np(VI) reaction and redetermined the acid dependence. The previously determined dependence in H_2O (*30*) could be interpreted in terms of either consecutive or parallel rate-determining reactions (*51*). We have now used the newer data and a least-squares procedure to compare the two mechanisms. In H_2O, consecutive reactions fit the data better than parallel reactions; the root-mean-square deviations are 3.63 and 3.81% respectively. In D_2O the corresponding deviations are 7.79% and 4.18%. It is concluded that, unlike the analogous U(IV)–Pu(VI) reaction (*51*), there is no strong evidence for consecutive reactions and a binuclear intermediate. This reaction has been reinvestigated by Rykov and Yakovlev (*76*), who report higher rate constants under comparable conditions.

Reactions of Plutonium Ions

Oxidations of Pu(III). Dukes (*13*) has studied the Pu(III)-HNO_2 reaction in HCl, $HClO_4$, and HNO_3 solutions. The rate laws in the first two acids were essentially the same and were explained by postulating NO^+ + Pu(III) = NO + Pu(IV) to be the rate-determining step. In the presence of NO_3^- a faster rate-determining step is apparently possible; it may be N_2O_4 + Pu(III) = NO_2^- + NO_2 + Pu(IV).

Cleveland (*7*) has reported preliminary results on the oxidation of Pu(III) by XeO_3 at 30°C. in perchlorate solutions of 2*M* ionic strength. Some sort of Xe(V) is produced in the rate-determining step, which then reacts rapidly with five additional Pu(III) to give Pu(IV). Interference from the competitive oxidation of Pu(IV) was minimized by working at high Pu(III)/Pu(IV) ratios.

The slow oxidation by Cl_2 has been described by Mazumdar and Pisharody (*45, 46*). Unfortunately, neither the presentation of the data nor its interpretation is clear. The rate law is incorrectly derived from the proposed mechanism, which in turn violates the principle of microscopic reversibility.

Reductions of Pu(IV). Rabideau and Kline have studied the reduction of Pu(IV) by the formally similar reducing agents V(III) (*73*) and

Ti(III) (*71*). These analogous reactions show different hydrogen ion dependences. The Ti(III) reaction is almost exclusively inverse first power while for V(III), terms inverse first power and inverse second power in acid concentration are important in the rate law.

In chloride solutions Sn(II) reduces Pu(IV) at conveniently measurable rates (*72*). After allowance was made for chloride complexing of the reactants it was concluded that activated complexes composed of Pu(IV), Sn(II), and four and five chloride ions are involved.

Fe(II) reacts with Pu(IV) at rates which show inverse first power hydrogen ion dependence (*54*). In chloride solutions a term first power in chloride but zero power in hydrogen ion becomes important. Thus, for this reaction, Cl can replace OH in the activated complex.

Reductions of Pu(VI). Rabideau and Kline (*70*) studied the reduction of Pu(VI) by Ti(III) for comparison with the previous results for the analogous reaction of V(III) (*67*). The rate-determining step produces Pu(V), which is rapidly reduced by Ti(III) to Pu(IV). This is in contrast to most other reducing agents which react slower with Pu(V) than with Pu(VI). Since the product, Pu(IV), is also reduced by Ti(III), a competitive-consecutive system results. A method for treating the data was developed which used a computer programmed for numerical integration. Unlike the analogous V(III) reaction, the rate law was found to have only a single important term, inverse in hydrogen ion concentration.

Rabideau and Masters (*74*) found that the oxidation of Sn(II) by Pu(VI) is very similar to what they observed for Pu(IV). A very important feature is their evidence that a two-electron process is involved. Although the reduction of Pu(V) is slower than that of Pu(VI), no Pu(V) was formed.

The net reaction for the reduction of Pu(VI) to Pu(V) by Fe(II) is quite simple; in spite of this a complicated three-term hydrogen ion dependence was found (*56*). A mechanism which involves both outer-sphere and inner-sphere activated complexes is favored. The inner-sphere complexes are supported by evidence for consecutive reactions and a binuclear intermediate.

Reactions of Americium(V)

The reduction of Am(V) by H_2O_2 has been studied in 0.1*M* $HClO_4$ by Zaitsev *et al.* (*99*). The rate is probably first order in each of the reactants, but it is complicated by some radiolytic decomposition of H_2O_2. The temperature dependence was determined, but the acid dependence was not.

Coleman (*11*) has used a sample of the relatively long-lived (7951 yr.) Am^{243} to study the disproportionation of Am(V) without the excessive radiolysis which made earlier results difficult to interpret (*98*). In 2*M* perchlorate solutions the rate was found to be second power in Am(V) and approximately 2.5 power in acid concentration. This latter dependence differs from those of the analogous reactions of U(V) (*59*) and Pu(V) (*66*) which are predominantly first power in hydrogen ion concentration. The temperature dependence was determined at a single hydrogen ion concentration; so activation parameters for the individual rate determining reactions cannot be estimated with reasonable precision without making further assumptions.

Interpreting the Rate Laws

The rate constants and empirical rate laws shown in Table I describe the experimental observations, but they need further interpretation in order to extract the maximum amount of information from them. Adopting the language of the absolute reaction rate theory (*16*), we assume that for each rate-determining step the reactant species are in quasi-equilibrium with the activated complex and that the rate of this step is proportional to the concentration of the activated complex. Often, rapid equilibria preceed the actual rate-determining step; these can be added to the actual activation process to give a net activation process written in terms of the principal species in the solution:

$$\mathrm{m}A + \mathrm{n}B + \mathrm{p}C + \ldots = [\text{Act. Complex}]^* + \mathrm{q}L + \mathrm{r}M + \ldots$$

and the rate will be proportional to

$$\frac{[A]^m[B]^n[C]^p\ldots}{[L]^q[M]^r\ldots},$$

where *A, B, C,* are initial reactants, and *L, M,* are products of the pre-equilibria. Since the net activation process must formally balance, the composition of the activated complex can be determined from the rate law. This formulation has the advantage that the actual reactant species need not be known; in fact these species cannot be determined from the rate law alone.

This discussion shows that the empirical rate laws must be re-expressed, where necessary, as a collection of terms which are appropriate functions of the concentrations of species actually present in the solutions. The observed nonintegral dependences shown by some of the stoichiometric concentrations may be caused by (a) equilibria in which an appreciable fraction of one of the reactants is present as more than one species; complex formation and hydrolysis are examples of such equilibria, (b) more than one kinetically important activated complex, or

(c) changes in the pertinent activity coefficient ratios. This last effect is usually considered to be small at constant ionic strength for reactions among ions of the same sign (*54*). Further data pertinent to this point are clearly needed.

Although the rate law for a reaction does not give its detailed mechanism, it does give the composition of the activated complexes at the highest barriers as shown above, and in addition, the pattern of paths for the reaction. By pattern of paths, as contrasted to mechanism, we mean the various ways in which reactants get to products without considering intermediates which are in rapid equilibrium with the reactants or which react rapidly to give products. If only a single activated complex is kinetically important, only one pattern is possible: reactants → products. If more than one activated complex is involved, the possible patterns of paths are analogous to the possible ways in which electrical resistors can be connected. In this analog the resistors correspond to kinetic barriers (activated complexes), the junctions correspond to intermediates, and the terminals correspond to reactants or products.

For two activated complexes there are two distinguishable patterns; for three activated complexes four patterns are generally distinguishable; for four activated complexes ten patterns, and so on. The first three of these sets of patterns are shown in Figure 1. The patterns have been classified according to the number of activated complexes and the number of intermediates involved. Note that none of these patterns are kinetically distinguishable from their mirror images (*22*).

An important feature of these electrical analogs is that when the steady-state approximation is valid the reciprocals of the indicated resistances are the analogs of $k[A]^m[B]^n[C]^p$ . . . , where $A, B, C,$ . . . are the initial reactants, and k is the effective rate constant for the formation of the activated complex directly from the initial reactants, even if intermediates are involved. This means that the over-all rate law is found by combining the individual rate terms according to the rules for combining the analogous reciprocal resistances.

The activation parameters, ΔF^*, ΔH^*, and ΔS^* for the various net activation processes are determined from the values and temperature coefficients of the effective rate constants using the equations provided by the absolute reaction rate theory (*16*).

Table II lists the net activation processes, patterns of paths, and activation parameters derived from the data in Table I.

Empirical Correlations

Hydrogen Ion Dependences. The hydrogen ion dependences given in Table I and indicated by the net activation processes in Table II are

Table I. Observed Rate Laws, Rate

Reactant	*Rate Law*	k, *1M H^+*,[a] *25°C.* (*in* M *and sec.*)
*Oxidations of U(IV), –d[U(IV)]/*dt =		
U(VI)	$k[U(IV)]^{0.93}[U(VI)]^{0.92}[H^+]^{-3.03}$	2.1×10^{-7}
Np(IV)	$k[U(IV)][Np(IV)][H^+]^{-2.5}$	5.0×10^{-5}
Np(V)	$k[U(IV)][Np(V)][H^+]^{-2}$	8.0×10^{-6}
Fe(III)	$k[U(IV)][Fe(III)][H^+]^{-1.81}$	12.8
Pu(VI)	$k[U(IV)][Pu(VI)][H^+]^{-1.2}$	3.1
Pu(IV)	$k[U(IV)][Pu(IV)][H^+]^{-1.93}$	31.5
V(V)	$k[U(IV)][V(V)][H^+]$	2.0×10^{4}
Np(VI)	$k[U(IV)][Np(VI)][H^+]^{-0.97}$	22.0
Tl(III)	$k[U(IV)][Tl(III)][H^+]^{-1.39}$	3.9×10^{-2}
Ce(IV)	$k[U(IV)][Ce(IV)][H^+]^{-1.2}$	8.7×10^{3}
H_2O_2	$k[U(IV)][H_2O_2][H^+]^{-0.21}$ (approx.)	0.8 – 2.3
Br_2	$k[U(IV)][Br_2][Br^-]^0[H^+]^{-2}$	5.3×10^{-4}
O_2	$k[U(IV)][O_2][H^+]^{-1}$	2.4×10^{-2}
ClO_3^-	$k[U(IV)][ClO_3^-][H^+]^{+1}$	2.9×10^{-3}
ClO_2^-	$k[U(IV)][ClO_2^-][H^+]^{-0.13}$	19.0
$S_2O_8^{2-}$	$k[U(IV)][S_2O_8^{2-}][H^+]^0$	7.2×10^{-3}
BrO_3^-	$k[U(IV)][BrO_3^-][H^+]^{0.43}$	2.6×10^{-1}
	or $[U(IV)][BrO_3^-](k_0 + k_2[H^+]^2)$	2.1×10^{-1} (k_o)
		5.3×10^{-2} (k_2)
*Oxidations of U(V), –d[U(V)]/*dt =		
U(V)	$k[U(V)]^2[H^+]^{0.82}$	2.4×10^{2}
Fe(III)	$k[U(V)][Fe(III)]$	5.0×10^{4}
V(IV)	$k[U(V)][V(IV)][H^+]^{0.2}$	2.5×10^{4}
Np(V)		(Measurable at 25°C.)
*Reductions of U(VI), –d[U(VI)]/*dt =		
V(II)	$k[U(VI)][V(II)][H^+]^{0.01}$	7.4×10^{1}
V(III)	$k[U(VI)][V(III)][H^+]^{-1.8}$	2.8×10^{-1}
Sn(II)	$k[U(VI)][Sn(II)][HCl]^{-3.5}$	1.7×10^{-5}
*Reductions of Np(V), –d[Np(V)]/*dt =		
Cr(II)	$k[Np(V)][Cr(II)][H^+]^{-1}$	1.1×10^{3}
Np(III)	$k[Np(V)][Np(III)][H^+]^{1.05}$	4.3×10^{1}
V(III)	$[Np(V)][V(III)][H^+]^0$	3.0×10^{-1}
		6.0×10^{-2}
	$\times (k + k'[Np(IV)][H^+]^{-1.5}/[V(IV)])$	1.6×10^{-1} (k')
I^-	$k[Np(V)]^{0.86}[I^-]^{1.55}[H^+]^{2.61}$	1.7×10^{-3}
*Oxidations of Np(IV), –d[Np(IV)]/*dt =		
Fe(III)	$k[Np(IV)][Fe(III)][H^+]^{-3}$	5.7×10^{-2}
Np(V)	$k[Np(IV)]^{1.5}[Np(V)]^{0.5}[H^+]^{-2}$	6.45×10^{-8}
	$+ k'[Np(V)]^2[H^+]$	1.1×10^{-5} (k')
*Reduction of Np(IV), –d[Np(IV)]/*dt =		
Cr(II)	$k[Np(IV)][Cr(II)][H^+]^{-1.27}$	4.3
*Oxidation of Np(III), –d[Np(III)]/*dt =		
Fe(III)	$k[Np(III)][Fe(III)][H^+]^{-0.95}$	6.8×10^{2}
*Oxidations of Np(V), –d[Np(V)]/*dt =		

Constants, and Activation Energies

E_a, *kcal./mole*	μ, M	*Ref.*	*Comment*
38.0	2.00	*43*	
16.0	1.00	*79*	
33.0	1.00	*79*	
23.6	1.02	*5*	
19.1	2.00	*51*	Evidence for binuclear intermediate
24.8	2.00	*53*	
13.0	1.00	*62*	Preliminary result
18.8	2.00	*87*	
22.5	2.90	*25*	
15.4	2.00	*3*	
16–19	2.00	*4*	
—	2.00	*20*	
22.4	0.50	*24*	
—	0.50	*15*	
11.0	1.00	*19*	
—		*34*	In H_2SO_4
27.2	2.00	*76*	
9.0	2.00	*59*	Extrap. to 0*M* U(VI)
—	2.00	*60*	Estimated from the effect of Fe(III) and V(IV) on V(III)–U(VI) reaction
—	2.00	*60*	
		92	Preliminary result
7.8	2.00	*58*	
22.1	2.00	*60*	Evidence for binuclear intermediate
18.0	7.00	*48*	*k* value is for 1*M* Cl^- and 7*M* H^+
—	0.20	*94*	
6.4	2.00	*27*	
15.2	3.00	*1*	
	1.00		
	3.00		
28.3	3.00	*78*	
35.0	1.00	*31*	Corrected for back reaction
37.4	1.20	*85*	Exchange
18.2			
18.0	1.00	*93*	
15.0	2.00	*61*	

Table I.

Reactant	*Rate Law*	k, *1M* H^+,[a] *25°C. (in* M *and sec.)*
Cr(VI)	$\frac{k[Np(V)][Cr(VI)][H^+]^{-1.6}}{1 + k'[Np(VI)][H^+]^{-1.8}/[Np(V)]}$	4.3
V(V)	$k[Np(V)][V(V)][H^+]^{2.3}$	2.0
NO_2^-–NO_3^-	$k[Np(V)][H^+]^{-4}$	1.0×10^{-5}
Np(VI)	$k[Np(V)][Np(VI)][H^+]^{0.13}$	9.0×10^{1}
Reductions of Np(VI), –d*[Np(VI)]*/dt =		
V(III)	$k[Np(VI)][V(III)][H^+]^{-1.47}$	2.45×10^{1}
Np(IV)	$k[Np(VI)][Np(IV)][H^+]^{-2.14}$	4.9×10^{-2}
H_2O_2	$\frac{k[Np(VI)][H_2O_2][H^+]^{-1}}{1 + k'[Np(V)]/[Np(VI)]}$	8.9 1.9 (k')
Oxidations of Pu(III), –d*[Pu(III)]*/dt =		
Pu(VI)	$k[Pu(III)][Pu(VI)][H^+]^{0}$	2.7
Pu(V)	$k[Pu(III)][Pu(V)][H^+]^{0.97}$	4.5×10^{-2}
Pu(IV)	$k[Pu(III)]^{-1}[Pu(IV)]^{-0.8}[H^+]^{-1}$	1.0×10^{3}
HNO_2	$k[Pu(III)][HNO_2]^{0.83}[HCl]^{1.28} \times (1 + k'[NO_3])$	3.0×10^{-1}
Oxidations of Pu(III), –d*[Pu(III)]*/dt =		
XeO_3	$k[Pu(III)][XeO_3][H^+]^{0}$	1.6×10^{-2}
Cl_2	$k[Pu(III)][Cl_2]^{0}[HCl]^{0}$ (?)	7.0×10^{-6}
O_2	$[Pu(III)]^2[O_2]^{1.05}[H^+]^{-0.1} \times (k[SO_4^{2-}]^2 + k'[SO_4^{2-}]^3)$	6.0×10^{3} 1.9×10^{5} (k')
Reductions of Pu(IV), –d*[Pu(IV)]*/dt =		
Fe(II)	$k[Pu(IV)][Fe(II)][H^+]^{-0.92}$	4.7×10^{1}
V(III)	$k[Pu(IV)][V(III)][H^+]^{-1.43}$	6.2×10^{1}
Ti(III)	$k[Pu(IV)][Ti(III)][H^+]^{-1.09}$	6.6×10^{1}
Pu(IV)	$k[Pu(IV)]^2[H^+]^{-3.14}$	5.4×10^{-5}
Sn(II)	$k[Pu(IV)][Sn(II)][H^+]^{0}[Cl^-]^{1.9}$	1.7×10^{1}
Reductions of Pu(V), –d*[Pu(V)]*/dt =		
Pu(V)	$k[Pu(V)]^2[H^+]^{1.1}$	8.0×10^{-3}
Fe(II)	$k[Pu(V)][Fe(II)][H^+]^{-1}$	3.0×10^{1}
Reductions of Pu(VI), –d*[Pu(VI)]*/dt =		
V(III)	$k[Pu(VI)][V(III)][H^+]^{-1.3}$	2.24
Ti(III)	$k[Pu(VI)][Ti(III)][H^+]^{-1.05}$	1.1×10^{2}
Fe(II)	$k[Pu(VI)][Fe(II)][H^+]^{-0.36}$	1.66×10^{3}
Sn(II)	$k[Pu(VI)][Sn(II)][H^+]^{0}[Cl^-]^{1.46}$	6.7×10^{1}
Reductions of Am(V), –d*[Am(V)]*/dt =		
Am(V)	$k[Am(V)]^2[H^+]^{2.5}$	5.7×10^{-4}
H_2O_2	$k[Am(V)][H_2O_2][H^+]^{?}$	4.1×10^{-3}

[a] For solutions with $\mu < 1M$, this is the hypothetical value for $1M$ H^+ in a solution with the ionic strength listed.

Continued

E_a, *kcal./mole*	μ, M	*Ref.*	*Comment*
11.6	2.00	*91*	$k' = 7.6 \times 10^{-1}$
11.7	2.00	*12*	Values are for HNO_3 solution
12.0	2.90	*81*	Values are for 2.9*M* HNO_3
10.6	3.00	*8, 9, 10*	Values apply to 0°C. exchange
19.0	2.00	*80*	
25.5	2.00	*28, 29, 30*	
12.4	3.00	*99*	
5.4	1.00	*68*	
—	1.00	*64, 65*	From reverse reaction and equilibrium quotient
5.0	2.00	*37*	Exchange
~6.0	varied	*13*	
—	2.00	*7*	Values for 30°C.
15.0	1.00	*45, 46*	Values for 1*M* HCl
19.0	2.00	*49, 50*	$[O_2]$ in *M*
19.6	2.00	*54*	
21.2	2.00	*73*	
17.3	1.02	*71*	
—	1.00	*64, 65*	
20.0	2.00	*67*	Values are for 1*M* Cl^-
19.6	1.00	*66*	
—	1.00	*62*	Preliminary result
16.1	2.00	*67*	
10.9	2.00	*70*	
7.5	2.00	*56*	Evidence for binuclear intermediate
10.6	2.00	*74*	Evidence for a 2-electron process
14.0	2.00	*11*	Value extrapolated to 25°C.
13.0	0.10	*99*	Values apply to 0.1*M* HCl

Pattern	No. of Kinetically Distinguishable Activated Complexes	No. of Intermediates	Electrical Analog	Rate Law
1-0	1	0		R_1
2-0	2	0	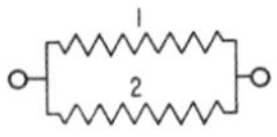	$R_1 + R_2$
2-1	2	1		$\frac{1}{\frac{1}{R_1} + \frac{1}{R_2}}$
3-0	3	0	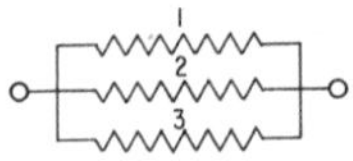	$R_1 + R_2 + R_3$
3-1-a	3	1	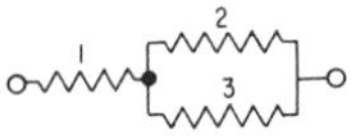	$\frac{1}{\frac{1}{R_1} + \frac{1}{R_2 + R_3}}$
3-1-b	3	1	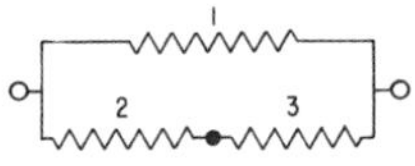	$R_1 + \frac{1}{\frac{1}{R_2} + \frac{1}{R_3}}$
3-2	3	2	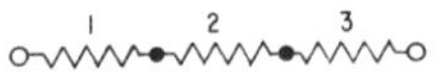	$\frac{1}{\frac{1}{R_1} + \frac{1}{R_2} + \frac{1}{R_3}}$

Figure 1. Various patterns of paths

All R_i are of the form $k_i[A]^{m_i}[B]^{n_i}[C]^{p_i}$ . . . , *where* A, B, C, *etc. are initial reactants.*

nearly all consistent with the proposition that the gain or release of hydrogen ions in an activation process will lie between zero and the total number gained or released in the corresponding over-all process. For example, Reactions 7-12 and 14-19, in Table II, all involve the overall release of four hydrogen ions, while the activated complexes are all formed with the prior release of from one to three hydrogen ions. Conspicuous exceptions to this generalization are shown by the oxidation of U(IV) by VO_2^+ and by ClO_3^- and by Reactions 2, 3, 5, 27, 28, and 29. These latter exceptions illustrate the tendency of activated complexes to hydrolyze and to reduce an otherwise high charge. In this connection no reliable evidence has been found for an activated complex with a net charge greater than 6+.

It is reasonable to suppose that the smaller the driving force for a reaction the more the activated complex will resemble the products. This supposition is borne out fairly well by the class of reactions in which an actinide(IV) ion is oxidized to the (V) state—Reactions 7-18 in Table II. For the five reactions for which ΔF° is greater than −1 kcal./mole, three out of a total of four hydrogen ions are released in the net activation process. For ΔF° less than −2 kcal./mole, the correlation is marred only by the three reactions for which both one and two hydrogen ions are released in simultaneous activation processes. This supposition rationalizes the fact that the disproportionation reactions of U(V) and Pu(V) are predominantly first power in the hydrogen ion concentration, while the analogous disproportionation of Am(V) is both second and third power.

The Entropies of the Activated Complexes. An approximate correlation had been noted previously (*52*) between the formal entropies of activated complexes and their charges. Data obtained since that time enable this correlation to be examined for activated complexes carrying charges from 0 to 6+. Values calculated for S^*_{complex} are given in Table II and plotted in Figure 2. The discordant point 21 corresponds to the minor path for the V(III)-Np(VI) reaction and has an uncertainty of at least 16 *e.u.* The uncertainties for points 8 are about 13 *e.u.* and are correlated such that if the true value of one is larger than indicated, that for the other is smaller. It is apparent that although charge is an important factor in determining the entropy of an activated complex, other less obvious ones are important also.

Free Energies of Activation. It is of interest to consider a set of similar reactions and determine the effect of the free energy changes on their rates. Reactions 7–18 are the largest such set of actinide ion reactions for which quantitative data are available. In this set an actinide(IV) ion, M^{4+}, is oxidized to the corresponding MO_2^+ ion by a reactant which does not undergo a drastic change in structure. A plot of ΔF^* *vs.* ΔF° for these reactions is given in Figure 3. The number of hydrogen ions released in the various net activation processes range from one to three and are indicated by the numbers in parentheses. All 15 points fall within 3.5 kcal./mole of a straight line with a slope of 1/2, irrespective of the number of hydrogen ions released. A slope of 1/2 is required if the value for a reaction and its reverse are to fall on the same straight line.

The relation shown here suggests that a measure of the intrinsic rate of a reaction, corrected for its driving force, is given by $\overline{\Delta F^*} = \Delta F^* - 0.5\,\Delta F^\circ$. This amounts to taking the average ΔF^* for the reaction in the forward and reverse directions. Under conditions where Marcus' relation: $k_{12} = (k_{11}k_{12}K_{12}f)^{1/2}$ (*42*) is applicable, $\overline{\Delta F^*} = \frac{1}{2}(\Delta F^*_{11} + \Delta F^*_{22} - RT \ln f)$. Values for these "intrinsic" activation free energies are given in Table III. This table shows some patterns of relative reactivity as well as some apparent anomalies. For example, the relative intrinsic

Table II. Thermodynamic Quantities of

	Process	*Pattern*[a]	μ, M
no M—O bonds formed or broken			
1.	$UO_2^{2+} + V^{2+} = UO_2^{+} + V^{3+}$		
	$UO_2^{2+} + V^{2+} = [*]^{4+}$	1–0	2.00
2.	$Pu^{4+} + Fe^{2+} = Pu^{3+} + Fe^{3+}$		
	$Pu^{4+} + Fe^{2+} + H_2O = [*]^{5+} + H^{+}$	2–0	2.00
2b.	$Np^{4+} + Cr^{2+} = Np^{3+} + Cr^{3+}$		
	$Np^{4+} + Cr^{2+} + H_2O = [*]^{5+} + H^{+}$	2–0	1.00
	$Np^{4+} + Cr^{2+} + H_2O = [*]^{4+} + 2H^{+}$		
2c.	$Np^{3+} + Fe^{3+} = Np^{4+} + Fe^{2+}$		
	$Np^{3+} + Fe^{3+} + H_2O = [*]^{5+} + H^{+}$	1–0	
3.	$PuO_2^{2+} + Fe^{2+} = PuO_2^{+} + Fe^{3+}$		
	$PuO_2^{2+} + Fe^{2+} = [*]^{4+}$	3–2	2.00
	$PuO_2^{2+} + Fe^{2+} = [*]^{4+}$		
	$PuO_2^{2+} + Fe^{2+} + H_2O = [*]^{3+} + H^{+}$		
4.	$Pu^{4+} + PuO_2^{+} = Pu^{3+} + PuO_2^{2+}$		
	$Pu^{4+} + PuO_2^{+} = [*]^{5+}$	1–0	1.00
5.	$Pu^{3+} + Pu^{4+} = Pu^{4+} + Pu^{3+}$		
	$Pu^{3+} + Pu^{4+} + H_2O = [*]^{6+} + H^{+}$	1–0	2.00
6.	$NpO_2^{+} + NpO_2^{2+} = NpO_2^{2+} + NpO_2^{+}$		
	$NpO_2^{+} + NpO_2^{2+} = [*]^{3+}$	1–0	3.00
MO_2^{+} formed from M^{4+}			
7.	$U^{4+} + NpO_2^{2+} + 2H_2O = UO_2^{+} + NpO_2^{+} + 4H^{+}$		
	$U^{4+} + NpO_2^{2+} + H_2O = [*]^{5+} + H^{+}$	1–0	2.00
8.	$Am^{4+} + AmO_2^{2+} + 2H_2O = 2AmO_2^{+} + 4H^{+}$		
	$Am^{4+} + AmO_2^{2+} + H_2O = [*]^{5+} + H^{+}$		
	$Am^{4+} + AmO_2^{2+} + H_2O = [*]^{4+} + 2H^{+}$	2–0	2.00
9.	$Np^{4+} + NpO_2^{2+} + 2H_2O = 2NpO_2^{+} + 4H^{+}$		
	$Np^{4+} + NpO_2^{2+} + H_2O = [*]^{4+} + 2H^{+}$	2–0	2.00
	$Np^{4+} + NpO_2^{2+} + H_2O = [*]^{4+} + 2H^{+}$		
	$Np^{4+} + NpO_2^{2+} + H_2O = [*]^{3+} + 3H^{+}$		
10.	$U^{4+} + PuO_2^{2+} + 2H_2O = UO_2^{+} + PuO_2^{+} + 4H^{+}$		
	$U^{4+} + PuO_2^{2+} + H_2O = [*]^{5+} + H^{+}$	2–1	2.00
	$U^{4+} + PuO_2^{2+} + H_2O = [*]^{4+} + 2H^{+}$		
11.	$Pu^{4+} + PuO_2^{2+} + 2H_2O = 2PuO_2^{+} + 4H^{+}$		
	$Pu^{4+} + PuO_2^{2+} + 2H_2O = [*]^{3+} + 3H^{+}$	1–0	1.00
12.	$U^{4+} + UO_2^{2+} + 2H_2O = 2UO_2^{+} + 4H^{+}$		
	$U^{4+} + UO_2^{2+} + 2H_2O = [*]^{3+} + 3H^{+}$	1–0	2.00
	$U^{4+} + UO_2^{2+} + 2H_2O = [*]^{3+} + 3H^{+}$	2–1(?)	2.00
13.	$U^{4+} + CeOH^{3+} + H_2O = UO_2^{+} + Ce^{3+} + 3H^{+}$		
	$U^{4+} + CeOH^{3+} + H_2O = [*]^{6+} + H^{+}$	1–0	2.00
14.	$U^{4+} + Pu^{4+} + 2H_2O = UO_2^{+} + Pu^{3+} + 4H^{+}$		
	$U^{4+} + Pu^{4+} + H_2O = [*]^{6+} + 2H^{+}$	1–0	2.00
15.	$U^{4+} + Fe^{3+} + 2H_2O = UO_2^{+} + Fe^{2+} + 4H^{+}$		
	$U^{4+} + Fe^{3+} + H_2O = [*]^{6+} + H^{+}$	2–0	1.02
	$U^{4+} + Fe^{3+} + H_2O = [*]^{5+} + 2H^{+}$		
16.	$Np^{4+} + Fe^{3+} + 2H_2O = NpO_2^{+} + Fe^{2+} + 4H^{+}$		
	$Np^{4+} + Fe^{3+} + 2H_2O = [*]^{4+} + 3H^{+}$	1–0	1.00

Over-all Processes and Net Activation Processes

ΔF, kcal./mole	ΔH, kcal./mole	ΔS, e.u.	S* comp.[b] e.u.	ΔF*,[c] kcal./mole	Ref.
−7.3	−14.0	−24.0[d]			
14.9	7.1	−26.1 ± 0.4[e]	−70	18.6	*58*
−4.9	−4.0	3.0			
15.1	19.1	13.0 ± 1	−82	17.6	*54*
−13.0	−11.9	4.0			
16.7	16.2	−1.6 ± 1.4	−93	23.2	*93(r)*[f]
17.7	20.6	9.8 ± 3.3	−82	24.2	
−14.2	−15.3	−4.0			
13.7	14.6	3.0 ± 0.3	−87	20.8	*61*
−3.3	−13.3	−34.0			
13.3	4.4	−30.0 ± 1.6	−84	15.0	
12.4	8.6	−12.6 ± 2	−67	14.0	*56*
13.4	9.4	−13.4 ± 2	−50	15.0	
−1.6	8.7	+34.0			
15.3	13.6	−6.0 ± 1	−106	16.1	*68*
0.0	0.0	0.0			
13.4	7.4	−20.4 ± 4	−127	13.4	*37(r)*[f]
0.0	0.0	0.0			
14.0	10.6	−12.0 ± 3	−29	14.0	*8, 9, 10, 52*
−12.9	1.7	49.0			
16.0	18.2	74.0 ± 1	−69	22.4	*87*
−12.9	8.2	68.0			
11.6	20.0	28.0 ± 13	−42	18.0	*11(r)*
11.4	20.0	30.0 ± 13	−40	17.8	
−9.2	7.5	56.0			
19.2	24.7	18.4 ± 1	−62	23.8	*28, 29, 30*
18.5	24.3	19.0 ± 5	−61	23.1	*76*
19.2	30.9	39.0 ± 5	−25	23.8	
−7.8	6.9	49.0			
16.6	17.6	3.4 ± 0.4	−87	20.5	*61*
16.0	21.3	17.6 ± 1.2	−72	19.9	
5.8	19.0	44.0			
26.6	37.8	38.0 ± 9	−40	23.7	*66*
11.9	26.7	49.6			
26.8	37.5	36.0 ± 1.7	−28	20.8	*43*
26.2	37.7	38.6 ± 1.5	−25	20.2	*59*
−24.0	−6.0	62.0			
12.2	14.0	6.0 ± 2	−116	24.2	*3*
−9.2	16.2	85.0			
15.4	24.3	30.0 ± 2	−118	20.0	*12*
−4.4	20.2	83.0			
17.0	18.0	3.0 ± 9	−130	19.2	*5(r)*
16.0	24.1	27.0 ± 2	−106	18.2	
−0.7	26.0	90.0			
19.1	34.6	52.0 ±	−69	19.4	*31*

Table II.

	Process	Pattern[a]	μ, M
17.	$Np^{4+} + Np^{4+} + 2H_2O = NpO_2^{+} + Np^{3+} + 4H^{+}$		
	$Np^{4+} + Np^{4+} + 2H_2O = [*]^{5+} + 3H^{+}$	1–0	2.00
18.	$Pu^{4+} + Pu^{4+} + 2H_2O = PuO_2^{+} + Pu^{3+} + 4H^{+}$		
	$Pu^{4+} + Pu^{4+} + 2H_2O = [*]^{5+} + 3H^{+}$	1–0	1.00
19.	$U^{4+} + Tl^{3+} + 2H_2O = UO_2^{2+} + Tl^{+} + 4H^{+}$		
	$U^{4+} + Tl^{3+} + H_2O = [*]^{6+} + H^{+}$	2–0	2.90
	$U^{4+} + Tl^{3+} + H_2O = [*]^{5+} + 2H^{+}$		
MO^{2+} formed from M^{3+}			
20.	$PuO_2^{2+} + Ti^{3+} + H_2O = PuO_2^{+} + TiO^{2+} + 2H^{+}$		
	$PuO_2^{2+} + Ti^{3+} + H_2O = [*]^{4+} + H^{+}$	1–0	1.00
21.	$NpO_2^{2+} + V^{3+} + H_2O = NpO_2^{+} + VO^{2+} + 2H^{+}$		
	$NpO_2^{2+} + V^{3+} = [*]^{5+}$		
	$NpO_2^{2+} + V^{3+} + H_2O = [*]^{4+} + H^{+}$	2–0	2.00
22.	$PuO_2^{2+} + V^{3+} + H_2O = PuO_2^{+} + VO^{2+} + 2H^{+}$		
	$PuO_2^{2+} + V^{3+} + H_2O = [*]^{4+} + H^{+}$	2–0	2.00
	$PuO_2^{2+} + V^{3+} + H_2O = [*]^{3+} + 2H^{+}$		
23.	$UO_2^{2+} + V^{3+} + H_2O = UO_2^{+} + VO^{2+} + 2H^{+}$		
	$UO_2^{2+} + V^{3+} + H_2O = [*]^{4+} + H^{+}$	2–1	2.00
	$UO_2^{2+} + V^{3+} + H_2O = [*]^{3+} + 2H^{+}$		
24.	$Pu^{4+} + Ti^{3+} + H_2O = Pu^{3+} + TiO^{2+} + 2H^{+}$		
	$Pu^{4+} + Ti^{3+} + H_2O = [*]^{6+} + H^{+}$	1–0	1.02
25.	$Pu^{4+} + V^{3+} + H_2O = Pu^{3+} + VO^{2+} + 2H^{+}$		
	$Pu^{4+} + V^{3+} + H_2O = [*]^{6+} + H^{+}$	2–0	2.00
	$Pu^{4+} + V^{3+} + H_2O = [*]^{5+} + 2H^{+}$		
Other Reactions			
26.	$NpO_2^{+} + V^{3+} + 2H^{+} = Np^{4+} + VO^{2+} + H_2O$		
	$NpO_2^{+} + V^{3+} = [*]^{4+}$	1–0	3.00
27.	$NpO_2^{+} + U^{4+} = Np^{4+} + UO_2^{+}$		
	$Np^{4+} + U^{4+} + 2H_2O = Np^{3+} + UO_2^{+} + 4H^{+}$		
	$NpO_2^{+} + U^{4+} + H_2O = [*]^{3+} + 2H^{+}$	(note [g])	1.00
	$Np^{4+} + U^{4+} + H_2O = [*]^{6+} + 2H^{+}$		
28.	$Np^{4+} + NpO_2^{+} = NpO_2^{+} + Np^{4+}$		
	$Np^{4+} + NpO_2^{2+} + H_2O = [*]^{4+} + 2H^{+}$	(note [g])	1.20
	$2NpO_2^{+} + H^{+} = [*]^{3+}$		
29.	$U^{4+} + UO_2^{2+} = UO_2^{2+} + U^{4+}$		
	$2U^{4+} + UO_2^{2+} + 2H_2O = [*]^{6+} + 4H^{+}$	1–0	0.14
30.	$NpO_2^{2+} + H_2O_2 = NpO_2^{+} + HO_2 + H^{+}$		
	$NpO_2^{2+} + H_2O_2 = [*]^{+} + H^{+}$		
	$2NpO_2^{2+} + H_2O_2 = [*]^{2+} + NpO_2^{+} + H^{+}$	2–1	3.00
31.	$NpO_2^{+} + HCrO_4^{-} = NpO_2^{2+} + Cr(V)$		
	$NpO_2^{+} + HCrO_4^{-} + 2H^{+} = [*]^{2+} + H_2O$	2–1	2.00
	$2NpO_2^{+} + HCrO_4^{-} + 4H^{+} = [*]^{3+} + NpO_2^{2+} + 2H_2O$		
Reactions involving Cl^{-}, net rate determining reactions not known			
32.	$Pu^{4+} + Fe^{2+} + Cl^{-} = [*]^{5+}$		2.00
33.	$UO_2^{2+} + V^{2+} + Cl^{-} = [*]^{3+}$		2.00
34.	$NpO_2^{+} + NpO_2^{2+} + Cl^{-} = [*]^{2+}$		3.00

Continued

ΔF, kcal./mole	ΔH, kcal./mole	ΔS, e.u.	S* comp.[b] e.u.	ΔF*,[c] kcal./mole	Ref.
13.5	41.0	94.0			
28.7	46.9	63.0 ± 2	−72	22.0	*27*
4.5	28.3	80.0			
24.0	—	—	—	21.8	*64, 65*
−43.0	−12.5	102.0			
19.7	24.7	17.0 ± 4	−88		*25(r)*
19.7	20.5	3.0 ± 4	−102		
−18.7	(−9.4)	(31)			
14.7	10.3	−14.7 ± 1.3	−88	24.0	*70*
−17.9	−9.0	31.0			
16.5	32.0	52.0 ± 16	−26	25.4	*80(r)*
15.7	13.0	−9.0 ± 6	−59	24.6	
−12.7	−2.6	32.0			
17.1	15.6	−5.0 ± 4	−81	23.4	*67(r)*
18.3	—	—		24.6	
6.9	16.0	32.0			
16.6	17.7	3.8 ± .9	−62	13.1	*60*
18.3	22.1	12.9 ± .5	−52	14.8	
−20.3	(−0.3)	(67)			
15.0	16.7	6.0 ± 2	−125	25.2	*71*
−14.3	6.0	68.0			
15.7	17.2	5.0 ± 3	−128	22.8	*73(r)*
15.3	21.6	21.0 ± 2	−112	22.4	
−8.8	15.3	−24.0			
18.2	14.6	−12.3 ± 2.6	−81	22.6	*1*
−3.8	−5.8	−7.0			
9.7	36.0	87.0			
24.4	32.2	26.2	−41	26.3	*79*
23.2	15.2	−27.0	−174	18.4	
0.0	0.0	0.0			
16.0	19.9	31.1 ± 1.7	−67	16.0	*85*
24.2	17.6	−22.2 ± .07	−30	24.2	
0.0	0.0	0.0			
25.1	32.8	26.0 ± 2	−118	25.1	*75*
8.4	—	—			
16.6	11.8	−16.1 ±	+35	12.4	*100*
17.0	13.3	−12.2	−2	—	
—	—	—			
16.8	13.4	−11.7	−16	—	*91*
17.0	11.4	−18.7 ± 3	−31	—	
14.2	14.4	0.6 ± 5	−98	—	*54*
14.3	10.6	−12.4 ± 1	−39	—	*58*
13.6	9.0	−14.0 ± 10	−18	—	*8, 9, 10*

Table II.

	Process	Pattern[a]	μ, M
35.	$PuO_2^{2+} + Sn^{2+} + 4Cl^- = [*]^0$	2–0	2.00
	$PuO_2^{2+} + Sn^{2+} + 3Cl^- = [*]^+$		
36.	$Pu^{4+} + Sn^{2+} + 5Cl^- = [*]^+$	2–0	2.00
	$Pu^{4+} + Sn^{2+} + 4Cl^- = [*]^{2+}$		
37.	$U^{4+} + BrO_3^- = [*]^{3+}$	2–0	4.00
	$U^{4+} + BrO_3^- + 2H^+ = [*]^{5+} + H_2O$		

[a] See Figure 1.
[b] Formal entropy of the activated complex, S^* comp. $= \Delta S^* + \sum S°$ reactants $-$ $\sum S°$ other products in net activation process.
[c] Average value for forward and reverse reactions, $\Delta F^* = \Delta F^* - 0.5\ \Delta F°$.
[d] $\Delta F°$, $\Delta H°$, and $\Delta S°$ were calculated from data in (*31*) for actinide ions and from data in Ref. *36* for other ions. Where necessary values were estimated using correlations given in Ref. *36*.

rates of reduction of PuO_2^{2+} by various reducing agents is $Fe^{2+} > Pu^{3+} > U^{4+} > Pu^{4+} > V^{3+} > Ti^{3+}$. The sequence for Pu^{4+} is the same except for inversion of the first two members. When the two couples, U^{4+}–UO_2^+ and V^{3+}–VO^{2+}, are compared in their reactions with PuO_2^{2+}, Pu^{4+}, NpO_2^{2+}, NpO_2^+, and UO_2^{2+}, it is seen that NpO_2^+ reacts slower than expected with U^{4+}, and V^{3+} reacts faster than expected with UO_2^{2+}. It is clear that further data are needed.

The dimensions of the rate constants from which the ΔF^* values were calculated are sec.$^{-1}$, M sec.$^{-1}$, or M^2 sec.$^{-1}$, depending on whether the hydrogen ion dependence is –1, –2, or –3, respectively. This means that the use of different concentration units would not change the ΔF^* values for the processes in which one hydrogen ion is released but would change those for three twice as much as those for two hydrogen ions released. The observation is that the ΔF^* values, based on mole/liter, all fall near the same straight line in spite of the different hydrogen ion dependences. This suggests either a cancellation of effects, or that the choice of mole/liter fortuitously makes the correction to a concentration independent basis small. The correction necessary to put all the activation free energies on the same basis is difficult to estimate since it involves the translational contribution to the entropies of the various solutes.

Reactions 20–25 involve the oxidation of V^{3+} or Ti^{3+} to VO^{2+} or TiO^{2+} (?) by actinide(VI) or (IV) ions, MO_2^{2+} or M^{4+}. Examination of ΔF^* *vs.* $\Delta F°$ shows that the V^{3+}–UO_2^{2+} Reaction, 23, is anomalously fast, but that the other ΔF^* values are correlated with $\Delta F°$ as before, irrespective of the number of hydrogen ions released in the net activation processes.

Continued

ΔF, kcal./mole	ΔH, kcal./mole	ΔS, e.u.	S^* comp.[b] e.u.	ΔF^*,[c] kcal./mole	Ref.
12.2	14.6	8.0 ± 5.5	+28	—	74(r)
12.7	14.0	4.4 ± 7	+11		
13.1	24.1	37.0	12.0	—	72
13.6	26.9	44.7	6.6		
18.0	27.6	32.1 ± 0.3	−10.0		76
18.7	22.8	13.9 ± 0.3	−45.0		

[e] Estimates of the uncertainties are given for the entropy values only; those for ΔH^* may be estimated by multiplying by T; those for ΔF^* are generally very much smaller.
[f] (r) indicates recalculated from the original data.
[g] See original reference.

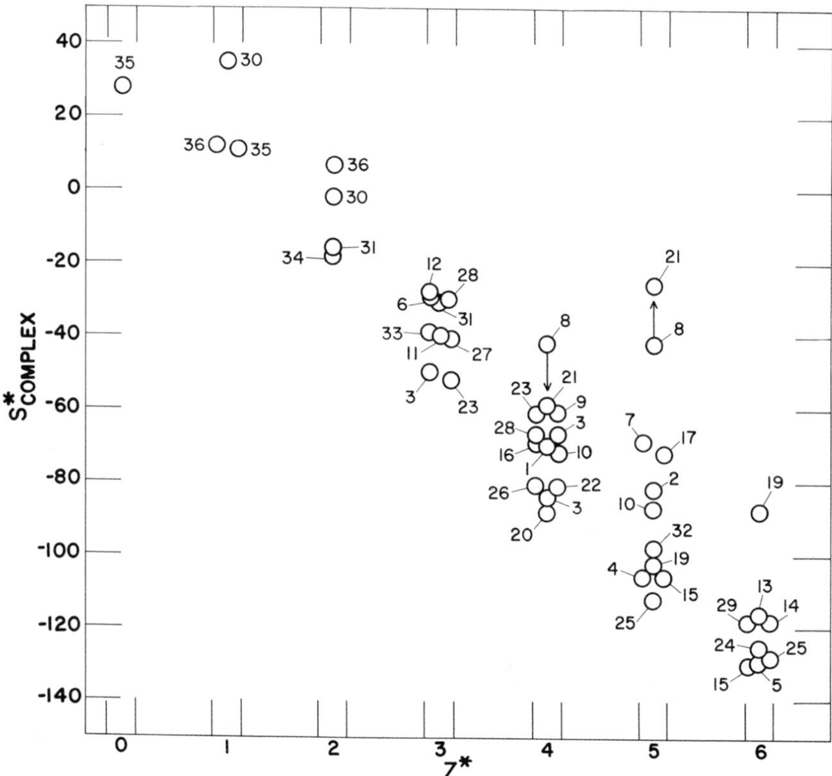

Figure 2. Formal entropies vs. charge for the activated complexes described in Table II. S* *complex* = ΔS* + Σ S° *reactants* − Σ S° *products other than activated complex*

The numbers refer to the Table

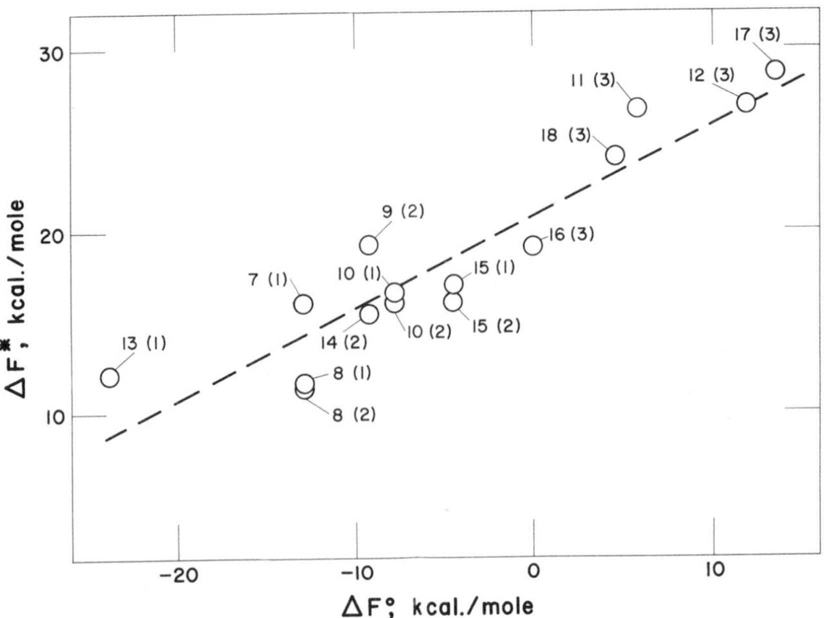

Figure 3. ΔF^* vs. ΔF° *for the reactions in which actinide (V) ions are formed from actinide (IV) ions*

The numbers in parentheses indicate the hydrogen ions released in the net activation processes; the others refer to Table II

Reactions 1-6 do not involve the making or breaking of metal-oxygen bonds. The free energies of activation for these reactions show no correlation with either ΔF° or with the number of hydrogen ions released. Thompson (95) has offered the following explanation for the observation that a correlation exists between ΔF^* and ΔF° for processes involving the formation or rupture of a metal-oxygen bond, but not for the other reactions in which there is no such rupture. He states that the linearity of the appropriate plot for reactions 7–18 amounts to the approximation: $0.50\Delta F^*_1 + 0.50\Delta F^*_2 - 1.15T \log f =$ constant, in accordance with Marcus theory (if applicable). Since ΔF^*_1 appears to be large for the M^{4+}–MO_2^+ conversion, perhaps it represents the main contribution to the constant, and the ΔF^*_2 and $\log f$ terms tend to cancel one another within the uncertainty of the plot. In reactions 1–6, ΔF^*_1 (corresponding to the actinide couple) would not be as large, and the differences between the ΔF^*_2 and $\log f$ terms would be numerically more significant.

Heats of Activation. Figure 4 shows a plot of ΔH^* *vs.* ΔH° for Reactions 7–17 in which an actinide metal-oxygen bond is formed. These data scatter considerably more than the corresponding free energy data but do show a distinct dependence on both ΔH° and on the number of hydrogen ions released in the net activation process. The latter dependence is independent of the concentration units chosen. Average values of $\overline{\Delta H^*}$ ($= \Delta H^* - 0.5\ \Delta H^\circ$) were found to be 14.5, 17.0, and 25.1 kcal./mole for the net activation processes in which one, two, and three hydrogen ions are released.

For Reactions 20–25 the heats are similar to the free energies in that, except for Reaction 23, ΔH^* is correlated with ΔH°; the average ΔH^* is 16.1 kcal./mole for one hydrogen ion released. The heats of activation for the reactions in which metal-oxygen bonds are neither formed or broken (1–6) do not appear to be correlated with ΔH°.

Entropies of Activation *vs.* Heats of Activation. Kazakov, Peshchevitskii, and Erhenburg (*36*) plotted ΔS^* *vs.* ΔH^* for 34 actinide oxidation-reduction reactions and found a correlation which they expressed by $\Delta S^* = -50 + 3.44 \times 10^{-3}\ \Delta H^*$; this is equivalent to ΔF^* (at 208°K.) $= 14{,}900 - 0.025\ \Delta H^*$ cal./mole, or that ΔF^* (298°K.) is essentially constant. The observed range is 12 to 21 kcal./mole; so we believe that the "correlation" reported merely reflects the fact that for the reactions studied, the range of ΔF^* is small compared with those of ΔH^* or $T\Delta S^*$.

Binuclear Species

One particularly interesting aspect of recent work with the actinide "–yl" ions has been the discovery of a number of binuclear species formed from two cations. Such species, when they occur in relatively high concentrations, are readily detected by physical means such as spectrophotometry. Some are reaction intermediates which occur only at low steady-state concentrations. These can sometimes be detected if the pattern of paths is such that the intermediate disappears by more than one reaction, as in patterns 2-1, 3-1, and 3-2 in Figure 1.

Physical Evidence. Spectrophotometric and EMF methods have been used to show that Np(V) will react with a number of cations to give readily detectable equilibrium concentrations of binuclear complexes such as Np(V) · U(VI), Np(V) · Fe(III), and Np(V) · Cr(III) (*89*). This last complex, probably $CrONpO^{4+}$, forms or dissociates at a relatively low rate, presumably owing to substitution inertness at Cr or Np. The same complex is also formed when Cr(II) and Np(VI) are mixed; the complex is not the only product since $Cr(H_2O)_6^{3+}$, Np(IV), and Np(V) are formed as well.

In the analogous reaction between Cr(II) and U(VI) a U(V) · Cr(III) intermediate forms almost quantitatively if U(VI) is in excess (*55*). However, unlike Np(V), U(V) is unstable with respect to disproportionation and the intermediate decomposes to Cr(III), U(VI), and U(IV) with a half-time of about 5 min. at 0°C. Although U(V) is

Table III. Intrinsic Activation

	AmO_2^+–AmO_2^{2+}	PuO_2^+–PuO_2^{2+}	Pu^{4+}–PuO_2^+	Pu^{3+}–Pu^{4+}
U^{4+}–UO_2^+	—	20.5,[a] +1[b] 19.9, 0	—	20.0, 0
UO_2^+–UO_2^{2+}	—	—	—	—
Np^{3+}–Np^{4+}	—	—	—	—
Np^{4+}–NpO_2^+	—	—	—	—
NpO_2^+–NpO_2^{2+}	—	—	—	—
Pu^{3+}–Pu^{4+}	—	16.1, 0	21.8, −1	13.4, −1
Pu^{4+}–PuO_2^+	—	23.7, −1	—	
PuO_2^+–PuO_2^{2+}	—	—		
Am^{4+}–AmO_2^+	18.0, +1 17.8, 0			
Fe^{2+}–Fe^{3+}	—	15.0, 0 14.0, 0 15.0, −1	—	17.6, −1
V^{2+}–V^{3+}	—	—	—	—
V^{3+}–VO^{2+}	—	23.4, 0 24.6, −1	—	22.8, 0 22.4, −1
Ti^{3+}–TiO^{2+}	—	24.0, 0	—	25.2, 0
Ce^{3+}–$CeOH^{3+}$	—	—	—	—
Cr^{2+}–Cr^{3+}	—	—	—	—

[a] This is the intrinsic activation free energy, $\Delta F^* = \Delta F^* - \frac{1}{2}\Delta F^\circ$.

oxidized rapidly by Tl(III) or V(IV), the intermediate reacts directly with these reagents only very slowly. The spectrum of U(V) · Cr(III) was found to be similar to that of many Cr(III) ions, showing peaks at about 410 and 600 mμ.

A complex which is probably analogous to the Np(V) · U(VI) mentioned above is formed in solutions of U(V) and U(VI) (59). Spectrophotometric and kinetic measurements showed the formula to be $U_2O_4^{3+}$ and the association quotient to be about 16 M^{-1} at 25°C. and 2*M* ionic strength. The corresponding value for Np(V) · U(VI) is 0.7 M^{-1} ($\mu = 3M$). Again, complexing of U(V) significantly reduces its reaction rate; at 25°C. in 1*M* acid the U(V) disproportionation rate is about 30 times greater than for its reaction with the complex. The spectrum of the complex shows a peak at 737 mμ with $\epsilon = 27$ M^{-1} cm.$^{-1}$.

Kinetic Evidence. The observed rate laws for the U(IV)–Pu(VI), V(III)–U(VI), and Fe(II)–Pu(VI) reactions are of the form required for 2-1, 2-1, and 3-1 patterns of paths. For the first two reactions here, the compositions of the two activated complexes differ by a single hydrogen ion. The composition of an intermediate cannot be inferred from the rate law alone, but it is almost certain to be the same as one or the

Free Energies, Kcal./mole				
NpO_2^+–NpO_2^{2+}	Np^{4+}–NpO_2^+	Np^{3+}–Np^{4+}	UO_2^+–UO_2^{2+}	U^{4+}–UO_2^+
22.4, +1	26.3, −2		20.5, −1	—
—	—	—	—	
—	22.0, −1	—		
23.1, 0	—			
23.8, −1				
14.0, 0				
—	19.4, −1	20.8, −1	—	19.2, +1
				18.2, 0
—	—	—	18.6, 0	—
25.4, +1	22.6, −1	—	13.1, 0	—
24.6, 0			14.8, −1	—
—	—	—	—	
—	—	—	—	24.2, +½
—	—	23.2, −1		
		24.2, −2		

[b] The number of hydrogen ions incorporated into the activated complex, averaged for the forward and reverse reactions.

other of the activated complexes involved: $UOH \cdot PuO_2^{5+}$ or $U(OH)_2 PuO_2^{4+}$ and $VOH \cdot UO_2^{4+}$ or $VO \cdot UO_2^{3+}$.

It is interesting that although the Np(IV)–Np(VI) reaction provides no evidence for an intermediate analogous to the U(V) · Pu(V) one mentioned above, the high acid term in the rate law for the Np(IV)–Np(V) exchange is $k[Np(V)]^2[H^+]$ (85). This term strongly suggests the rate-determining formation of a Np(V) dimer which exchanges rapidly with Np(IV). Similarly, the V(III)–Pu(VI) reaction shows no evidence for an intermediate even though the V(III)–U(VI) reaction does.

The Fe(II)–Pu(VI) reaction is interesting in that although the overall reaction appears to be a simple electron transfer, an accurate representation of the data requires a three-term rate law: $-d[Pu(VI)]/dt = [Pu(VI)][Fe(II)][A + (B + C[H^+])^{-1}]$. This rate law can be rearranged to the form for either pattern 3-1-a or 3-1-b, in which the hydrogen ion dependence of both R_1 and R_2 or R_3 is zero and that of the remaining R-term is −1. The intermediate in this reaction appears to be analogous to the Fe(III) · Np(V) species mentioned above.

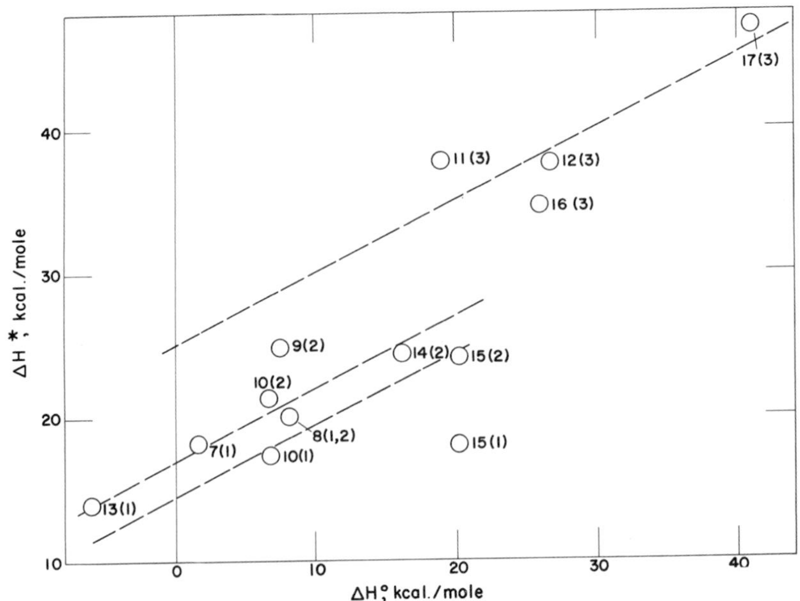

Figure 4. ΔH* vs. ΔH° *for the reactions in which actinide (V) ions are formed from actinide (IV) ions*

The numbers in parentheses indicate the hydrogen ions released in the net activation processes; the others refer to Table II

The U(V) disproportionation rates can best be described by a rate law consistent with a 2-1 pattern and a U(V) · U(V) intermediate, although other rate laws fit nearly as well (*59*).

The detection of binuclear intermediates is important since it provides evidence for inner-sphere mechanisms; conversely, outer-sphere mechanisms preclude their formation. It is significant that formally identical reaction sets do not necessarily all display binuclear intermediates. Not only might this be caused by a lack of the proper kinetic requirements for detectability but also by a lack of occurrence. This can be rationalized by pointing out that it is not necessary for these reaction sets to occur all by inner-sphere or all by outer-sphere mechanisms. In fact, examples of single reactions which apparently occur simultaneously by both mechanisms are Np(VI)–Cr(II) (*89, 90*), Pu(VI)–Fe(II) (*56*), and V(IV)–V(II) (*57*).

Acknowledgments

Helpful discussions with James C. Sullivan and Harold L. Friedman are gratefully acknowledged. We also thank Marilyn Treiman for assistance in the literature search.

Literature Cited

(1) Appelman, E. H., Sullivan, J. C., *J. Phys. Chem.* **66,** 442 (1962).
(2) Bachmann, K., Lieser, K. H., *Ber. Bunsenges. Physik. Chem.* **69,** 522 (1965).
(3) Baker, F. B., Newton, T. W., Kahn, M., *J. Phys. Chem.* **64,** 109 (1960).
(4) Baker, F. B., Newton, T. W., *J. Phys. Chem.* **65,** 1897 (1961).
(5) Betts, R. H., *Can. J. Chem.* **33,** 1780 (1955).
(6) Biddle, P., Miles, J. H., Waterman, M. J., *J. Inorg. Nucl. Chem.* **28,** 1736 (1966).
(7) Cleveland, J. M., *J. Am. Chem. Soc.* **87,** 1816 (1965).
(8) Cohen, D., Sullivan, J. C., Hindman, J. C., *J. Am. Chem. Soc.* **77,** 4964 (1955).
(9) Cohen, D., Sullivan, J. C., Hindman, J. C., *J. Am. Chem. Soc.* **76,** 352 (1954).
(10) Cohen, D., Sullivan, J. C., Hindman, J. C., *J. Am. Chem. Soc.* **78,** 1543 (1956).
(11) Coleman, J. S., *Inorg. Chem.* **2,** 53 (1963).
(12) Dukes, E. K., *U.S. At. Energy Comm. Rept.* **DP-434,** Nov., 1959.
(13) Dukes, E. K., *J. Am. Chem. Soc.* **82,** 9 (1960).
(14) Federova, L. A., Kanevskii, E. A., *Kinetika i Kataliz.* **3,** 332 (1962).
(15) Federova, L. A., *Radiokhimiya* **6,** 42 (1964).
(16) Glasstone, S., Laidler, K., Eyring, H., "The Theory of Rate Processes," McGraw-Hill Book Co., New York, N. Y., 1941.
(17) Gordon, G., Taube, H., *J. Inorg. Nucl. Chem.* **16,** 272 (1961).
(18) Gordon, G., *Inorg. Chem.* **2,** 1277 (1963).
(19) Gordon, G., Feldman, F., *Inorg. Chem.* **3,** 1728 (1964).
(20) Gordon, G., Andrews, A., *Inorg. Chem.* **3,** 1733 (1964).
(21) Gunn, S. R., Cunningham, B. B., *J. Am. Chem. Soc.* **79,** 1563 (1957).
(22) Haim, A., *Inorg. Chem.* **5,** 2081 (1966).
(23) Hall, G. R., Markin, M. R., *J. Inorg. Nucl. Chem.* **4,** 296 (1957).
(24) Halpern, J., Smith, J. G., *Can. J. Chem.* **34,** 1419 (1956).
(25) Harkness, A. C., Halpern, J., *J. Am. Chem. Soc.* **81,** 3526 (1959).
(26) Hindman, J. C., Proc. Second UN Geneva Conference, Vol. **28,** Session C-10, P/941, (1958).
(27) Hindman, J. C., Sullivan, J. C., Cohen, D., *J. Am. Chem. Soc.* **80,** 1812 (1958).
(28) Hindman, J. C., Sullivan, J. C., Cohen, D., *J. Am. Chem. Soc.* **81,** 2316 (1959).
(29) Hindman, J. C., Sullivan, J. C., Cohen, D., *J. Am. Chem. Soc.* **79,** 4029 (1957).
(30) Hindman, J. C., Sullivan, J. C., Cohen, D., *J. Am. Chem. Soc.* **76,** 3278 (1954).
(31) Huizenga, J. R., Magnusson, L. B., *J. Am. Chem. Soc.* **73,** 3202 (1951).
(32) Imai, H., *Bull. Chem. Soc., Japan* **30,** 873 (1957).
(33) Jones, F. A., Amis, E. S., *J. Inorg. Nucl. Chem.* **26,** 1045 (1964).
(34) Kanevskii, E. A., Federova, L. A., *Radiokhimiya* **2,** 559 (1960).
(35) Katz, J. J., Seaborg, G. T., "The Chemistry of the Actinide Elements," Methuen and Co. Ltd., London, 1957.
(36) Kazakov, V. P., Peshchevitskii, B. I., Erenburg, A. M., *Radiokhimiya* **6,** 291 (1964).
(37) Keenan, T. K., *J. Phys. Chem.* **61,** 1117 (1957).
(38) Kern, D. M. H., Orlemann, E. F., *J. Am. Chem. Soc.* **71,** 2102 (1949).
(39) Koryta, J., Koutecky, J., *Coll. Czech. Chem. Commun.* **20,** 423 (1955).
(40) Latimer, W. M., "Oxidation Potentials," 2nd Ed., Prentice-Hall, Inc., New York, N. Y., 1952.

(41) Love, C. M., Quinn, L. P., Brubaker, C. H., *J. Inorg. Nucl. Chem.* **27,** 2183 (1965).
(42) Marcus, R. A., *J. Phys. Chem.* **67,** 853 (1963).
(43) Masters, B. J., Schwartz, L. L., *J. Am. Chem. Soc.* **83,** 2620 (1961).
(44) Mathews, D. M., Hefley, J. D., Amis, E. S., *J. Phys. Chem.* **63,** 1236 (1959).
(45) Mazumdar, A. S. G., Pisharody, K. P. R., *J. Inorg. Nucl. Chem.* **26,** 1903 (1964).
(46) Mazumdar, A. S. G., Pisharody, K. P. R., *J. Inorg. Nucl. Chem.* **24,** 1617 (1962).
(47) Minc, S., Sobkowski, J., Stok, M., *Nukleonika* **10,** 747 (1965).
(48) Moore, R. L., *J. Am. Chem. Soc.* **77,** 1504 (1955).
(49) Newton, T. W., Baker, F. B., *J. Phys. Chem.* **60,** 1417 (1956).
(50) Newton, T. W., Baker, F. B., *J. Phys. Chem.* **61,** 381 (1957).
(51) Newton, T. W., *J. Phys. Chem.* **62,** 943 (1958).
(52) Newton, T. W., Rabideau, S. W., *J. Phys. Chem.* **63,** 365 (1959).
(53) Newton, T. W., *J. Phys. Chem.* **63,** 1493 (1959).
(54) Newton, T. W., Cowan, H. D., *J. Phys. Chem.* **64,** 244 (1960).
(55) Newton, T. W., Baker, F. B., *Inorg. Chem.* **1,** 368 (1962).
(56) Newton, T. W., Baker, F. B., *J. Phys. Chem.* **67,** 1425 (1963).
(57) Newton, T. W., Baker, F. B., *Inorg. Chem.* **3,** 569 (1964).
(58) Newton, T. W., Baker, F. B., *J. Phys. Chem.* **69,** 176 (1965).
(59) Newton, T. W., Baker, F. B., *Inorg. Chem.* **4,** 1166 (1965).
(60) Newton, T. W., Baker, F. B., *J. Phys. Chem.* **70,** 1943 (1966).
(61) Newton, T. W., Daugherty, N. A., *J. Phys. Chem.* (to be published).
(62) Newton, T. W., Baker, F. B. (preliminary observation).
(63) Pence, D. T., Booman, G. L., *Anal. Chem.* **38,** 1112 (1966).
(64) Rabideau, S. W., *J. Am. Chem. Soc.* **75,** 798 (1953).
(65) Rabideau, S. W., *J. Am. Chem. Soc.* **77,** 6145 (1955).
(66) Rabideau, S. W., *J. Am. Chem. Soc.* **79,** 6350 (1957).
(67) Rabideau, S. W., *J. Phys. Chem.* **62,** 414 (1958).
(68) Rabideau, S. W., Kline, R. J., *J. Phys. Chem.* **62,** 617 (1958).
(69) Rabideau, S. W., Asprey, L. B., Keenan, T. K., Newton, T. W., Proc. Second UN Geneva Conference, Vol. **28,** Session C-10, P/2247 (1958).
(70) Rabideau, S. W., Kline, R. J., *J. Phys. Chem.* **63,** 1502 (1959).
(71) Rabideau, S. W., Kline, R. J., *J. Phys. Chem.* **64,** 193 (1960).
(72) Rabideau, S. W., *J. Phys. Chem.* **64,** 1491 (1960).
(73) Rabideau, S. W., Kline, R. J., *J. Inorg. Nucl. Chem.* **14,** 91 (1960).
(74) Rabideau, S. W., Masters, B. J., *J. Phys. Chem.* **65,** 1256 (1961).
(75) Rona, Elizabeth, *J. Am. Chem. Soc.* **72,** 4339 (1950).
(76) Rykov, A. G., Yakovlev, G. N., *Radiokhimiya* **8,** 20, 27 (1966).
(77) Rykov, A. G., Vasil'ev, V. Ya., Yakovlev, G. N., *Radiokhimiya* **8,** 33 (1966).
(78) Shastri, N. K., Wear, J. O., Amis, E. S., *J. Inorg. Nucl. Chem.* **24,** 535 (1962).
(79) Shastri, N. K., Amis, E. S., Wear, J. O., *J. Inorg. Nucl. Chem.* **27,** 2413 (1965).
(80) Sheppard, J. C., *J. Phys. Chem.* **68,** 1190 (1964).
(81) Siddall, T. H., III, Dukes, E. K., *J. Am. Chem. Soc.* **81,** 790 (1959).
(82) Sobkowski, J., *Roczniki Chemii* **37,** 1019 (1963).
(83) Sobkowski, J., *Roczniki Chemii* **40,** 271 (1966).
(84) Stephanou, S. E., Asprey, L. B., Penneman, R. A., AECU-925, (1950).
(85) Sullivan, J. C., Cohen, D., Hindman, J. C., *J. Am. Chem. Soc.* **76,** 4275 (1954).
(86) Sullivan, J. C., Cohen, D., Hindman, J. C., *J. Am. Chem. Soc.* **79,** 3672 (1957).

(87) Sullivan, J. C., Zielen, A. J., Hindman, J. C., *J. Am. Chem. Soc.* **82,** 5288 (1960).
(88) Sullivan, J. C., Hindman, J. C., Zielen, A. J., *J. Am. Chem. Soc.* **83,** 3373 (1961).
(89) Sullivan, J. C., *Inorg. Chem.* **3,** 315 (1964).
(90) Sullivan, J. C., *J. Am. Chem. Soc.* **84,** 4256 (1962).
(91) Sullivan, J. C., *J. Am. Chem. Soc.* **87,** 1495 (1965).
(92) Sullivan, J. C., (private communication to be published).
(93) Thompson, R. C., Sullivan, J. C., *J. Am. Chem. Soc.* **89,** 1096 (1967).
(94) Thompson, R., Sullivan, J. C., *J. Am. Chem. Soc.* **89,** 1098 (1967).
(95) Thompson, R., (private communication).
(96) Wear, J. O., *J. Chem. Soc.* **1965,** 5596 (1965).
(97) Wear, J. O., *Sandia Corp.* SC-RR-65-219 (1965).
(98) Zaitsev, A. A., et al., *Radiokhimiya* **2,** 339 (1960).
(99) Zaitsev, A. A., et al., *Radiokhimiya* **2,** 348 (1960).
(100) Zielen, A. J., Sullivan, J. C., Cohen, D., Hindman, J. C., *J. Am. Chem. Soc.* **80,** 5632 (1958).

RECEIVED October 13, 1966. This work was performed under the auspices of the U. S. Atomic Energy Commission.

21

A Contribution to the Study of the Oxidation Potential of the Berkelium (III)–(IV) Couple in Various Media

C. MUSIKAS and R. BERGER

Department de Chimie, Services de Chimie des Combustibles Irradies, Section d'Etudes Chimiques et Radioactives, Commisariat a l'Energie Atomique, Centre d'Etudes Nucléaires, Fontenay aux Roses, France

*Indirect determinations of the formal oxidation potential of Bk(IV)–Bk(III) couple in sulfuric and nitric acids have been made by tracer measurement. From the Bk(IV)/Bk(III) ratios and the corresponding Ce(IV)/Ce(III) ratios at equilibrium conditions one can calculate the oxidation potential of the Bk(IV)–Bk(III) couple. The Bk(IV)/Bk(III) ratio can be determined by extracting Bk(IV) by an appropriate organic solvent. The formal oxidation potentials of the Bk(IV)–Bk(III) couple in 1*N *and 0.5*N *sulfuric acid were found to be 1.42 and 1.44 volts using trilaurylmethylammonium sulfate in carbon tetrachloride as a solvent. In 6*N *nitric acid the oxidation potential of the couple was found to be 1.56 volts by using 0.18*M *tributylphosphate. Whereas, in 1*N *to* 2N *nitric acid berkelium was not oxidized by cerium(IV).*

Oxidation of berkelium to the tetravalent state was demonstrated in 1950 by Thompson, Cunningham, and Seaborg (*7*). Using ceric iodate as a tetravalent species carrier for tracer experiments, they found that in 8*N* HNO_3 medium the formal oxidation potentials of the Ce(IV)–Ce(III) and the Bk(IV)–Bk(III) couples were nearly the same.

In the same year Jones and Cunningham continued these experiments (*2*) and found that the cerium and the berkelium adsorption on zirconium phenylarsonate carrier were similar regardless of the oxidizing agent (bichromate, chlorate, hypochlorite, or bromate), or the medium (1*N* nitric acid, 1*M* lithium perchlorate–perchloric acid at hydrogen ion concentrations from 0.1*N* to 1*N*). From these experiments they concluded that the oxidation potential of the Bk(IV)–Bk(III) couple did not differ by more than 60 mv. from that of the Ce(IV)–Ce(III) couple.

In order to complete these experiments we undertook tracer level measurements of the formal oxidation potential of the Bk(IV)–Bk(III) couple in nitric acid and sulfuric acid solutions, using the Ce(IV)–Ce(III) couple as a mediator. The tetravalent species were extracted by organic solvents.

A similar method was used by Matsuura and Haissinsky in 1958 (*4*) and by Haissinsky and Pluchet in 1962 (*1*) for determining the formal oxidation potentials of the Po(VI)–Po(IV) and the Pa(V)–Pa(IV) couples respectively.

We took advantage of the property of different solvents to extract selectively the tetravalent actinide and lanthanide elements. Some of them are sufficiently stable in the presence of oxidizing agents. Among the organonitrogen and organophosphorus compounds we used were trilaurylmethylammonium (TLMA) salts and tributyl phosphate (TBP) in carbon tetrachloride.

Principle of the Method

The formal oxidation potential of the Bk(IV)–Bk(III) couple can be deduced from Nernst's law if the distribution equilibria between the aqueous phase and the nonmiscible organic phase is reached. This can be written as:

$$Ef_{\mathrm{Bk}} = Ef_{\mathrm{Ce}} + \frac{RT}{F} \log \frac{[\mathrm{Ce(IV)}]_a}{[\mathrm{Ce(III)}]_a} \times \frac{[\mathrm{Bk(III)}]_a}{[\mathrm{Bk(IV)}]_a} \qquad (1)$$

in which the concentrations are aqueous concentrations after extraction.

The different terms of Equation 1 were obtained as follows—Ef_{Ce}, formal potential of the Ce(IV)–Ce(III) couple in the medium, was taken from publications; $[\mathrm{Ce(IV)}]_a$ and $[\mathrm{Ce(IV)}]_o$ have been measured by direct absorption spectrophotometry; $[\mathrm{Ce(III)}]_a$ was calculated by difference between total cerium, titrated by potentiometry, and tetravalent cerium; $[\mathrm{Bk(IV)}]_a$ was calculated from the solvent beta counting, allowing for the measured distribution coefficient of Bk(IV); $[\mathrm{Bk(III)}]_a$ was determined by subtracting the $[\mathrm{Bk(IV)}]_a$ value from the aqueous counting; in all cases $[\mathrm{Ce(III)}]_o$ and $[\mathrm{Bk(III)}]_o$ were found to be negligible.

Total oxidation and extraction equilibrium were verified by plotting:

$$\log_{10} \frac{[\mathrm{Bk(IV)}]_a}{[\mathrm{Bk(III)}]_a} \ vs.\ \log_{10} \frac{[\mathrm{Ce(IV)}]_a}{[\mathrm{Ce(III)}]_a}$$

and checking to see that the slope of the straight line was close to 1.

Preliminary Experiments

To determine the aqueous and organic concentrations of the tetravalent cerium and berkelium with sufficient accuracy, it was necessary

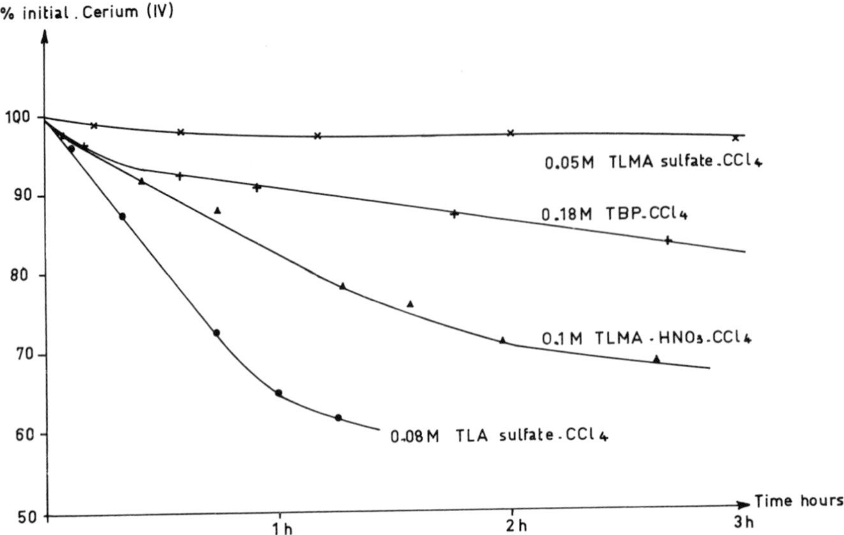

Figure 1. Reduction rate of cerium(IV) in various organic solvents

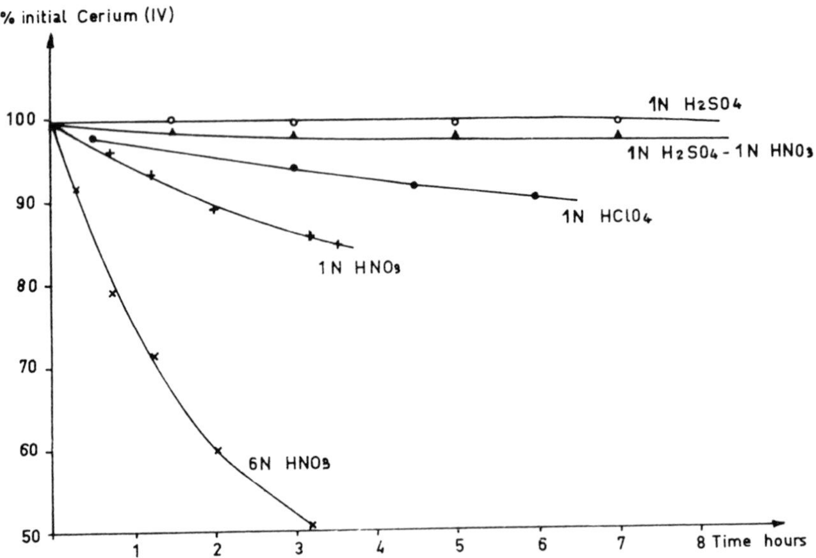

Figure 2. Reduction rate of cerium(IV) in various aqueous media

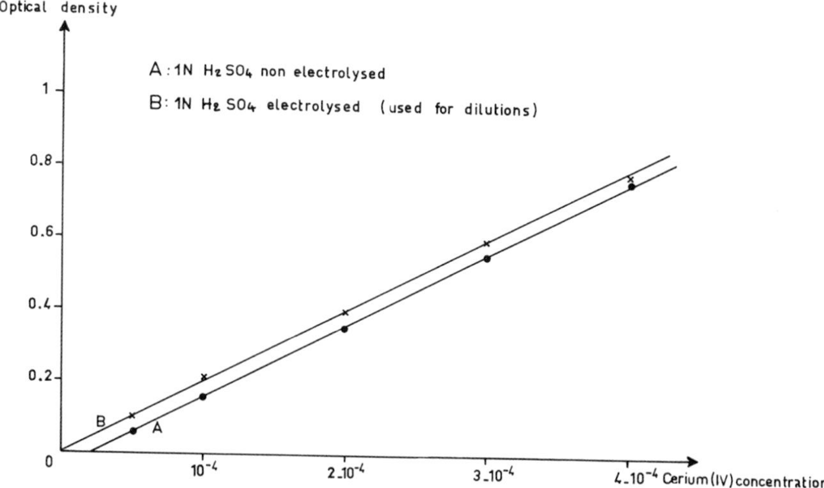

Figure 3. Effect of the electrolytic oxidation of sulfuric acid on Beer's straight lines at 380 mμ for cerium(IV)

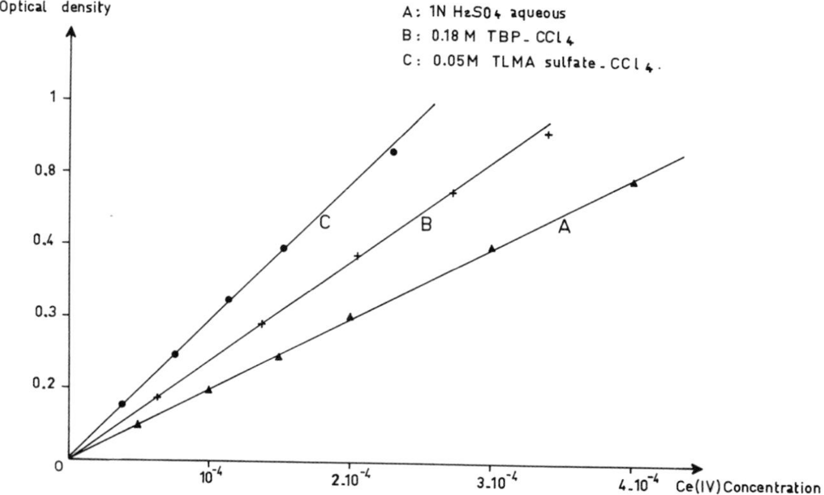

Figure 4. Absorption of cerium(IV) at 380 mμ in various media

to find a solvent in which the distribution coefficients of these two tetravalent species between the solvent and the chosen aqueous medium was in the range 0.1 to 10. In addition the oxidation rate of the solvent by the tetravalent elements should be sufficiently low. For sulfuric acid solutions, trilaurylmethylammonium sulfate in carbon tetrachloride was preferred to trilaurylamine sulfate because it is less sensitive to oxidation by cerium(IV) (Figure 1). In the case of nitric acid, tributyl phosphate in carbon tetrachloride gives higher distribution coefficients for berkelium than trilaurylmethylammonium nitrate in the same diluent.

Because the reduction rate of cerium(IV) in these solvents is not negligible, it is necessary to take samples for beta counting and spectrophotometric analysis at the same time. The concentration of cerium(IV) was determined by direct absorption spectrophotometry at 380 mμ, both in aqueous and in organic solutions. This wavelength was chosen in order to avoid any interference by the reagents.

In sulfuric acid, tetravalent cerium is more stable than in the other aqueous solutions (Figure 2). For this reason 1*N* H_2SO_4 was chosen as the medium for spectrophotometric measurements. Nevertheless it was necessary to oxidize electrolytically all the reagents before the spectrophotometric measurements. This is illustrated by Figure 3 in which the optical densities *vs.* the cerium(IV) concentrations are plotted.

The verification of Lamber Beer's law is shown in Figure 4. Organic solutions of cerium were prepared by extracting cerium(IV) from titrated aqueous solutions and standardized by beta counting of ^{141}Ce tracer. Standardization curves were plotted from three values for further spectrophotometric determinations of cerium(IV).

The berkelium(IV) extraction coefficients have been determined by stripping solvents previously loaded with tetravalent cerium and berkelium in the presence of sodium bismuthate. Sodium bismuthate has been found to be an efficient oxidizing agent for trivalent cerium. Because of its small solubility it does not affect the distribution coefficients of tetravalent cerium. These two properties have been demonstrated by comparing the distribution coefficients of cerium(IV) measured by spectrophotometry with those of cerium oxidized by sodium bismuthate and measured by beta counting of the ^{141}cerium isotope tracer. The data are summarized in Table I and indicate no real difference in the distribution coefficients of cerium obtained by these two methods when using trilaurylmethylammonium salts–carbon tetrachloride as solvent.

Table I. Effect of Sodium Bismuthate on the Distribution Coefficients of Cerium(IV)

		E_a° Ce(IV)	
Organic	*Aqueous*	*Spectrophotometric Determination of Ce(IV)*	*Beta Counting of ^{141}Ce (+ Na BiO_3)*
0.05*M* TLMA–Sulfate	0.5*N* H_2SO_4	7.7	7.4
0.1*M* TLMA–Sulfate	1*N* H_2SO_4	2.6	2.7
0.1*M* TLMA–HNO_3	1*N* HNO_3	110	78
0.1*M* TLMA–HNO_3	6*N* HNO_3	200	240

Table II. 0.1*M* Trilaurylmethylammonium Nitrate–Carbon Tetrachloride Extraction of Cerium and Berkelium from Nitric Acid Solutions in the Presence of Sodium Bismuthate

Aqueous	$E_a°$ *Ce(IV)*	*% of Initial Bk Extracted*
1*N* HNO_3	110	1
1*N* HNO_3 (without $NaBiO_3$)	110	1
1*N* HNO_3 + 1.5*M* $Al(NO_3)_3$	100	65
4*N* HNO_3	100	12
4*N* HNO_3 + 1.5*M* $Al(NO_3)_3$	100	20
6*N* HNO_3	100	6
6*N* HNO_3 + 1.5*M* $Al(NO_3)_3$	100	9
8*N* HNO_3		3.6
10*N* HNO_3		2

Ce(IV) initial aqueous concentration = $6.0 \times 10^{-3}M$
$E_a°$ Ce(III) < 0.005 when $[HNO_3] < 6N$

Experimental

Apparatus. The following apparatus was utilized for this study: a PRT 2000 type potentiostat (Tacussel) for the electrolysis; a Graphispectral spectrophotometer (Jouan) for the absorption measurements; a TS 6 type millivoltmeter (Tacussel) for potentiometric analysis; a 2π windowless flow gas counter (S.A.I.P.) for measuring the soft beta from ^{249}Bk; and a bell type Geiger counter for ^{141}Ce and ^{144}Ce beta counting.

Reagents. BERKELIUM. An amount of 5μ Ci of berkelium 249 was supplied by Euratom. Its purity was checked by alpha and beta counting and by alpha and gamma spectrography. The yield of soft beta was greater than 98%. The sample was dissolved in 6*N* nitric acid, and the conversion to sulfuric acid medium was made by fuming down one aliquot three times and dissolving the residue in the appropriate solution.

CERIUM. Cerium 141 and 144 isotopes were supplied by the "Département des Radioéléments" of Saclay. Cerous nitrate solutions were prepared by dissolving the reagent (Prolabo No. 22585). Ceric nitrate was obtained by electrolytic oxidation of the previous solution in a cell with separated compartments. Ceric sulfate and ferroammonium sulfate solutions were prepared from the guaranteed reagent (Merck No. 2274 and No. 3793). Cerous sulfate was obtained similarly by electrolytic reduction.

TRILAURYLMETHYLAMMONIUM SALTS. A solution of 0.1*M* trilaurylmethylammonium chloride in carbon tetrachloride was prepared for each experiment by dissolving the reagent (Rhône-Poulenc). Trilaurylmethylammonium nitrate and sulfate solutions were obtained by mixing four times the previous organic solution (3 v/v) respectively with 4*N* HNO_3 and 1*M* Na_2SO_4. In addition, the solvents were pre-equilibrated by mixing them twice (3 v/v) with the corresponding acid solutions.

TRIBUTYL PHOSPHATE. The reagent tributylphosphate (Eastman Kodak) was purified by scrubbing with sodium carbonate solution (5% v/v) and then with distilled water and by distillation *in vacuo*.

MISCELLANEOUS. The carbon tetrachloride and acids used were reagents of grade RP (Prolabo). (CCl_4 No. 22521, HNO_3 No. 20420, H_2SO_4 No. 20700).

Procedure. Aqueous phases were prepared from samples of cerium(IV), cerium(III), berkelium, and acid and diluted by distilled water to the proper concentrations. Samples of cerium were chosen in order to obtain different cerium(IV)/cerium(III) ratios. The solutions were allowed to stand for six hours to reach the oxidation equilibrium. A 2 cc. sample of the solvent was added to the same volume of aqueous solution and mixed for 15 minutes. After separation by a centrifuge, samples of both phases were taken for the beta counting of berkelium and the spectrophotometric determination of cerium(IV). In addition, one aliquot of the loaded solvent was taken for determining the distribution coefficient of berkelium(IV).

Results

Sulfuric Acid Solutions. Data obtained with 0.1*M* and 0.05*M* trilaurylmethylammonium sulfate-carbon tetrachloride for determining the formal oxidation potential of the Bk(IV)–Bk(III) couple in 1*N* and 0.5*N* H_2SO_4 is summarized in Table III; the corresponding curves of:

$$\log_{10} \frac{[\mathrm{Bk(IV)}]_a}{[\mathrm{Bk(III)}]_a} \quad vs. \quad \log_{10} \frac{[\mathrm{Ce(IV)}]_a}{[\mathrm{Ce(III)}]_a}$$

are plotted in Figures 5 and 6. The slopes are 0.92, calculated by the least squares method (Figure 5) and close to 1 (Figure 6), graphically estimated, for 1*N* and 0.5*N* H_2SO_4, respectively.

From these data it appears that in sulfuric acid the formal oxidation potentials of the Bk(IV)–Bk(III) couple differ from those of the Ce(IV)–Ce(III) couple by 0.022 and 0.017 volts, respectively in 1*N* H_2SO_4 and 0.5*N* H_2SO_4 media. Assuming the published values of 1.44 and 1.46 volts for the formal oxidation potentials of the Ce(IV)–Ce(III) couple in 1*N* and 0.5*N* H_2SO_4 respectively (*3, 6*), we obtain

$$Ef_{\mathrm{Bk}} = 1.42 \text{ volts in } 1N\ \mathrm{H_2SO_4}$$

$$Ef_{\mathrm{Bk}} = 1.44 \text{ volts in } 0.5N\ \mathrm{H_2SO_4}$$

Nitric Acid Solutions. The data obtained with 0.18*M* tributyl phosphate–carbon tetrachloride are summarized in Table IV. It is apparent that in 6*N* HNO_3

$$Ef_{\mathrm{Bk}} - Ef_{\mathrm{Ce}} = -0.023 \text{ volts}$$

In this case the slope of the straight line representing

$$\log_{10} \frac{[\mathrm{Bk(IV)}]_a}{[\mathrm{Bk(III)}]_a} \quad vs. \quad \log_{10} \frac{[\mathrm{Ce(IV)}]_a}{[\mathrm{Ce(III)}]_a}$$

is estimated to be 1.1 (Figure 7).

By accepting 1.58 volts as the formal oxidation potential of the Ce(IV)–Ce(III) couple (6) we obtain:

$$Ef_{\mathrm{Bk}} = 1.56 \text{ volts in } 6N \ \mathrm{HNO_3}$$

On the other hand very little berkelium is extracted by tributyl phosphate from 1*N* to 2*N* HNO_3 as shown in Table IV. The determination of the formal oxidation potential of the Bk(IV)–Bk(III) couple in this medium is not reliable. Assuming that all the berkelium extracted is tetravalent and that the distribution coefficient of berkelium(IV) is the same as that of cerium(IV), calculation shows that the difference between the formal oxidation potential of the two couples should be greater than +0.08 volts.

Table III. Trilaurylmethylammonium Sulfate–Carbon Tetrachloride Extraction of Cerium and Berkelium from Sulfuric Acid Solutions

Aqueous: 1N H_2SO_4 Solvent: 0.1M TLMA Sulfate–CCl_4			*Aqueous: 0.5N H_2SO_4 Solvent: 0.05M TLMA Sulfate–CCl_4*		
$\frac{[Ce(IV)]_a}{[Ce(III)]_a}$	E_a° Bk(IV)	$\frac{[Bk(IV)]_a}{[Bk(III)]_a}$	$\frac{[Ce(IV)]_a}{[Ce(III)]_a}$	E_a° Bk(IV)	$\frac{[Bk(IV)]_a}{[Bk(III)]_a}$
0.022	1.35	0.035	0.0087	4.9	0.02
0.052	1.41	0.08	0.014	5.1	0.038
0.040	1.32	0.15	0.036	5.3	0.065
0.065	1.22	0.21	0.08	6.4	0.13
0.13	1.40	0.24	0.085	6.1	0.15
0.11	1.28	0.31	0.1	5.5	0.17
0.12	1.47	0.44			
0.17	1.28	0.48			
0.19	1.36	0.6			
0.24	1.25	0.75			
0.34	1.50	0.65			
0.44	1.18	0.85			
0.65	1.23	1.10			
0.85	1.43	1.35			

E_a° Bk(III) < 0.005 in all cases.

Discussion

In 1*N* to 2*N* nitric solutions, berkelium was not extracted either in TLMA nitrate or TBP, whereas cerium was extracted. Furthermore, the berkelium(IV) already extracted from 6*N* HNO_3 into TBP was completely back-extracted by 1*N* HNO_3, while cerium was not stripped as much. A similar experiment made after adding sodium bismuthate proved that aqueous cerium was entirely at the four valence state, while berkelium showed a low distribution coefficient (smaller than 0.01) corresponding mainly to the trivalent state. This result was confirmed by a

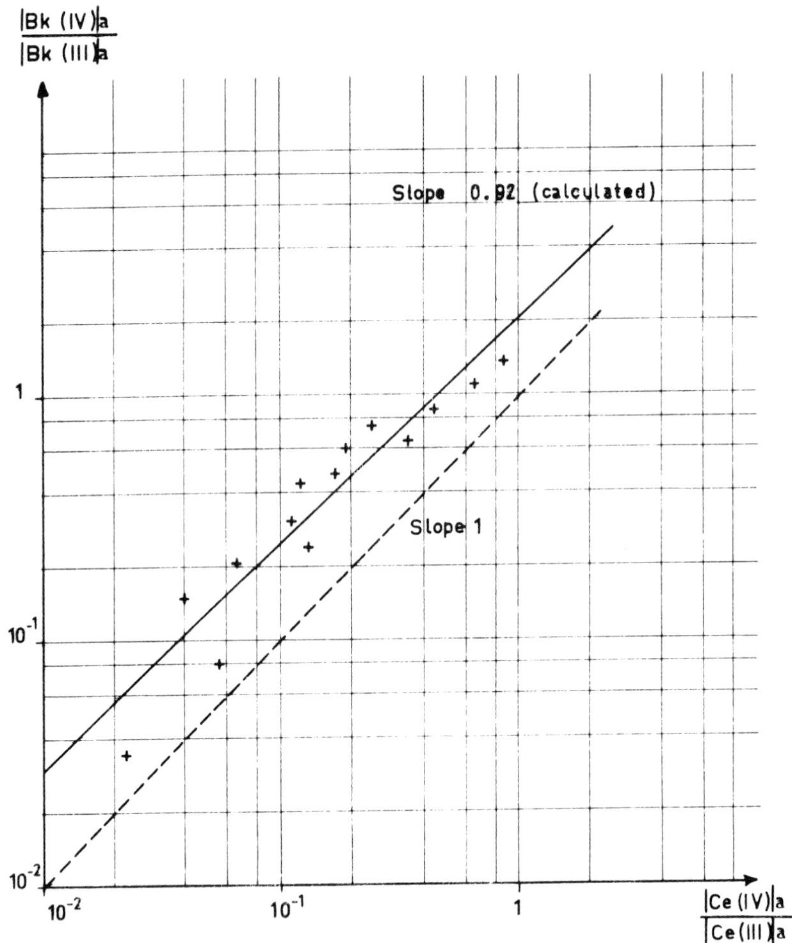

Figure 5. Formal potential of the Bk(IV)–Bk(III) couple in 1N H_2SO_4

tracer experiment, carried out with ^{249}Bk and ^{144}Ce isotopes. Cerium was extracted from 1*N* HNO_3 into TLMA in the presence of sodium bismuthate whereas berkelium was not.

The last three experiments seem to confirm that the difference in behavior between berkelium and cerium in 1*N* to 2*N* nitric acid solutions does not result from a difference in the reaction rate. It is more probably caused by the higher formal oxidation potential of the Bk(IV)–Bk(III) couple. At such a high formal oxidation potential tetravalent berkelium should be less stable than tetravalent cerium, even if the difference is smaller than the estimated value (+0.08 volts).

These results suggest that the standard potentials of the Ce(IV)–Ce(III) and the Bk(IV)–Bk(III) couples should be rather different.

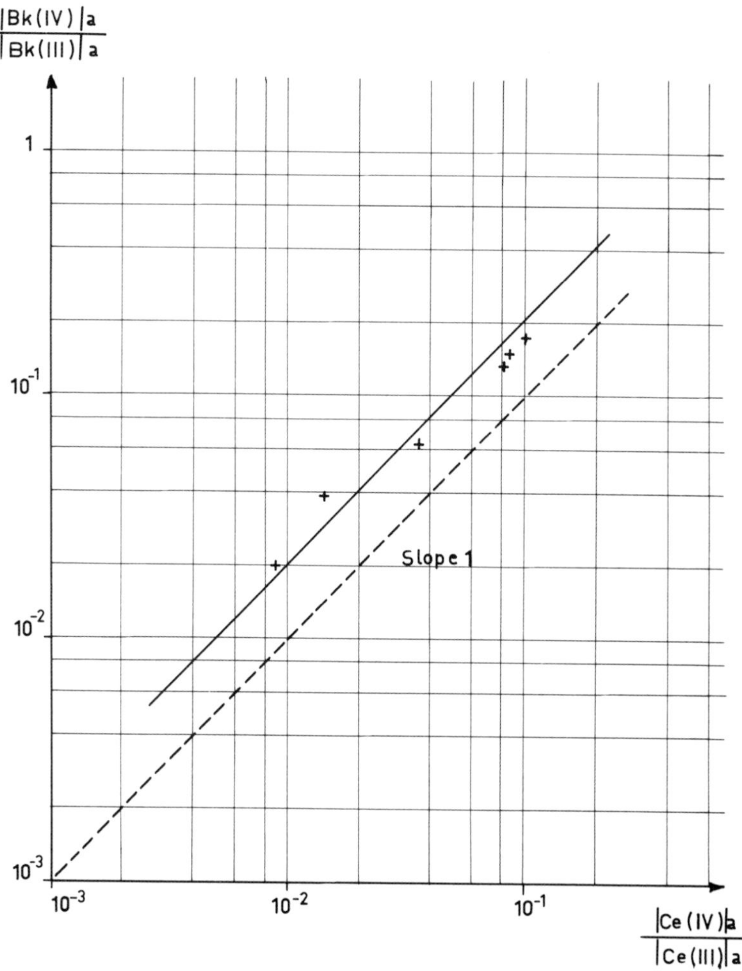

*Figure 6. Formal potential of the Bk(IV)–Bk(III) couple in 0.5*N *H_2SO_4*

The fact that in complexing medium the two couples have close values could imply that the Bk(IV) complexes are more tightly bound than those of the Ce(IV).

Although berkelium(IV) was obtained in concentrated nitric acid (*4, 6*), it was not extracted in TLMA nitrate CCl_4 whereas cerium(IV) was extracted. When decreasing the acidity for the same nitrate ion concentration [*e.g.*, in 1*N* HNO_3 + 1.5*M* $Al(NO_3)_3$ solution], berkelium(IV) was extracted (Table II). This phenomenon could be attributed to the competition between the nitric acid and the tetravalent berkelium species which could be extracted.

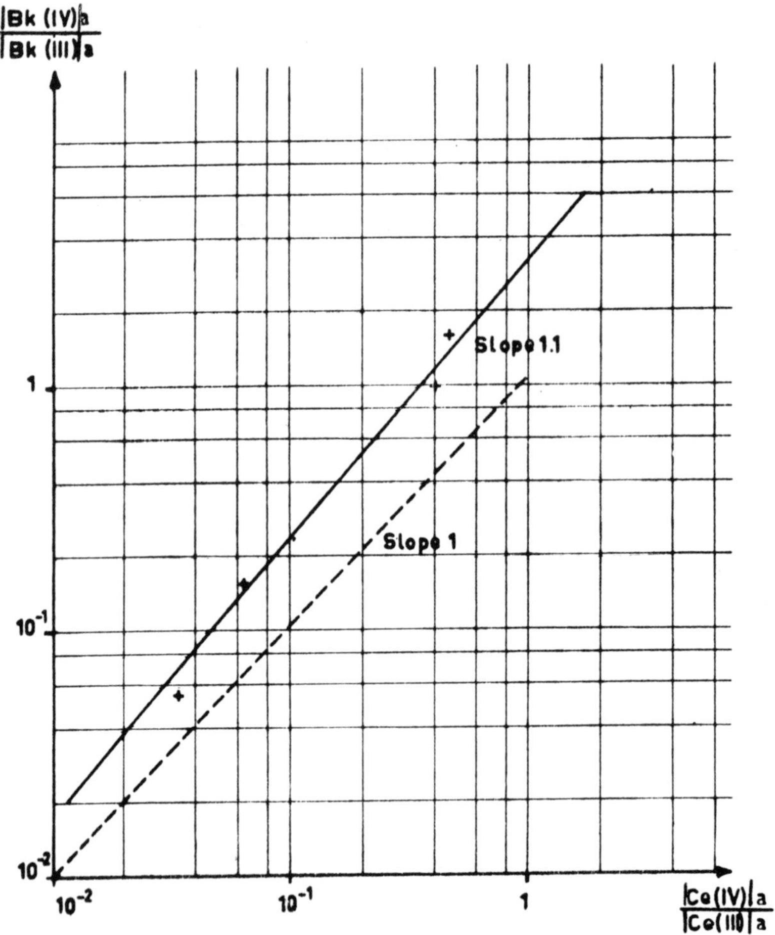

Figure 7. Formal potential of the Bk(IV)–Bk(III) couple in 6N HNO_3

The accuracy of the method was checked from the data plotted in Figure 5. Calculation gives a mean value for

$$Ef_{Bk} - Ef_{Ce} = 0.023 \text{ volts}$$

with a standard deviation of:

$$\sigma = \pm 0.009 \text{ volts}$$

The scattering of the results depends upon the soft beta counting of ^{249}Bk which is sensitive to the self absorption of the source; the spectrophotometric determination of unstable cerium(IV); and the great number of experimental determinations needed for calculating the potential.

Table IV. 0.18*M* Tributyl Phosphate–Carbon Tetrachloride Extraction of Cerium and Berkelium from Nitric Acid Solutions

Aqueous[b]	$E_a°$ *Ce(IV)*	$\frac{[Ce(IV)]_a}{[Ce(III)]_a}$	*% of Initial Bk Extracted*	$E_a°$ *Bk(IV)*	$\frac{[Bk(IV)]_a}{[Bk(III)]_a}$
$1N\ HNO_3 + Ce(IV)$	0.2		1		
$1N\ HNO_3 + Ce(IV) + Ce(III)$	0.2	2.7	1		0.05[a]
$1N\ HNO_3 + 1.5M\ Al(NO_3)_3 + Ce(IV) + NaBiO_3$	—	—	70		
$2N\ HNO_3 + Ce(IV) + NaBiO_3$	1.9		2.5		
$2N\ HNO_3 + Ce(IV) + Ce(III)$	1.9	0.55	3		0.02[a]
$6N\ HNO_3 + Ce(IV) + Ce(III)$	8.9	0.034		1.3[c]	0.055
– d° –	8.4	0.065		1.2	0.16
– d° –	8.1	0.4		1.25	1.0
– d° –	8.4	0.465		1.05	1.6

[a] Estimated values assuming that only Bk(IV) is extracted and that $E_a°$ Bk(IV) = $E_a°$ Ce(IV).
[b] Total cerium initial aqueous concentration = $6.0 \times 10^{-3}M$. $E_a°$ Ce(III) < 0.01 in all cases.
[c] In $6N\ HNO_3$ $E_a°$ Bk(III) < 0.005.

Acknowledgments

The authors wish to thank A. Chesné for the helpful discussions and M. Marteau for experimental assistance. J. Kooi is gratefully acknowledged for supplying berkelium-249, thus encouraging this work.

Literature Cited

(1) Haissinsky, M., Pluchet, E., *J. Chim. Phys.* **76,** 608 (1962).
(2) Jones, M. E., Cunningham, B. B., *U. S. At. Energy Comm.* **AECD-2913** (1950).
(3) Kunz, A. H., *J. Am. Chem. Soc.* **53,** 98 (1931).
(4) Matsuura, N., Haissinsky, M., *J. Chim. Phys.* **55,** 475 (1958).
(5) Peppard, D. F., Moline, S. W., Mason, G. W., *J. Inorg. Nucl. Chem.* **4,** 344 (1957).
(6) Smith, G. F., Getz, C. A., *Ind. Eng. Chem. Anal.* **10,** 191 (1938).
(7) Thompson, S. G., Cunningham, B. B., Seaborg, G. T., *J. Am. Chem. Soc.* **72,** 2798 (1950).

RECEIVED December 27, 1966.

22

Condensed Phase Equilibria in the Molybdenum Hexafluoride-Uranium Hexafluoride System

L. E. TREVORROW, M. J. STEINDLER, and D. V. STEIDL

Chemical Engineering Division, Argonne National Laboratory, Argonne, Ill.

J. T. SAVAGE

University of Oregon, Eugene, Ore.

The temperature-composition phase diagram constructed from thermal arrests observed in the MoF_6–UF_6 system is characteristic of a binary system forming solid solutions, a minimum-melting mixture (22 mole % UF_6 at 13.7°C.), and a solid-miscibility gap. The maximum solid solubility of MoF_6 in the UF_6 lattice is about 30 mole % MoF_6, whereas the maximum solid solubility of UF_6 in the MoF_6 lattice is 12 to 18 mole % UF_6. The temperature of the solid-state transformation of MoF_6 increases from ~ -10°C. in pure MoF_6 to ~ -5°C. in mixtures with UF_6, indicating that the solid solubility of UF_6 is greater in the low temperature form of MoF_6 than in the high temperature form of MoF_6. This solid-solubility relationship is consistent with the crystal structures of the pure components: The low temperature form of MoF_6 has an orthorhombic structure similar to that of UF_6.

Investigations of condensed phase equilibria in several systems involving UF_6 and other components are recorded. The binary systems, BF_3–UF_6 (*9, 13*), ClF_3–UF_6 (*21*), HF–UF_6 (*15*), BrF_3–UF_6 (*4*), BrF_5–UF_6 (*4*), and Br_2–UF_6 (*5*), have been studied. The ternary system ClF_3–HF–UF_6 (*16*) has also been studied. In all of these cases, the binary mixtures show the formation of a simple eutectic without solid solubility.

Investigations of condensed phase equilibria in binary systems involving UF_6 and another hexafluoride are few. Although it has been reported that the system NpF_6–UF_6 involves solid solutions (*10*), a phase diagram is not available. A recent study (*18*) showed that the system PuF_6–UF_6 forms a continuous series of solid solutions.

This paper describes the results of an experimental study of condensed phase equilibria in the system MoF_6–UF_6 carried out by thermal analysis and x-ray diffraction analysis. A temperature-composition phase diagram is constructed from the temperatures of observed thermal arrests in MoF_6–UF_6 mixtures, and the basis for the formation of this particular type of diagram is traced to the physical properties of the pure components. The solid-solubility relations indicated by the diagram are traced to the crystal structures of the pure solids.

Experimental Details

Materials. The UF_6 used in this work was a portion of a larger batch originally obtained from Oak Ridge National Laboratory. Almost two-thirds of the original batch had been distilled away in previous experimental work, presumably contributing to the purification of the UF_6 from low boiling impurities (*e.g.*, HF, CF_4, F_2). Emission-spectrographic analysis of the material indicated that the predominant impurities were P, at a concentration of <400 p.p.m., and As, B, Cs, Pd, Re, Sb, Sn, and Th, each present at concentrations of <100 p.p.m. Two determinations of the triple point of a sample of the UF_6 yielded values of 64.1°C. and 64.2°C. The best literature value (*19*) for this is 64.05°C.

The MoF_6 used in this work was a high purity material obtained commercially. Analysis of the material by emission spectrography indicated that the concentrations of the predominant impurities were P, <20 p.p.m.; Cs, Re, and Sb, <10 p.p.m.; U, <5 p.p.m.; Sn, W, Zn, <4 p.p.m.; and all other impurities <2 p.p.m. The triple point of the material was 17.4 ± 0.5°C. Literature values for the triple point are 17.4°C. (*3*), 17.5°C. (*2*) and 17.57°C. (*14*).

Containment of Materials. All experimental work with hexafluorides was carried out in a metal manifold constructed of nickel tubing and fittings which could be evacuated by both mechanical and diffusion pumps. The manifold incorporated Monel diaphragm valves and a number of 1 in. diameter valves with brass bodies, Monel bellows, and Teflon seats. The hexafluorides were transferred between vessels in the manifold by vacuum distillation at room temperature.

Thermal Analysis Apparatus. Mixtures to be examined by thermal analysis were contained in a nickel sample tube with a bottom well to admit the tip of the thermocouple. The sample tube was bolted through a Teflon-gasketed flange to a bellows-valve which could be attached to a vacuum manifold by a flare fitting. The volume of the sample tube was about 4.9 ml. when the valve was closed.

Sample tubes containing the hexafluoride mixtures were positioned in cavities of a cylindrical nickel block. The temperature of the block was varied as a linear function of time with the aid of heating and cooling coils, a program controller, a control unit, and a silicon-controlled rectifier.

Iron-Constantan thermocouples, which had been calibrated against an N.B.S.-standardized platinum resistance thermometer, measured both the sample temperature and the difference in temperature between sample and reference tubes. The thermocouple wires were embedded in magnesia and electrically insulated from their Inconel sheaths. The signal of the thermocouple in the sample tube could be determined either by a recording potentiometer or by a manual potentiometer and null meter.

For differential thermal analysis, two tubes were positioned symmetrically in the nickel block. One tube contained the mixture to be examined by thermal analysis; the other was used as a reference. Satisfactory baseline behavior in the record of the differential thermocouple was obtained by operating with the reference tube filled with air at 1 atm. pressure. The voltage indicating the difference between the sample and reference thermocouples was fed into a d.c. amplifier, capable of multiplying the difference signal by factors varying from 2.5 to 100. The amplified signal was displayed by a suitable strip chart recorder.

Thermal Analysis. A new or reassembled sample tube received the following conditioning treatment. It was evacuated, filled with gaseous fluorine to a pressure of about 1 atm., and periodically heated with a hot-air blower. After 1–15 hours, the fluorine was removed, and the tube was evacuated and weighed to obtain a tare.

A sample tube was charged as follows. A sample of UF_6 was measured by a PVT method, using a ballast tank and gage, then condensed into a sample tube cooled in liquid nitrogen or a dry ice slush bath. The sample tube was removed from the vacuum manifold and weighed on an automatic balance to determine the weight of the UF_6 sample. The sample tube was then reattached to the vacuum manifold, and a sample of MoF_6 was measured and condensed into the sample tube in a manner similar to that described for the UF_6. The sample tube was again weighed to determine the weight of the MoF_6 sample by difference. The total weight of each mixture was about 3.5 grams.

After a sample tube had been charged, it was heated to 70°C. to melt both components. The tip of the tube was then placed against a block of dry ice. This procedure vibrated the tube, mixed the components, and condensed them into the bottom of the tube. The tube was warmed again and maintained at a temperature of 70°C. for an hour; then the sample block assembly was heated or cooled at a programmed rate to observe the thermal arrests from which solidus and liquidus temperatures were obtained. Programmed thermal analysis was carried out two to five times on each mixture. Some of the thermal analyses were carried out at a heating rate of 0.6°C. per minute; most of the analyses were carried out at a heating rate of 0.3°C. per minute.

X-ray Diffraction. To obtain x-ray diffraction patterns for the hexafluorides, samples were sealed into quartz capillary tubes constructed from lengths of quartz tubing pulled into capillary tips with 0.15 to 0.25 mm. i.d., and wall thicknesses of 0.02 to 0.05 mm. The large end (9 mm. o.d.) of each length of quartz tubing was attached to the nickel vacuum manifold by a vacuum coupling using a neoprene O-ring coated with Kel-F No. 90 grease (Minnesota Mining and Mfg. Co.) which is resistant to fluorinating agents. After the manifold and capillary tubing were evacuated to a pressure of 3×10^{-4} torr, the capillary was baked either by a hot-air blower or a low temperature flame. The hexafluoride was transferred by vacuum distillation at room temperature through the vacuum manifold and was condensed into the tip of the capillary. With the bottom of the capillary immersed in liquid nitrogen, it was sealed off with an oxy-gas flame.

Mixtures of MoF_6 and UF_6 were prepared for x-ray diffraction analysis as follows. A sample of MoF_6 was measured by a PVT method and condensed into a nickel tube where it was isolated by a valve. A UF_6 sample was measured similarly and subsequently condensed into the nickel tube. The MoF_6 and UF_6 samples were then allowed to vaporize so that they filled the volumes of both a ballast tank and the nickel tube. The MoF_6–UF_6 vapors remained in this volume to mix at ambient temperature for 15 to 48 hours. A small sample of the hexafluoride mixture was trapped in the capillary tube, condensed into the tip, and the capillary was sealed off as described above.

The capillaries were positioned in a 114.6-mm. Debye-Scherrer camera, and x-ray diffraction photographs were obtained using filtered radiation from CuKα and CoKα sources. Subambient temperatures were maintained in the camera by cooled nitrogen gas which flowed into the camera through a port in the cover plate. The camera temperature was controlled by regulating the flow rate of nitrogen gas. An iron-Constantan thermocouple taped to a surface inside the camera indicated the temperature. Both the camera and nitrogen gas lines were insulated with a foam rubber covering.

Determination of Solid Density of High Temperature Form of MoF_6. The density of solid MoF_6 above its transformation point was determined from measurements of the volume and weight of a single sample. The volume of solid MoF_6 was measured by observing the height of the sample in a calibrated quartz tube which was joined by a brass vacuum coupling to a valve and flare fitting so that it could be attached to the vacuum manifold.

After the sample of MoF_6 had been condensed into the quartz tube on the vacuum line, the valve was closed to isolate the sample, and the tube was removed from the vacuum manifold and weighed to obtain the weight of the MoF_6 by difference. The tube was then clamped in an upright position, and the MoF_6 was solidified. Void formation in the solid was minimized by a slow, progressive immersion of the tube in an ice bath. After the MoF_6 had completely frozen, the tube was immersed in a water bath of desired temperature, and the height of the solid surface with respect to the tip of the tube was measured with the cathetometer.

Results

Thermal Analysis. Interpreting cooling curves, especially those of UF_6–rich mixtures, was difficult because of extensive supercooling of the small samples ($\sim$3.5 grams total). The supercooling could not be controlled either by manual bumping or by an electric core-box vibrator.

Table I. Temperature of Thermal

Mole Fraction UF_6	*Liquidus*		*Solidus*	
	Cooling	*Heating*	*Heating*	*Cooling*
0.964		63.2 ± 0.6	58.0 ± 0.1	
0.910		62.4 ± 1.9	49.1 ± 0.6	14.2 ± 0.0[s]
0.880		59.4 ± 0.6	43.0 ± 5.0	
0.873	60.8		12.3 ± 0.1	13.2 ± 0.2[s]
0.853		60.4 ± 2.4	43.0 ± 3.3	14.3 ± 0.1[s]
0.809		55.4 ± 0.4	29.0 ± 4.0	14.4 ± 0.3[s]
0.769		55.5 ± 0.8	26.6 ± 5.5	14.4 ± 0.0
0.729	52.1		12.4	13.8 ± 0.2
0.719		53.2 ± 2.3	22.7 ± 2.6	14.5 ± 0.1
0.599		49.5 ± 2.1	13.5 ± 0.2	14.2 ± 0.2
0.583	46.4			13.7 ± 0.2
0.516		46.0 ± 0.7	13.6 ± 0.0	14.2
0.490	40.0			13.7 ± 0.2
0.451		43.6 ± 1.8	13.7 ± 0.1	14.2 ± 0.2
0.404	31.4		14.2 ± 0.1	13.9 ± 0.1
0.354		33.3 ± 2.2	13.6	14.2 ± 0.2
0.337	27.0 ± 1.6			13.6 ± 0.6
0.331	29.2			13.8 ± 0.2
0.308	21.3 ± 4.1	23.8 ± 1.3	13.6 ± 0.0	14.5 ± 0.1
0.282	19.3 ± 2.5			14.5 ± 0.2
0.276	21.9 ± 0.4		12.5 ± 0.3	13.9 ± 0.4
0.263	>16.8	14.2 ± 0.1	13.7 ± 0.1	14.4
0.237	16.0	14.1 ± 0.5	13.6 ± 0.4	14.4 ± 0.1
0.231	16.0			13.4 ± 0.3
0.200				13.0 ± 0.5
0.198		14.2 ± 0.4	13.0 ± 0.6	
0.173		14.8 ± 0.4	13.4 ± 0.1	
0.166		14.8 ± 0.4	13.2 ± 0.4	
0.152		15.2 ± 0.0	13.8 ± 0.0	
0.146				
0.116		15.7	14.5	
0.109		15.6 ± 0.0	14.7 ± 0.1	
0.0972				
0.0702		16.7 ± 0.3	14.7 ± 0.5	
0.0661		16.8 ± 0.3	15.8 ± 0.2	
0.0554		17.2	16.0	
0.0551		16.6 ± 0.6	15.7 ± 0.4	
0.0527		17.6 ± 0.5	16.1 ± 0.1	
0.0326		17.1 ± 0.2	16.4 ± 0.2	
0.0296		17.7	16.2	
0.0				

[s] Indicates small thermal arrest.

Because of the sharp maximum temperature in the cooling curves, the freezing point of a mixture could not be obtained with accuracy by a simple extrapolation of each cooling curve. The extrapolation procedure

Arrests in MoF_6-UF_6 Mixtures (°C.)

Solid Trans.		*Solid Trans.*	
Cooling	*Heating*	*Cooling*	*Heating*
5.5 ± 2.6[s]			
6.3[s]		−2.7[s]	
2.5 ± 0.4[s]		−3.6 ± 0.3[s]	
3.6 ± 1.6[s]		−2.0 ± 0.1[s]	
2.4 ± 0.2[s]		−2.2 ± 0.3[s]	
4.0 ± 1.8[s]		−2.1 ± 0.4[s]	
5.9 ± 0.6[s]		−5.6 ± 2.1[s]	
		−3.3 ± 2.1[s]	
7.7[s]		−4.3	−8.3[s]
		−2.0 ± 2.1[s]	
8.0 ± 0.6[s]		−3.2 ± 1.9[s]	−7.9
7.4 ± 0.8[s]		−3.5 ± 0.7	−7.0 ± 0.7
8.3 ± 0.3[s]		−4.1 ± 0.6	−8.3 ± 0.6
4.9 ± 0.9[s]		−5.1 ± 1.4	
7.3 ± 0.6[s]		−4.1 ± 1.7	
7.7[s]			
7.3 ± 0.6[s]		−3.7	
5.1 ± 1.0[s]		−8.0 ± 0.3	−6.8 ± 0.1
		−4.8 ± 0.5	−4.9
6.8 ± 2.1[s]		−5.1	
7.9[s]		−4.9 ± 0.6	
9.7 ± 0.7		−2.3 ± 1.5	
7.5 ± 3.0			
6.0 ± 1.6			
4.7 ± 0.7			
+3.4 ± 0.4	5.1 ± 0.3	−3.1 ± 0.6	−7.6 ± 0.1
5.8 ± 1.3		−3.2 ± 1.2	
−0.5 ± 0.3	−2.1	−5.7 ± 0.6	−5.5
−1.9 ± 0.0	−0.5 ± 1.4	−6.3 ± 0.3	−6.6 ± 0.4
−2.5 ± 0.0		−6.1	
		−6.2 ± 0.4	−6.9
	−0.6 ± 0.4	−6.2 ± 0.1	−7.6 ± 0.4
		−7.4 ± 0.2	−8.5
		−6.7 ± 0.0	−8.1
		−7.0 ± 2.3	−7.3 ± 0.6
		−8.8 ± 0.2	−7.9 ± 0.2
		−9.0 ± 0.2	
		−10.8 ± 0.1	−9.8 ± 0.05

of Andrews *et al.* (*1*) was used to obtain liquidus points from cooling curves with the modification that the extent of supercooling was not halted by seeding, but was allowed to proceed to various temperatures to be halted by random stimuli.

Although cooling curves indicated liquidus points and solid-state transformations, the supercooling effect obscured the indication of solidus points. Many of the thermal analyses were carried out by obtaining heating curves to determine both liquidus points and solidus points. The liquidus points obtained from heating curves agreed satisfactorily with those obtained from cooling curves.

Voltages of the sample thermocouple corresponding to thermal arrests were converted to temperatures using N.B.S. Circular No. 561 (*17*). Table I lists the temperatures of thermal arrests for the entire range of composition between 0 and 100 mole % UF_6. The values listed in Table I are averages of several measurements, and the uncertainty values are standard deviations of the averages. The uncertainty values associated with the liquidus points obtained by the extrapolation procedure (*1*) have not been estimated.

The temperatures of thermal arrests are plotted as a function of composition in Figure 1. The lines have been drawn to suggest the location of equilibrium phase boundaries, and the best interpretation of the thermal analysis data. The resulting diagram is characteristic of a system exhibiting solid solubility with a minimum melting point and a solid-miscibility gap.

Changes in the composition of the condensed phases caused by differential vaporization of UF_6 and MoF_6 were estimated: The location of points on the liquidus curve in UF_6–rich mixtures would be affected more than any others by composition changes, but they differed by less than 1% from the mole fraction values calculated from the total weights of the components. Since changes of this size are not greater than the uncertainty of locating the liquidus curve in this region owing to errors in freezing point determination, the effects of vaporization on the composition were considered unimportant in constructing the phase diagram from the thermal analysis data.

X-ray Diffraction of Pure MoF_6, High Temperature Form. X-ray diffraction powder photographs of MoF_6 taken at 10°C. can be indexed on the basis of a body-centered cubic unit cell with a lattice constant, $a = 6.23 \pm 0.01$A. The similarity of the MoF_6 diffraction pattern to that of molybdenum metal indicates that the molybdenum atoms in the hexafluoride, as in the metal, are located at the body center and corners of a cube.

X-ray Diffraction of Pure MoF_6, Low Temperature Form. X-ray diffraction powder photographs taken below −10°C. are indexable on the basis of an orthorhombic unit cell. Lattice constants from a pattern obtained at −20°C. are $a = 9.65 \pm 0.02$A., $b = 8.68 \pm 0.03$A., and $c = 5.05 \pm 0.02$A. An orthorhombic MoF_6 diffraction pattern was calculated using the atomic coordinates derived by Hoard and Stroupe (*8*) for UF_6.

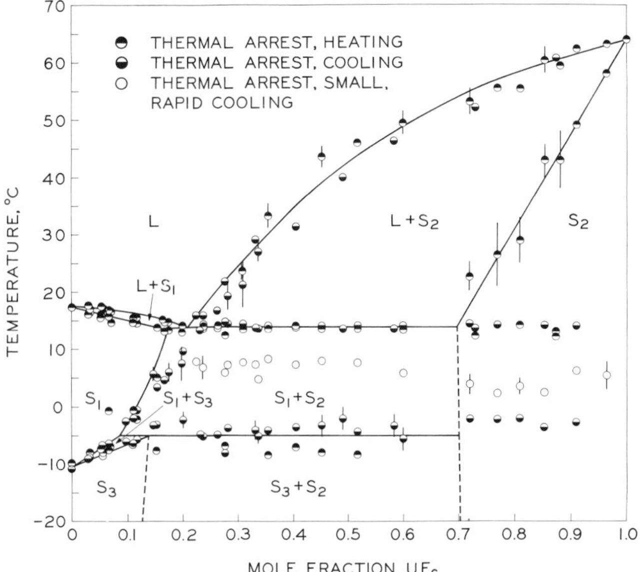

Figure 1. Phase equilibria in the condensed system UF_6–MoF_6

The agreement of calculated and observed values for MoF_6 listed in Table II indicate that the low temperature structure of MoF_6 is similar but not necessarily identical to the orthorhombic structure of UF_6.

The crystal structure change associated with the solid-state transformation of pure MoF_6, *i.e.*, body-centered cubic above the transformation to orthorhombic below it, is analogous to the cubic-to-orthorhombic transformation reported (*20*) for the 5*d* hexafluorides, WF_6, ReF_6, OsF_6, IrF_6, and PtF_6. Another investigation has shown that the solid-state transformation in MoF_6 involves the crystal structure change from body-centered cubic to orthorhombic (*see* Ref. *14*).

X-ray Diffraction of MoF_6-UF_6 Mixtures. X-ray diffraction patterns obtained from mixtures with 5 mole % UF_6 at 6°C. and 14 mole % UF_6 at 0 to 7°C. appeared to be the same as patterns obtained from the high temperature form of pure MoF_6. X-ray diffraction patterns obtained from a mixture with 91 mole % UF_6 at 0° to 5°C. appeared to be the same as a pattern obtained for pure UF_6.

Solid Density of High Temperature MoF_6. The density of solid MoF_6 was obtained from weight and volume measurements at two temperatures above its transformation point. At +8°C., the density was 2.91 grams/cc., and at 0°C., the density was 2.88 grams/cc. The change from 2.91 to 2.88 grams/cc. reflects both the temperature coefficient of density and the error of the measurement. The density calculated from x-ray diffraction data obtained on pure MoF_6 at +10°C. on the basis of a body-centered cubic unit cell containing 14 atoms (2 × MoF_6) was 2.88 grams/cc. The agreement between this calculated value and that obtained from weight and volume measurements confirms the cubic structure for the high temperature form of pure MoF_6.

Table II. Powder Diffraction Data[a] for Low Temperature (Orthorhombic) Form of MoF_6, (Data Obtained at −20°C.)

hkl	$d(A)$ *obs.*	$d(A)$ *calc.*	I *obs.*[b]	I *calc.*
101	4.48	4.47	W	38
011	4.36	4.36	W	24
020		4.34		57
210	4.19	4.22	S	100
111	3.98	3.98	M	66
201	3.48	3.49	W	16
121	3.11	3.11	F	29
221	2.708	2.719	M	11
301		2.713		13
311	2.580	2.589	F	14
230	2.473	2.481	F	18
112	2.349	2.351	F	12
321	2.298	2.300	F	14
202	2.234	2.237	W	12
231		2.227		23

[a] Obtained with cobalt Kα radiation.
[b] S = strong, M = medium, W = weak, F = faint.

Discussion

Nonequilibrium Thermal Arrests. A number of small thermal arrests were observed at ~12 to 14°C. and also at ~+5°C. in the region labelled S_2 on the diagram (Figure 1) where, according to the interpretation suggested, only the primary solid solution S_2 is stable. These thermal arrests are attributed to fractional crystallization which occurs if diffusion in the solid phase is not fast enough to allow the establishment of equilibrium between solid and liquid phases during crystallization. In the extreme case of no solid-state diffusion, the first nucleus (or nuclei) of solid formed when the mixture is cooled is completely removed from the reaction. As cooling proceeds, the crystal nucleus becomes the core of a layered structure, each succeeding layer being poorer in the higher melting component (UF_6). With the removal of UF_6-rich liquid from the reaction, the composition of the remaining liquid proceeds along the liquidus curve, approaching the composition of the minimum-freezing mixture as a limit, with the freezing point of remaining liquid approaching the eutectic point as a limit. For a mixture with a total composition of 80 or 90 mole % UF_6, the last small amount of liquid to freeze may have the composition of the eutectic mixture (~22 mole %).

If annealing has not occurred in the solid phase before heating the mixture to obtain a melting curve, the first of the solid to melt will be the outer layer with the composition and melting point of the eutectic mixture. Thus, on heating UF_6–rich mixtures, the first, slight absorption of thermal energy was observed at the eutectic point, but the major and definite thermal arrests occurred at higher temperatures; these latter points were assumed to indicate the location of the solidus curve.

The thermal arrests obtained at ~−5°C. in the region S_2 are attributed to the transformation of S_1 to S_3 in the nonequilibrium mixture of S_2 plus MoF_6–rich solid.

Effect of UF_6 on the MoF_6 Solid-State Transformation. The temperature of the solid-state transformation of pure MoF_6 obtained by thermal analysis was −10.8 ± 0.1°C. from cooling curves and −9.8 ± 0.05°C. from heating curves. The value of −9.8°C. is considered the better one since supercooling occurred while determining cooling curves. Literature values for this solid-state transformation are −8.7°C., obtained from the intersection of vapor pressure curves (*3*), −9.6°C., obtained in calorimetric measurements (*2*), and −9.68°C., also obtained in calorimetric measurements (*14*).

The results of thermal analysis show that the temperature of the solid state transformation in MoF_6 is higher (~−5°C.) in UF_6 mixtures than it is in pure MoF_6. An increase of the transformation temperature of a component A in mixture with another component B indicates that component B is more soluble in the low temperature form of component A (*13*). It is concluded, on the basis of the observed raising of the transformation temperature (not on the basis of a chemical analysis of solids S_1 and S_3), that UF_6 is more soluble in the low temperature form of MoF_6 than in the high temperature form.

This conclusion might be anticipated on the basis of the crystal structures: A solid of orthorhombic structure (UF_6) is expected to be more soluble in another solid of orthorhombic structure (low temperature form of MoF_6) than in a solid of cubic structure (high temperature form of MoF_6).

Comparison of Solid-Solubilities. The limit of solid miscibility has been related to the energy of distortion of the crystal lattice when atoms of a second component are introduced into the lattice; Scott (*6*) and Lawson (*11*) have expressed the distortion energy as a function of the molal volumes of the two components. Both authors recognized that the solubility of small atoms in a lattice of large atoms is greater than the solubility of large atoms in a lattice of small ones. The same relationship presumably holds for molecular lattices. The solid-solubility relations indicated in Figure 1 are in accord with this thesis. The molal volumes (7) are 84 cc. for MoF_6 and 96 cc. for UF_6. Figure 1 indicates that the maximum solubility ($\sim$30 mole % MoF_6) of the smaller MoF_6 molecule in the primary solid solution S_2 (presumably the UF_6 lattice) is greater than the maximum solubility ($\sim$12 to 18 mole % UF_6) of the larger UF_6 molecule in either of the primary solid solutions, S_1 or S_3 (presumably MoF_6 lattices).

Correlation of X-ray Diffraction Patterns from MoF_6-UF_6 Mixtures with the Phase Diagram. X-ray diffraction patterns from mixtures with 5 mole % UF_6 at 6°C. and 14 mole % UF_6 at 0° to 7°C. appeared to be the same as those obtained from the high-temperature form of MoF_6, suggesting a cubic structure. According to Figure 1, the stable phase in these mixtures is the primary solid solution S_1 which would be expected to have the lattice of the high temperature form of pure MoF_6.

The x-ray diffraction pattern from a mixture with 91 mole % UF_6 at 0° to 5°C. appeared to be the same as that obtained for pure UF_6. Figure 1 shows that the stable phase in this mixture is the primary solid solution S_2 which would be expected to have the lattice of pure UF_6.

Acknowledgment

The authors are grateful to Irving Knudsen for the source of UF_6; to George Redding and Milton Haas for some of the instrumental operations; to William Gunther for providing a vacuum manifold; to James Riha for contributing to the design of the sample tubes; to Robert Schablaske and Ben Tani for x-ray diffraction analyses; and to A. E. Martin for discussion regarding construction of the phase diagram from the thermal analysis data.

Literature Cited

(1) Andrews, D. H., Kohman, G. T., Johnson, J., *J. Phys. Chem.* **29,** 914 (1925).
(2) Brady, A. P., Myers, O. E., Clauss, J. K., *J. Phys. Chem.* **64,** 588 (1960).
(3) Cady, G. H., Hargreaves, G. B., *J. Chem. Soc.* **1961,** 1563 (1961).
(4) Fischer, J., Vogel, R. C., *J. Am. Chem. Soc.* **76,** 4829 (1954).
(5) *Ibid.,* p. 4862.
(6) Hildebrand, J. H., Scott, R. L., "The Solubility of Nonelectrolytes," 3rd Ed., p. 304. Reinhold, New York, 1960.
(7) *Ibid.,* p. 436.
(8) Hoard, J. L., Stroupe, J. D., *U. S. At. Energy Comm. Rept.* **TID-5290,** 325 (1958).
(9) Hutchison, C. A., Jr., *U. S. At. Energy Comm. Rept.* **TID-5224,** 85 (1952).

(10) Hutchison, C. A., Jr., Tsang, T., Weinstock, B., *J. Chem. Phys.* **37**, 555 (1962).
(11) Lawson, A. W., *J. Chem. Phys.* **15**, 831 (1947).
(12) Lewis, G. N., Randall, M., "Thermodynamics," 2nd ed., p. 235, McGraw-Hill, New York, 1961.
(13) Katz, J. J., Rabinowitch, E., "The Chemistry of Uranium," p. 445, Dover Publications, New York, 1961.
(14) Osborne, D. W., Schreiner, F., Malm, J. G., Selig, H., Rochester, L., *J. Chem. Phys.* **44**, 2802 (1966).
(15) Rutledge, G. P., Jarry, R. L., Davis, W., Jr., *U. S. At. Energy Comm. Rept.* **K-845** (1951).
(16) Rutledge, G. P., Davis, W., Jr., *J. Phys. Chem.* **63**, 166 (1959).
(17) Shenker, H., Lauritzen, J. I., Jr., Corruccini, R. J., Lonberger, S. T., "Reference Tables for Thermocouples," *Natl. Bur. Std. Circ.* **561**, (1955).
(18) Trevorrow, L. E., Steindler, M. J., Steidl, D. V., Savage, J. T., *U. S. At. Energy Comm. Rept.* **ANL-7234** (1966).
(19) Weinstock, B., Weaver, E. E., Malm, J. G., *J. Inorg. Nucl. Chem.* **11**, 104 (1959).
(20) Weinstock, B., *J. Phys. Chem. Solids* **18**, 86 (1961).
(21) Wendolkowski, W. S., Barber, E. J., *J. Phys. Chem.* **62**, 750 (1958).

RECEIVED October 14, 1966. This work was performed under the auspices of the U. S. Atomic Energy Commission, under Contract No. W-31-109-eng-38.

23

Uranyl Metaborate and Sodium Uranyl Borate

HENRY R. HOEKSTRA

Argonne National Laboratory, Argonne, Ill.

Uranyl metaborate, $UO_2(BO_2)_2$, is prepared by heating U_3O_8 with an excess of boric oxide in air at 900°–1100°C. In the presence of excess B_2O_3 the salt is thermally stable to 1100°C. in air and to ~950°C. in a nitrogen atmosphere. Without excess B_2O_3, decomposition begins at 750°C. in air. The greenish-yellow crystals of $UO_2(BO_2)_2$ are insoluble in water but hydrolyze slowly to $UO_2(OH)_2 \cdot H_2O$. The crystal symmetry is believed to be monoclinic. The infrared spectrum of $UO_2(BO_2)_2$ is compared with spectra of ring-type ($NaBO_2$) and chain-type (CaB_2O_4) metaborates. The synthesis of several alkali uranyl borates (MUO_2BO_3) is described, and the infrared spectrum of the sodium salt is analyzed with the aid of a borate preparation enriched in B^{10}.

Few references to uranium borates appear in the literature. Larson (*12*) reported that yellow crystals, whose composition was assumed to be $3UO_3 \cdot B_2O_3$ (uranyl orthoborate), were obtained among other products from a melt of uranium niobate in boric oxide. Bruhat and Dubois (*2*) stated that perborate solutions react with uranium oxide to give an anhydrous stable yellow salt of the composition UBO_4. No further information has appeared on either of these compounds.

Experimental

The compounds used in this investigation (H_3BO_3, UO_3, U_3O_8, CaO, and the alkali metal carbonates) were reagent grade chemicals. Boric acid, U_3O_8, and Li_2CO_3 were used directly, UO_3, Na_2CO_3, and K_2CO_3 were dried at 500°C., and CaO was dried at 900°C. prior to use. A sample of boric acid enriched in B^{10} to 92% was used in several borate preparations. The indicated isotopic ratio was confirmed by mass spectrographic analysis.

The products prepared in the experiments described below were investigated by powder x-ray diffraction methods. A Phillips 114.59 mm.

camera was used with nickel-filtered copper radiation to obtain the powder patterns. Infrared spectra of the products were obtained on a Beckman IR-12 spectrophotometer. Potassium bromide disks (200 mgm.) containing 0.4 to 1% of the borate salt permitted investigation of the spectra between 4000 and 300 cm.$^{-1}$, while Nujol mulls spread on polyethylene disks were used in the 300 to 200 cm.$^{-1}$ region of the spectra. The borate salts used in the spectral studies were pulverized for 1 minute in a Wiglbug amalgamator to improve the quality and detail of the infrared spectra.

Preparation of Uranyl Metaborate. An anhydrous boric oxide glass is prepared by thermal decomposition of boric acid in a platinum dish. The uranium oxide powder is then spread on the surface of the boric oxide, and the reactants are heated in air at ~1000°C. until Reaction 1

$$2U_3O_8 + 6B_2O_3 + O_2 \rightarrow 6UO_2(BO_2)_2 \qquad (1)$$

is complete. Conversion to the metaborate takes place slowly. A thin film of finely powdered U_3O_8 reacts completely within several hours, but a thicker layer of sintered U_3O_8 may require several weeks to reach completion. Since boric oxide volatilizes slowly at the temperature required to effect this reaction, an excess of the sesquioxide is necessary. A 5- to 10-fold excess of B_2O_3 gives complete conversion to $UO_2(BO_2)_2$ within a reasonable time. A loose fitting cover can be used to minimize B_2O_3 loss while permitting access of the oxygen required in the reaction. The useful working temperature range is 900° to 1100°C. Below 900°C. the reaction rate is too slow, while above 1100°C. the salt is not formed and actual decomposition is observed, even in the presence of excess B_2O_3.

After complete conversion to $UO_2(BO_2)_2$ is achieved, the uranyl salt is freed from B_2O_3 by dissolving the excess sesquioxide in absolute methanol. Reasonable care should be taken to minimize access of moisture to the metaborate during the purification step, but completely anhydrous conditions are not required. A sample of $UO_2B_2O_4$ prepared as described above gave the following analytical results: uranium found 66.80%, theoretical 66.93%, and boron found 6.02%, theoretical 6.08%.

Attempts to prepare uranyl borate from UO_3 instead of U_3O_8 were only partially successful. The trioxide is more reactive than U_3O_8 and eliminates the necessity for an oxidation step in the metaborate synthesis reaction, but the low thermal stability of UO_3 restricts the reaction temperature to <650°C. Infrared and x-ray analyses of products obtained after heating UO_3 and B_2O_3 mixtures for several days at 650°C. indicated that only a minor conversion to the metaborate had been effected.

The "two container" procedure demonstrated that gaseous boric oxide can be used as well as the molten oxide to obtain conversion of U_3O_8 to the metaborate. The U_3O_8 powder was placed in a small platinum dish suspended within a larger dish containing the B_2O_3 glass. The larger dish was covered with platinum foil and heated at 1000°C. A slow conversion of U_3O_8 to the metaborate was achieved, but several months were required to complete the reaction. This technique eliminates the necessity for a methanol purification step.

Each of the procedures described above leads to the formation of a microcrystalline $UO_2(BO_2)_2$ powder. All attempts to prepare larger crystals of the salt by long continued heating just below 1100°C. proved unsuccessful; no appreciable crystal growth could be detected. Larger crystals can be obtained by adding a small amount of sodium ion, in the form of $Na_2U_2O_7$ or $Na_2B_4O_7$, to the reaction mixture. After several weeks at 1000°C., thin greenish-yellow flakes and needles of uranyl metaborate can be isolated from the mixture by a methanol purification. X-ray and infrared analysis have confirmed the identity of this product even though (*see* below) larger amounts of sodium ion lead to the synthesis of another salt.

Table I. X-Ray Diffraction Data on Uranium Borates

Uranyl Metaborate				*Sodium Uranyl Borate*			
Intensity	*D*	*Intensity*	*D*	*Intensity*	*D*	*Intensity*	*D*
W	5.228	VVW	1.664	M	5.738	VW	1.828
W	4.858	VW	1.639	W	5.343	VVW	1.787
M	4.372	F	1.625	VW	5.085	VW	1.767
M	3.815	F	1.592	M	4.223	VW	1.736
W	3.300	F	1.555	M	4.070	VW	1.720
W	3.098	F	1.552	M	3.919	VW	1.696
M	2.920	VVW	1.526	S	3.409	B-W	1.666
VVW	2.733	VVW	1.519	VW	3.040	F	1.647
VW	2.635	VW	1.503	W	2.947	F	1.600
VW	2.602	VVW	1.473	VW	2.891	F	1.585
W	2.569	VVW	1.465	F	2.842	F	1.574
VVW	2.454	VVW	1.439	VW	2.786	VVW	1.539
VW	2.320	VVW	1.402	M	2.583	F	1.525
VW	2.205	F	1.400	F	2.540	VVW	1.521
VW	2.102	VW	1.381	W	2.493	F	1.494
VVW	2.086	F	1.351	F	2.424	VW	1.460
W	2.050	F	1.337	F	2.384	VVW	1.446
VVW	1.982	F	1.330	W	2.291	F	1.433
VW	1.940	F	1.320	W	2.244	VVW	1.403
VW	1.921	W	1.303	F	2.130	F	1.374
VW	1.887	VW	1.249	VW	2.104	VVW	1.364
VW	1.867	F	1.229	VW	2.086	F	1.339
VVW	1.778	VW	1.221	F	2.044	VVW	1.328
F	1.759			VVW	2.007	VVW	1.325
B-W	1.736			VW	1.976	F	1.306
VVW	1.686			F	1.925	F	1.295
VVW	1.676			W	1.880	VVW	1.249

Preparation of Sodium and Calcium Metaborate. These compounds can be prepared by weighing and mixing the calculated amounts of Na_2CO_3 or CaO with H_3BO_3. The mixtures are heated carefully to liberate volatile products; the residue is then heated strongly to form the molten metaborate. The composition of the product can be determined by measuring weight loss during the reaction. Any boric oxide lost during the sample ignition is replaced by adding more boric acid and refusion to form a homogeneous product. Powder patterns of $NaBO_2$ and

$Ca(BO_2)_2$ prepared by this procedure were found to be in excellent agreement with data given by Marezio, Plettinger, and Zachariasen (*15*).

Preparation of Sodium Uranyl Borate. Equivalent amounts of sodium, uranium, and boron (weighed as Na_2CO_3, UO_3, and H_3BO_3) are mixed and ground in a mortar, then heated in a gold crucible at gradually increasing temperatures to drive off volatile products. The solid product is heated at 900°C. for a day to give a bright yellow crystalline powder. Similar procedures can be utilized to prepare the lithium and potassium uranyl borates.

Results and Discussion

Crystal Structure. Crystallographic studies on a number of metal borates have established that each boron atom is bonded either to three oxygen atoms in a planar BO_3 group or to four oxygen atoms in a tetrahedral configuration. In some instances both arrangements are found in a single compound. Boron-oxygen bond lengths vary from 1.27 to 1.59A., and Zachariasen has correlated observed bond lengths with bond strengths (*21*). Anhydrous orthoborates may have three equal boron-oxygen bonds, as in $ScBO_3$ and $InBO_3$ (*5*), or two B—O bonds which are either shorter or longer than the third, as in $Co_3(BO_3)_2$ or $Mg_3(BO_3)_2$ (*1*).

The oxygen to boron ratio of the metaborates (2:1) requires that at least one of the oxygen atoms must be shared between two boron atoms to obtain the customary boron coordination number. Metaborates with the triangular BO_3 group crystallize in (*a*) a trimeric ring structure, or (*b*) a chain structure. Sodium and potassium metaborates and orthorhombic

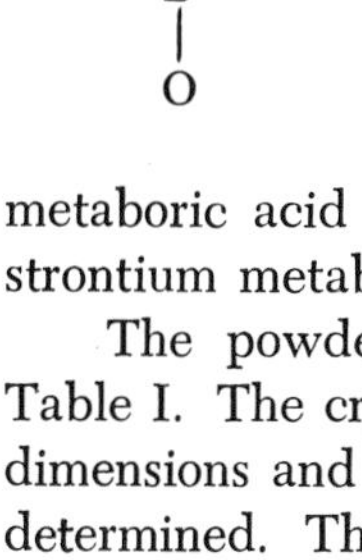

(a)

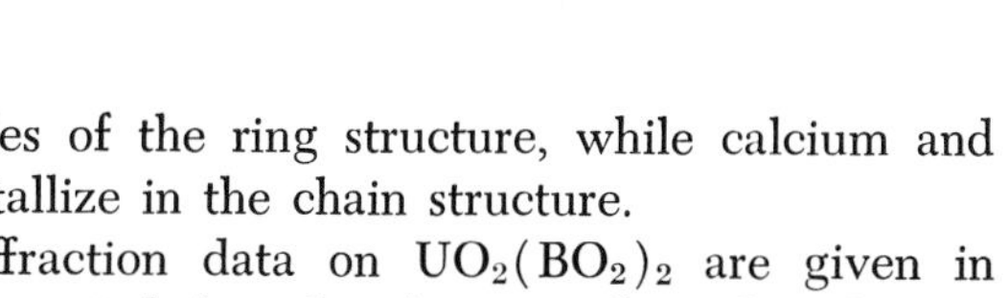

(b)

metaboric acid are examples of the ring structure, while calcium and strontium metaborates crystallize in the chain structure.

The powder x-ray diffraction data on $UO_2(BO_2)_2$ are given in Table I. The crystal symmetry is believed to be monoclinic, but the cell dimensions and atomic arrangement in the crystal lattice have not been determined. The single crystals of uranyl metaborate prepared thus far have provided little assistance in determining its structure since the crystals exhibit extensive twinning. Studies to determine whether uranyl metaborate crystallizes in the ring or chain configuration are continuing.

Only microcrystalline powders of $NaUO_2BO_3$ (*see* Table I for powder data) have been obtained to date, and the crystal symmetry is unknown.

Thermal Stability. Uranyl metaborate is one of the most stable (thermally) uranyl salts; the pure salt begins to show evidence of decomposition only when heated above 750°C. Even at 800°C., only 3% decomposition is observed after two days. The reverse reaction occurs to 1100°C. in air when excess B_2O_3 is present, thus showing that this instability is occasioned by loss of B_2O_3 from the crystal. The equilibrium pressure of boric oxide over the metaborate between 800° and 1100°C. must be less than that of pure B_2O_3. An equation derived by Nesmeyanov and Firsova (*16*) from effusion data on boric oxide gives a vapor pressure of approximately 0.0002 mm. at 1000°C. and 0.002 mm. at 1100°C.; these values must constitute the upper limit for the uranyl metaborate equilibrium decomposition pressure. No measurable decomposition of $UO_2(BO_2)_2$ was detected after two hours at 925°C. in a nitrogen atmosphere, but substantial decomposition occurred after two hours at 1000°C.

Reaction with Water. Uranyl metaborate is virtually insoluble in water at 25°C., but the salt hydrolyzes slowly over several days to form uranyl hydroxide.

$$UO_2(BO_2)_2 + 5H_2O \rightarrow UO_2(OH)_2 \cdot H_2O + 2H_3BO_3 \qquad (2)$$

The hydrated product (which may also be designated as $UO_3 \cdot 2H_2O$ or $H_2UO_4 \cdot H_2O$) was identified by its powder pattern and its infrared spectrum.

Sodium uranyl borate is insoluble in water at 25°C. and gave no evidence of hydrolysis even after a five-day exposure to liquid water. The potassium salt showed slight evidence of hydrolysis in this time, as did the lithium salt.

Infrared Spectra. The interpretation of infrared and Raman spectra of borates and related compounds has been confined largely to the less complex configurations, *e.g.*, substances containing individual BO_3, BO_2X, or BOX_2 groups (*4, 6, 13, 14, 18, 19*). The planar BO_3, with D_{3h} symmetry, has four normal modes of vibration. The symmetric stretch (ν_1) is inactive in the infrared, but the out-of-plane bend (ν_2), the asymmetric stretch (ν_3) and the in-plane bend (ν_4) are infrared active. The vibrational frequencies of two of the fundamentals (ν_2 and ν_3) are directly affected by a change in mass of the central atom in the planar group. Thus a change from $B^{11}O_3$ to $B^{10}O_3$ should produce an increase of approximately 4% in the out-of-plane bending and asymmetric stretching frequencies, while the other two modes are virtually unaffected.

The B—O asymmetric stretching vibration is usually observed in the 1380 to 1310 cm.$^{-1}$ region of the infrared spectrum. The frequency is somewhat lower ($\sim$1250 cm.$^{-1}$) in the metal orthoborates. In-plane and out-of-plane bending vibrations occur in the 750 to 600 cm.$^{-1}$ portion of the spectrum. The asymmetric stretching frequency is substantially lower (at $\sim$1000 cm.$^{-1}$) in compounds containing tetrahedral B—O bonds.

Spectra of substituted borates are more complex as the symmetry is lowered to C_{2v} or C_s; the symmetric stretching mode becomes infrared active, and the two degenerate modes can each separate into two bands to give a total of six absorption maxima. A similar result can be observed in the crystalline orthoborates where the selection rules are governed by site symmetry rather than point symmetry of the borate ion. In addition, unequal bond lengths in BO_3^{3-} ion can lower the symmetry and lead to as many as six absorption bands in the infrared spectrum.

Relatively little information has appeared on the infrared spectra of the metaborates. In addition to several survey investigations which include a number of metaborate spectra (*8, 20*), some tentative band assignments have been reported for several compounds containing the trimeric metaborate (boroxole) ring (*6, 7, 11, 17*). The chain-type metaborate spectra have not been studied in any detail. Fourteen vibrational modes are possible in the D_{3h} boroxole ring, seven of which are active in the infrared ($2A_2''$ and $5E'$). Some or all of the remaining seven bands may become active owing to site group considerations, and splitting of the five E' bands is possible. As a result metaborate infrared spectra can be complex, and their interpretation is less certain than orthoborate spectra. In general, the boron-oxygen stretching vibrations occur in the 1500 to 1100 cm.$^{-1}$ portion of the spectrum. The bending modes are found at lower frequencies, with some as low as 200 cm.$^{-1}$. Further details are discussed below.

Uranyl, Sodium and Calcium Metaborate. The spectra of uranyl, sodium, and calcium metaborates are illustrated in Figure 1, and Table II lists the absorption maxima for three compounds. The bands in the 92% B^{10} compounds are also located. Data on the sodium and calcium salts, as representative of the ring and chain metaborate structures, are in agreement with results reported by Goubeau and Hummel (*6*). The spectra given by Wier and Schroeder (*20*) are more complex and may not represent pure phases.

It is evident from the characteristic strong absorption in the 1400 to 1200 cm.$^{-1}$ region of the spectrum that $UO_2(BO_2)_2$ contains 3-coordinated rather than 4-coordinated boron atoms, but that it cannot be classed as a ring- or chain-type structure simply by a cursory comparison of the three spectra. The broad features of the three spectra are similar, but each differs in details. One distinctive difference in the uranyl salt is the presence of a relatively strong band at 950 cm.$^{-1}$. This absorption is assigned to the asymmetric stretching mode of the uranyl group (*10*). The uranyl bond length can be estimated with the aid of an equation (*3*) derived from Badger's rule, *i.e.*,

$$R_{uo}(\text{A.}) = \frac{53.3}{\nu_A{}^{2/3}} + 1.17$$

In this equation ν_A is the asymmetric stretching frequency in cm.$^{-1}$, and 53.3 and 1.17 are constants characteristic of the bonding atoms. The calculated uranyl bond length is 1.72A. The strong band at 243 cm.$^{-1}$ may arise, at least in part, from the bending mode of this uranyl group.

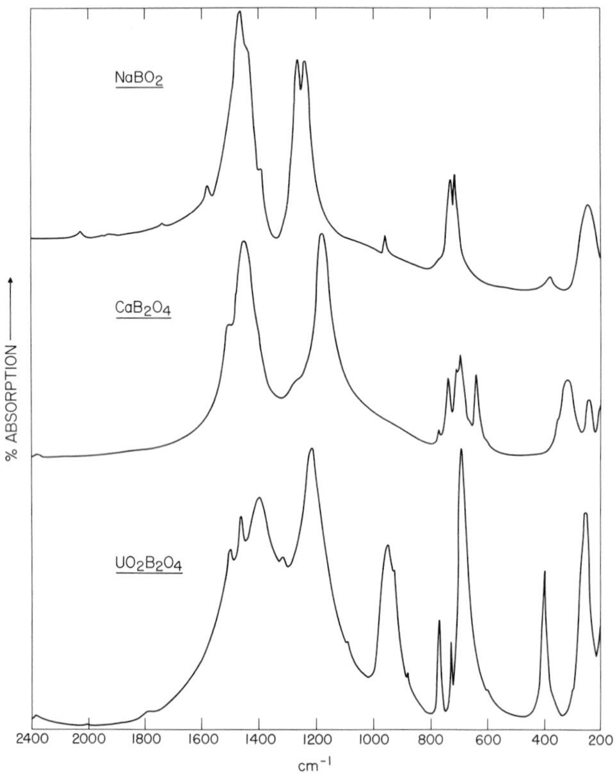

Figure 1. Infrared absorption spectra of metaborates

The three metaborate spectra each have two strong bands in the asymmetric B—O stretching region (~1450 and ~1220 cm.$^{-1}$). The higher frequency band is identified with the side-chain or branch oxygen atom, while the lower frequency band is identified with a ring or chain stretching mode. In the absence of any definitive structural data, any attempt to assign the remaining uranyl metaborate bands would be classed as highly speculative at present.

Table II. Infrared Bands in Sodium, Calcium and Uranyl Metaborates (cm.$^{-1}$)

Sodium Metaborate			*Calcium Metaborate*			*Uranyl Metaborate*		
B^{11}	*Intensity*	B^{10}	B^{11}	*Intensity*	B^{10}	B^{11}	*Intensity*	B^{10}
2035	VW	2065	2350	VW		2355	VW	
1730	VW	1730				1788	VW	
1565	W	1565	1497	sh		1495	W	1508
						1456	W	1457
1450	S	1482	1440	S	1483	1392	S	1418
1423	sh	1432						
1380	sh	1375				1313	VW	
1255	S	1267	1270	sh				
1228	S	1238	1165	S	1193	1210	S	1230
950	W	950				950	S	950
			765	W	780	763	M	767
715	M	727	732	M	739	720	M	727
700	M		700	M	707			
			686	M	694	687	S	695
			633	M	639			
368	W	370				403	M	403
			308	M	308			
238	M	238	235	W	238	243	S	245

Table III. Infrared Vibrations of Boroxole Ring Structure

ν	*Species*	*Description*	*Goubeau & Hummel*	*Present*
6	A_2''	B-ring O out-of-plane bending	—	700
7	A_2''	B-branch O wagging	(473)	(184)
8	E'	B-branch O stretching	1425, 1450	1423, 1450
9	E'	B-ring O stretching	1227, 1255	1255
10	E'	B-ring O stretching	702, 720	1228
11	E'	B-ring O bending	—	715
12	E'	B-branch O rocking	—	238

The spectral data on the two $NaBO_2$ preparations do show that the assignments of Goubeau and Hummel (*6*), based on spectra taken in the NaCl region, are not entirely correct. Table III indicates the bands assigned, as well as the revised assignments based on the spectra described in Table II. Goubeau and Hummel's placement of ν_7 at 473 cm.$^{-1}$ was based on the assignment of a weak band at 946 cm.$^{-1}$ to $2\nu_7$. The $NaBO_2$ spectrum of Figure 1 indicates that no band is found at 473 cm.$^{-1}$.

The weak absorption at 946 cm.$^{-1}$ can be ascribed to ν_{10}, as Parsons did for metaboric acid, or to the symmetric stretching mode (ν_1) which is weakly active because of site symmetry considerations. I prefer the latter explanation because the band is unaffected by a shift in boron isotope ratio. The revised frequency for ν_7 is 184 cm.$^{-1}$ on the assumption that the weak band at 368 cm.$^{-1}$ is $2\nu_7$. This frequency is in better agreement with Parson's assignment for the vibration in metaboric acid. The two ring stretching modes (ν_9 and ν_{10}) are assigned to the twin maxima at 1255 and 1228 cm.$^{-1}$, and the branch oxygen stretching vibration (possibly split at the 1423 cm.$^{-1}$ shoulder) to the 1450 cm.$^{-1}$ band. The band at 700 cm.$^{-1}$ is assigned to ν_6 because it shows a marked isotope effect. Here again, the assigned frequency is close to that given by Parsons for $(HBO_2)_3$. The frequency assigned to ν_{11} (715 cm.$^{-1}$) is unusually high, but no good alternative seems to exist.

According to the Teller-Redlich product rule (9) a B^{10}/B^{11} frequency ratio of ~1.04 should be observed in the product of the two A_2'' vibrations, and ~1.07 in the product of the five E' vibrations. The spectral assignments proposed here give ratios of 1.04 and 1.06 respectively.

Sodium Uranyl Borate. The infrared spectra of sodium uranyl borate (the normal and B^{10} enriched salts) are given in Figure 2, and Table IV

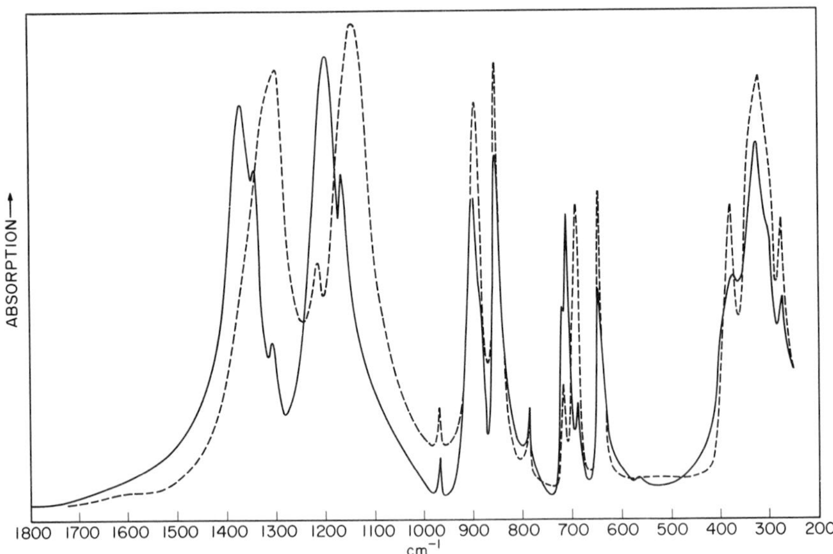

Figure 2. Infrared absorption spectra of sodium uranyl borate

$NaUO_2BO_3$
- - - - - - - 82% B^{11}
——— 92% B^{10}

Table IV. Infrared Maxima (in cm.$^{-1}$) of Alkali Uranyl Borates

$LiUO_2BO_3$		$NaUO_2BO_3$				KUO_2BO_3	
cm.$^{-1}$	*Intensity*	*B^{11}cm.$^{-1}$*	*Intensity*	*B^{10}cm.$^{-1}$*	*Intensity*	*cm.$^{-1}$*	*Intensity*
		1370	sh	1350	S	1380	sh
				1332	VW		
1300	S	1288	S	1297	VW	1290	S
1220	W	1203	W	1188	S	1207	W
1170	S	1133	S	1156	W	1135	S
960	W	958	W	958	W	951	VW
925	M	884	S	890	S	893	M
860	M	842	S	841	S	840	MS
797	VW	773	W	775	W	762	VW
710	W	706	W	709	VW	724	W
				701	MS		
685	M	680	MS	680	W	699	M
630	MW	635	M	637	M	638	MW
362	M	368	M	367	M	326	M
310	M	312	S	314	S	292	S
270	W	265	M	264	M	250	M
243	W						

lists the absorption maxima found in these alkali uranyl borates. The double salt spectra can be divided into four portions:

1500–1100 cm.$^{-1}$	Boron-oxygen stretching modes
1000– 800 cm.$^{-1}$	Uranyl asymmetric stretching, possibly B—O sym. stretching
750– 600 cm.$^{-1}$	Boron-oxygen bending
500– 200 cm.$^{-1}$	Uranium-secondary oxygen stretching, uranyl bending.

It is assumed in the following discussion that these borate double salts contain individual BO_3 groups. The tetrahedral B—O configuration can be eliminated from consideration because of the strong absorption maxima at 1288 and 1133 cm.$^{-1}$. The two spectra of the sodium salt indicate that both high frequency bands arise from B—O asymmetric stretching modes because they both show the 4% isotope shift. The weak maximum at 960 cm.$^{-1}$ is probably ν_1, the symmetric stretching vibration. The borate spectrum is thus governed by C_{2v} or C_s selection rules.

The two maxima at 900 and 850 cm.$^{-1}$ show little or no isotope shift and occur in the frequency range expected for the asymmetric uranyl stretching mode. It does not seem likely that the 850 cm.$^{-1}$ band arises from the symmetric U—O stretch activated by site symmetry because the absorption is too strong. Other possibilities are that the uranyl group is not symmetrical, the O—U—O bonds are not collinear, or two different uranyl groups (sites) occur in the crystal. The data are insufficient to permit a choice at this time.

The band near 700 cm.$^{-1}$ is assigned to the out-of-plane bending in BO_3^{3-} since it shows an isotope shift, while the 650 cm.$^{-1}$ band is an in-plane bending mode without isotope effect. The weak band at 780 cm.$^{-1}$ may represent the remaining in-plane bending vibration.

The low frequency maxima are assigned to the U—O_{II} stretching modes (*i.e.,* to those oxygen atoms bonded weakly to uranium at right angles to the uranyl bonds) and to the uranyl bending vibration.

The spectra of $LiUO_2BO_3$ and KUO_2BO_3 are similar to the sodium salt spectrum—an indication that the uranyl and borate site symmetries are similar in the three compounds.

Literature Cited

(1) Berger, S. V., *Acta Chem. Scand.* **3,** 660 (1949).
(2) Bruhat, J., Dubois, H., *Compt. rend.* **140,** 506 (1905).
(3) Carnall, W. T., Neufeldt, S. J., Walker, A., *Inorg. Chem.* **4,** 1808 (1965).
(4) Finch, A., Pearn, E. J., *Spectrochim Acta* **19,** 1621 (1963).
(5) Goldschmidt, V. M., Hauptmann, H., *Nachr. Ges. Wiss. Gottingen* **53** (1932).
(6) Goubeau, J., Hummel, D., *Z. Phys. Chem.* **20,** 15 (1959).
(7) Goubeau, J., Keller, H., *Z. Anorg. Chem.* **272,** 303 (1953).
(8) Hart, P. B., Smallwood, S. E. F., *J. Inorg. Nucl. Chem.* **24,** 1047 (1962).
(9) Herzerg, G., "Infrared and Raman Spectra," p. 231, Van Nostrand, Princeton, 1945.
(10) Hoekstra, H. R., *Inorg. Chem.* **2,** 492 (1963).
(11) Lappert, M. F., *J. Chem. Soc.* **1958,** 2791 (1958).
(12) Larsson, A., *Z. Anorg. Chem.* **12,** 188 (1896).
(13) Lehmann, W. J., Onak, T. P., Shapiro, I., *J. Chem. Phys.* **30,** 1215, 1219 (1959).
(14) Lehmann, W. J., Weiss, H. G., Shapiro, I., *J. Chem. Phys.* **30,** 1222, 1226 (1959).
(15) Marezio, M., Plettinger, H. A., Zachariasen, W. H., *Acta Cryst.* **16,** 390, 594 (1963).
(16) Nesmeyanov, A. N., Firsova, L. P., *Zh. Fis. Khim.* **34,** 1032 (1960).
(17) Parsons, J. L., *J. Chem. Phys.* **33,** 1860 (1960).
(18) Pistorius, C. W. F. T., *J. Chem. Phys.* **31,** 1454 (1959).
(19) Steele, W. C., Decius, J. C., *J. Chem. Phys.* **25,** 1184 (1956).
(20) Wier, C. E., Schroeder, R. A., *J. Res. Natl. Bur. Std.* **68A,** 465 (1964).
(21) Zachariasen, W. H., *Acta Cryst.* **16,** 385 (1963).

RECEIVED October 24, 1966. Based on work performed under the auspices of the U. S. Atomic Energy Commission.

24

Octahedral Hexahalide Complexes of the Trivalent Actinides

J. L. RYAN

Battelle Memorial Institute, Pacific Northwest Laboratory, Richland, Wash.

The trivalent actinides, like the trivalent lanthanides, form only weak chloride complexes in aqueous solution, and although there is evidence of slight formation of anionic complexes in concentrated LiCl from anion exchange data, no anionic chloride complexes have previously been positively identified. Ryan and Jørgensen have recently prepared the trivalent lanthanide hexachloro and hexabromo complexes and studied their absorption spectra. This paper discusses preliminary results of the extension of this work to the trivalent actinides.

Octahedral hexahalide complexes are of considerable interest because the known high symmetry allows many theoretical arguments to be applied to the energy levels. As an example, in the 4*f* and 5*f* group elements the electric dipole components of the internal *f* electron transitions are forbidden by parity considerations in octahedral complexes with a center of inversion, and the spectrum in the region of these transitions is dominated by weak vibronic transitions. Tetravalent actinide hexahalide spectra of this type have been studied extensively (*1, 5, 6, 7, 9, 10, 11, 12*).

The trivalent actinides and lanthanides form only weak chloride complexes in aqueous solution. Although the trivalent actinides are absorbed moderately strongly by anion exchange resins from concentrated LiCl, the MX_2^+ complex appears to be the highest complex present to a measurable extent in the aqueous chloride solutions (*2*). The bromide complexes appear to be even weaker (*3*). The only other evidence for anionic trivalent actinide chloro or bromo complexes has been in the system of UCl_3 in fused CsCl (*4*). Ryan and Jørgensen have recently prepared the trivalent lanthanide hexachloro and hexabromo complexes and studied their absorption spectra (*8*).

This paper is a preliminary report of the extension of this work to the trivalent actinides. Further work is in progress and will be presented in greater detail later.

Hexachloro and hexabromo complexes of the trivalent actinides can be prepared both in triphenylphosphonium salts and in solution in high dielectric, weakly complexing solvents. The triphenylphosphonium salts can be prepared by precipitation from nearly anhydrous ethanol solutions of the actinide trihalide and triphenylphosphonium halide which are almost saturated with the respective hydrogen halide. The actinide trihalide solution in ethanol can be prepared by dissolving the metal, the anhydrous or hydrated halide, the oxyhalide, or in the applicable instances the sesquioxide in ethanol containing the appropriate hydrogen halide. The presence of the anhydrous hydrogen halide is necessary to decrease the coordinating power of impurities (chiefly water) and of the ethanol through formation of oxonium and ethyloxonium ions. At the time of this writing the $PuCl_6^{3-}$, $PuBr_6^{3-}$, and $AmCl_6^{3-}$ salts have been prepared on a macro scale, and the salt of $AmBr_6^{3-}$ has been prepared on a micro scale. The $PuCl_6^{3-}$ and $PuBr_6^{3-}$ salts were prepared starting with Pu metal and allowing it to react with the respective hydrogen halide in ethanol containing the triphenylphosphonium halide. The pale grey salts are oxidized easily by air to yellow $PuCl_6^{2-}$ and bright red $PuBr_6^{2-}$, respectively. Hence, they must be handled in an inert atmosphere, at least until they are completely dry. The corresponding UCl_6^{3-} salt could not be made this way because of oxidation to U(IV) even in the absence of air. The neptunium salts have not been attempted.

The MX_6^{3-} complexes can be prepared in solution in acetonitrile or preferably in the higher dielectric solvent, 85% succinonitrile–15% acetonitrile, starting with the triphenylphosphonium salts, the hydrated or anhydrous halides, or (particularly in the case of the bromides) the oxyhalides. The latter solvent is preferable if the triphenylphosphonium salts are used as starting material because of their higher solubility than in acetonitrile. The hexachloro complexes are stable in these solvents in the presence of a moderate excess of chloride. The hexabromo complexes are stable in the presence of a large excess of bromide if the system is quite dry but are better stabilized by the presence of anhydrous HBr which reacts with electron donor groups. When the MCl_6^{3-} complexes are prepared in solution starting with the anhydrous chlorides, a small amount of HCl can be used to react with any oxychloride present, but a large excess of HCl destroys the complex by lowering Cl^- activity through formation of species such as HCl_2^-. In the bromide system these species are not of sufficient strength to compete with the metal ions, and the MBr_6^{3-} complexes are stable in the presence of a large excess of HBr. The

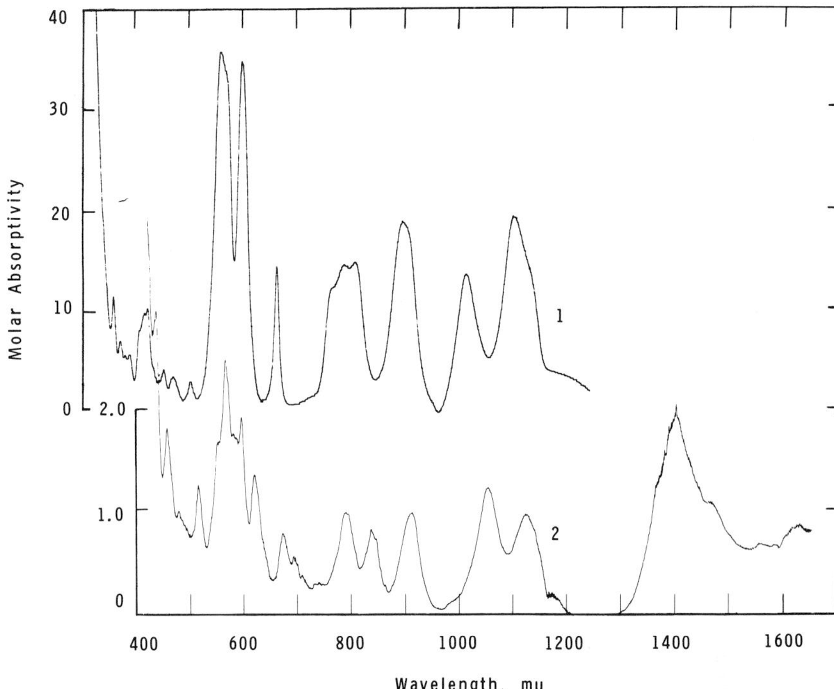

Figure 1. Absorption spectra of plutonium(III). (1) Pu(III) in 1M $HClO_4$; (2) the $PuCl_6^{3-}$ ion in 85% succinonitrile-15% acetonitrile. This solution was prepared by dissolving $PuCl_3$ in the solvent saturated with $(C_2H_5)_4NCl$ and containing a small amount of anhydrous HCl. The $PuCl_6^{3-}$ spectrum was corrected for 2.0% Pu(IV) (as $PuCl_6^{2-}$) which appears to constitute a slight overcorrection, and because of this the fine structure in the 670-870 mμ region may not be exactly correct for $PuCl_6^{3-}$

$PuCl_6^{3-}$ and $PuBr_6^{3-}$ ions in these solutions are readily oxidized to Pu(IV), and the solutions must be handled in an inert atmosphere.

The absorption spectra of these complexes can be obtained in the visible and near infrared region using solutions of the triphenylphosphonium salts, but if the ultraviolet spectrum is desired, the complex must be formed in solution using an aliphatic quaternary ammonium halide and the actinide trihalide or oxyhalide.

The absorption spectrum of Pu(III) in the region of the $f \rightarrow f$ transitions (visible and near infrared) is generally considered to be only slightly sensitive to complexing. The absorption spectrum of the $PuCl_6^{3-}$ ion in this region is markedly different from the spectra of Pu(III) in aqueous solutions of various complexing agents, as seen in Figure 1. The molar absorptivities are on the average about 18-fold less in the $PuCl_6^{3-}$ complex than in the Pu(III) aquo ion, and the number and shape of the peaks are changed and they are shifted in energy (Figure 1). A similar pronounced decrease in intensity of the $AmCl_6^{3-}$ spectrum *vs.* that of the Am(III) aquo ion was observed. This marked decrease in intensity of the $f \rightarrow f$ transitions of the hexahalide complexes *vs.* the aquo ion (and other Pu(III) complexes formed in aqueous solutions such as sulfate, nitrate, etc.) is quantitative evidence of octahedral or near octahedral symmetry with a center of inversion in the hexahalides and of the lack of such symmetry in most Pu(III) complexes. This indicates that the Pu(III) aquo ion and most other Pu(III) complexes are not octahedral, and as for the trivalent lanthanides (5), six is not a common coordination number of the trivalent actinides.

Further studies of the spectra of the trivalent actinide hexahalide complexes are being carried out and will be presented in greater detail later.

Literature Cited

(1) Jørgensen, C. K., *Acta Chem. Scand.* **17**, 251 (1963).
(2) Marcus, Y., *J. Inorg. Nucl. Chem.* **28**, 209 (1966).
(3) Marcus, Y., [private communication].
(4) Morrey, J. R., [unpublished results].
(5) Pappalardo, R., Jørgensen, C. K., *Helv. Phys. Acta.* **37**, 79 (1964).
(6) Pollack, S. A., Satten, R. A., *J. Chem. Phys.* **36**, 804 (1962).
(7) Ryan, J. L., *Inorg. Chem.* **3**, 211 (1964).
(8) Ryan, J. L., Jørgensen, C. K., *J. Phys. Chem.* **70**, 2845 (1966).
(9) Ryan, J. L., Jørgensen, C. K., *Mol. Phys.* **7**, 17 (1963).
(10) Satten, R. A., *J. Chem. Phys.* **29**, 658 (1958).
(11) Satten, R. A., Schreiber, C. L., Wong, E. Y., *J. Chem. Phys.* **42**, 162 (1965).
(12) Satten, R. A., Young, D., Gruen, D. M., *J. Chem. Phys.* **33**, 1140 (1960).

RECEIVED October 10, 1966. Work performed under U. S. Atomic Energy Commission Contract AT(45-1)-1830.

25

Anionic Acetato Complexes of the Hexavalent Actinides

Anion Exchange and Amine Extraction of Hexavalent Actinide Acetates

J. L. RYAN and W. E. KEDER

Battelle-Northwest Laboratories, Richland, Wash.

Spectrophotometric studies were used to identify the anionic hexavalent actinide acetate complexes present in aqueous and nonaqueous solutions, anion exchange resins, and amine extracts. The previously unreported tetraacetato complexes, $MO_2(C_2H_3O_2)_4^{2-}$, *were identified in all these systems. The formation constant for the reaction* $UO_2(C_2H_3O_2)_3^- + C_2H_3O_2^- \rightarrow UO_2(C_2H_3O_2)_4^{2-}$ *in acetonitrile was found to be* 2.0 ± 0.2. *The ratio of tetraacetato to triacetato complex in anion exchange resins was found to be independent of aqueous acetate concentration but depended somewhat on aqueous acidity. The ratio of these species in amine extracts was almost independent of all variables except the ionizing power of the diluent used. The formation constant of the tetraacetato complex in the amine extract increases with decreasing dielectric constant of the diluent.*

Hexavalent actinides can be extracted into long chain amines (*11*) and loaded into anion exchange resins from acetic acid solutions with resin distribution coefficients approaching 10^3. Salts of the general formula $M[UO_2(C_2H_3O_2)_3]_m$ are well known, and the existence of the triacetato complex in aqueous solutions has been shown with no evidence of higher complexes (*1, 3, 5, 22*). A few salts containing four acetate ions per uranyl ion have been reported (*4, 12*). The Pb and Mn salts were reported by Nichols and Howes without analysis (*12*) based on the old work (about 1885) of Rammelsberg who analyzed a Cd salt and assigned a similar formula to the Pb and Mn salts. Nichols and Howes could not prepare the Cd salt (*12*) and in a later work reported the Pb and Mn salts as triacetates (*13*). Dieke and Duncan reported several uranyl salts as tetraacetates with no basis for this assignment except for a reference to Ref. *12* above in the case of the Pb salt. It was found in the present work that the Pb salt is a triacetato salt, and it is probable that all of these reports of tetraacetato uranyl salts are in error.

The triacetato uranyl complex (*24*) is structurally similar to the trinitrato uranyl complex (*6*) (three bidentate ligands arranged equatorially around the uranyl O—U—O axis). It was expected that the visible, near ultraviolet spectrum of the triacetato uranyl complex would be similar to the spectrum of $UO_2(NO_3)_3^-$ as are the spectra of $UO_2(SO_4)_3^{4-}$, $UO_2(CO_3)_3^{4-}$, and other uranyl complexes which apparently have the same structure (*17*). The absorption spectrum of uranyl acetate extracted into tri-*n*-octylamine in xylene from dilute acetic acid is different from the trinitrato uranyl spectrum. This indicates that the triacetato uranyl complex is probably not the species involved. By analogy to the uranyl nitrate system (*14*), formation of a tetraacetato uranyl complex might be expected. The purpose of this work is to determine the nature of the anionic hexavalent actinide acetate complexes and to identify the species involved in the amine extraction and anion exchange of the hexavalent actinides from acetate systems.

Experimental

Reagents. Commonly available reagents were all reagent grade. Cesium acetate and lithium acetate were prepared by neutralizing the corresponding C. P. hydroxides with acetic acid, followed by evaporating and drying at 110°C. at 200 mm. pressure. Tetraethylammonium acetate was prepared by neutralizing Eastman 10% tetraethylammonium hydroxide with acetic acid, evaporating on a hot plate until boiling ceased, and drying at 110°C. at 200 mm. pressure for about 5 hours. Prolonged drying under these conditions causes gradual decomposition and discoloration. The resulting material was an almost colorless oily liquid when cooled to room temperature, which crystallized upon absorption of atmospheric moisture. The compound appears to be the same as that reported by Steigman and Hammett (*20*) as the monohydrate. It crystallized when cooled to −80°C. and did not remelt when warmed to 25°C. When a nonaqueous solution of tetraethylammonium acetate of known concentration was desired, the salt was prepared as above with a measured volume of standardized tetraethylammonium hydroxide, and the entire preparation was dissolved to volume in the nonaqueous solvent.

Preparation of Cesium and Quaternary Ammonium Actinide(VI) Acetate Salts. Tetraethylammonium uranyl acetate was prepared by evaporating to dryness a solution of uranyl acetate containing tetraethylammonium acetate in slight excess. The residue was dissolved in boiling absolute ethanol, and the product was precipitated by cooling in a dry ice bath. The product was filtered and recrystallized again from ethanol.

The salt was dried at 120°C. at 200 mm. pressure. Analysis: calculated for $(C_2H_5)_4NUO_2(C_2H_3O_2)_3$: U, 41.23; found: U, 41.29.

Cesium uranyl triacetate was precipitated by adding a solution of cesium acetate containing a small amount of acetic acid to a solution of uranyl acetate in water. This previously reported compound was not analyzed.

Cesium neptunyl acetate was prepared as follows. Neptunium(VI) nitrate was prepared by heating anion-exchange purified (*15*) neptunium(IV) and (V) nitrate in 0.5*M* HNO_3 to 100°C. for one hour. The Np(VI) was precipitated with CsOH. The precipitate was separated, washed with water, and redissolved in a minimum of concentrated acetic acid. This solution was diluted tenfold with water, and the precipitation, washing, and dissolution in concentrated acetic acid were repeated. Excess cesium acetate was added, and the green product was filtered, washed with ethanol and then acetone, and dried over $Mg(ClO_4)_2$. Analysis: calculated for $CsNpO_2(C_2H_3O_2)_3$: Cs, 23.0; Np, 40.9. Found: Cs, 23.2; Np, 39.7.

Cesium plutonyl triacetate (pink) was prepared in the same manner as the neptunyl analog except the anion-exchange purified (*18*) Pu(IV) nitrate was oxidized to Pu(VI) nitrate by ozone at about 80°C. Analysis: calculated for $CsPuO_2(C_2H_3O_2)_3$: Cs, 22.9; Pu, 41.2. Found: Cs, 23.6; Pu, 41.3.

Cesium and lithium analyses were by flame photometry. Uranium (*2*), neptunium (*21*), and plutonium (*19*) analyses were by controlled potential coulometric titration.

Solvents. Acetonitrile and nitromethane were Eastman spectro grade. Succinonitrile was Eastman white label.

Amine Extraction. Tri-*n*-octylamine was prepared by repeated washing of tri-*n*-octylammonium chloride with 1*N* NH_4OH followed by washing with water. Uranium extraction experiments were performed with U-233 tracer which contained a small amount of hydrochloric acid. Successive backwashing of extracts with acetic acid was used to eliminate the chloride. Np-237 and Pu-239 were oxidized with ozone and backwashed two or three times to eliminate lower oxidation states.

Spectrophotometric Measurements. Spectrophotometric measurements were made with a Cary Model 14 recording spectrophotometer. Absorption spectra of solutions were obtained in silica cells. Absorption spectra of the crystalline salts were obtained using mixtures of the materials with petrolatum between glass or silica plates using the Cary Model 1417200 source. Blanks for the solid spectra were $CaCO_3$ mulls in petrolatum plus aqueous starch solution if necessary to produce a flat base line. The reference was adjusted so the base line was flat in the 520 to 600 mμ region where the U(VI) acetate complexes do not absorb. Slit widths for spectra of solids were typically < 0.1 mm.

Results and Discussion

Identification of Species. Figure 1 shows the absorption spectra of solid $CsUO_2(C_2H_3O_2)_3$ and $(C_2H_5)_4NUO_2(C_2H_3O_2)_3$ in acetonitrile solution. Other solid triacetato salts produce essentially the same spectrum, which is also obtained when the tetraalkylammonium salt is dissolved in nitromethane, acetone, acetic anhydride, and succinonitrile. This distinctive spectrum is similar to those of $UO_2(NO_3)_3^-$ (*7, 14*), $UO_2(SO_4)_3^{4-}$ (*17*), $UO_2(CO_3)_3^{4-}$, and $UO_2(ClO_4)_3^-$ (*23*), and it appears that this spectrum is peculiar to uranyl(VI), which is bonded through oxygen to three bidentate ligands lying in a plane perpendicular to the O—U—O axis. Trinitrato (*6*) and triacetato (*24*) uranyl ions have this geometry, while no ions which could not fit this pattern are known to have a similar spectrum.

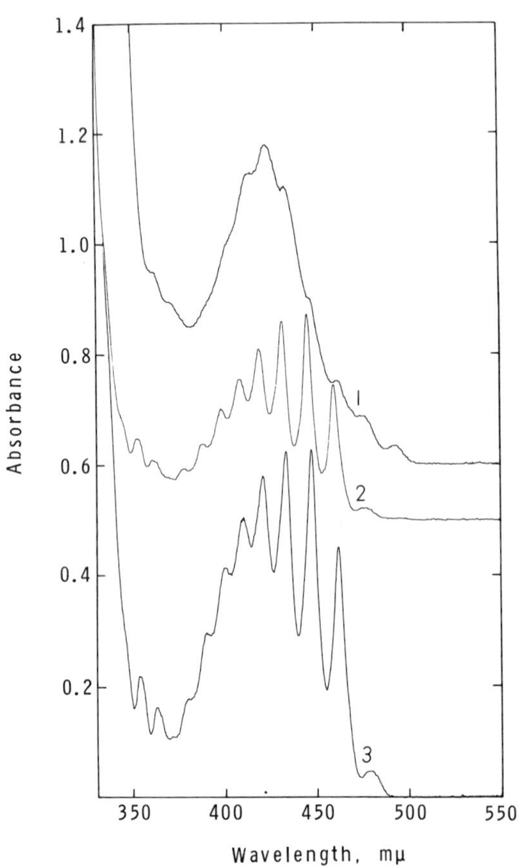

Figure 1. Absorption spectra of the $UO_2(C_2H_3O_2)_3^-$ ion compared with that of a tri-n-octylamine extract of U(VI) from 1M $HC_2H_3O_2$; (1) 0.022M U(VI) in 5% tri-n-octylamine in xylene (1 cm. cell), (2) 0.024M $(C_2H_5)_4NUO_2(C_2H_3O_2)_3$ in acetonitrile (1 cm. cell), and (3) solid $CsUO_2(C_2H_3O_2)_3$

It was observed in preliminary work (*9, 10*) that the spectrum of uranyl(VI) extracted into TOA-xylene from acetic acid is definitely not that of the triacetato anion (Figure 1). The general lack of strong vibrational features in both this spectrum and that of $UO_2(NO_3)_4^{2-}$, combined with the relatively higher molar absorptivity of both of these relative to those of the corresponding trisubstituted complexes, strongly indicate the presence of the tetraacetato uranyl ion in the TOA-xylene extract.

To identify this unknown species, an attempt was made to prepare a tetraacetato salt. In the uranyl nitrate system the compound $[(C_2H_5)_4N]_2UO_2(NO_3)_4$ could be prepared (*13*) by fusing an equimolar mixture of $(C_2H_5)_4NUO_2(NO_3)_3$ and $(C_2H_5)_4NNO_3$. $(C_2H_5)_4NUO_2(C_2H_3O_2)_3$ does not melt without decomposition, so an aqueous solution was prepared containing equimolar $(C_2H_5)_4NUO_2(C_2H_3O_2)_3$ and $(C_2H_5)_4NC_2H_3O_2$ with a small excess of acetic acid. This was dried at 110°C. at 200 mm. pressure. The product was a viscous oil which did not crystallize at 25°C. The absorption spectrum of this material between fused-quartz plates was found to be identical to that of uranyl extracted from 1*M* acetic acid into tri-*n*-octylamine in xylene. A series of solutions was prepared which contained $(C_2H_5)_4NC_2H_3O_2$ to $(C_2H_5)_4NUO_2(C_2H_3O_2)_3$ ratios from 0 to 2 and a small excess of acetic acid. These were dried at 100°C. at 200 mm., and the absorption spectra were obtained. The sample with no excess tetraethylammonium acetate produced crystalline $(C_2H_5)_4NUO_2(C_2H_3O_2)_3$, and its spectrum was obtained in petrolatum. The samples containing between 3 and 4 moles of acetate per mole of uranium were mixtures of crystalline material and a viscous liquid, and the spectra were run between quartz plates without mixing with petrolatum. The ratio of the absorbance at 460 mμ, where the triacetato complex has a strong peak, to that at 453 mμ, where it has a minimum, is plotted against acetate to uranium ratio in Figure 2. It is apparent from this plot that a tetraacetato uranyl complex forms. The samples having an acetate to U ratio of 4.0 and 4.1 appeared to disproportionate slightly and had a few small crystals of $(C_2H_5)_4NUO_2(C_2H_3O_2)_3$ present. Their spectra are not the pure tetraacetato spectrum. At higher acetate to U ratios no crystals were present, and no further change in spectrum occurred with increased acetate (up to an acetate to uranium ratio of 100) indicating lack of higher complexes. The spectrum of samples having an acetate to U ratio of 4.5 or greater is that of the pure tetraacetato uranyl complex.

When $(C_2H_5)_4NC_2H_3O_2$ is added to a solution of $(C_2H_5)_4NUO_2(C_2H_3O_2)_3$ in a relatively noncomplexing solvent, such as acetonitrile or nitromethane, the strong vibrational peaks of the triacetato complex decrease in intensity, and the over-all absorbance increases. At high acetate concentrations the spectrum approaches that of the pure tetraacetato complex obtained above but still contains a small amount of triacetato complex. If a high dielectric-constant solvent of low complexing power such as 85% succinonitrile-15% acetonitrile (*16*) is used, $CsUO_2(C_2H_3O_2)_3$ is soluble. The same effect can be observed by adding $CsC_2H_3O_2$, although the reaction cannot be carried as far toward the tetraacetato complex because of the solubility limit of $CsC_2H_3O_2$.

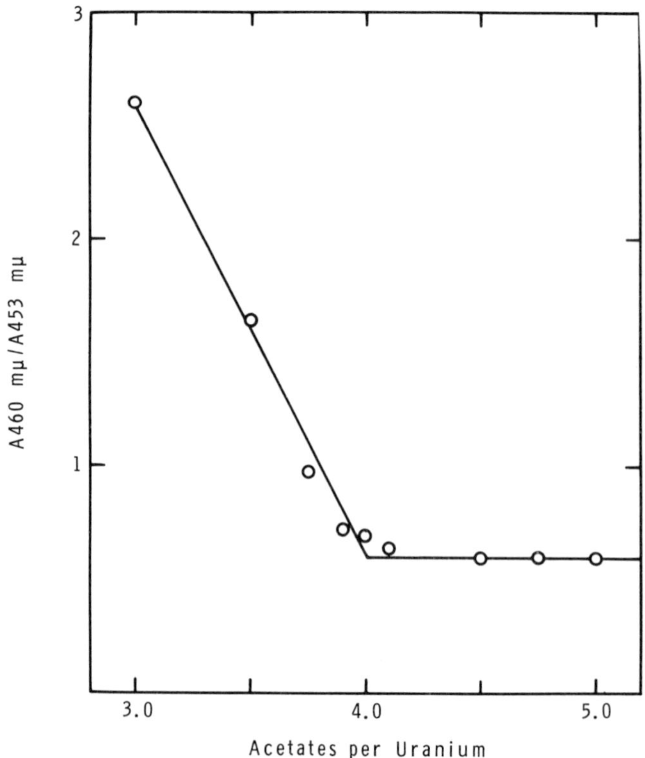

Figure 2. Ratio of absorbance at 460 mμ to that at 453 mμ of residues produced by evaporating mixtures of $(C_2H_5)_4NUO_2(C_2H_3O_2)_3$ *and* $(C_2H_5)_4NC_2H_3O_2$

A series of acetonitrile solutions was prepared which contained known concentrations of $(C_2H_5)_4NUO_2(C_2H_3O_2)_3$ and tetraethylammonium acetate. The spectrum of a solution containing no tetraethylammonium acetate was taken to be that of pure $UO_2(C_2H_3O_2)_3^-$, and the spectrum in liquid tetraethylammonium acetate [probably the monohydrate (*20*)] with an acetate to U ratio of about 100 was taken to be that of pure $UO_2(C_2H_3O_2)_4^{2-}$. The absorption spectra of the pure triacetato complex, the pure tetraacetato complex, and one mixture are compared in Figure 3. With the molar absorptivities of the pure complexes obtained in this manner, the fraction of each complex present in all the acetonitrile solutions can be calculated at any wavelength where there is an appreciable difference in the molar absorptivity of the two complexes. This was done at 494 mμ where the tetraacetato complex has an absorption maximum and the triacetato complex has almost no absorption. This wavelength was chosen because it was one of the few wavelengths where the absorption spectrum of neither of the complexes was extremely steep thus

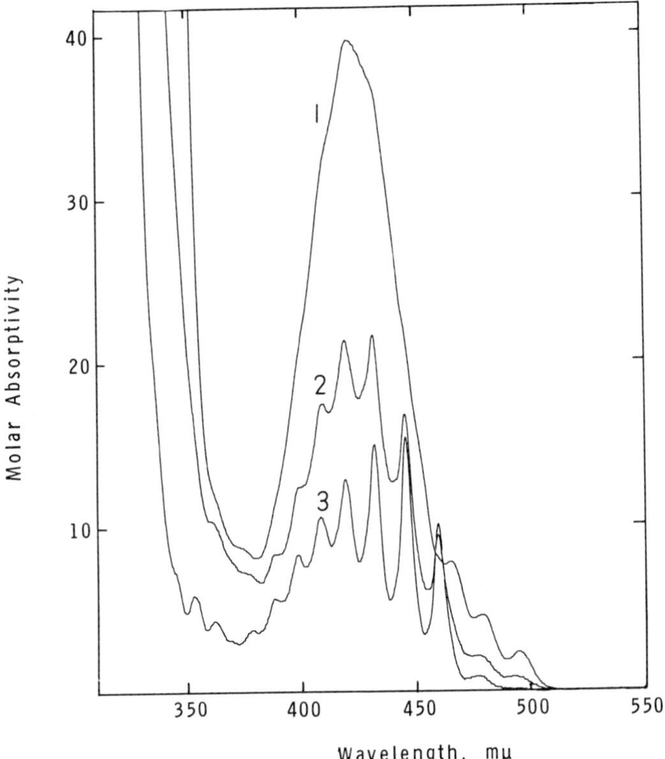

Figure 3. Absorption spectra of 0.0240M $(C_2H_5)_4NUO_2(C_2H_3O_2)_3$ in (1) pure liquid $(C_2H_5)_4NC_2H_3O_2 \cdot H_2O$, and in acetonitrile solutions containing (2) 0.225M and (3) 0.000M $(C_2H_5)_4NC_2H_3O_2$

minimizing errors caused by small errors in wavelength. (This is also true at 420 mμ, but here discoloration of the tetraethylammonium acetate produces absorption, and there was some problem in ensuring this was correctly blanked out at the highest tetraethylammonium acetate concentrations.) Checks were made at several wavelengths other than 494 mμ, and the results agreed within experimental accuracy with those obtained at 494mμ. The formation constant,

$$K = \frac{[UO_2(C_2H_3O_2)_4^{2-}]}{[UO_2(C_2H_3O_2)_3^-][C_2H_3O_2^-]}$$

was calculated for each acetate concentration examined (Table I).

Table I. Formation of Tetraacetato Uranyl Complex in Acetonitrile

Initial Molarity $(C_2H_5)_4NC_2H_3O_2$	% $UO_2(C_2H_3O_2)_3^-$	% $UO_2(C_2H_3O_2)_4^{2-}$	K
0.000	100.0	0.0	
0.045	92.9	7.1	1.77
0.090	83.3	16.7	2.34
0.225	66.7	33.3	2.25
0.450	56.0	44.0	1.79
0.900	35.7	64.3	2.00
2.25	17.9	82.1	2.04
			Av. = 2.0 ± 0.2

Aqueous Solutions. Ahrland (*1*) has concluded that $UO_2(C_2H_3O_2)_3^-$ is the highest uranyl acetate complex present in aqueous solutions and that this species constitutes > 95% of the total uranyl species at 0.3*M* and higher acetate. The triacetato uranyl complex does not contain water and the tetraacetato complex undoubtedly does not. Because of this, the formation constant of the tetraacetato complex from the triacetato complex might be expected to be of about the same order of magnitude in water as in acetonitrile. Also the tetraacetato complex might be expected to form to an appreciable extent at high aqueous acetate concentrations. Any difference between acetonitrile and water should be caused by the effects on the formation constant caused by a difference in ionizing power of the solvent as affected by dielectric constant, solvent structure, etc., since water is not directly involved in the equilibrium. Aqueous lithium acetate-acetic acid solutions of U(VI) were examined spectrophotometrically for evidence of the tetraacetato uranyl complex. Acetic acid concentration was kept at least twice the lithium acetate concentration, except for the highest lithium acetate concentration examined, to prevent hydrolysis (*1*). Solutions ranging in acetate concentration from $UO_2(C_2H_3O_2)_2$ in acetic acid to 5.4*M* $LiC_2H_3O_2$ were examined at 0.040*M* uranium in all cases. Some of the spectra are shown in Figure 4, and it is apparent that at least three uranyl species are present in this concentration range.

At low acetate concentration (uranyl acetate in acetic acid) little if any triacetato complex is present as seen by the absence of the four strong vibrational peaks at about 420, 432, 445, and 460 mμ. As the acetate level is increased, these strong triacetato peaks build into the

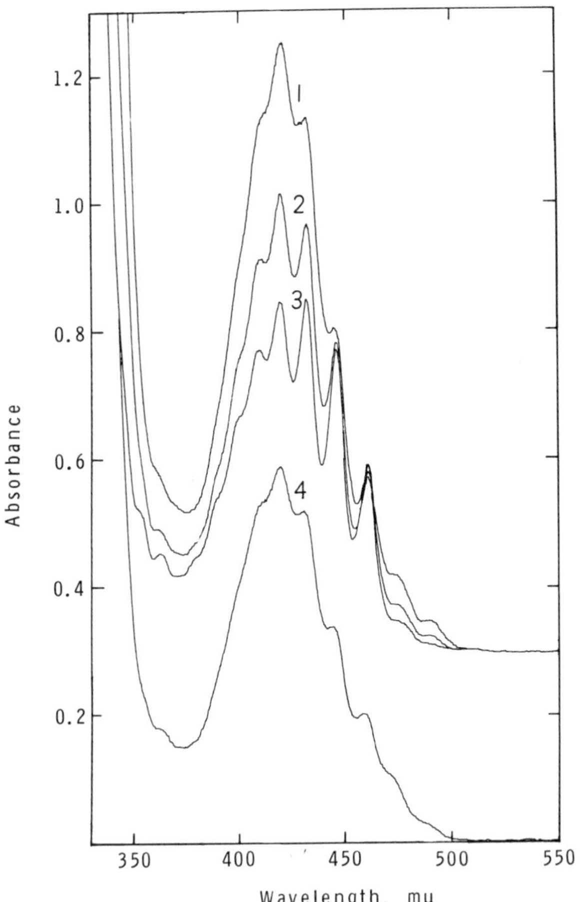

Figure 4. Absorption spectra of 0.040M aqueous U(VI) acetate solution in 1 cm. cells: (1) 5.4M $LiC_2H_3O_2$—3.5M $HC_2H_3O_2$, (2) 3.0M $LiC_2H_3O_2$—6.0M $HC_2H_3O_2$, (3) 0.165M $LiC_2H_3O_2$—0.6M $HC_2H_3O_2$, and (4) 0.6M $HC_2H_3O_2$

spectra. The absorbance at 420 mμ decreases somewhat, goes through a minimum at about 0.1–0.3*M* acetate, and increases markedly at higher acetate concentrations. This increase in absorbance appears to be caused by the formation of the tetraacetato uranyl complex. The triacetato complex appears to be decreasing at the highest lithium acetate concentrations, and a large fraction of the total uranium is present as the tetraacetato complex.

A quantitative interpretation of these spectra is not feasible for two reasons. First, there are at least three species present including at least one complex which contains less than three acetates, and the spectrum of this complex (or complexes) is not known. Second, any change in the triacetato or tetraacetato spectra from those measured as described previously would further complicate a quantitative interpretation. There does appear to be an energy shift amounting to about 2 mμ in the tetraacetato spectrum in going from acetonitrile to water. Even a slight broadening of the sharp triacetato vibrational peaks would also cause large errors. A semiquantitative interpretation indicates that the tetraacetato, triacetato, and at least one lower complex coexist in appreciable amounts in the same solutions with the amount of triacetato complex apparently increasing up to about 1*M* acetate. The amount of the triacetato uranyl complex never appears to exceed about 50–60% of the total uranium unless the acetic acid to lithium acetate ratio is increased to well above 2. At high acetate concentrations, a large amount of the $UO_2(C_2H_3O_2)_4^{2-}$ complex is present. At 5.4*M* $LiC_2H_3O_2$–3.5*M* $HC_2H_3O_2$, the $UO_2(C_2H_3O_2)_4^{2-}$ appears to constitute about 50% or more of the total uranium, and in 3*M* $LiC_2H_3O_2$–6*M* $HC_2H_3O_2$ about 20% as determined by the increased absorbance at 420 mμ and at 494 mμ. Increasing the acetic acid concentration at a constant lithium acetate concentration increases the amount of triacetato complex. This occurs at the expense of lower complexes by decreasing water activity since water is no doubt present in the lower acetate complexes. This may also decrease acetate activity by hydrogen bonding to the acetic acid and simultaneously favor the triacetato complex over the tetraacetato complex. The formation constant for the tetraacetato complex from the triacetato complex appears somewhat smaller in water than in acetonitrile but apparently not by more than a factor of 10.

Anion Exchange Resin Studies. Figure 5 shows the absorption spectra of U(VI) loaded into Dowex 1, X-4 (50 to 100 mesh) anion exchange resin from several acetate solutions. Both the triacetato and tetraacetato uranyl complexes are absorbed by the anion exchange resin. An increase in the fraction of triacetato complex occurs with an increase in the acetic acid concentration of the solutions. The fraction of each complex can be approximated by measuring the ratio of the absorbances at 460 mμ and 454 mμ and comparing with the values obtained in acetonitrile. This calculation is not exact because the spectra of the two pure species in the resin may be different from those in acetonitrile. In contact with 17.5*M* acetic acid the resin contains about 9% tetraacetato complex, in 10*M* acetic acid about 13%, and in 1*M* acetic acid about 25%. This increase is also observed by the build-in of the tetraacetato peak at 494 mμ where the triacetato complex does not absorb. In solutions having a lithium acetate to acetic acid ratio of 1/2, the U(VI) in the resin was about 30% in the tetraacetato form from 0.16–3.0*M* lithium acetate.

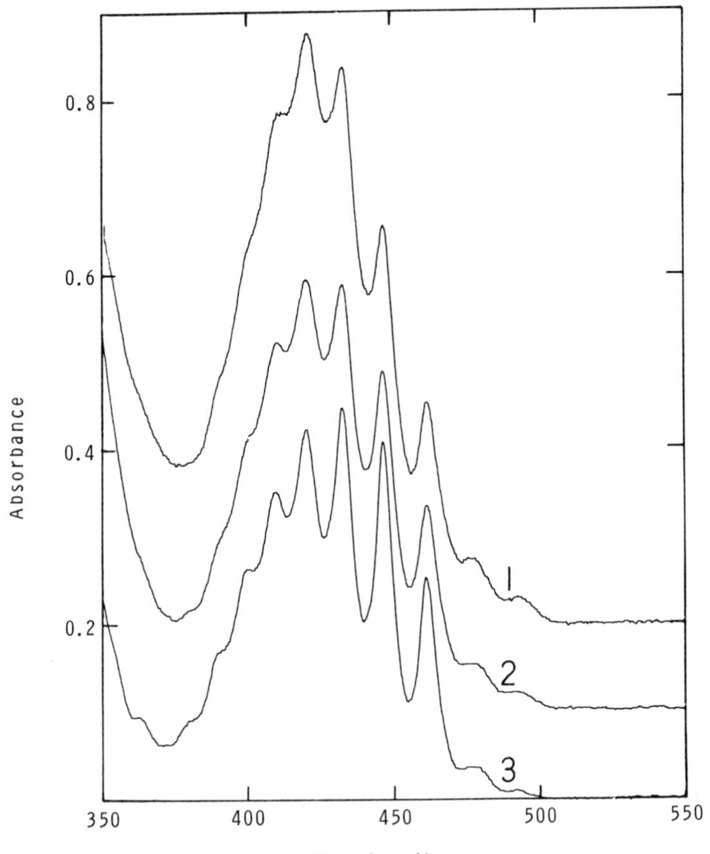

Figure 5. Absorption spectra of U(VI) absorbed in Dowex 1, X-4 (50-100 mesh) from acetate solutions: (1) 4.0M $LiC_2H_3O_2$—2.0M $HC_2H_3O_2$, (2) 0.6M $HC_2H_3O_2$, and (3) 17M $HC_2H_3O_2$. U(VI) concentrations in resin phase are approximately equal

With 5*M* lithium acetate and $< 4M$ acetic acid, the U(VI) in the resin was about 40% in the tetraacetato form.

The decrease in tetraacetato complex in the resin phase with increased acetic acid concentration is probably attributed to lowered acetate activity in the resin phase caused by hydrogen bonding of invading acetic acid to the resin acetate. A similar but more pronounced effect occurs in the uranyl sulfate system owing to conversion of resin sulfate to bisulfate (*17*). The only clear cut effect of a wide variance in the lithium acetate concentration seems to be a decrease of the acetic acid effect. This is probably caused by tying up of acetic acid by hydrogen bonding to acetate from lithium acetate thereby decreasing its effect on resin acetate. A similar marked lack of dependence of the uranyl sulfate species in resin on total aqueous sulfate occurs (*17*). It appears that the ratio of complex species in anion exchange resins (where more than one species is absorbed) is determined by resin ligand activity, and this is not much affected by aqueous ligand concentration but may be markedly affected by other factors such as aqueous acid concentration.

The uranyl nitrato and acetato anionic complexes are similar. From low acid 5*M* metal nitrate (*14*) or acetate solutions the relative ratios of $UO_2(NO_3)_4^{2-}$ to $UO_2(NO_3)_3^-$ and $UO_2(C_2H_3O_2)_4^{2-}$ to $UO_2(C_2H_3O_2)_3^-$ in the resin phase closely reflect the difference in formation constants of the tetra complexes from the tri complexes. This is despite the fact that the formation constants of the triacetato complex and the trinitrato complex from the respective lower complexes are obviously different and the aqueous phase contains mainly anionic species in the acetate case but essentially no anionic species in the nitrate case (*14*).

Amine Extraction. Extraction of uranium(VI) and plutonium(VI) from acetic acid with tri-iso-octylamine in xylene has been studied previously by Moore (*11*), who suggests that the extracted species is the triacetato ion. The spectra in Figure 1 show this is not the predominate species extracted into TOA-xylene solutions (*9*). Comparing the spectrum of this extracted uranium with the spectra of pure tetraacetato and triacetato complexes in Figure 3 shows that the TOA-xylene extracts a mixture of these ions that is largely tetraacetato uranyl complex.

We noted earlier that the principle uranyl(VI) species extracted from acetic acid by TOA-xylene is different from that extracted by TOA-chloroform (*10*). To explore the effect of the solvent further we have now measured the spectra of uranium(VI) extracted with solutions of TOA in different solvents. In these experiments a 0.10*M* uranyl acetate solution in 1*N* acetic acid was extracted with an equal volume of 0.10*M* TOA in each of the several solvents, and the spectra of both phases were measured. In most cases the extracted uranium was found to be a mixture of tri- and tetraacetato complexes. Some examples of these spectra are shown in Figure 6.

Using the technique employed earlier in this paper we have calculated the fraction of the extracted U which is in the tetraacetato form. These results are shown in Table II. The values are not precise since small solvent-dependent frequency shifts occur relative to the spectra of the pure species which were obtained in nitrile solutions. If the data in the table are plotted, a smooth curve can be drawn through all of the points, within the estimated precision, except those from the haloform solutions. The fraction of the tetraacetato complex decreases uniformly

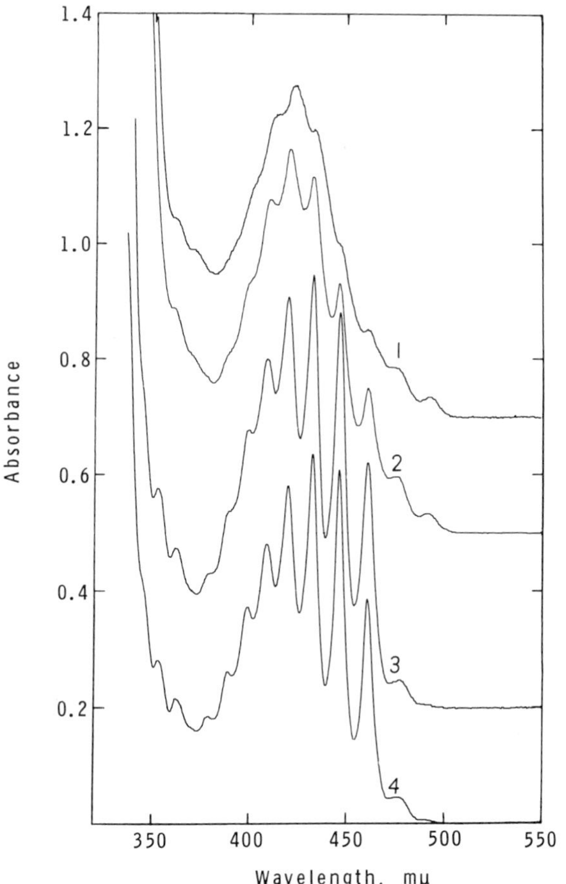

Figure 6. Absorption spectra of U(VI) extracted from 1M $HC_2H_3O_2$—0.10M U(VI) into 5% tri-n-octylamine in: (1) xylene, (2) isopropl ether, (3) chloroform, and (4) hexone

with increase of dielectric constant of the solvent with no apparent relationships to the molecular form of the solvent, except for $CHCl_3$ and $CHBr_3$. Since only anionic complexes can be present in the organic phase, what we observe is simply a decrease of the formation constant of the reaction $UO_2(acetate)_3^- + acetate^- \rightarrow UO_2(acetate)_4^{2-}$ with increasing ionizing power of the solvent. A simple electrostatic argument would predict this result. The same behavior appears to hold for the acetonitrile and aqueous solutions discussed above, although conditions there are different and a strict comparison is difficult. The occurrence of extra low fractions of the tetraacetato complex in the haloform solutions might be expected from the fact that hydrogen bonding between acetate ions and haloform molecules lowers the acetate activity below what it would otherwise be.

One would expect the organic phase of other amine extraction systems in which more than one metal anion can be formed to exhibit similar equilibria. It is fortunate that in this system not only is the solvent not present in the coordination sphere of either complex but also the equilibrium constant between the two is of an order of magnitude which allows concentration of both to be measured readily by spectrophotometric methods. This allows the effect of the dielectric constant of the solvent on the ratio of the species to be studied easily without the perturbing effect of specific interactions caused by differences in the tendency of the solvents to enter the coordination sphere.

Table II. Uranyl(VI) Species Extracted from 1*N* Acetic Acid into 0.2*N* Tri-*n*-Octylammonium Acetate Solutions

Solvent	*Dielectric Constant*	*Fraction of U as Tetraacetato Complex*
Pentane	1.84	0.91[a] 0.11[b]
Carbon tetrachloride	2.24	.73
Tetrachloroethylene	2.30	.70
Toluene	2.38	.62
o-Xylene	2.57	.63
Trichloroethylene	3.42	.35
Isopropyl ether	3.88	.42
Bromoform	4.39	.14
Chloroform	4.81	.08
Chlorobenzene	5.6	.26
α-Chlorotoluene	7.0	.08
1,2-Dichloroethane	10.6	.0
Methyl isobutyl ketone	13.1	.0
Cyclopentanone	16.3	.05

[a] Pentane phase.
[b] Third phase containing most of the TOA and uranium.

In the present work we have measured the distribution ratios (D) by tracer techniques for extraction of U(VI), Np(VI), and Pu(VI) from 1 or 2*N* acetic acid into TOA-xylene over a concentration range 0.002–0.20*M* TOA and for extraction of U(VI) into TOA-$CHCl_3$ over the same concentration range. Plots of log D *vs.* log TOA concentration gave straight lines with slopes between 1.3 and 1.6. The nature of the extracted complex is not clearly shown by these slopes; therefore, this data is not shown. Non-integral slopes were not unexpected since previous experience has shown that the slopes of such curves often do not indicate the proper identity of the extracted species (*8*). This has usually been attributed to a difference in the state of aggregation of the TOA-containing species before and after metal extraction. In the present case, extraction of a mixture of anionic species is a complicating factor, but change of species extracted is not reflected by a large change in concentration dependence of *D*.

Distribution ratio values for extraction of the three hexavalent metals from 1*N* acetic acid by 0.1*M* TOA-xylene were all about 1, indicating little separation among the metals. For extraction of U(VI) by 0.1*M* TOA-$CHCl_3$, *D* was nearly 10.

Moore has shown that thet extractability of U(VI) by 5% tri-*iso*-octylamine in xylene passes through a maximum at about 0.5*N* aqueous acetic acid, and it continues to decrease to 14*N* acid. Our spectral measurements show that the species extracted by TOA in either xylene or chloroform are nearly independent of aqueous acid concentration, although the triacetato complex seems to be slightly favored by increase of acid to 10*N*. There is also a small increase in the percentage of the triacetato ion extracted when uranium to amine ratio is increased.

When extraction is by TOA in low dielectric constant solvents—*e.g.*, pentane—a third phase is formed, leaving only a dilute major organic phase. In this case the spectra show that the U(VI) species in the two organic phases are different, with mainly tetraacetato in the dilute organic phase and mainly triacetato in the heavy, viscous third phase.

Cesium triacetato neptunyl(VI) and plutonyl(VI) were prepared, and spectra were measured in 85% succinonitrile-15% acetonitrile solutions. Both metals were extracted from 1*N* acetic acid into CCl_4 and $CHCl_3$ solutions of TOA, and the spectra of these solutions were also measured. The neptunium spectra are not distinctive and hence are omitted. The spectra of tri-*n*-octylammonium plutonyl acetate in CCl_4 and in $CHCl_3$ are compared with that of $PuO_2(C_2H_3O_2)_3^-$ ion in Figure 7. The predominate species that extracts into $CHCl_3$ solution is clearly the triacetato complex. The principal species that extracts into CCl_4 is a different one, which by analogy with the uranyl case and by comparison with the spectra of 85% succinonitrile-15% acetonitrile solutions of $CsPuO_2(C_2H_3O_2)_3$ containing excess cesium or tetraethylammonium acetates would be the tetraacetato ion. The outstanding difference in these spectra is the sharp intense peak at 840 mμ in the latter ($\epsilon \sim 220$). The relatively high absorptivity of this peak makes it easy to measure small amounts of the tetraacetato species in the presence of the other. Small amounts of triacetato in the presence of the tetraacetato complex would best be measured by difference using the 840 mμ peak. We have not measured the absorptivity of this peak precisely enough; therefore, we have estimated the relative amounts of plutonyl acetate species in the CCl_4 solutions from the spectrum of the triacetato complex present. It

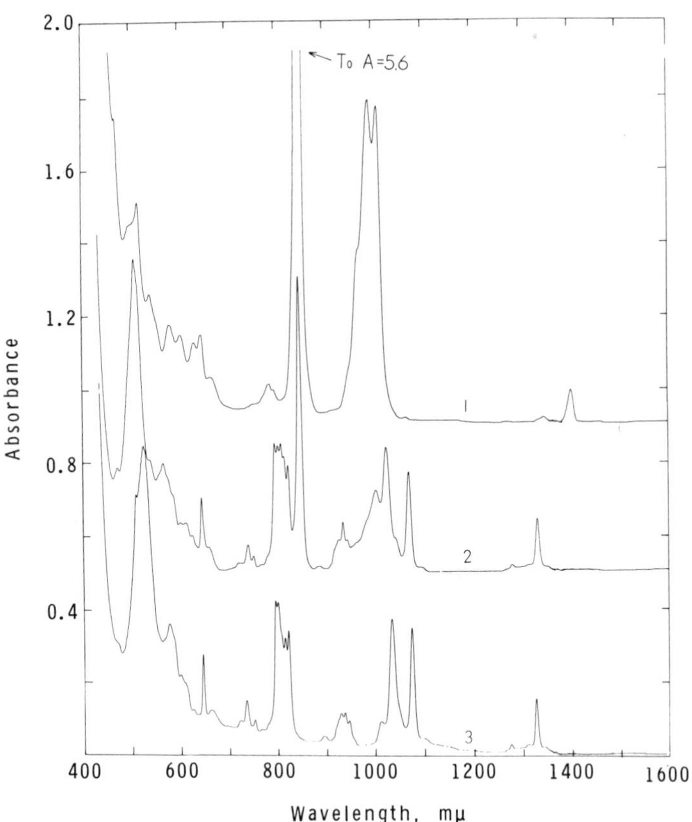

Figure 7. Absorption spectra of Pu(VI) acetates: (1) Pu(VI) extracted from 1M $HC_2H_3O_2$ into 10% tri-n-octylamine in carbon tetrachloride and into (2) 10% tri-n-octylamine in chloroform, and (3) $CsPuO_2(C_2H_3O_2)_3$ in 85% succinnonitrile-15% acetonitrile. Pu concentration is approximately 0.03M in each case (1 cm. cell)

appears that each solution contains about 10% of the minor species, and the behavior of plutonyl(VI) is, therefore, not different from that of uranyl(VI).

The actinide(VI) acetate system discussed here and the actinide(VI) sulfate system to be discussed later (*17*) represent the only cases known to us in which observable mixtures of labile anionic complexes of a given metal are extracted from an acid solution by susbtituted amines. The present system represents the only one in which the diluent is the only major factor controlling the ratio of species in the organic phase. The principle mechanism by which the nature of the diluent appears to determine the ratio of species in the organic phase in this system is by the effect of ionizing power of the diluent (as measured to a first approximation by its dielectric constant) on the formation constant of the tetraacetato complex from the triacetato complex.

Literature Cited

(1) Ahrland, S., *Acta Chem. Scand.* **5,** 199 (1951).
(2) Booman, G. L., Holbrook, W. B., Rein, J. E., *Anal. Chem.* **29,** 219 (1957).
(3) Brintzinger, H., Jahn, F., *Z. Anorg. Allgem. Chem.* **231,** 342 (1937).
(4) Dieke, G. H., Duncan, A. B. F., "Spectroscopic Properties of Uranium Compounds," pp. 133-136, McGraw-Hill, New York, 1949.
(5) Golovnya, V. A., Shubochkin, L. K., *Russ. J. Inorg. Chem. (English Transl.)* **8,** 579 (1963).
(6) Hoard, J. L., Stroupe, J. D., "Spectroscopic Properties of Uranium Compounds," pp. 13-15, McGraw-Hill, New York, 1949.
(7) Kaplan, L., Hildebrandt, R. A., Ader, M., *J. Inorg. Nucl. Chem.* **2,** 153 (1956).
(8) Keder, W. E., Ryan, J. L., Wilson, A. S., *J. Inorg. Nucl. Chem.* **20,** 131 (1961).
(9) Keder, W. E., Wilson, A. S., *Nucl. Sci. Eng.* **17,** 287 (1963).
(10) Keder, W. E., Wilson, A. S., Burger, L. L., *Symp. Aqueous Reprocessing Irradiated Fuels, Brussels, European Nucl. Energy Agency* (1963).
(11) Moore, F. L., *Anal. Chem.* **32,** 1075 (1960).
(12) Nichols, E. L., Howes, H. L., *Carnegie Inst. Technol., Wash., Publ. No.* **298** (1919).
(13) Nichols, E. L., Howes, H. L., Wick, F. G., *Phys. Rev.* **14,** 201 (1919).
(14) Ryan, J. L., *J. Phys. Chem.* **65,** 1099 (1961).
(15) Ryan, J. L., *U. S. At. Energy Comm. Res. Develop. Rept.* **HW-59193** (1959).
(16) Ryan, J. L., Jørgensen, C. K., *J. Phys. Chem.* **70,** 2845 (1966).
(17) Ryan, J. L., Keder, W. E. (to be published).
(18) Ryan, J. L., Wheelwright, E. J., *U. S. At. Energy Comm. Res. Develop. Rept.* **HW-55893** (1959).
(19) Scott, F. A., Peekema, R. M., *Proc. Second Intern. Conf. Peaceful Uses At. Energy, Geneva* **28,** 573 (1958).
(20) Steigman, J., Hammett, L. P., *J. Am. Chem. Soc.* **59,** 2536 (1937).
(21) Stromatt, R. W., *U. S. At. Energy Comm. Res. Develop. Rept.* **HW-59447** (1959).
(22) Tishkoff, G. H., "Pharmocology and Toxicity of Uranium Compounds," Part 1, Chapter 1, Appendix B, McGraw-Hill, New York, 1949.
(23) Vdovenko, V. M., Skoblo, A. I., Suglobov, D. N., *Radiochemistry (USSR) (English Transl.)* **6,** 658 (1964).
(24) Zachariasen, W. H., Plettinger, H. A., *Acta Cryst.* **12,** 526 (1959).

RECEIVED September 12, 1966. Work was performed under Contract No. AT(45-1)-1830 for the U. S. Atomic Energy Commission.

INDEX

A

Absorption peaks, neptunium 259
Absorption spectra
  of hexavalent actinides 336
  lanthanide and actinide 86
  of trivalent actinides in octahedral symmetry 333
Absorption spectrum
  americium (III) 265
  neptunium 257-9
  uranium (IV) 265
Acetato complexes of the hexavalent actinides, anionic 335
Actinide
  absorption spectra 86
  -cesium complexes 337
  chemistry 1
    in saturated KF solution 256
  elements, electronic structure of. 180
  elements, fluorite-related oxide phases of the 67, 73
  fluoride complexes, tetra- and pentavalent 248
  ion reactions, activation free energies of 290
  ion reactions
    entholpy of activation for 282-7
    entropy of activation for 282-7
    free energy of activation for .. 282-7
    rate laws and constants for ... 276-9
  ions, optical and electron paramagnetic resonance spectroscopy 203
  pentachlorides, oxygen donor complexes of 7
  spectroscopy 189
  -lanthanide oxide phases, ternary 78
  tetrachloride-acetamide complexes 4
Actinide (III) halo complexes 3
Actinide (V)
  dioxofluoro complexes 7
  nitrato complexes 8
  oxochloro complexes 7
Actinide (VI) acetates, amine extraction of 335
Actinide (VI) acetates, anion exchange of 335
Actinides
  absorption spectra of hexavalent. 336
  anionic acetato complexes of the hexavalent 335
  octahedral hexahalide complexes of the trivalent 331
Actinides *(Continued)*
  in octahedral symmetry, absorption spectra of trivalent 333
Activated complexes, entropies of . 281
Activation for actinide ion reactions
  entholpy of 282-7
  entropy of 282-7
  free energy of 282-7
Activation, free energies of 281
  actinide ion reactions 290
Activation process
  net 274
  thermodynamic constants of 282-7
Alkali fluorides, protactinium (IV) fluoride complexes with 248
Alkaline americates 231, 233
Alkaline earth americates 231, 235
Alkaline earth halide solid solutions 51
Alkali uranyl borates, infrared maxima in 329
$AmBr_6^{3-}$ 332
$AmCl_6^{3-}$ 332
Americates, alkaline 231, 233
Americates, alkaline earth 231, 235
Americium 201
  aluminate 232, 236
  aqueous oxidation-reduction reactions of 268, 273
  borate 232, 236
  compounds, self-irradiation damage of 243
  dihalides 2
  hafnate 232, 237
  in KF solution 266
  oxides, reactions of 230
  oxides, solid-state chemistry of .. 228
  protactinate 241
Americium (II) 205
Americium (III)
  absorption spectrum 265
  niobate 240
  phosphate 243
  tantalate 240
  vanadate 243
  zirconate 237
Americium (IV) germanate 232, 236
Americium (IV) silicate 232, 236
Americium (VI) chlorocomplex .. 8
$Am_2Hf_2O_7$ 245
Amine extraction of actinide (VI) acetates 335
Aminocarboxylic acid chelates 169
AmO_2 244
AmO_2–ThO_2 solid solution 239

AmO_x 76
Analog for complicated rate laws, electrical 275
Anion exchange of actinide (VI) acetates 335
Anionic acetato complexes of the hexavalent actinides 335
Anionic chlorocomplexes 3
Aqueous oxidation-reduction reactions of uranium, neptunium, plutonium, and americium ... 268
Arrests in MoF_6–UF_6 thermal ..312, 316

B

Berkelium, tributyl phosphate–carbon tetrachloride extraction of 307
Berkelium, trilaurylmethylammonium nitrate–carbon tetrachloride extraction of ..301, 303
Berkelium (III)–(IV) couple, oxidation potential of the 296
Berkelium (III)–(IV), solvent extraction in determining the potential of 297
BFTA chelates of europium 156
Binuclear intermediates 289
Bismuthate *vs.* distribution coefficients of Ce(IV), sodium 300
Borates
infrared maxima in alkali uranyl 329
uranium 320
x-ray diffraction of 328
Boroxole ring structure 327

C

Calcium metaborate 322
infrared spectrum of 325
Californium compounds 2
Calorimetric titrations 128
Carbides, thermodynamics of lanthanide 41
Carbon tetrachloride extraction of Ce and Bk,
tributyl phosphate- 307
trilaurylmethylammonium nitrate- 301, 303
Cation effect on laser action of Eu chelates 160
Cerium halides 56
CeI_2, resistivity of 58
Cerium oxides 70, 72
Cesium-actinide complexes 337
Ce, tributyl phosphate-carbon tetrachloride extraction of 307
Ce, trilaurylmethylammonium nitrate-carbon tetrachloride extraction of 301, 303
Ce(IV)–(III) couple 296
Ce(IV), sodium bismuthate *vs.* distribution coefficients of 300
CFW 104
Chalcogenides, heat capacities of europium 40
Chalcogenides, lanthanide 26
Charge compensation 52
Charge transfer energies 137
Chelates
cation effect on laser action of .. 160-1
of β-diketones, volatile rare earth 141
effect of deuteration on laser threshold of Eu 162
energy transfer in Eu 164
of europium, BFTA 156
fluorescence of Ln 157
heavy atom effect in Ln 165
intersystem crossing in Ln 164
as laser materials, europium 155
nonradiative processes in Ln ... 158-9
phosphorescence of Gd 165
phosphorescence of Ln 157, 163
Chemical thermodynamics of the lanthanides 25
Chlorocomplexes, anionic 3
Chromium-uranium oxides 211
Cobalt-uranium oxides 211
Complexes
cesium-actinide 337
of the hexavalent actinides, anionic acetato 335
inner-sphere 133
of the lanthanides, thermodynamic parameters of 127, 134
plutonyl acetate 349
rare earth 169
of rare earth ions with octamethylpyrophosphoramide . 13
of the trivalent actinides, octahedral hexahalide 331
Concentrated salt solutions, chemistry in 256
Condensed phase equilibria in the MoF_6–UF_6 system 308
Configuration of energy levels 181
Constants for actinide ion reactions, rate 276-9
8-Coordination of Ln (III) 156
Copper-uranium oxides 211
Cryothermal magnetic anomalies .. 28
Crystal structure of metal borates . 323
Crystal structure of uranium-transition element double oxides . 216
Curium 201
oxides 77
protactinium to 248
Curium(III) 206
Curium(IV) 206

D

Decomposition of UO_{2+x} 40
Dehydration, fluoride ion 134
Deuteration on laser threshold of Eu chelates, effect of 162
Diiodides of La and Ce 58
Diiodides, metallic 59
β-Diketones, europium(III) complexes of 145

β-Diketones, volatile rare earth chelates of ... 141
Disordered phases of rare earth oxides ... 70
Disproportionation of neptunium(V) ... 253
Distribution coefficients of Ce(IV), sodium bismuthate *vs.* ... 300
Divalent lanthanide ions ... 51
ground state of ... 54
Divalent state ... 2
Donor properties of pyrophosphate derivatives ... 13
Double oxides, uranium-transition element ... 211

E

Eigenvectors ... 91
Electric dipole transitions ... 92
Electron configurations ... 182
Electronic configuration of metallic halides ... 60
Electronic spectra of lanthanides in the vapor phase ... 102
Electronic structure of actinide elements ... 180
Electron paramagnetic resonance spectroscopy of actinide ions, optical ... 203
Electrostatic parameters ... 88-9, 91
Energy levels
configuration of ... 181
parameters for ... 181
in trivalent lanthanides and actinides ... 86, 91
Energy matrix ... 184
Energy transfer in Eu chelates ... 164
Energy transfer in Ln chelates ... 156
Enthalpies ... 136
Enthalpy of activation for actinide ion reactions ... 282-7
Enthalpy of formation ... 136
Entropies of
activated complexes ... 281
lanthanide halides ... 43
lanthanide metals ... 33
lanthanide oxides ... 31-2
lanthanide(III) oxides ... 30
Entropy
of activation for actinide ion reactions ... 282-7
evaluation ... 29
of formation ... 135
Equilibria in the Mo_6–UF_6 system, condensed phase ... 308
Ethyl sulfates, heat capacities of rare earth ... 44
Europium
BFTA chelates of ... 156
chalcogenides, heat capacities of 40
chelates
cation effect on laser action of 160-1
effect of deuteration on laser threshold of ... 162
Europium (*Continued*)
energy transfer in ... 164
as laser materials ... 155
laser threshold of ... 157
solvent effect on laser action of 157
Europium(III) complexes of β-diketones ... 145
Europium(III), nonradiative processes in ... 166
EuS, heat capacity of ... 40
Extraction of Ce and Bk, trilauryl-methylammonium nitrate–carbon tetrachloride ... 301, 303

F

f-d separation ... 201
Fluorescence of Ln chelates ... 157
Fluoride complexes
of the lanthanides, thermodynamic parameters of ... 127, 134
lattice constants of ... 249-50
molecular volumes ... 250
tetra- and pentavalent actinide .. 248
Fluoride ion dehydration ... 134
Fluorides, stability constants of lanthanide ... 132
Fluorite-related oxide phases ... 67
Fluoro complexes, uranium(V) ... 7
fod chelates, volatility of ... 153
fod rare earth complexes ... 147
Forced electric dipole intensity mechanism ... 114
Free energies of actinide ion reactions, activation ... 290
Free energies of activation ... 281
Free energy of activation for actinide ion reactions ... 282-7
Fused state, reduction in the ... 52

G

Gadolinium chelates, phosphorescence of ... 165
Gadolinium metal, heat capacity of 32
Gadolinium(III), paramagnetism of 165
Garnets, heat capacities of lanthanide iron ... 44
Gas chromatography ... 141
Gaseous chelates of Pr, Nd, Sm, Eu, Dy, Ho, Er, Tm ..111, 114, 115, 117
Gaseous trihalides of Pr, Nd, Er, Tm ... 105, 113
Ground state of divalent lanthanide ions ... 54

H

ΔH_{cov} ... 138
Halides
electronic configuration of metallic ... 60
entropies of lanthanide ... 43
thermal properties of lanthanide 42
Halide systems, physical characterization of rare earth metal-metal 56

Halo complexes, actinide(III) 3
Halo complexes, lanthanide(III) .. 3
Hamiltonian 87, 205
Heat capacities of
  europium chalcogenides 40
  lanthanide iron garnets 44
  rare earth ethyl sulfates 44
Heat capacity
  of EuS 40
  of gadolinium metal 32
  magnetic 28
    contributions to 30
  of terbium metal 32
Heavy atom effect on Ln chelates . 165
Hexaborides, thermodynamics of
    lanthanide 41
Hexaborides, Schottky anomalies
    in lanthanide 42
Hexafluorides 308
Hexahalide complexes of the trivalent actinides, octahedral .. 331
Hexavalent
  actinides, absorption spectra of . 336
  actinides, anionic acetato complexes of the 335
  state 8
H(fod) 143
High temperatures for lanthanide
    metals, thermodynamics at ...36, 39
H(thd) 143
Hydrides, thermal properties of
    lanthanide 43
Hydrogen ion dependencies 275
Hyperfine structure 191
Hypersensitive transitions in
    gaseous lanthanides 103, 118

I

Iminodiacetic acids, *N*-substituted. 169
Infrared
  maxima in alkali uranyl borates . 329
  spectra of metaborates 325
  spectra of uranium-transition
      element double oxides 222
  spectrum of sodium uranyl borate 328
  spectrum, uranium 266
Inhomogeneous dielectric intensity
    mechanism 113
Inner-sphere complexes 133
Intermediate phase $LaI_{2.42}$ 57, 62
Interstitial fluoride ions 52
Intersystem crossing in Ln chelates 164
Iron garnets, heat capacities of
    lanthanide 44
Isotope shifts 192

K

KF solution
  americium in 266
  actinide chemistry in saturated .. 256
  neptunium in 257
  reactions in 260
  uranium in 264

L

LaI_2, resistivity of 58
$LaI_{2.42}$, intermediate phase 57, 62
Lanthanide
  absorption spectra 86
  carbides, thermodynamics of ... 41
  chalcogenides 26
  chelates
    energy transfer in 156
    fluorescence of 157
    heavy atom effect on 165
    intersystem crossing in 164
    nonradiative processes in 158-9
    phosphorescence of 157, 163
  chemistry 1
  complexes of OMPA, NMR
      spectra 20
  contraction *vs.* volatility 151
  dihalide 2
  fluorides, stability constants of .. 132
  halides, entropies of 43
  halides, thermal properties of .. 42
  hexaborides, Schottky anomalies
      in 42
  hexaborides, thermodynamics of. 41
  hydrides, thermal properties of . 43
  ions, divalent 51
  ions, ground state of divalent ... 54
  iron garnets, heat capacities of.. 44
  metals
    entropies of 33
    thermodynamics at high temperatures for 36, 39
    vapor pressures of 40
  monochalcogenides 40
  oxide phases, ternary actinide- .. 78
  oxides
    entropies of 31-2
    thermochemical data of 33-5
    vaporization of 38
  perchlorate complexes 15
  perchlorates 128
  pnictides, thermodynamics of .. 41
Lanthanide(III)
  8-coordination of 156
  halo complexes 3
  oxides 27
  oxides, thermodynamics at high
      temperatures of 36
Lanthanides
  chemical thermodynamics of the 25
  τ_λ parameters for 93, 99
  thermodynamic parameters of
      fluoride complexes of the 127, 134
  in the vapor phase, electronic
      spectra of 102
Lanthanum halides 56
LaO_x, vaporization of 39
Laser action of Eu chelates
  effect of ring substitution on ... 158-9
  cation effect on 160-1
  solvent effect on 157

Laser materials, europium chelates as 155
Laser threshold of Eu chelates 157
effect of deuteration on 162
LaS, vaporization of 41
Lattice constants of fluoride complexes 249-50
Lattice constants of MoF_6 314
Li_4AmO_5 245
Light trivalent actinides, $^{T}\lambda$ parameters for 97
Lithium uranyl borate 323

M

Magnetic
anomalies, cryothermal 28
contributions to heat capacity .. 30
heat capacity 28
Manganese-uranium oxides 211
Matrix, energy 184
Metaborates, calcium and sodium . 322
Metaborates, infrared spectra of .. 325
Metal borates, crystal structure of . 323
Metal, heat capacity of gadolinium 32
Metal, heat capacity of terbium .. 32
Metallic diiodides 59
Metallic halides, electronic configuration of 60
Metal-metal halide systems, physical characterization of rare earth 56
Metals
entropies of lanthanide 33
thermodynamics at high temperatures for lanthanide ...36, 39
vapor pressures of lanthanide .. 40
MoF_6, lattice constants of 314
MoF_6–UF_6 system, condensed phase equilibria in the 308
Molecular volumes of fluoride complexes 250
Monochalcogenides, lanthanide ... 40

N

Na_2PrF_6 123
$Na_7Pr_6F_{31}$ 123
$Nd(ClO_4)_3 \cdot 3OMPA \cdot H_2O$ 23
Neodymium halides 56
Nephelauxetic effects 137
Neptunium
absorption peaks 259
absorption spectra 257-9
aqueous oxidation-reduction reactions of 268, 271
in KF solution 257
reactions 260
solid compounds of 261
trioxide 8
Neptunium(V), disproportionation of 253
Neptunium(V) fluoride complexes. 253
Neptunyl fluoride 8
Nickel-uranium oxides 211
Nonradiative processes in Eu(III). 166
Nonradiative processes in Ln chelates 158
Nonstoichiometry 68, 56
Np-K fluorides, x-ray patterns for . 261-5
NpO_2 74

O

Octahedral hexahalide complexes of the trivalent actinides 331
Octahedral symmetry, absorption spectra of trivalent actinides in 333
Octamethylpyrophosphoramide, complexes of rare earth ions with 13
OMPA 13
Optical and electron paramagnetic resonance spectroscopy of actinide ions 203
Oscillator strength 93
of f←f transitions 102, 106, 118
Oxidation potential of the berkelium (III)-(IV) couple 296
Oxidation-reduction reactions of U, Np, Pu, Np, and Am, aqueous 268
Oxide phases of rare earth and actinide elements, fluorite-related. 67
Oxides
entropies of lanthanide 31-2
thermochemical data of lanthanide 33-5
thermodynamics at high temperatures of lanthanide (III) .. 36
vaporization of lanthanide 38
Oxygen donor complexes of actinide
pentachlorides 7
tetrachlorides 5

P

Paramagnetism of Gd(III) 165
Pentavalent actinide fluoride complexes 248, 253
Pentavalent state 5
Perchlorates, lanthanide 14, 128
Phosphorescence of Gd chelates .. 165
Phosphorescence of Ln chelates .157, 163
Photoreduction 52
Physical characterization of rare earth metal-metal halide systems 56
Plutonium
aqueous oxidation-reduction reactions of 268, 272
spectrum 194
tetrachloride complexes 4
trioxide 8
Plutonium(IV) 208
Plutonium(V) fluoride complexes . 253
Plutonyl acetate complexes 349
Pnictides, thermodynamics of lanthanide 41
Potassium uranyl borate 323

Potential of Bk(III)-(IV), solvent extraction in determining the . 297
Potentiometric titrations 128
Praseodymium halides 56
Praseodymium oxides 70
Praseodymium(IV) compounds, spectra of 122
PrF_4 . . . . 3, 123
Protactinium
  to curium 248
  oxide 73
  pentahalides 5
Protactinium(IV) halides 3
Proton magnetic resonance spectra of lanthanide complexes of OMPA 20
Proton NMR shifts 20
$PuBr_6^{3-}$ 332
$PuCl_6^{3-}$ 332
PuO_{2-x} 75
Pyrophosphate derivatives, donor properties of 13

R

Rare earth
  chelates of β-diketones, volatile . 141
  complexes 169
  elements, fluorite-related oxide phases of the 67
  ethyl sulfates, heat capacities of 44
  ions with octamethylpyrophosphoramide, complexes of . . 13
  metal-metal halide systems, physical characterization of. 56
  oxides, disordered phases of the . 70
Rate laws
  and constants for actinide ion reactions 276-9
  electrical analog for complicated 275
  interpreting the 274
Reactions
  of americium oxides 230
  in KF solution 260
  of U, Np, Pu, and Am, aqueous oxidation-reduction 268
  of uranyl metaborate with water 324
Reduction
  in the fused state 52
  rate of cerium(IV) 300
  in the solid state 53
Resistivity of LaI_2 and CeI_2 58
Ring substitution on laser action of Eu chelates, effect of 158-9

S

Salt solutions, chemistry in concentrated 256
Schottky anomalies 27
  in lanthanide hexaborides 42
Self-irradiation damage of Am compounds 243
Shell concept 142
Sodium bismuthate *vs.* distribution coefficients of Ce(IV) 300
Sodium metaborate 322
  infrared spectrum of 325
Sodium uranyl borate 320
  infrared spectrum of 328
Solid
  compounds of neptunium 261
  solubilities 317
  solutions, alkaline earth halide . . 51
  state
    chemistry of americium oxides 228
    reduction in the 53
    transformations 317
Solvent
  effect on laser action of Eu chelates 157
  extraction 129
  extraction in determining the potential of Bk(III)-(IV) . 297
Spectra
  of hexavalent actinides, absorption 336
  of praseodymium (IV) compounds 122
  of trivalent actinides in octahedral symmetry, absorption 333
Spectroscopy, actinide 189
Spectroscopy of actinide ions, optical and electron paramagnetic 203
Spin orbit parameter 88-9, 91
Stability constants of lanthanide fluorides 132
Structure of
  actinide elements, electronic . . . 180
  metal borates, crystal 323
  Pr(IV) complexes 123
N-Substituted iminodiacetic acids . 169

T

TBP 297
Terbium metal, heat capacity of . . 32
Terbium oxides 70, 72
Ternary actinide-lanthanide oxide phases 78
Tervalent state 2
Tetraethylammonium acetate 336
Tetravalent
  actinide fluoride complexes 248
  praseodymium compounds, spectra of 122
  state 3
thd rare earth complexes 147
Thermal
  analysis 309
  arrests in MoF_6–UF_6 . . . . 312, 316
  properties of lanthanide
    halides 42
    hydrides 43
  stability of uranium-transition element double oxides 221
  stability of uranyl borates 324

Thermochemical data of lanthanide oxides 33-5
Thermogravimetric analysis 145
Thermodynamic constants of activation processes 282-7
Thermodynamic parameters of fluoride complexes of the lanthanides 127, 134
Thermodynamics
  at high temperatures for lanthanide metals 36, 39
  high temperatures of lanthanide(III) oxides 36
  of lanthanide
    carbides 41
    hexaborides 41
    pnictides 41
  of the lanthanides, chemical 25
Thermoluminescence of Am(III) . 205
ThI_2 2
ThI_3 2
Thorium oxide 73
τ_λ parameters 103, 118
  for lanthanides 93, 99
  for light trivalent actinides 97
TLMA 297
Transition element double oxides
  crystal structure of uranium- ... 216
  infrared spectra of uranium- ... 222
  thermal stability of uranium- ... 221
  uranium- 211
Tributyl phosphate-carbon tetrachloride extraction of Ce and Bk 307
Trioctylamine 336
Trilaurylmethylammonium nitrate-carbon tetrachloride extraction of Ce and Bk 301, 303
Tris bidentate complexes 142
Trivalent actinides
  energy levels in 86
  octahedral hexahalide complexes of the 331
  in octahedral symmetry, absorption spectra of 333
Trivalent lanthanides, energy levels in 86

U

UF_6–MoF_6 system, condensed phase equilibria in the 308
$UO_{2\pm x}$ 73
UO_{2+x}, decomposition of 40
Uranium
  aqueous oxidation-reduction reactions of 268-9
  borates, x-ray diffraction 328
  infrared spectrum 266
  in KF solution 264
  -transition element double oxides 211
    crystal structure of 216
    infrared spectra of 222-3
    thermal stability of 221
Uranium(IV) absorption spectra .. 265
Uranium(V) fluoride complexes .. 252
Uranium(V) halocomplexes 6
Uranyl
  acetate complex 335
  borates, infrared maxima in alkali 329
  borates, thermal stability of 324
  halide complexes 9
  metaborate 320
  infrared spectrum of 325
  with water, reaction of 324

V

Vaporization of
  lanthanide oxides 38
  LaO_x 39
  LaS 41
Vapor phase, electronic spectra of lanthanides in the 102
Vapor pressures of lanthanide metals 40
Vibronic intensity mechanism 116
Visible spectra data 22
Volatility of fod chelates 153
Volatility *vs.* lanthanide contraction 151
Volatile rare earth chelates of β-diketones 141

W

Water, reaction of uranyl metaborate with 324

X

X-ray diffraction of MoF_6 ......314, 316
X-ray diffraction of uranium borates 322
X-ray patterns for Np-K fluorides . 261-5

Z

Zeeman effect 191
Zinc-uranium oxides 211